Standard Encyclopedia of the World's Mountains

Contributors

Humphrey Beckett
Sir Gavin de Beer
Ernle Bradford
Ronald W. Clark
Simon Clark
Roger P. Coleman
T. Dodson
Joyce Dunsheath
Robin Fedden
Geoffrey Grigson

Nicholas Guppy
Brigadier Sir John Hunt
Peter Hunt
Anthony Huxley
Frank Illingworth
F. Kingdon-Ward
Mrs F. Kingdon-Ward
Sir Harry Luke
Dr A. J. Marshall
Professor Kenneth Mason

Professor N. E. Odell
George Pendle
E. W. Shanahan
Eric Shipton
Dr W. T. Stearn
Cecil Stewart
J. C. Stuttard
Paul Tabori
Dr J. Monroe Thorington
Francis Watson

Standard Encyclopedia of the World's

Mountains

Edited by Anthony Huxley

G. P. Putnam's Sons

New York

Contents

List of Color Plates

Introduction

The existence of mountains is testimony to the almost unbelievable forces that fashioned our planet, to the recurrent paroxysms that squeezed rock like clay in the fist, thrusting, grinding, contorting the earth's crust, flinging old sea levels among new heights – slow-motion paroxysms taking hundreds of thousands of years, but still almost more than we can grasp, though present-day outbursts of volcano or earthquake, making an atom bomb seem puny in comparison, awe us with their reminder of the vast forces still pent up within the earth.

Man is newer than the most recent ranges, and to him mountains have been primarily barriers, at first isolating tribes and countries, then to be laboriously crossed for invasion or commerce. Peoples settled mountain areas as they populated most areas of the earth capable of supporting life, building a specialized existence dominated by the pronounced change of the seasons, adapting their agriculture to the terrain; sometimes, like some South Americans, their own bodies developed in an exceptional way to meet the needs of high altitude and rarefied air.

The peaks above, however, were left almost entirely alone, and often considered unpleasant. The Greeks, for instance, had hardly a good word for them, regarding them as the haunts of robbers, planting shrines on their heights as tests of devotion, and allocating their highest summits, bleak and icy as they were in reality, to their bickering, interfering deities. The Hebrews, on the other hand, took pleasure in mountains, equating them with holiness and righteousness; the Old Testament has many allusions in terms such as "The mountains shall bring peace to the people." Moses received the Commandments on a mountain, and the God-head dwelt in the peaks.

Holy men of many religions built monasteries and hermitages among the mountains, where until this century complete isolation could be achieved. To the superstitious peasant, however, the high places were haunts of spirits, or were simply shunned for their inhospitability, while more intellectual men took little interest, on the whole, until the eighteenth century.

The history of the relationship of man with mountain is summarized in the article "Mountains and Mountaineering" (page 13) and there is no need to repeat it in detail here. This article should, perhaps, be the first to be read, for it sets the scene for the rest of the volume. The important fact is that, after various small beginnings, and a new taste for the picturesque in the Gothic Revival, mountains became popular in the nineteenth century, and have steadily become more so. There are various reasons for this astonishing change. The taste for high scenery is an acquired one and in the last two centuries it developed alongside an ever-increasing interest in nature. This was coupled with greater wealth and leisure, and quickly improving methods of transport. All these factors started a surge to the mountains, to which today innumerable people with a fortnight's holiday contribute, going to.

climb, ski, or to enjoy them in quieter ways. Tourism is one of Switzerland's biggest industries.

Climbing began this surge and is still the most important human activity connected with the mountains themselves. The original incentive of the climber was undoubtedly the conquest of a new peak, and even today this element is important, though the prize is often an ascent by a new and more difficult route. But it was not long before the element of pleasure became equally important. The pioneer Swiss became the professionals; the British – the first of other nationalities to take to climbing – added mountaineering to their other sports.

The earliest climbers were sometimes scientifically inclined. Horace Bénédict de Saussure, after his ascent of Mont Blanc – the third – in 1787, spent some three hours carrying out simple scientific tests. J. D. Forbes, a great explorer in the Alps – and in his day, the eighteen-thirties and 'forties, the Alps were still virtually unknown and unmapped – did some interesting research on glaciers. Another great mountaineer, Professor John Tyndall, was primarily a scientist, always observing and collecting information as he climbed.

These, and many others, wrote about their experiences and so spread this new fashion. Some of their writings are of a high literary order, especially perhaps because they were still full of wonder and the mountains full of unknowns and surprises. Martin Conway, Edward Whymper and Leslie Stephen are some of the best of these Alpine authors, while some more recent writers have achieved the same quality – Tom Longstaff and Eric Shipton among them.

Some climbers have sought to explain their pleasure in terms of a higher mystique; the simplest explanation ever given is that of George Leigh Mallory, who climbed a peak "because it is there." Most climbers are satisfied with exhilaration and achievement; others find mental and even spiritual contentment among the peaks; a few, driven on by who knows what demons, must court danger at all costs, and subjugate rock needle or overhung cliff by sheer strength and cunning.

But mountains are not only for climbers. There are those who prefer merely to gaze without exertion; others walk and scramble around the peaks; some will enjoy studying geology and geography at first hand, or the flowers, both beautiful and specialized, which are such a delightful feature of mountain country.

The many possible reasons for being interested in mountains are, indeed, behind the production of this volume. It aims at being a standard reference book with a high degree of accuracy in its factual information, which includes the geographical status of each peak, glacier or pass mentioned, its geology, special fauna and flora, its historical importance, and of course who first discovered, explored or climbed it – anything, in fact, of interest about the mountain in question. To balance these hard facts use has been made in many articles of quotations, and in this way something, I hope, will be transmitted of the essentially individual nature of mountain climbing and exploration, and of the immense human effort which often goes into it.

There are over 300 major articles, of which several – such as those on the Rocky Mountains, Andes, Alps and Himalayas – describe the great ranges as entities, relate them to world geography and refer to the more important individual peaks. To supplement these articles there is a gazetteer with over

1,500 entries. A glossary explains unfamiliar geographical and mountaineering terms; there are short biographical notes on some of the most important mountaineering personalities; and reference maps show the positions of the principal mountains. Numerous photographs depict some of the most important and interesting peaks and ranges, while a number of the illustrations are of historical interest. Finally, there is a comprehensive index. The spelling of place names and the alphabetical order are based on the Columbia Lippincott Gazetteer.

Today, we can fly over mountain ranges and, if we have any imagination, obtain some idea of the extent of the forces which created these backbones of the continents. But we need to go among them for a proper knowledge of their brooding vastness on the one hand, and of their beauty on the other: the contrast of valley and peak, glacier and scree, snow and forest, with river, waterfall and flowery meadow setting them off. This book, I hope, will serve as an introduction to those not familiar with the mountains, and a valuable reference to those who are.

Anthony Huxley

Crossing a snowbridge over a crevasse

Mountains
and Mountaineering

The shape and structure of the hills and mountains of the world, from the gleaming peaks of the Himalayas to the rounded ridges of England's South Downs and America's White Mountains, are all end-products of two opposing forces. The geological strains and stresses formed during the long story of the earth have thrust up the rocks; and wind and water, acting on them through countless aeons, have carved them slowly but relentlessly into the shapes we know today, living examples of the fact that "the everlasting hills" is a poet's phrase rather than a fact of life.

The local causes which have helped to form any one mountain or range of mountains are thus both complex and technical, but the results have long been simply classified into three groups. There are the mountains of accumulation, typified by volcanoes; usually isolated peaks, they consist of the material ejected from the earth or otherwise gathered together. There are the folded mountains, usually appearing as ranges, the outcome of the great terrestrial strains which have produced anticlines and synclines, those crests and troughs of the earth's crust. And there are the mountains of erosion, formed primarily by the weathering away of their substance by wind and water throughout the years.

The three causes of mountain-building are not, of course, mutually exclusive, and each may have played its part in forming any summit that we see today. Many of the greatest ranges – the Alps, the Himalayas and the Andes – have been produced primarily by successive upthrusts of the earth, each separated by long periods during which the forces of erosion have been at work. Older rock may be thrust over younger rock, weathering will act differentially on differing

strata, and the result will present an almost infinitely complex picture of the earth's story. In general, the highest mountains are the most recently formed, and their physical features accord more accurately than do those of older ranges with the physical nature of the terrain we see today. Thus the geology of the Himalayas, that range which is relatively young in years although great in height, can be linked visibly to its topography. In Scotland's Ross and Cromarty, where the ancient Torridonian sandstone lies on the even more ancient Lewisian gneiss, the topographical and geological maps show little obvious conformity.

The raw materials of which mountains – and the rest of the earth – are composed, are generally divided into three groups: the igneous, the sedimentary, and the metamorphic. The first of these consists of rocks, such as granite, or serpentine, which have solidified from the molten rock-mass below the earth's crust, either below ground under pressure, on their way to the earth's surface, or even after reaching the surface. The second group consists of substances such as limestone, dolomite, clay or shale, which have been deposited as beds, frequently as sediments, beneath the surface of the oceans. Thirdly, there are the metamorphic rocks, which have been produced either from the igneous or the sedimentary – by heat, by pressure, or, in some cases, by the action of water which, by dissolving some components and replacing them with others, has altered the composition of the original material. Many igneous and sedimentary rocks thus have their metamorphic counterparts, such as gneiss, which results when the quartz and feldspar of igneous granite are separated and rearranged, and slate, which is produced when sedimentary shale is transformed by tremendous pressure.

This great variety in the materials of which mountains are formed became of significance when they were first quarried to produce building stone, or mined for industrial purposes. And in an age when mountains are climbed for pleasure, the hardness or softness of the rock and the manner in which it weathers (providing, for instance, the sharp handholds of granite or the rounded bosses of sandstone) have additional importance.

Yet for by far the greater span of human life on earth, the geological structure of mountains had little relevance to either of the contrasting positions which they occupied in man's scheme of things. Until the sport of mountaineering was born in the mid-nineteenth century, partly as a by-product of the industrial revolution (escapism from an increasingly industrialized England), mountains in most parts of the world were either revered as "the abode of the gods" or cursed as objectionably large rugosities which impeded the free flow of trade and travel. Naturally enough, those which offered few routes below the permanent snowline were given over to the gods, for above it man moved into a world of glacier and ice whose physical properties he could not understand and with whose difficulties he was ill-equipped to deal. The rest were traversed if absolutely necessary, as were the Alps, for instance, which stand as a barrier between the plains of northern Europe and the Italian peninsula. They were usually crossed in fear, and the account of Master John de Bremble's journey across the Great St Bernard Pass in 1188 typified a reaction that was to persist for centuries. "Lord, restore me to my brethren, that I may tell them that they come not to this place of torture," he prayed.

There were exceptions to this attitude. Philip of Macedon ascended Mount Haemus in the Balkans, hoping for a view of both the Aegean and the Adriatic. In the thirteenth century Peter III of Aragon climbed Pic Canigou in the Pyrenees. A century later Petrarch went to the summit of Mont Ventoux in Provence, while Leonardo da Vinci climbed an outlier of Monte Rosa, possibly reached 10,000 feet near the Col d'Olen, and reported a "large mass of ice formed by layers of Hail" that may well have been a glacier. Roche Melon in the Graians was climbed in 1358. And in 1492 Charles VII of France, passing through the Dauphiné, was so struck by the massive flat-topped bastion of Mont Aiguille that he ordered his Chamberlain, the Lord of Dompjulian and Beaupré, to make its ascent. This the chamberlain duly did, with a party that used "subtle means and engines" – pitons and the like, no doubt – on what was a genuine rock climb. The ascent was not repeated until 1834.

These climbs were, however, the activities of exceptional men performing unconventional deeds once in a lifetime. It was in the sixteenth century that there grew up a small "school" whose members looked on mountains with unjaundiced eyes. Based on Zürich, they had as their first leader the eminent naturalist, Conrad Gesner, a man whose letter to a friend, written in 1541, sums up his own spirit and that of his companions. "I have resolved for the future, so long as God grants me life, to ascend divers mountains every year, or at least one, partly for the worthy exercise of the body and recreation of the mind," he wrote. "What must be the pleasure, think you, what the delight of a mind rightly touched, to gaze upon the huge mountain masses for one's show and, as it were, lift one's head into the clouds. . . Philosophers will always feast the eye of body and mind on the goodly things of this earthly paradise; and by no means least among these are the abruptly soaring summits, the trackless steeps, the vast slopes rising to the sky, the rugged rocks, the shady woods." This was a long way from the attitude of De Bremble, and it comes as no surprise to learn that a generation later another Zürich scholar, Josias Simler, wrote a little volume, *Concerning the Difficulties of Alpine Travel and the Means by which they may be Overcome*, which is really the first manual of movement above the snowline.

The Zürich enthusiasm faded out, and it was only in the mid-eighteenth century that there began the scientific examination of mountains which was to lay the foundations for the sport of mountaineering. This examination began in 1760 when Horace Bénédict de Saussure, a Genevese naturalist, offered a reward to anyone who could find a way to the top of Mont Blanc, and it continued on almost entirely scientific lines for almost a century. From the early nineteenth century onwards, however, more and more men – and, fairly early, women – began to travel above the snowline under the influence of what we should now call sporting instincts. The lines cannot be clearly drawn, and well before mid-century there is a definite overlap between scientific and sporting interests. James David Forbes first traveled in the Alps on purely scientific missions; yet after he had stayed with Agassiz at the "Hôtel des Neuchâtelois," a rugged cave-bivouac on the Unteraar Glacier, from which he made the first British ascent of the Jungfrau, he wrote: "I here willingly record that I shall never forget the charm of those savage scenes. The varying effects of sunshine, cloud and storm upon the sky, the mountains and the glacier; the rosy tints of sunset, the cold hues of moonlight, on a scene which included no trace of animation and of which our party were the sole spectators." This was in the early eighteen-forties: 20 years later John Tyndall was delighting not only in the majesty of the mountains but in the hard, dangerous struggle of climbing the most difficult peaks he could find.

All this activity of the mid-nineteenth century would have been impossible, however, had it not been for the encouragement of Saussure almost a century earlier. Twenty-six years were to pass before his offer of a reward brought results, and Dr Michel Paccard of Chamonix at last stood with Jacques Balmat on the summit of the highest mountain in western Europe. Saussure made

the third ascent of the mountain the following year (the second having been made a few days earlier by a couple of local men).

"What I really saw, and saw as never before," he later wrote, "was the skeleton of all those great peaks whose connection and real structure I had so often wanted to comprehend. I hardly believed my eyes. It was as though I were dreaming when I saw below me the Midi, the Argentière, and the Géant, peaks whose very bases I had before found it so difficult and dangerous to reach."

Then he set about three-and-a-half hours of concentrated scientific work, testing the boiling-point of water, the temperature of the snow, and the pulse of his guides.

Saussure's ascent of Mont Blanc and his subsequent travels through the Alps – he spent nearly a fortnight camping and taking scientific observations on the 11,060-foot Col du Géant – showed that worthwhile scientific information could be obtained by travel above the snowline. His exploits therefore led directly to the explorations of such mountain travelers as F. J. Hugi, the Soleure geologist; Louis Agassiz; and Forbes, Tyndall and T. G. Bonney, who between them helped to found the science of glaciology.

Saussure's influence went deeper still, however. By demonstrating that it was possible to reach the summit of Mont Blanc and not only live but enjoy the sensation, he set the fashion for purely "sporting" ascents of the mountain. The influence of these, multiplying quickly after the end of the Napoleonic wars, spread to other mountains and other regions of the Alps. The Meyer brothers of Aarau climbed in the Bernese Oberland merely "for fun" and made ascents of the Jungfrau and the Finsteraarhorn, while from the eighteen-twenties onwards more and more British visitors to Europe ventured above the snowline not to make scientific observations but because they felt drawn towards exploration of the scarcely-known world that they discovered there.

All was now ready for the great upsurge of

interest in mountaineering as a sport which was to produce its "Golden Age." Before considering this, however, one should notice that Ramond de Carbonnières had begun his pioneer exploration of the Pyrenean summits before the end of the eighteenth century, and had made the first ascent of Mont Perdu, the third highest in the range, two years later; that the exploration of the Austrian summits of the Alps had been started at the turn of the century; and that across the Atlantic the first steps into the mountains were being taken as a part of ordinary exploration, the first ascent of a 14,000-foot peak in what is now the United States having been made in 1820 when Edwin James climbed Pikes Peak.

The "Golden Age" of mountaineering, during which most of the great summits of the Alps were climbed for the first time, during which sporting, as distinct from scientific, interests became overwhelming, and during which many of the present customs and conventions of the sport were established, lasted for little more than ten years. It can conveniently, but not quite accurately, be claimed to start with Alfred Wills' famous ascent of the Wetterhorn above Grindelwald; and it ended in 1865 with the first ascent of the Matterhorn and the tragic accident on the descent in which four of the party were killed.

During the years between, the Mönch, the Dom, the Eiger, Monte Viso, the Schreckhorn, the Dent d'Hérens, the highest peak of Monte Rosa, and many other Alpine summits great and small, mediocre and sublime, were climbed for the first time, by amateurs who provided organization and map-reading ability and who were led by guides with local knowledge and muscle power. A large majority of these ascents were made by Englishmen, solid, middle-class representatives of "the workshop of the world," and it is possible to argue at length over the driving-power which sent them to the summits of so many mountains and impelled their influence around the world. It seems likely that the twin revelations of Darwinism and the new archeology were in many cases intimately involved. "The attributes with which men commonly clothe the idea of God, majesty, solitude, radiance, darkness and storm, seem inherent in the mystery of the mountains," said the late Lord Schuster in his Romanes lecture on "Mountaineering" at Oxford University in 1948. "Further, until Copernicus rearranged the universe for the western world, it was easy to believe that you got nearer to heaven the higher you climbed. Thus, much of the literature of the pioneers is filled with an ingenuous piety. And those who, in the intellectual struggles of the mid-nineteenth century, had rejected the traditional creed were still none the less moved by their surroundings." In the nineteen-twenties George Leigh Mallory, asked why he wanted to climb Everest, could answer an importunate journalist with his "Because it is there." For the Victorians who founded the sport, the motives were infinitely more complex.

The aura of scientific investigation was retained, not merely as an alibi by those who wished to justify climbing as what Sir Frederick Pollock called "a taste and a pursuit," but by those, such as Professor Tyndall, for whom it still remained a major, although not the sole, reason for mountaineering. The *Alpine Journal*, first published in 1863 by the Alpine Club (founded five years previously), then carried, as it still carries today, the sub-title "A Record of Mountain Adventure and Scientific Observation." It was even suggested that the club might form a scientific recruiting ground, and when Tyndall was invited to become Vice-President, he was informed: "Many men (originally mere climbers) are beginning to take an interest in the physical questions that have to be decided in the Alps. In a few years there will be an organization which you will be able to wield with effect."

This approach irked many members, such as Leslie Stephen who, after he had parted company with the Church, found much of his own mental solace among "the cathedrals of God." So much so, that at the Club's Winter Dinner of 1861 he gave a mock-heroic account of a climb,

The clubroom at Zermatt in 1864

saying that he would no doubt be questioned by "those fanatics who, by a reasoning process to me utterly inscrutable, have somehow irrevocably associated Alpine travel with science. To them I answer, that the temperature was approximately (I had no thermometer) 212 degrees Fahrenheit below freezing point. As for ozone, if any existed in the atmosphere, it was a greater fool than I take it for." Tyndall, shocked, resigned from the Club in protest.

This heroic era, an era in which it seemed that the sporting and scientific approaches to mountaineering might become irreconcilable, ended with the Matterhorn accident. It was the last great peak of the Central Alps that had remained unclimbed. Edward Whymper, who joined forces with Charles Hudson's party to make the ascent, had himself made seven previous efforts to climb it. There was rivalry with the Italians, trying to make the first ascent from the other side of the peak. And an English "milord," Lord Francis Douglas, was among those killed. All these things combined to give the accident the maximum publicity, so that *The Times* could ask of mountaineering in its famous leading article: "Is it

life? Is it duty? Is it commonsense? Is it allowable? Is it not wrong?"

The Matterhorn accident, in the opinion of later experts, held back the tide of mountaineering for a generation. And, when the tide was moving again, it was seen to have assumed a different shape and character.

Throughout the last third of the nineteenth century a number of new trends can be distinguished in what was becoming a largely sporting pastime. One of these was the ascent of minor mountains which would previously have been ignored by climbers because of their physical insignificance. Minor points on major peaks assumed separate life, and it became more frequent for new "summits" to be named only after they had been climbed.

Secondly, there developed the practice of ascending old mountains by new and (since first ascents invariably took the easiest way) by more difficult routes. A typical pyramidal mountain has three ridges and three faces, all culminating at the summit and each presenting a new set of problems to the climber. The opportunities of the "Silver Age" were thus more numerous if less

17

Tourists at Chamonix in the eighteen-eighties

individually valuable than those of its predecessor.

Both of these developments involved the climbing of more and yet more difficult rocks, a process that has been continuing ever since. That this was feasible was due, at least in part, to the growth of rock climbing in Britain. In this small island whose highest summit of Ben Nevis reaches only 4,406 feet, some few hundred feet below the permanent snowline, and in which all but a few summits can be reached without the use of the hands, the prime motive of the early mountaineers was missing. Only walking, not "climbing," was normally needed to reach the summit, and the conquest of difficult rocks thus became an end in itself.

The Victorians who scaled the Alps during the eighteen-sixties and 'seventies had sometimes visited Scotland, North Wales, and the Lakes during the winter so that they could practice step-cutting in the snow- and ice-filled gullies. Then, in 1881, Walter Parry Haskett Smith, a 22-year-old Oxford student, organized a reading party to the Lakes and spent two summer months at Wasdale Head. Here, near the hub of Lakeland, and surrounded by such rock masses as Great Gable and Scafell, Haskett Smith scrambled. The following year he returned to climb up the easier gullies and rocks on which, during the following two decades, the principles of British cragsmanship were formulated. Elsewhere, particularly in the Dolomites and the Austrian Alps, mountaineers developed their technical ability on rock climbs below the snowline, but until the end of the century and, in fact, until the outbreak of the First World War, British influence in the Alps remained a major one.

Two other features of the three decades that followed the end of the Golden Age must be mentioned. One was the coming of the woman mountaineer, of Miss Marguerite ("Meta") Brevoort, who had left her native New York with her young nephew, W. A. B. Coolidge, in 1864; of her great rival Miss Lucy Walker; of Miss Straton, Miss Emmeline Lewis-Lloyd, and the Pigeon sisters; and, towards the end of the century, of Miss Hawkins-Whitshed, Mrs Burnaby, Mrs Main and Mrs Le Blond, all names borne at different times by the high-spirited, thrice-married mountaineer who helped found the Ladies' Alpine Club.

Secondly there was the popularization of mountaineering as such, and the spread and development of interest in mountains to other spheres of activity. The Alpine Club – not, it should be stressed, the British or the London Alpine Club – retained its exclusive position; but it was followed by the great Continental Clubs, Austrian, German, Italian and French, associations rather than clubs, demanding only nominal mountaineering qualifications, and numbering their members by thousands rather than by hundreds. Simultaneously, throughout the last three decades of the nineteenth century, there developed what might be called a number of mountain-specializations. The Rev. W. A. B. Coolidge, the American who became an Oxford don, devoted himself to the untilled field of mountaineering history. Vittorio Sella followed the example of the Bisson brothers and became the greatest living mountain-photographer. Mountain-writers and mountain-artists multiplied.

This extension of interest in mountains and in the experiences which came from climbing them was accompanied by the steady exploration of ranges beyond the Alps. The Caucasus were climbed by Douglas Freshfield (who as early as 1868 made the first ascent of the eastern peak of Elbrus), by W. F. Donkin, Henry Fox and A. F. Mummery. The mountains of Norway were explored by Cecil Slingsby, a Yorkshireman who also played an important part in the "Silver Age" of Alpine climbing and in the development of mountaineering in Britain; and the Pyrenees were climbed by a long succession of British enthusiasts beginning with Charles Packe.

This period also saw the birth of genuine mountaineering in the United States, much of it springing from the State and Federal surveys, particularly the California Geological Survey, which employed such mountaineers as Clarence King, William Brewer and Richard Cotter. Mount Rainier was climbed in 1870, Mount Whitney, among the highest in the United States, in 1873, while Half Dome, in Yosemite, was conquered two years later. The exploration of the mountains of Alaska began seriously with John Muir's visits of 1879 and 1880, and although the conquest of Mount McKinley was reserved for the twentieth century, Mount St Elias was successfully climbed by the Duke of the Abruzzi's Italian party in 1897. In South America the pioneers were largely British, such men as Whymper, E. A. Fitzgerald and Lord Conway, who had learned the craft in the Alps, while the foundations of mountaineering in Japan were laid by another Englishman, the Rev. Walter Weston. In New Zealand, however, it was the American tradition that was followed, many of the pioneers being the surveyors who opened up the country and who climbed almost as part of their everyday duty.

It was in the Himalayas that the most significant steps were taken before the turn of the century. As in the United States, the first ascents had been made by the surveyors and mapmakers. The Schlagintweits traveled extensively here in the eighteen-fifties, but it was only in 1883 that the first purely mountaineering party visited the range, led by W. W. Graham, whose claimed 24,000-foot ascent of Kabru is still disputed. It was in the following decade that the "modern" story of Himalayan exploration began with the expedition led by Martin Conway, later Lord Conway of Allington. One object was to discover the effects of altitude, and the expedition thus reverted, as it were, to the ideals of the Alpine explorers of half a century earlier. Pioneer Peak was ascended, and at 22,600 feet it was the highest mountain except Kabru that had then been climbed. Conway was knighted for his achievement. ("I was given reason to expect that I should be made a K.C.S.I. . . but the number for the year was made up without me and I was offered an ordinary knighthood as a stop-gap," he wrote later. "It served me well enough.") Himalayan climbing was fairly launched.

It is from this period that the efforts to climb Mount Everest begin. In 1893 Captain (later General) the Hon. Charles Granville Bruce unsuccessfully applied for permission to travel through Tibet. Fourteen years later it was proposed that an attempt should be made to climb Everest in celebration of the fiftieth anniversary of the Alpine Club's formation. This also failed, and it was only after the end of the First World War that permission was granted for the first of the British expeditions to approach the mountain.

The numerous, but unavailing, efforts to climb Everest form the most publicized feature of mountaineering between the two world wars. Throughout the nineteen-twenties and 'thirties they produced a ferment of interest in mountaineering in the United States and in Britain and the other countries of Europe. In North America the highest peak of all, 20,290-foot Mount McKinley, had been climbed in 1913 by a party that included Archdeacon Hudson Stuck, but numerous and attractive peaks remained in Alaska, the Rockies of both Colorado and Canada, and the Tetons and other ranges of North America that had so far received relatively little attention from mountaineers. These were now attacked by an ever-increasing number of enthusiasts.

In Britain, also, the open-air movement of the inter-war years attracted large numbers of climbers, a fact indicated by the dozens of small clubs which began to grow up in most of the larger cities. On the Continent, the great upsurge of mountaineering interest had two causes. First there was that illustrated by Pierre Dalloz, one of the leaders of the French Groupe de Haute Montagne, whose generation grew to manhood as the First World War ended. Of difficult and dangerous mountaineering, Dalloz wrote: "It gave us the complete fulfilment of our dream, it proved to us our worth, and in spite of the event which had robbed us of war, it allowed us to taste the intoxicating pleasures of the heroic life." To this attitude there was soon to be added the political view, summed up by the Italian journal which proudly announced that "The medal for valor in sport, the highest distinction accorded by the Duce to exceptional athletes who break world records or are victors in international contests, will be awarded to climbers who vanquish mountains by new ascents of the sixth standard."

The outcome of these two new incentives, which now supplemented Mallory's "because-it-is-there" reason for mountaineering, was twofold. One was a dramatic increase in the difficulty and danger of the climbs attempted, partly owing to the increased use of mechanical aids, partly to the new ways in which danger was considered. Previously, mountaineers had been willing to chance their own failings, their inability to climb in difficult places; but they had been chary of exposing themselves to dangers, such as expected stone-falls or avalanches, about which their own skill could do nothing. Playing Russian roulette with a mountain had until now had few attractions. This attitude changed in the nineteen-thirties under the spur of international rivalry, the result being an ominous increase in deaths in the Alps, where the great north faces were attempted for the first time.

In the Himalayas, the Germans sent massive but unsuccessful expeditions to Kanchenjunga and Nanga Parbat, on both of which a number of men were lost. The practice of using small expeditions was encouraged by the British, notably by Frank Smythe, whose party in 1931 climbed Kamet, at 25,447 feet the highest peak then scaled; by Eric Shipton; and by H. W. Tilman who, with a small Anglo-American party, climbed Nanda Devi in 1936.

The coming of the Second World War directed attention to the military need for Alpine troops and, more generally, to the physical benefits of mountaineering. The result was that by 1945 many thousands of men in all the combatant countries had been introduced to the elements of mountaineering – most Commandos and Special Service units being trained at least in rock climbing and often in snow- and ice-work as well.

The impact of the war on mountaineering was to be demonstrated more forcibly, however, by the technological advances which it produced. This was to be seen most clearly during the assault on the Himalayas which was resumed in nineteen-forties and 'fifties. The conquest of Everest by Sir John Hunt's expedition in 1953 was due not only to clear planning and cool courage but also to such things as synthetic materials (nylon linings for clothes, microcellular rubber for boot-soles, and Alkathene containers), light-weight metals, pint-size radios, and numerous other products which had been developed largely as a result of wartime needs.

All these things were to be a feature of the "Golden Age of Himalayan mountaineering" which was opened by the success on Everest. K2, the second highest mountain in the world, was climbed by an·Italian party; Kanchenjunga by a British party. The Germans at last succeeded on Nanga Parbat. The British-Pakistani expedition climbed Rakaposhi, and the Americans "Hidden Peak" (Gasherbrum I). The Italians climbed Gasherbrum IV and the Japanese Chogolisa. In the latter years of the nineteen-fifties, the great (and hitherto almost unconsidered) summits of the Himalayas and the Karakoram fell with the speed of the Alpine summits almost exactly a century earlier.

The process is still continuing, and it would be wrong to say that its end can be seen. The unclimbed but worthwhile peaks of the Himalayas can still be numbered by the score whereas in the Alps, roughly a century ago, their counterparts could be counted on the fingers of one hand. For the mountaineer, it is an altogether encouraging prospect.

Rock climbing in England's Lake District

Mountaineering Pioneers

Abruzzi, H. R. H. Prince Luigi Amedeo of Savoy-Aosta, Duke of the (1873–1933) Mountaineer and mountain traveler who served an apprenticeship in the Alps in 1892 and 1894, climbing the Matterhorn by the Zmutt ridge in the latter year with A. F. Mummery and Norman Collie. In 1897 made the first ascent of Mount St Elias with an expedition that included the photographer Vittorio Sella. Visited the Arctic in 1899, and in 1906 led the first major mountaineering expedition to the Ruwenzori. Three years later led a large party to the Karakoram which surveyed the glaciers around K2 and reached a height of 24,600 feet on the Golden Throne – some 700 feet higher than any summit at that time reached by man.

Agassiz, Jean Louis Adolphe (1807–73) Swiss geologist who in 1840 established his Hotel des Neuchâtelois – a converted rock gîte – on the ice of the Unteraar glacier, and used it as a base from which he and his companions made glaciological observations.

Almer, Christian (1826–98) Grindelwald guide who in 1854, together with his brother-in-law Ulrich Kaufmann, joined Alfred Wills' party in the classic fourth ascent of the Wetterhorn. Made many first ascents with such mountaineers of the "Golden Age" as the Rev. Hereford George, Leslie Stephen and Edward Whymper. Was engaged in 1868 by Coolidge and Miss Brevoort, and subsequently became their regular guide, making with them the first ascent of the central peak of the Meije in 1870 and taking part in the opening-up of the Dauphiné. In 1896, aged 70, ascended the Wetterhorn on his Golden Wedding anniversary, together with his wife, aged 71.

Anderegg, Melchior (1828–1914) Meiringen guide, with Christian Almer possibly the most important of the "Golden Age." His first ascents included the Alphubel, the Blümlisalphorn and the Oberaarhorn with Leslie Stephen, the Monte Della Disgrazia with Stephen and E. S. Kennedy, the Dent d'Herens, Mont Mallet, and Mont Blanc from the Brenva Glacier.

Ball, John (1818-89) Mountaineer, Alpine traveler and botanist who had crossed the main Alpine chain 48 times by 32 different passes and had traversed nearly 100 lateral passes when the first volume of his *Alpine Guide* appeared in 1863. The first President of the Alpine Club.

Balmat, Jacques (1762–1834) Chamonix guide who, together with Dr Paccard, made the first ascent of Mont Blanc on August 8, 1786.

Band, George (born 1931) British mountaineer who took part in the 1953 Everest expedition and, two years later, made the first ascent of Kanchenjunga with Joe Brown.

Banks, Mike British mountaineer, officer in the Royal Marines, who first climbed at the Commando Cliff Assault Center. Has since mountaineered extensively in Britain, Greenland, the Alps and elsewhere. Made the first ascent of Rakaposhi, with Surgeon-Lieutenant T. W. Patey, in 1958.

Bauer, Paul German mountaineer who led two expeditions to Nanga Parbat in 1937 and 1938.

Bonney, The Rev. Thomas George (1833–1921) Mountaineer and geologist who between 1856 and 1911 made about 110 ascents, 65 of them above 10,000 feet, and crossed more than 170 passes. Much of his scientific work is contained in *The Building of the Alps* and *The Alpine Regions*.

Bourdillon, T. D. (1926–56) British mountaineer who made many exceptional guideless climbs in the Alps in the nineteen-fifties. Responsible, with his father, for the closed-circuit oxygen sets used on the 1953 Everest expedition, during which, with Charles Evans, he reached the South Peak.

Brevoort, Marguerite ("Meta") (1825–76) Aunt of the Rev. W. A. B. Coolidge and one of the finest women mountaineers of her day. Left the United States with her sister and nephew in 1864 and settled in Europe. Her "firsts" included the ascent of the central peak of the Meije in 1870 and the first traverse of the Matterhorn by a woman in 1871.

Brown, Joe (born 1930) English mountaineer who revolutionized British rock climbing after the Second World War by greatly raising the standard. Took part in the successful 1955 expedition to Kanchenjunga and was one of the first two men to reach the summit. The following year was one of the first two men to reach the west summit of the Muztagh Tower during the expedition which also ascended the main summit, some ten feet higher.

Bruce, Charles Granville (1866–1939) Army officer, Himalayan explorer and mountaineer. With Conway in the Karakoram in 1892, and with Mummery and Collie on the first attempt on Nanga Parbat three years later. Made two proposals for exploring Everest in the early nineteen-hundreds, these being vetoed on political grounds. Was largely responsible for the first training of the Sherpas as mountaineers. Was invalided out of the Army in 1920 by a medical board which recommended a quiet and sedentary life, and subsequently led the 1922 and 1924 expeditions to Mount Everest.

Buhl, Hermann (1924–57) Innsbruck mountaineer with a record of many exceedingly difficult climbs in the Alps. In 1953 made the solitary and unparalleled first ascent of Nanga Parbat.

Carbonnières, Ramond de (1762–1827) Mountain explorer of the Pyrenees who made the first ascent of Mont Perdu in 1802.

Clark, Ronald William (born 1916) British mountain historian, author of a number of books dealing with nineteenth-century climbers including *The Victorian Mountaineers*, *The Early Alpine Guides*, *Six Great Mountaineers* and *An Eccentric in the Alps*, a biography of the Rev. W. A. B. Coolidge.

Collie, John Norman (1859–1942) Scientist and mountaineer whose extensive climbing included much early work in Skye and on the Scottish mainland, the first ascent of the Dent du Requin and the first traverse of the Grepon in 1892. In 1895 he went with Mummery, Bruce and Geoffrey Hastings to Nanga Parbat, and two years later led the first British party to the Canadian Rockies – the first of five visits.

Compagnoni, Achille (born 1915) Italian guide, skiing instructor and inn-keeper who, together with Lino Lacedelli, made the first ascent of K2 in 1954.

Conway, Sir Martin (later **Lord Conway of Allington**) (1856–1937) Mountaineer and art connoisseur whose knowledge of the Alps led him, in 1886, to propose publication of a series of Climbers' Guides to the European chain. His *Zermatt Pocket-Book* was the forerunner of these, which were written in collaboration with Coolidge and eventually appeared as the *Conway and Coolidge's Climbers' Guides*. In 1892 he led the first major mountaineering expedition to the Karakoram, surveying many hundreds of square miles and ascending Pioneer Peak, at 22,600 feet the highest then climbed. Two years later he traversed "the Alps from End to End" and in 1896 made the first crossing of Spitsbergen, to which he returned the following year. In 1898 he visited the Andes, making the first ascent of Illimani, climbing Aconcagua and then sailing south to Tierra del Fuego.

Coolidge, The Rev. William Augustus Brevoort (1850–1926) Born near New York and brought to Europe by his mother and aunt – the latter being Marguerite ("Meta") Brevoort, one of the best women mountaineers of the eighteen-seventies – at the age of 14. Crossed the Col du Géant at the age of 15, and, though short of sight, stature and breath, made 1,700 Alpine expeditions, including 600 *grandes courses*, during the following 30 years. Together with Miss Brevoort and their dog Tschingel, was largely responsible for the exploration of the Dauphiné between 1870 and 1876. Editor of the *Alpine Journal* from 1880 to 1889. Editor, with Martin Conway, of the first series of climbing guides to the Alps. The greatest of all Alpine historians, author of scores of erudite articles, books and notes dealing with the development of mountaineering. Resigned from the Alpine Club in 1899 and from Honorary Membership in 1910 during the course of persistent and much-enjoyed battles with the rest of the Alpine world over points of scholarship. Settled in Grindelwald in 1895, where he wrote, together with much else, his two important works, *Josias Simler et les Origines de l'Alpinisme jusqu'en 1600* (1904) and *The Alps in Nature and History* (1908). Known to his contemporaries as "the name on the back of a guide-book," "the Magdalen hedgehog," "the fiery lamb" and "the Sage of Grindelwald." According to his obituary notice in *The Times*, he "could do anything with a hatchet except bury it."

Croz, Michel (1830–65) Chamonix guide, employed by Whymper on many of his most famous expeditions including (with Christian Almer) the great journey through the Dauphiné with A. W. Moore and Horace Walker in 1864. Was killed in the Matterhorn disaster the following year.

Dent, Thomas Clinton (1850–1912) Made the first ascent of the Aiguille du Dru in 1878 after 18 unsuccessful attempts. Visited the Caucasus in 1886, 1888, 1889 and 1895, the third visit being made partly to discover the fate of W. Donkin and H. Fox, two other British mountaineers, who had disappeared the previous year. Originated the idea of the Alpine Distress Signal.

Desio, Ardito (born 1898) Italian geologist and mountaineer who has climbed in the Alps and in Persia, and who has led 11 expeditions, the most important being the one whose members successfully climbed K2, the second highest mountain in the world, in 1954.

Donkin, William Frederick (1845–88) Mountaineer, scientist and photographer who sent to the Winter Exhibition of the Alpine Club in 1879 a unique collection of Alpine panoramas and other photographs taken in the preceding few years. Visited the Caucasus in 1888 with H. Fox and Clinton

Dent (who had to return on account of illness). Made an attempt on Koshtan-Tau, bivouacked below the summit and was lost, with the rest of the party, during a second attempt on the peak.

Dyhrenfurth, Professor G. O. German mountaineer and geologist who has led numerous expeditions to the Himalayas and Karakoram, notably the international expedition to Kanchenjunga in 1930.

Evans, Dr Charles (born 1918) British mountaineer who has climbed extensively in the Alps and in Wales. Was deputy leader of the 1953 Everest expedition and, as a member of the first assault party, reached the south summit with Tom Bourdillon. Two years later led the successful expedition which reached the summit of Kanchenjunga.

Filippi, Filippo de (1869–1938) Italian surgeon, scholar and mountain traveler who took part in the Duke of Abruzzi's expedition to Mount St Elias in 1907, wrote the official account of the Duke's expedition to the Ruwenzori (in which De Filippi did not himself take part) and took part in the Abruzzi expedition to the Karakoram in 1909. In 1913–14 led a major scientific expedition through Kashmir, Baltistan and Ladakh to the heart of Central Asia.

Finch, George Ingle (born 1888) British mountaineer and scientist. Member of the 1922 Everest expedition, on which he led the second climbing party to 27,300 feet.

Fitzgerald, E. A. (1871–1931) Mountaineer who accompanied Martin Conway on parts of his journey along "the Alps from End to End" in 1894. The following year he visited New Zealand with Matthias Zurbriggen, intent on making the first ascent of Mount Cook, but was forestalled by local mountaineers. Three years later he visited South America with the intention of climbing Aconcagua. His party carried out much useful scientific work, but the first ascent of Aconcagua itself was made by Zurbriggen alone.

Forbes, James David (1809–68) Scottish scientist and traveler, one of the first to describe regular journeys above the snowline. Made numerous minor ascents – as well as the first British ascent of the Jungfrau – in the Alps and Norway. Employed Auguste Balmat on research into glacier movement and was involved with Tyndall in the great glacier controversy of the eighteen-fifties. First Honorary Member of the Alpine Club.

Freshfield, Douglas (1845–1934) Mountaineer and traveler who during the last third of the nineteenth century climbed extensively in the Alps and in Scotland, as well as in the Caucasus (1868, 1887 and 1889), the Himalayas, where in 1899 he and his party circumambulated Kanchenjunga, and the Pyrenees (1892). Wrote on many subjects dealing with mountains and mountain history, and was active in the politics of exploration, mountaineering and geographical education.

Gesner, Conrad (1516–65) Zurich naturalist and professor whose enthusiasm for mountaineering was expressed in a famous letter to a friend in which he said that "I have resolved for the future, so long as God grants me life, to ascend divers mountains every year, or at least one, in the season when vegetation is at its height, partly for botanical observation, partly for the worthy exercise of the body and recreation of the mind."

*Sir Edmund Hillary (left), Sir John Hunt
and Sherpa Tenzing, after their ascent
of Mount Everest in 1953*

Green, The Rev. William Spotswood (1847–1919) British mountaineer who in 1882 reached to within a few hundred feet of the summit of Mount Cook, New Zealand, being forced back by lack of time. In 1888 made an exploratory tour of the Selkirks during which he made the first ascent of Mount Bonney and the first passage of the Asulkan Pass.

Hadow, Douglas (1846–65) A young man who made his first tour of the Alps in 1865 under the tutelage of the Rev. Charles Hudson. Took part in the first ascent of the Matterhorn on July 13–14 and was one of the four men killed on the descent, the accident generally being attributed to a slip on Hadow's part.

Hartog, John M. British mountaineer who led the first ascent of the Muztagh Tower in 1956.

Hedin, Sven (1865–1952) Swedish explorer who before the age of 21 had traveled extensively in the Caucasus, western Persia and Mesopotamia. Was attached to the court of Nasr-ud-Din at Teheran in 1891 and subsequently climbed Demavend. In 1894 reached 20,160 feet on Muztagh Ata, a great achievement for that time. Mapped large areas of southern Tibet and Central Asia during numerous trans-desert journeys.

Herzog, Maurice French mountaineer who with Louis Lachenal made the first ascent of Annapurna in 1950.

Hillary, Sir Edmund (born 1919) First visited the Southern Alps of New Zealand in 1939. Made his first visit to the European Alps in 1950, and with two companions climbed five 4,000-meter peaks in five days. In 1951 was a member of a four-man team, two of whom made the first ascent of the 23,760-foot Mukut Parbat in the Kamet group. In the same year joined Eric Shipton's reconnaissance of Everest from the south and played a crucial part in finding the route through the ice-fall of the Khumbu Glacier.

After an attack on Cho Oyu, joined Hunt's 1953 Everest expedition, and with Tenzing reached the summit on May 29, and was subsequently knighted. In the following year took part in the Himalayan expedition which climbed Baruntse and broke three ribs during the rescue of a companion. In 1955 was chosen to lead the New Zealand component of the Commonwealth Antarctic Expedition, and set up a series of *caches* between Scott Base and the United States base at the South Pole, to which he subsequently traveled. Later took part in a number of Himalayan expeditions including, in 1960, one in search of the "Abominable Snowman."

Has recorded his adventures and travels in one chapter of Hunt's *The Ascent of Everest* and in his own *High Adventure; East of Everest* (written in collaboration with George Lowe) and *No Latitude for Error*.

Hudson, The Rev. Charles (1828–65) Possibly the greatest amateur mountaineer of his time. Made the first ascent of the highest point of Monte Rosa in 1855 and, in the same year, the first guideless ascent of Mont Blanc – the first from St Gervais. Together with E. S. Kennedy, the author of the classic *Where There's a Will, There's a Way; an Ascent of Mont Blanc by a new route without Guides*. Killed in the Matterhorn disaster of 1865.

Hugi, Francois-Joseph (1796–1855) Geologist who in 1828 unsuccessfully attacked the Jungfrau and the Finsteraarhorn. During a second attack on the latter peak the following year, two of his guides reached the summit.

Humboldt, Baron Friedrich Heinrich Alexander von (1769–1859) Prussian scientist and traveler who between 1799 and 1804 explored much of what is now Venezuela, Colombia, Ecuador and Peru. In 1802 climbed to within 1,000 feet of the summit of Chimborazo. In 1829 explored the mountains of Central Asia, and in his writings contributed much to geographical knowledge.

Hunt, Sir John (born 1910) Son of an Indian Army officer, Hunt began mountaineering with the traverse of Piz Palu at the age of 15, and three years later traversed the Meije. During the early nineteen-thirties made a series of Alpine climbs which brought him into the first rank of British mountaineers. In 1935 reached 24,500 feet on K36 in the Karakoram and in the following year made the first ascent of the south face of Kolahoi in Kashmir. Was rejected for the 1936 Everest attempt as medically unfit, but shortly afterwards reconnoitered Kanchenjunga with his wife. Wartime record included the post of Chief Instructor at the Mountain Warfare and Winter Warfare School in Braemar, in the Cairngorms, D.S.O. in Italy and C.B.E. in Greece, where he organized toughening courses on Mount Olympus. Later climbed in Sinai, Cyprus and the Alps.

After the Swiss failure on Everest in 1952, was appointed to lead the British 1953 expedition which succeeded in placing Hillary and Tenzing on the summit on May 29. Hunt's staff planning was an important factor in the victory, which brought him a knighthood, the Founders Medal of the Royal Geographical Society and the United States Hubbard Medal.

Following the publication of *The Ascent of Everest*, a 150,000-word account of the expedition which he wrote in less than two months, he became Awards Secretary of the Duke of Edinburgh Award Scheme. In 1956 was elected President of the Alpine Club, filling the post throughout the Club's centenary celebrations. In 1958 accompanied a private party of British mountaineers to the Caucasus.

Irvine, Andrew Comyn (1902–24) Skier, rock climber and mountain traveler who took part in the 1924 Everest expedition and who was lost with Mallory in an attempt to reach the summit.

Kellas, Dr A. M. (died 1921) Scottish mountaineer who climbed extensively in the Cairngorms and in Switzerland before carrying out a great deal of exploratory work in the Himalayas, notably in 1910, when he made the first ascents of ten mountains in Sikkim of more than 20,000 feet. Died from heart trouble during the journey across the Tibetan plateau while on the Everest Reconnaissance of 1921.

Kennedy, Edward Shirley (1817–98) Mountaineer who in 1857 made numerous guideless ascents with Charles Hudson. Two years later discussed with B. St J. and W. Mathews the formation of an Alpine Club. A few days later, during the fifth (first British) ascent of the Finsteraarhorn, "the formation of the new Club was actually determined upon."

King, Clarence (1842–1901) Geologist and mountaineer whose *Mountaineering in the Sierra Nevada* is the great mountain classic of the United States. Member of the famous California survey party of 1864 that included James T. Gardiner, Richard Cotter and William Brewer. Made first ascents of Mount Tyndall and many other peaks in California, Nevada and Utah.

Lacedelli Lino Italian mountaineer who took part in the first ascent of K2 in 1954.

Lachenal, Louis French mountaineer and guide of Chamonix who made the first ascent of Annapurna with Maurice Herzog in 1950.

Longstaff, Tom George (born 1875) Mountaineer who in 1907 made the first ascent of Trisul and who has climbed in the Alps, the Caucasus, the Himalayas, Greenland, Spitsbergen, and the Rocky Mountains.

Mallory, George Leigh (1886–1924) British mountaineer who climbed extensively in North Wales and the Alps during the first decade of the century. Was a member of the first reconnaissance of Mount Everest in 1921, and was largely responsible for finding what appeared to be a practicable approach to the summit via the North Col and the North Ridge. Took part in the first attempt to climb the mountain, made in 1922, and in the 1924 attempt. It was on this expedition that Mallory and Andrew Irvine disappeared while making a final effort to reach the summit. Mallory's ice-axe was found many years later, and from this and other circumstances it appears most likely that they were lost in an accident while still ascending. Mallory is remembered not only for his great climbing ability and his almost mystic preoccupation with Mount Everest, but also for his brusque remark "Because it is there," given in reply to an importunate American journalist who asked why men wanted to climb Everest at all.

Mathews, Charles Edward (1834–1905) Climbed regularly in the Alps between 1856 and 1901. In 1870 helped to found the "Society of Welsh Rabbits," whose object was to explore Snowdonia in winter and which was the precursor of many clubs devoted to climbing in Britain. Made 100 ascents of both Snowdon and Cader Idris.

Mathews, William (1828–1901) Birmingham mountaineer who climbed extensively in the Alps between 1854 and 1874. His letter to F. J. A. Hort in 1856 suggesting "an Alpine Club, the members of which might dine together once a year, say in London, and give each other what information they could," was the first proposal that such a club should be formed.

Merkl, Willi (1900–34) German mountaineer and rock climber who visited the Caucasus in 1929 and Nanga Parbat in 1932 and 1934, when he was killed on the mountain with a number of companions.

Meyer, Johann Rudolf and **Hieronymus** Two brothers from Aarau who in the early years of the nineteenth century traveled through the Bernese Oberland and wished "to learn the relations between the various vast basins of eternal snow, and to ascertain whether the peaks which rise out of them could be ascended." In 1811 they made the first ascent of the Jungfrau; their ascent being queried, they made the second the following year, taking a third man as witness. In 1812 they also made the first ascent of the Finsteraarhorn.

Moore, Adolphus Warburton (1841–87) Made numerous extensive Alpine tours between 1860 and 1881, notably that with Whymper and Horace Walker through the Dauphiné in 1864, during which the first ascent of the Écrins was made. Visited the Caucasus in 1868 with Douglas Freshfield and Comyns Tucker, making the first ascents of Kazbek and the east summit of Elbruz.

Moore, Terris (born 1908) Mountaineer who in 1932, with Richard Burdsall, made the first ascent of Minya Konka in the Sikang province of China. Has taken part in numerous other expeditions, including the United States Army Alaska Test Expedition, which ascended Mount McKinley in 1942.

Morshead, Henry Treise (1882–1931) Mountaineer and surveyor who in 1920 attempted to ascend Kamet with Dr Kellas, and who in 1922 took part in the first assault on Everest with Mallory and Colonel E. F. Norton.

Muir, John (1838–1915) Scottish-born traveler, naturalist and writer. Emigrated from Dunbar, Scotland, to the United States at the middle of the nineteenth century, and settled in Wisconsin, to whose university he later went. Joined the United States Coast and Geodetic Survey, for which he traveled extensively in Alaska, where he found and named the great Muir Glacier. In 1881 took part in the Arctic cruise of the United States Revenue cutter *Corwin*, which was seeking the De Long expedition. Later traveled extensively in "the mountains of California," the title of his most famous book, published in 1894. By 1897, Muir had contributed nearly 150 articles on the Sierra Nevada, Yosemite, and other mountainous areas to magazines, journals and newspapers. He was a naturalist in the older and less specialized sense of the word, and played a significant part in the National Parks movement in the United States and in those movements aimed at the conservation of the forests of the West. One of the founders of the Sierra Club, whose President he was for 22 years. By his writings, as much as by his travels, Muir helped to condition American thought on mountains and their place in society at a time when it was perhaps most susceptible to influence.

Mummery, Albert Frederick (1855–95) Exponent of "modern" methods of rock climbing who made first ascents of the Charmoz, the Grepon and the Dent du Requin among the Chamonix Aiguilles, and left on the Géant the card found by Alexander Sella two years later and inscribed: "Absolutely inaccessible by fair means." Made seven ascents of the Matterhorn and visited the Caucasus in 1888 and 1890. In 1895 made the first exploration of Nanga Parbat with Collie, Bruce and Hastings. Disappeared with a Gurkha during an attempted passage of the Diama Pass.

Noyce, Wilfrid (born 1919) Mountaineer, schoolmaster and author, who climbed extensively in Britain and the Alps immediately before the last war, during part of which he trained aircrews in mountain-craft in Kashmir. Was a member of the 1953 Everest expedition, and has since made many notable ascents in the Himalayas.

Outram, Sir James (1864–1925) Mountaineer who made the first ascent of Mount Assiniboine in 1901 and who subsequently made many first ascents in other parts of Canada – notably of the north peak of Mount Victoria and, with Norman Collie in 1902, of ten peaks including Mount Freshfield and Mount Forbes.

Paccard, Dr Michel Gabriel Chamonix doctor who, with Jacques Balmat, made the first ascent of Mont Blanc on August 8, 1876.

Packe, Charles (1826–96) Mountaineer largely responsible for the opening-up as a mountaineering district of the Pyrenees, to which he wrote one of the first guides.

Paradis, Maria Chamonix girl who in 1809 made the first woman's ascent of Mont Blanc. Jacques

Balmat induced her to make the ascent, saying: "Climb the mountain with us and then visitors will come and see you and give you money." She was taken to the top with considerable difficulty. "Thanks to the curiosity of the public," she said years later, while serving in her stall near the foot of the mountain, "I have made a nice profit out of it, which is what I intended to do."

Ruttledge, Hugh (1884–1961) Indian Civil Servant and mountaineer. Leader of the Mount Everest expeditions of 1933 and 1936.

Saussure, Horace Bénédict de (1740–99) Genevese naturalist whose offer of a reward to the first man to find a way to the summit of Mont Blanc, made in 1760, led to the first ascent of the mountain in 1786. Saussure made the third ascent the following year and in 1788 camped for nearly a fortnight on the Col de Géant in order to make scientific observations. Laid the foundations of Alpine exploration during numerous journeys described in his *Voyages dans les Alpes*.

Sella, Vittorio (1859–1943) Italian mountaineer and photographer whose first set-piece panoramas were taken from the summits near his home at Biella in 1879. Exposed many hundreds of glass plates, some 16 by 11½ inches, not only in the Alps but in the Caucasus, which he visited in 1889, 1890 and 1896, on Mount St Elias (1897) and the Ruwenzori (1906), and in the Himalayas and the Karakoram (1899 and 1909).

Shipton, Eric (born 1907) Took part in five expeditions to Central and East Africa between 1929 and 1932. Reached the summit of Kamet, the highest mountain then climbed, on Frank Smythe's expedition of 1931. Has carried out much exploratory work in the central Himalayas and was a member of the Everest expeditions of 1933, 1935 (which he led), 1936 and 1938. In 1951 led the expedition which confirmed that Everest could be approached from the south and, the following year, led the Cho Oyu expedition which gained further information about the route by which the summit of Everest was gained in 1953.

Simler, Josias (1530–76) Zurich scholar and mountain traveler whose book *Concerning the Difficulties of Alpine Travel and the Means by which they may be Overcome* was the first practical handbook on travel above the snowline.

Slingsby, William Cecil (1849–1929) British mountaineer largely responsible for the opening-up of the mountains of Norway some 80 years ago, and for making numerous first ascents there. Climbed extensively in the Alps, and took part in the first ascent of the Dent du Requin and the first traverse of the Aiguille du Plan. Made many ascents in the Lake District and Scotland which are of importance in the history of mountaineering in Britain.

Smythe, Francis Sydney (1900–49) British mountaineer, photographer and writer, who made a number of new routes in the Alps in the nineteen-twenties after being invalided out of the Royal Air Force, and joined Professor Dyhrenfurth's expedition to Kanchenjunga in 1930. Led the successful Kamet expedition in 1931, and took part in the 1933, 1936 and 1938 expeditions to Mount Everest. Climbed also in the Canadian Rockies and the Lloyd George Mountains of British Columbia. His books, many of them largely photographic, helped to make him the best known writer on mountains since the days of Whymper.

Stein, Sir Aurel (1862–1943) Traveler, explorer and archeologist who between 1888 and 1928 carried out extensive research and exploration throughout large areas of Central Asia.

Stephen, Sir Leslie (1832–1904) English mountaineer and man of letters, remembered for his first ascents during the "Golden Age" – including the Alphubelhorn, the Blümlisalphorn and the Schreckhorn – for his book *The Playground of Europe* and for his review of Whymper's *Scrambles* in the *Alpine Journal*.

Stuck, Archdeacon Hudson American Archdeacon of the Yukon who in 1913 took part in the first ascent of Mount McKinley with Harry Karstens, Robert Tatum and Walter Harper.

Tenzing, Norkay (born 1914) Sherpa of Darjeeling who took part as a porter in the Everest Reconnaissance of 1935, and subsequently joined most Everest expeditions. Climbed the east peak of Nanda Devi with the French expedition in 1951 and the following year, accompanying the Swiss expedition to Everest, reached to within 1,000 feet of the summit with the Swiss guide Ramond Lambert. Member of the 1953 expedition, and with Sir Edmund Hillary made the first ascent of the mountain on May 29.

Terray, Lionel French mountaineer and guide of Chamonix, who took part in the French expedition to Annapurna in 1950.

Thorington, James Monroe (born 1894) Mountaineer who has climbed extensively in the Canadian Rockies and the mountains of British Columbia, as well as in Europe. Alpine historian with detailed knowledge of early Mont Blanc ascents.

Tilman, Harold William (born 1898) Mountaineer and traveler who has climbed in Africa (Mount Kenya, Mount Kilimanjaro and the Ruwenzori) as well as in the Himalayas. Took part in the successful Anglo-American expedition to Nanda Devi in 1936 as well as in its predecessor. Member of the 1935 Everest Reconnaissance and leader of the 1938 expedition.

Tucker, Charles Comyns (1843–1922) Companion on many climbs in the Eastern Alps of Douglas Freshfield, with whom he visited the Caucasus in 1868. Made an attempt on Ararat during the same year, but was forced back when 1,000 feet from the summit.

Tuckett, Francis Fox (1834–1913) Persistent mountaineer and Alpine traveler who between 1853 and 1891 climbed 269 peaks, 87 of them important ones, and crossed 687 passes. As an amateur scientist, made numerous observations throughout his travels, having been induced to do so by J. D. Forbes.

Tyndall, John (1820–93) One of the most influential mountaineers of the Victorian age. First visited the Alps in 1856 with T. H Huxley to make scientific observations. Made his third ascent of Mont Blanc in 1859 and spent 20 hours on the summit carrying out scientific work. His *The Glaciers of the Alps* produced one of the great controversies of the time. In 1860 reached 13,000 feet on the Matterhorn, the highest point then gained, and during the following year made the first ascent of the Weisshorn. Resigned from the Alpine Club in 1862 after a famous after-dinner speech by Leslie Stephen which caricatured scientific observation by mountaineers. Elected Honorary Member in 1887.

Ullman, James Ramsey (born 1907) American novelist and mountaineer. Author of *The Age of Mountaineering* and a biography of Tenzing, and editor of an anthology on Everest.

Ville, Antoine de Chamberlain of Charles VIII of France who in 1492 made the first ascent of Mont Aiguille on the orders of his master. The 6,880-foot mountain, 36 miles from Grenoble, with its flat top and perpendicular walls, was not climbed again until 1834.

Walker, Lucy The most famous woman mountaineer of the Victorian age, her most notable feat being the first woman's ascent of the Matterhorn in 1871, an ascent made with her brother, Horace Walker, and the guide Melchior Anderegg.

Washburn, H. Bradford, Jr. (born 1910) American mountaineer who climbed in the Alps in 1926, 1929 and 1931. Has carried out extensive exploration and mountaineering in Alaska including, in 1938, the first ascents of Mount Sandford and Mount Marcus Baker.

Whymper, Edward (1840–1911) English wood-engraver, traveler and mountaineer. Visited the Alps for the first time in 1860 to prepare sketches for *Peaks, Passes and Glaciers*. Made his first attempt on the Matterhorn in 1861 and six more attempts in subsequent years. By the summer of 1865 had

Edward Whymper

made first ascents of the Écrins, Mont Dolent, Aiguille de la Trelatete, Grand Cornier, the west summit of the Grandes Jorasses, and the Aiguille Verte, as well as first passages of numerous cols. On July 12, 1865, together with Lord Francis Douglas, joined Charles Hudson's party in the first ascent of the Matterhorn, made by the Swiss ridge. Hudson, Douglas Hadow, Lord Francis and Michel Croz, Whymper's guide, were killed following a slip, almost certainly by Hadow, during the descent, Whymper and the two Taugwalders, the other guides of the party, being saved only by the breaking of the rope.

Endless controversy was aroused by the accident – which has been the subject of books, films and a radio play – because of the number killed, the fact that one of the victims was a titled man, the rivalry with an Italian party which was trying to climb the mountain from the Italian side, and the unfortunate fact that the rope which broke was one of the thinnest among those available. There were also groundless rumors that one of the Taugwalders had "cut the rope," a possibility completely ruled out by the circumstances of the accident.

After the Matterhorn disaster, Whymper gave up regular high mountaineering in the Alps but visited Greenland and, in 1879-80, the Andes of Ecuador, where he made numerous first ascents, spent 36 nights above 14,000 feet and made important physiological observations. Visited the Canadian Rockies in 1901, 1904 and 1909 for the Canadian Pacific Railway.

Whymper's *Scrambles Amongst the Alps in the Years 1860-69*, published in 1871, is the classic account of Alpine exploration during the "Golden Age" of the last century. Together with Whymper's many lecture tours, it made him the best known of all mountaineers throughout the latter part of the nineteenth century.

Wills, The Rt. Hon. Sir Alfred (1828–1912) Made many ascents in the Alps during the eighteen-fifties, notably the fourth ascent of the Wetterhorn in 1854. The account of this climb given by Wills in *Wanderings Among the High Alps*, published two years later, did much to stimulate the growing interest in mountaineering.

Wood, Walter A., Jr. (born 1907) American geographer. Climbed in the Alps between 1924 and 1930, and has also taken part in expeditions to the Himalayas and Mount St Elias.

Workman, William Hunter (1847–1932) and **Fanny Bullock** (1859–1925) American husband and wife who between 1899 and 1912 made seven important exploratory expeditions in the Himalayas, covering an immense amount of new ground and making numerous first ascents. Notable among these was the visit to the Nun Kun massif in 1906, during which a first ascent was made of the second highest peak in the group at nearly 23,000 feet, an altitude record for women, which Mrs Workman gained at the age of 47. Nearly as important was the expedition of 1912, during which the 50-mile Siachen Glacier was fully explored and partially surveyed.

Young, Geoffrey Winthrop (1876–1958) British mountaineer and mountain writer. Played an important part in the foundation of Welsh rock climbing at end of the nineteenth century, and its development in the twentieth. With his *Roof-Climbers' Guide to Trinity* (1905) he popularized the sport of stegophily. Made an important series of first ascents in the Alps before the First World War, notably the south face of the Taschhorn and the Mer de Glace face of the Grepon. Lost a leg in the Italian campaign while commanding a Friends' Ambulance Unit but later made numerous climbs in Wales and the Alps, including the Matterhorn. Played an important part in the formation of the Climbers'

Club, the British Mountaineering Council and the Outward Bound Trust. His *Mountain Craft*, first published in 1920, is still the classic textbook of mountaineering precept and practice. Wrote numerous poems dealing with mountains and mountaineering, as well as various volumes of prose describing his experiences.

Younghusband, Sir Francis Edward (1863–1942) Himalayan mountain traveler who in 1887 made the first European crossing of the Muztagh Pass at the end of a journey from Peking, across the Gobi Desert to Kashgar. Played an important part in organizing the first expeditions to Mount Everest.

Zurbriggen, Matthias (died 1918) Guide from Macugnaga who accompanied Martin Conway to the Karakoram in 1892, and E. A. Fitzgerald to New Zealand and the Andes, making the first ascent of Aconcagua during the second of these journeys.

Glossary

Shoulder Belay

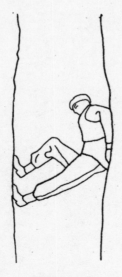

Chimney

Abseil see **Rappel**

Aiguille A sharp needle of rock or, as in the Chamonix aiguilles, a sharply pointed peak.

Anticline The crest of a fold of rock in the earth's surface: the reverse of a syncline, which is the trough of such a fold. The term geoanticline is sometimes used to describe a large anticline.

Arête also *Cresta* (Italian), *Crête* (French), *Grat* (German) and *Kamm* (German). A rocky ridge.

Avalanche A mass of snow, ice and/or rock, descending a mountain-slope under its own impetus. It can vary in size from the small rock-avalanche which is little more than an overgrown stone-fall to the massive snow-and-ice avalanche which can overwhelm entire villages.

Belay To belay is to secure oneself, or a fellow climber, by passing the rope round a suitable projection, or through a karabiner. A belay is also the name given to the projection of a karabiner so used. The principles of belaying, direct or indirect, have been developed so that they now include a large number of different methods.

Bergschrund The large crevasse found where the upper end of a glacier abuts against a higher snow- or ice-field or, in some cases, against a rock wall.

Boss A knob of rock.

Caldera A large crater, usually of volcanic origin, bounded by steep cliffs and frequently filled by a lake.

Chimney A vertical fissure in rock or ice which is at least wide enough to allow the insertion of a climber's body. It is thus wider than a crack and both narrower and of more definite shape than a couloir.

Chockstone A rock which has fallen and become jammed between the walls of a chimney or gully.

Cirque also *Corrie* (Scottish) and *Cwm* (Welsh). A deep, steepsided hollow at the head of a valley, frequently produced by glacier-erosion in the distant past, and often partly filled by a small lake.

Col A depression on a ridge linking two summits.

Cordillera A group of parallel mountain ranges.

Cornice A curving and overhanging mass of snow and ice formed on a mountain ridge by the action of wind and weather. Cornices may overhang by many feet, and can form a serious danger to the climber, who may believe he is standing on firm ground when he is, in fact, standing on a thin cornice overhanging space.

Corrie see **Cirque**

Couloir A wide, deep gully running vertically up the side of a mountain. Couloirs frequently contain snow and ice,

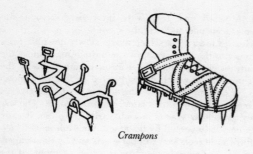

Crampons

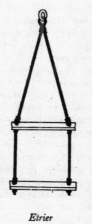

Etrier

and act as funnels for stone-falls and avalanche-debris.

Crampon A metal framework carrying steel spikes which can be attached to climbing boots with leather straps. The spikes, which are dug deeply into hard snow by the weight of the body, can eliminate the need for step-cutting, and thereby save time on a climb.

Cresta see **Arête**

Crête see **Arête**

Crevasse Vertical fissure in a glacier which may be hundreds of feet deep and from a few inches to many feet in breadth. Crevasses are caused by the slow movement of the glacier over the rock-bed on which it rests; this movement takes the glacier down slopes of varying angle, and between rock walls which may constrict its breadth or allow it to spread over a greater area. The resulting strains and stresses create the crevasses, groups of which are therefore usually to be found in the same sections of a glacier year after year. However, since the composition and extent of a glacier are due to a number of variable factors, the exact pattern of crevasses on a glacier is constantly changing.

Crux The vital pitch – or sometimes single move – on a rock climb, beyond which it will usually be more difficult to retreat than to advance.

Cwm see **Cirque**

Divide also *Watershed*. The high country separating two river systems or basins.

Dolerite Sill An intrusive layer of dolerite resting between parallel planes of a different rock.

Dyke A sheet of igneous rock forced upward towards the earth's surface through a cleft while in the process of solidifying. Often vertical or steeply-inclined, and anything from a fraction of an inch to many feet in thickness.

Escarpment A cliff-like inland ridge usually formed by the erosion of inclined strata of hard rocks. Consists frequently of a shorter, steeper slope known as the scarp face and a longer, more gradual slope known as the dip-slope.

Etriers Stirrups of wood and rope, having one or more rungs, which can be attached to pitons and used as footholds in the absence of satisfactory rock-holds.

Fault A dislocated stratum of rocks of which one part has been moved, either by pressure or by differential uplift, in relation to the other.

Firn see **Névé**

Fumaroles Small holes in the crust of the earth through which steam and gas are thrust up. Usually found in volcanic areas. The most famous group of fumaroles in the world is probably that in the Valley of Ten Thousand Smokes, Alaska.

Funicular see **Mountain Railways**

Funnel A rock formation shaped like a funnel.

Gabbro An igneous rock consisting basically of feldspar and diallage crystals.

Gendarme A rock tower or pinnacle on a ridge.

Geoanticline see **Anticline**

Geosyncline see **Syncline**

Gîte A small and frequently improvised bivouac-site where at least one night can be spent.

Glacier A mass of ice which moves slowly downhill from the upper to the lower parts of a mountain mass under the pressure of gravity. The ice is formed from snow by the great pressure to which it is subjected in the thick snow-fields on the upper slopes. This lowers the freezing point and melts the snow, which later solidifies into ice. The size of any particular glacier, which varies from one decade to the next, is governed by the amount of fresh snow which can form a reservoir at the upper levels and by the temperatures at the lower levels, near the end, or snout, of the glacier. Glaciers may therefore be either in advance or in retreat. A hanging glacier, as the name implies, is a minor glacier which has been left high above a main valley by the evolution of a mountain range.

Glacier Table A rock supported above a glacier on an ice-pedestal, the pedestal having been created by the protection from the sun given by the rock.

Glissade A method of descending snow-slopes. The feet, kept together, are pointed down the slope, and the ice-axe, held behind with the point against the slope, acts as a brake as the climber slides. Although a safe practice when used by experts, it is the cause of numerous accidents.

Gneiss A coarse-grained metamorphic rock of which there are many kinds; usually containing mica, quartz and feldspar.

Grande Course A major expedition as compared to a minor one. There is no simple permanent dividing line, although some expeditions, such as the traverse of the Matterhorn, are obviously *grandes courses* and others fall equally obviously below the standard needed to qualify.

Granite An igneous rock always containing quartz and feldspar as well as other substances. One of the hardest known rocks, it presents an ideal surface for rock climbing.

Grat see **Arête**

Greywacks An anglicized version of the German word *Grauwacke*, applied to certain sedimentary rocks.

Ice-fall The portion of a glacier where it passes over a particularly steep drop in the rock-bed on which it rests; the part, therefore, where the glacier is extensively cut up by crevasses.

Joch German word for a col. Also used, sometimes, for the lowest point on a ridge, which is not a true col – i.e. one over which a relatively easy passage can be made.

Kamm see **Arête**

Karabiner A metal snap-ring through which a climbing rope can be passed and which can be used, in conjunction with a piton or a rope-belay, to give additional security.

Karst A limestone area, named after the Karst district of Yugoslavia, in which most of the drainage is by underground streams and rivers.

Laccolith (also spelled laucolith) An intrusion of igneous rock, normally with domed top and flat base, thrust up from the earth's crust but not breaking the earth's surface.

Glissading

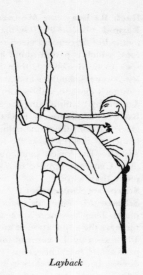

Layback

Layback A method of climbing a crack which can be used where the crack is situated in a corner and has a sharpish edge. This edge is gripped by the hands, the feet are pressed against the rock, and the body is raised against the pressure of the feet. Upward movement is strenuous, since more than the dead-weight of the body has to be borne by the arms.

Llyn see **Tarn**

Lochan see **Tarn**

Massif A mountain mass, broader than a range and frequently consisting of a plateau-like area from which the main peaks rise.

Mesa Spanish word for table used to describe flat-topped mountains which fall away steeply on all sides.

Moraine The accumulation of debris and rock fragments moved downhill by a glacier. When these fall from the mountainside on to the edges of a glacier they form lateral moraines. When two of these are brought together by the meeting of two glaciers, the result is a medial moraine which is formed down the center of the confluent glacier. At the snout of a glacier, the melting of the ice and the consequent dropping of the glacier-debris forms a terminal moraine.

Moulin A vertical and usually circular hole in a glacier made by a stream which has driven the hole to the rock-bed below the glacier.

Mountain Railways These consist of two main kinds: the funicular railway, in which a cord or cable is used to draw a carriage or carriages up an inclined slope; and the rack railway – alternatively described as cog railway or rack and pinion railway – in which additional traction is added to the normal wheel-to-rail adhesion by means of a cog mounted on the engine and engaging with a rack laid parallel to the track.

Munro A Scottish summit of 3,000 feet or more, named after the late Sir Hugh Munro, who compiled a list of such peaks at the end of the nineteenth century. The country contains 543 Munros, of which 276 are considered to be distinct mountains. The definition of a separate summit is complicated and sometimes contested.

Muskeg A boggy region, the word normally being applied to various parts of Canada.

Névé also *Firn* (German). Snow at the head of a glacier-filled valley, which is in process of being turned into ice and which will eventually form part of the upper glacier.

Overhang A rock protuberance which thrusts the climber out beyond the vertical.

Peneplain Rolling lowlands, almost forming a plain, which have been produced by extensive denudation.

Pitch Section of a climb between two successive stances, or places where a climber can stand in relative comfort and security.

Piton A short metal stanchion so designed that it can be driven, with a piton-hammer, into a rock-fissure or into ice. Pitons, which are used for belaying, frequently have attached to their blunt end a snap-ring through which the rope may be taken.

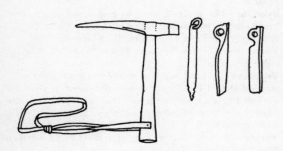

Piton hammer and pitons

39

Rappeling

Rack Railway see **Mountain Railways**

Rappel also *Abseil* (German). Descent *en rappel* is a method of descending steep rocks by the use of a doubled rope, which is passed round a projection at the top of the rock to be descended, then taken beneath the climber's legs, over his shoulder and across his back. Friction on the climber's clothes enables him to regulate the speed of his descent by manipulating the rope.

Roches Moutonées Rocks ground and rounded by glacier action, the name coming from the assumed resemblance to sheep's backs.

Saddle The lowest point on a ridge between two summits. Generally applied to a position more grassy and less rocky than a col.

Scarp see **Escarpment**

Schists Metamorphic rocks which can be split into thin plates. They have been formed from sedimentary or igneous rocks by the application of great heat and pressure. Normally known by the name of their principal constituent, e.g. mica schist, talc schist, etc.

Scree Loose slopes of rocks and boulders which rise to the foot of rock faces, and are produced by the material dislodged from above by weathering.

Serac An ice-tower formed on a glacier by the intersection of two or more glaciers.

Sierra Spanish word for a mountain range.

Slab A smooth rock lying at a relatively easy angle.

Snowline The line above which snow remains on the ground throughout the year. The altitude of the snowline in a range depends partly on its latitude, and partly on the extent of its annual rainfall. Other factors being equal, northward-facing slopes will have a lower snowline than the southern slopes of the same range.

Standards Rock climbs were for long classified as easy, moderate, difficult, very difficult, severe and very severe. Further classification led to such categories as "easy very difficult," and the method was eventually superseded on the Continent and elsewhere by numerical classification from Grade I to Grade VI, i.e. from easy to very severe.

Strike A horizontal line at right-angles to the dip of rock strata, the dip being the inclination of the strata into the ground.

Syncline The trough formed by rock strata which have been folded by movement of the earth's crust. The term geosyncline is sometimes used to describe a large syncline.

Tarn also *Llyn* (Welsh) and *Lochan* (Scottish). A small mountain lake.

Traverse A horizontal or near-horizontal movement across a face of rock, snow or ice. Also used to describe the crossing of a mountain peak – such as the ascent of the Matterhorn from Zermatt followed by the descent to the Valtournanche.

Verglas A thin film of ice formed on rocks by the weather conditions.

Watershed see **Divide**

Maps

The twelve maps on the following pages show as accurately as the scale permits the locations of the principal mountains and ranges of the world. The sketch map below indicates the area covered by each map. It should be noted that the maps are drawn to different scales. The contours marked also vary from map to map, and a scale will be found on each map. In the main section of this book – The World's Mountains – the heading to each entry carries a reference to the numbered square on the appropriate map.

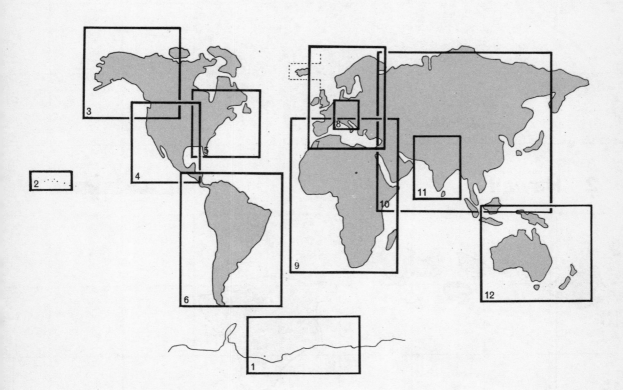

1 Antarctica

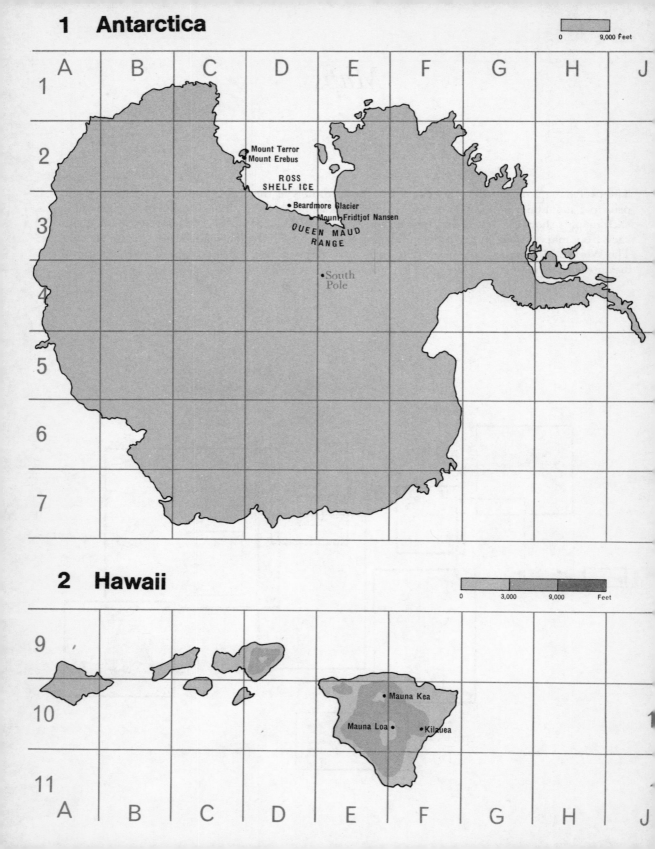

0   9,000 Feet

A   B   C   D   E   F   G   H   J

1
2   Mount Terror
   Mount Erebus
     ROSS
     SHELF ICE
3   • Beardmore Glacier
    • Mount Fridtjof Nansen
    QUEEN MAUD
     RANGE
4   • South Pole
5
6
7

2 Hawaii

0   3,000   9,000   Feet

9
10   • Mauna Kea
   Mauna Loa •   • Kilauea
11

A   B   C   D   E   F   G   H   J

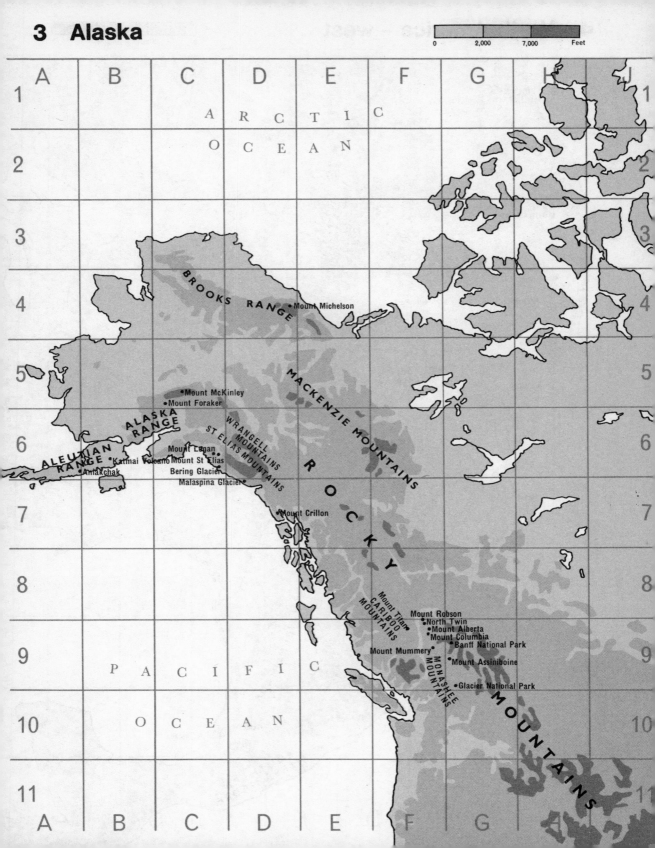

3 Alaska

0   2,000   7,000   Feet

	A	B	C	D	E	F	G	H	J
1									
2									

A R C T I C

O C E A N

BROOKS RANGE
•Mount Michelson

MACKENZIE MOUNTAINS

•Mount McKinley
•Mount Foraker

ALASKA RANGE

WRANGELL MOUNTAINS

ST ELIAS MOUNTAINS

ALEUTIAN RANGE

Mount Logan•
•Katmai Volcano Mount St Elias
Bering Glacier
•Aniakchak
Malaspina Glacier

R O C K Y

•Mount Crillon

Mount Tiam
CARIBOO MOUNTAINS
Mount Robson
North Twin
•Mount Alberta
•Mount Columbia
•Banff National Park
Mount Mummery•
•Mount Assiniboine

P A C I F I C

MONASHEE MOUNTAINS

•Glacier National Park

O C E A N

M O U N T A I N S

| | A | B | C | D | E | F | G | | |

4 North America – west

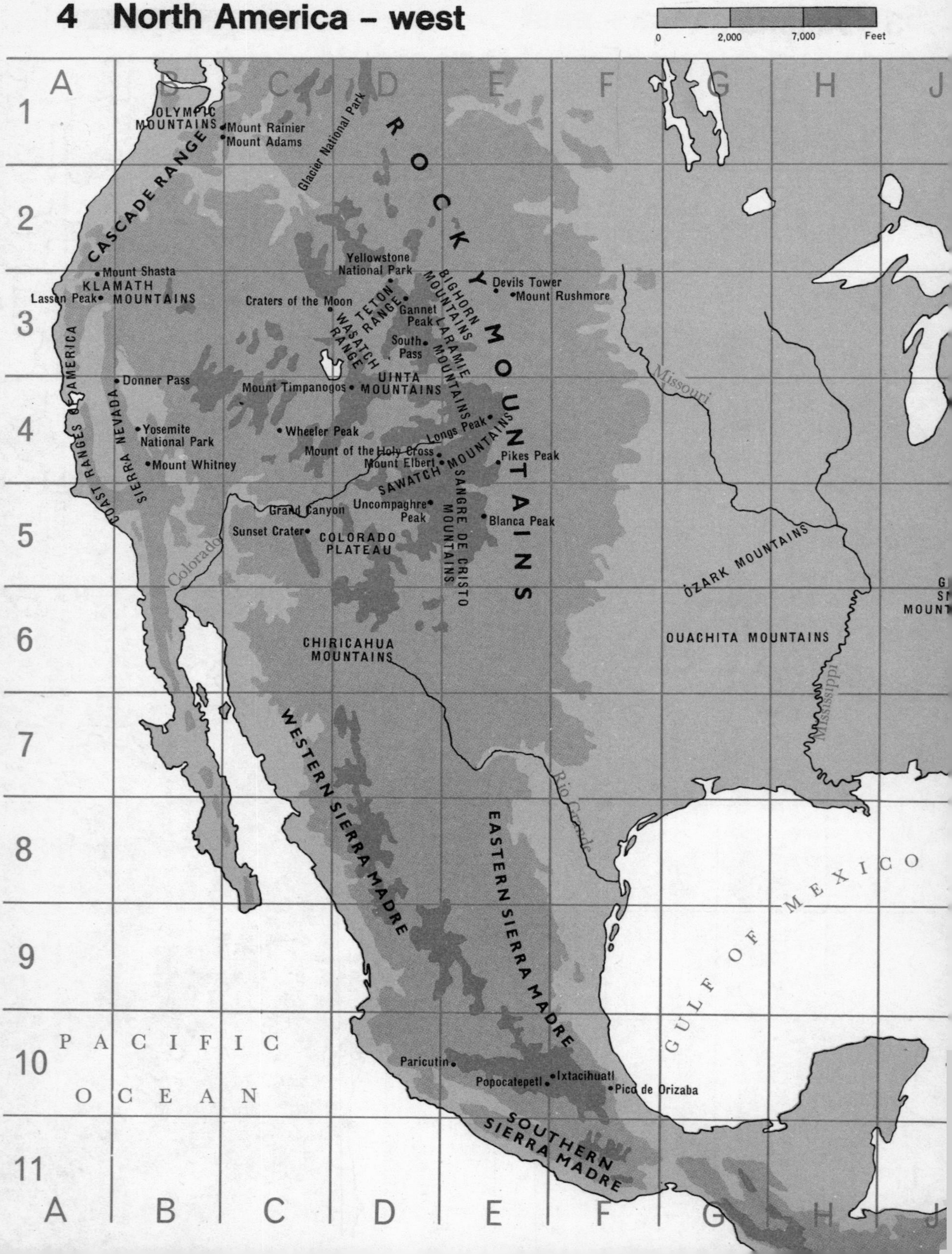

0   2,000   7,000   Feet

OLYMPIC MOUNTAINS
Mount Rainier
Mount Adams
CASCADE RANGE
Glacier National Park
ROCKY MOUNTAINS

Mount Shasta
KLAMATH MOUNTAINS
Lassan Peak
Craters of the Moon
Yellowstone National Park
TETON RANGE
Gannet Peak
BIGHORN MOUNTAINS
Devils Tower
Mount Rushmore
WASATCH RANGE
South Pass
LARAMIE MOUNTAINS

AMERICA
Donner Pass
Mount Timpanogos
UINTA MOUNTAINS

COAST RANGES OF
SIERRA NEVADA
Yosemite National Park
Wheeler Peak
Mount of the Holy Cross
Mount Elbert
Longs Peak
Pikes Peak
Mount Whitney
SAWATCH MOUNTAINS
SANGRE DE CRISTO MOUNTAINS

Grand Canyon
Uncompahgre Peak
Blanca Peak
Sunset Crater
COLORADO PLATEAU
Colorado

Missouri

OZARK MOUNTAINS
G.
SM
MOUNT

CHIRICAHUA MOUNTAINS
OUACHITA MOUNTAINS

Mississippi

WESTERN SIERRA MADRE

Rio Grande

EASTERN SIERRA MADRE

GULF OF MEXICO

PACIFIC

OCEAN

Paricutin
Popocatepetl
Ixtacihuatl
Pico de Orizaba

SOUTHERN SIERRA MADRE

5 North America – east

	B	C	D	E	F	G	H	J	
									1
									2
									3
									4
									5
									6
									7
									8
									9
									10
									11

LAURENTIAN MOUNTAINS

St. Lawrence

ADIRONDACK MOUNTAINS

GREEN MOUNTAINS

WHITE MOUNTAINS

•Mount Washington

CATSKILL MOUNTAINS

NY MOUNTAINS

ALLACHIAN MOUNTAINS

MOUNTAINS

A T L A N T I C

O C E A N

•Bonnet à l'Evêque

COCKPIT COUNTRY

BLUE MOUNTAINS

Soufrière II •
Soufrière I •

Mont Pelée•

Pitons•   •Soufrière III

•Soufrière IV

A B C D E F G H J

0   3,000   9,000   Feet

A B C D E F G H J

1

Pico Cristóbal Colón

PAKARAIMA MOUNTAINS

Mount Roraima

SIERRA NEVADA DE COCUY

2

3

OCEAN

Pichincha • Cayambe
Cotopaxi • Antisana
Chimborazo
Tungurahua

Amazon

4

P A C I F I C

Huascaran

Yerupajá

CUZCO

CORDILLERAS

Salcantay

Pumasillo

Illampu
El Misti • Illimani
Sajama

BOLIVIAN ALTIPLANO

A N D E S

SERRA DO RONCADOR

5

6

O C E A N

Parana

SERRA DO MAR

Sugar Loaf Mountain

7

Aconcagua
Uspallata • Pass
Tupungato

SIERRA DE CORDOBA

A T L A N T I C

8

9

O C E A N

10

11

A B C D E F G H J

7 Europe

0   1,500   6,000   Feet

A   B   C   D   E   F   G   H   J

ARCTIC OCEAN

Beerenberg

Askja
Hekla

ATLANTIC OCEAN

GALDHØPIGGEN
JOTUNHEIM
MOUNTAINS

NORTHERN
HIGHLANDS
CUILLIN
HILLS
CAIRNGORM
MOUNTAINS
Ben Nevis   Ben Macdhui
Ben Lawers

Slieve League

Scafell Pike
LAKE
Carrantuohill   DISTRICT.
Snowdon

PENNINE
CHAIN

HARZ
MOUNTAINS
Brocken   ERZGEBIRGE

Rhine

Loire

CARPATHIAN
MOUNTAINS

Mont Blanc
A L P S
Matterhorn

Danube

TRANSYLVANIAN
ALPS

Picos de Europa   Roncesvalles Pass
CANTABRIAN
MOUNTAINS   PYRENEES
CEVENNES
San Marino

DINARIC
ALPS
BALKAN
MOUNTAINS

Andorra
Maladeta
Cirque de Gavarnie

SIERRA DE
GUADARRAMA

APENNINES

Montenegro

RHODOPE
MOUNTAINS

Olympus   Mount Athos   IDA
MOUNTAINS

SIERRA
MORENA
Vesuvius

SIERRA
NEVADA

Stromboli

Parnassus
Helicon

TAURUS
MOUNTAINS

M E D I T E R R A N E A N   S E A

Mount Etna

ATLAS MOUNTAINS

Ushba
Mount Elbrus

A   B   C   D   E   F   G   H   J

8 The Alps

A B C D E F G H J

0   1,500   9,000   Feet

1

2

Rhine

3

4

5

VOSGES

6   Rhine   Danube   Danube

7   JURA   Pilatus
                          Eiger •Wetterhorn   SILVRETTA   •Grossglockner
                      Mönch •Schreckhorn   GROUP
                    Jungfrau •Finsteraarhorn   •Rhätikon   •Brenner Pass
              Dent du Midi •Aletschhorn •St Gotthard Pass RHAETIAN ALPS
8   BERNESE OBERLAND LEPONTINE ALPS   ALBULA ALPS   •Monte Piana
       Aiguille Verte •Monte Leone   BERNINA
     Brandes Jorasses •Dent   •Simplon Pass ALPS   DOLOMITES   JULIAN ALPS
     Aiguille du Midi Blanche •Weisshorn   P   S
        Mont Blanc •Dent •Matterhorn   •Piz Palu
     CHAIN OF MONT BLANC •Grand •Monte Rosa   •Ortler
     Great St Bernard Pass •Combin
       PENNINE   L
     Little St Bernard Pass ALPS
9   Aiguilles d'Arves• GRAIAN ALPS •Gran Paradiso   Rhône
       Meije• DU PELVOUX
     MASSIF •Ailefroide •Mont Cenis
       DAUPHINE •Roche Melon
         ALPS A
       COTTIAN   Po   ADRIATIC
10   •Mont Ventoux ALPS •Monte Viso   SEA
       MARITIME
         ALPS

11   •San Marino

A B C D E F G H J

9 Africa

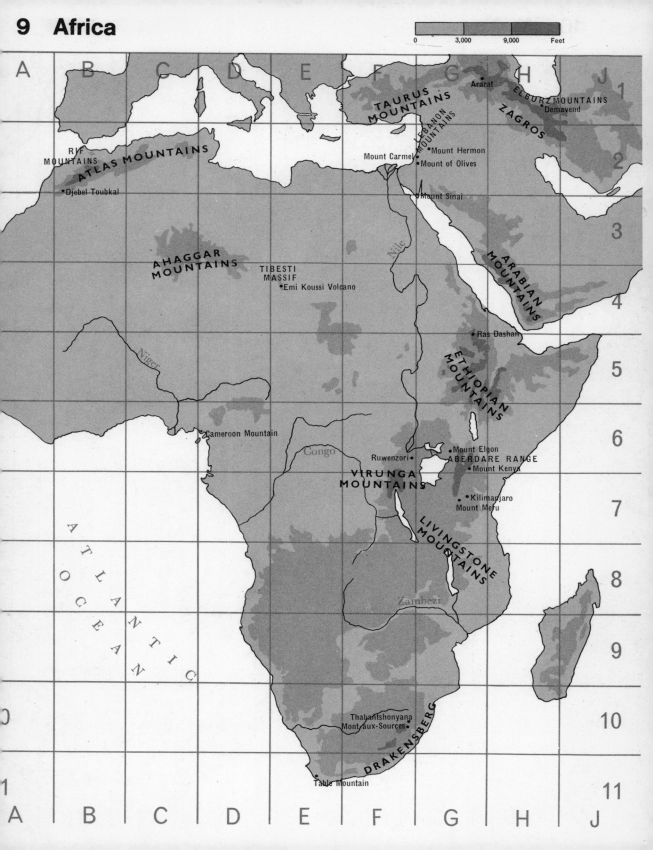

0   3,000   9,000   Feet

| | | | | | | | | | |
|A|B|C|D|E|F|G|H|J|

TAURUS MOUNTAINS

Ararat

ELBURZ MOUNTAINS

LEBANON MOUNTAINS

ZAGROS

Demavend

RIF MOUNTAINS

ATLAS MOUNTAINS

Mount Carmel
•Mount Hermon
•Mount of Olives

•Djebel Toubkal

•Mount Sinai

AHAGGAR MOUNTAINS

TIBESTI MASSIF

ARABIAN MOUNTAINS

Nile

•Emi Koussi Volcano

Niger

•Ras Dashan

ETHIOPIAN MOUNTAINS

•Cameroon Mountain

Congo

•Mount Elgon

Ruwenzori•

ABERDARE RANGE

•Mount Kenya

VIRUNGA MOUNTAINS

•Kilimanjaro
Mount Meru

LIVINGSTONE MOUNTAINS

A T L A N T I C

O C E A N

Zambezi

Thabantshonyana
Mont-aux-Sources

DRAKENSBERG

•Table Mountain

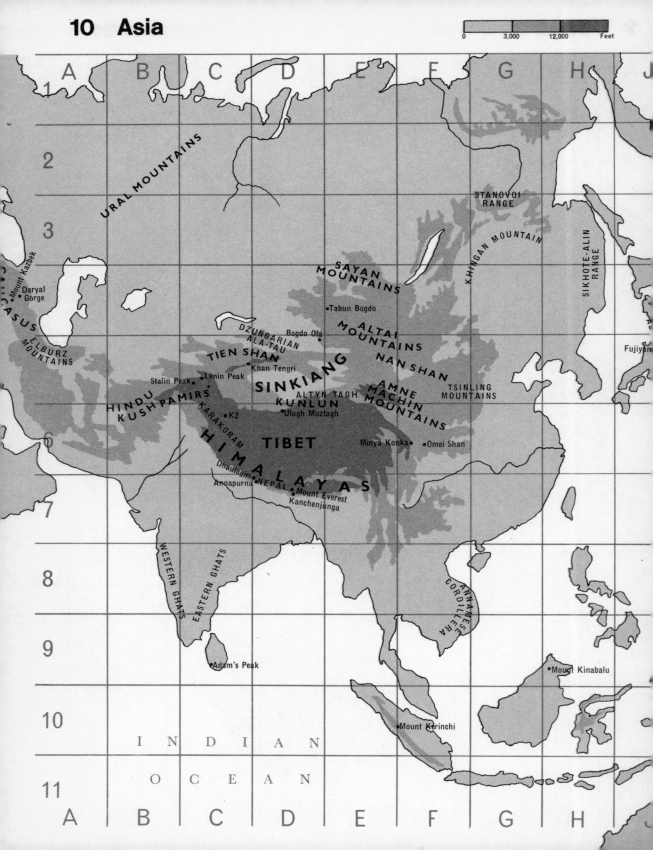

10 Asia

0   3,000   12,000   Feet

A   B   C   D   E   F   G   H   J

URAL MOUNTAINS

STANOVOI RANGE

CAUCASUS

Mount Kazbek

Daryal Gorge

KHINGAN MOUNTAIN

SIKHOTE-ALIN RANGE

ELBURZ MOUNTAINS

SAYAN MOUNTAINS

Tabun Bogdo

DZUNGARIAN ALA-TAU

Bogdo Ola

ALTAI MOUNTAINS

TIEN SHAN

NAN SHAN

Fujiyan

Khan Tengri

SINKIANG

Stalin Peak

Lenin Peak

HINDU KUSH PAMIRS

KARAKORAM

K2

KUNLUN

ALTYN TAGH

Ulugh Muztagh

AMNE MACHIN MOUNTAINS

TSINLING MOUNTAINS

TIBET

Minya Konka

Omei Shan

HIMALAYAS

Dhaulagiri

Annapurna

NEPAL

Mount Everest

Kanchenjunga

WESTERN GHATS

EASTERN GHATS

ANNAMESE CORDILLERA

Adam's Peak

Mount Kinabalu

Mount Kerinchi

I N D I A N

O C E A N

A   B   C   D   E   F   G   H

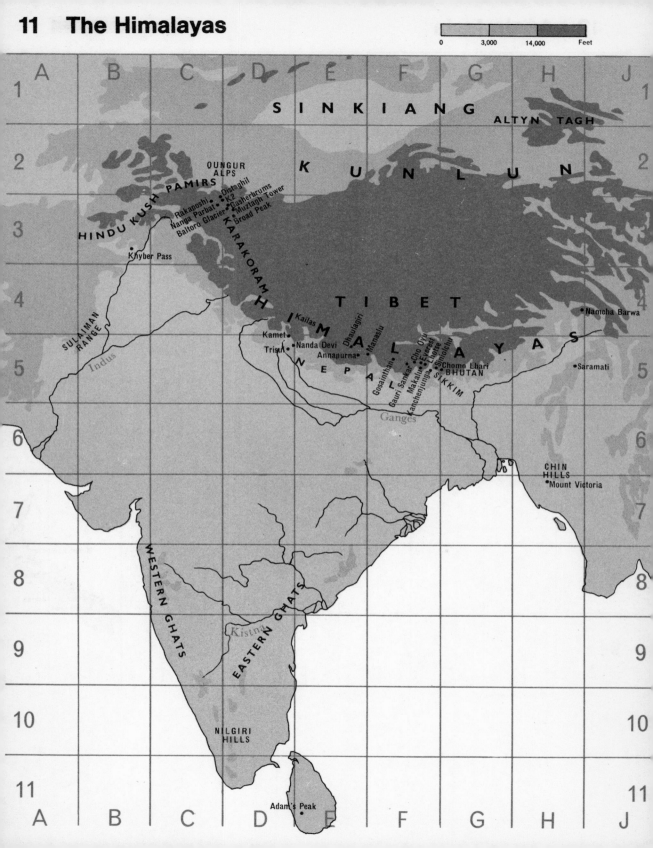

11 The Himalayas

Feet
0   3,000   14,000   Feet

A B C D E F G H J
1   1

SINKIANG
ALTYN TAGH

OUNGUR
ALPS
PAMIRS
HINDU KUSH
KUNLUN
K
2   2

Rakaposhi • Distaghil
Nanga Parbat • K2
• Gasherbrums
Baltoro Glacier • Muztagh Tower
• Broad Peak
3   3

• Khyber Pass
KARAKORAM

SULAIMAN
RANGE
H
I
Kailas
M
TIBET
• Namcha Barwa
4   4

Indus
Kamet •
Nanda Devi
Trisul •
• Dhaulagiri
A
Manaslu
• Cho Oyu
L
• Saramati
5   5

Annapurna •
Gosainthan •
Gauri Sankar • Everest
Makalu • Lhotse
Kanchenjunga • Sinolchu
Chomo Lhari
BHUTAN
SIKKIM
NEPAL
A
Y
A
S

Ganges

CHIN
HILLS
• Mount Victoria
6   6

7   7

WESTERN GHATS
EASTERN GHATS
8   8

Kistna
9   9

NILGIRI
HILLS
10   10

11   11

Adam's Peak •

A B C D E F G H J

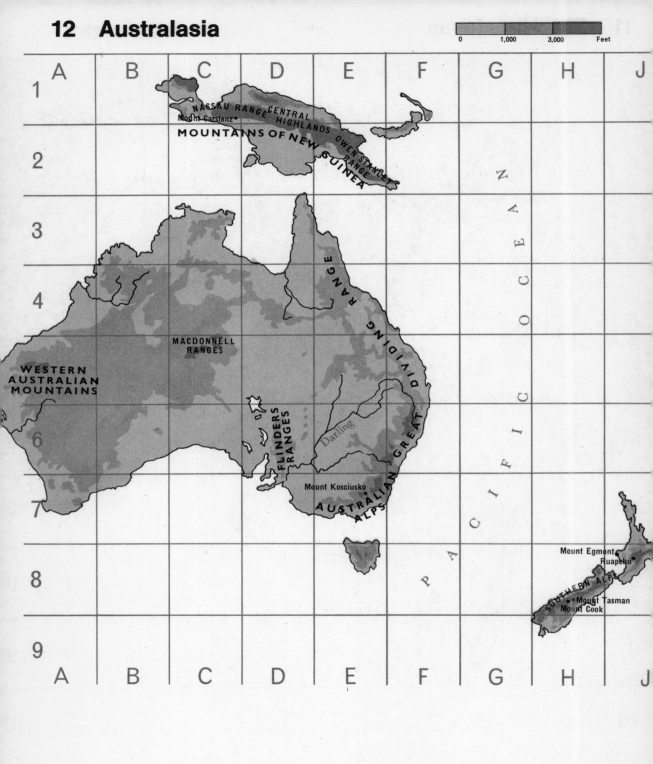

0   1,000   3,000   Feet

A   B   C   D   E   F   G   H   J

1
2
3
4
6
7
8
9

NASSAU RANGE
Mount Carstenz
CENTRAL HIGHLANDS
OWEN STANLEY RANGE
MOUNTAINS OF NEW GUINEA

MACDONNELL RANGES

WESTERN AUSTRALIAN MOUNTAINS

DIVIDING RANGE

FLINDERS RANGES

Darling

GREAT

Mount Kosciusko

AUSTRALIAN ALPS

PACIFIC OCEAN

Mount Egmont
Ruapehu
SOUTHERN ALPS
Mount Tasman
Mount Cook

The World's Mountains

The World's Mountains

Aberdare Range

*A section of the eastern rim of the Great Rift Valley.
Location Western central Kenya. Height 12,000–
13,000 feet average, rising to 13,244 feet. Map 9, G6.
Explored J. W. Gregory, Joseph Thomson, Dr Hans
Meyer, H. B. Muff and others, 1877–95.*

Lying almost due west of Mount Kenya, the
Aberdares form part of the rim which limits the
Great Rift Valley, that depression which runs
for more than 3,000 miles from the Middle East
to Central Africa and contains Lake Rudolf and
Lake Nyasa as well as many of the smaller
stretches of water which lie between the two.

The Aberdares were originally called the Sattima (or Settima) Range, and were renamed in
1894 after Henry Austin Bruce, Lord Aberdare,
a British politician of Welsh origin. A few miles
south of the equator they rise to 13,244 feet in
Sattima and 12,772 feet in Kinangop. They provide a pleasantly equable climate which has
made them for over 70 years a much sought-
after region for white settlers. Naivasha and Gil-
gil are the main towns from which the summits
of the Aberdares are usually reached.

Almost the whole of the range supports considerable vegetation, and the camphor forests which
stretch across its eastern slopes play a substantial
part in Kenya's economy. At greater heights, the
Kinangop Plateau has been turned into a center
for dairying, sheep farming and the growing of
pyrethrum and deciduous fruit.

Aconcagua

*Highest peak in the western hemisphere. Location
Andes of western Argentina, near the Chile border.*
*Height 22,835 feet. Map 6, C8. Climbed Mat-
thias Zurbriggen and Stuart Vines, 1897.*

"A white, sky-filling beacon, gigantic and alone,"
as James Ramsey Ullman described it, Aconcagua can be seen from the Pacific coast of Chile,
100 miles away, towering over the cities of Santiago and Valparaiso. It is the greatest and best-
known landmark on the continent. Its climbing
offers few technical difficulties, yet the great altitude, the bitter cold and the frequent and savage
storms make it one of the most gruelling ordeals
known to climbers.

The first attempt was made in 1883 under the
leadership of Paul Güssfeldt, a well-known German alpinist; his party was repulsed by storms
1,300 feet below the summit. A few more abor-
tive attempts followed, until in the winter of
1896–97 (the summer of the southern hemisphere) E. A. Fitzgerald set out to conquer the
mountain, accompanied by Stuart Vines, a younger British climber, and by a small group of
naturalists and a corps of Swiss and Italian guides
headed by Matthias Zurbriggen.

After three failures, Fitzgerald and Zurbriggen, racked by altitude-sickness and weakened
by poor food and exposure, started once again
from their base camp at 18,700 feet, high above
the deep ravine of the Horcones Valley.

"On reaching . . . 22,000 feet . . . I found that
it was absolutely impossible for me to proceed
further," Fitzgerald wrote later. "I sent Zurbriggen on at once to complete, if possible, the
ascent, although myself obliged to turn back.
I had the greatest difficulty in crawling down;
my knees were so weak that I repeatedly fell,
cutting myself with the sharp stones that covered
the mountainside. I crawled along in this miser-

The Adirondack Mountains in New York State, one of the most scenic areas in the eastern United States

able plight, steering for a big patch of snow. Here, unable to stand any longer from sheer exhaustion, I was obliged to lie down and roll down the mountainside."

But Zurbriggen made it. After many hours of weary plodding he reached the summit, planted his ice-axe on the top and built a small pyramid of stones. A month later, after another frustrated attempt, Vines and an Italian porter-guide, Nicola Lanti, made the second ascent of Aconcagua. This time the weather was fine and the view magnificent.

"The western and northwestern sides of the mountain fall away at an angle of 20° and are composed more or less of great slopes of loose stones which are kept clear of snow in summer by the winds that sweep them," wrote Fitzgerald (who never reached the summit himself). "To the south and southwest the sides are more precipitous, also fairly clear of snow and ice, forming one of the most imposing sights imaginable. Looking down this dizzy precipice, Mr Vines saw below him spurs of the mountain flanking the glacier beneath to the right and left, giving it

the appearance of a huge amphitheater . . . To the northwest the line . . . of the South Pacific Ocean . . . 100 miles distant . . . stood up high in the horizon, stretching away for over 150 miles. Range after range of mountain could clearly be seen between Aconcagua and the ocean. He seemed to look right into the valleys between these ranges . . ."

Since 1897 Aconcagua has often been climbed and it has become one of the most "international" of mountains. In 1906 a Swiss expedition was led by Helbling. In 1934 an Italian party took up two dogs – probably the greatest altitude reached by canines before the era of the sputniks. In 1951 a small hut was built at almost 22,000 feet by a group of Argentinian Army climbers, and in 1952 two priests carried up a statue of Our Lady of Carmel and placed it on the summit.

Adams, Mount

An ancient, inactive volcano with snow-capped cone. Location Southern Washington, in the Cascade

Range, 55 miles southwest of Yakima. Height 12,470 feet. Map 4, B1. Climbed Shaw, Aiken and Allen, 1854.

Mount Adams is the second highest peak of the Cascade Range. It is about 45 miles south of Mount Rainier and just west of the Yakima Indian Reservation. Its northern and southern slopes are more gradual than the eastern or western ascent. One of the peaks thrown up by the volcanic eruption on the Cascade Peneplain, it is a beautiful and typical example of a volcanic cone. As it lies on the eastern side of the Cascades, it does not get the extremely heavy rainfall of the western side of the range, but there is enough moisture to support extensive pine forests.

Adam's Peak

A conical mountain peak. Location Southern central Ceylon, 45 miles east of Colombo. Height 7,360 feet. Map 11, E11.

Adam's Peak is also known as Rama's Peak, while the Singhalese call it "Sri Padastanaya" or "Samanaliya." The conical summit terminates in an oblong platform 72 feet by 24 feet in which there is a hollow shaped like a human foot 5 feet 4 inches by 2 feet 6 inches. "When the Buddhists first came to Ceylon, in about the fourth century B.C., they claimed the footmark as that of Buddha," wrote Edward Carpenter in his *From Adam's Peak to Elephanta*. "Later on some Gnostic Christian sects attributed it to primal man; the Mohammedans, following this idea, when they got possession of the mountain, gave it the name of Adam's Peak; the Portuguese consecrated it to St Eusebius; and now the Buddhists are again in possession – though I believe the Mohammedans are allowed a kind of concurrent right."

The Moslems believe that Adam ended 1,000 years' penance here, while the Hindu followers of Brahma claim the footstep for their god, Siva.

For over 2,000 years there has been an uninterrupted flow of pilgrims to the sacred spot. The margins of the hollow are ornamented with gems and it is covered with an elaborate carved canopy. "On the natural platform just below," Carpenter continued, "are some curious bits of furniture; four old bronze standard lamps, of lotus-flower design, one at each corner of the platform, a bell, a little shrine and the priests' hut ... Very ancient gnarled rhododendron trees, 20 or 30 feet high, rooting in clefts and hollows, were in flower (carmine red) all round the top of the rock."

Adirondack Mountains

A group of mountains about 100 miles long and 75 miles wide, with over 100 peaks and many lakes. Location Northeast New York. Height Average 4,000 feet, with many peaks over 4,500 feet. Map 5, B3.

The Adirondacks are spread mainly over Clinton, Essex, Hamilton and Franklin counties of New York State. Generally, but mistakenly, regarded as part of the Appalachian system, they are related geologically to the Laurentian highlands. The entire hilly or mountainous region lying within St Lawrence, Lewis, Herkimer, Warren and the above four counties is usually referred to as the Adirondack Mountains. Under Mount Marcy lies a tiny oval lake which Verplanck Colvin, the naturalist who discovered it in 1872, named Lake Tear of the Clouds. It is the source of the great Hudson River.

Other peaks are Algonquin (5,112 feet), Boundary, Dix, Gray, Haystack, Skylight and Whiteface, all under 5,000 feet. Forests of beech, birch, cedar, hemlock, maple and pine are abundant on the slopes. There are many rivers and lakes as beautiful as their names: Mink Pond, Big Moose Lake, Tupper Lake, Lake Placid, Lake Racquette, Upper and Lower Saranac, Cold River, Otter Creek. Because of the mild and pure climate, many sanatoria for lung diseases have been established in the district, especially around the Saranac Lakes.

The early settlers, though they used the Mohawk and Hudson valleys as outlets to the west and south, found the Adirondacks too inaccessible and for a long time they were left uninhabited. Today dairy- and truck-farming are flourishing. Iron ore (rich in titanium compounds) has been discovered and mining has grown important in the northern part of the mountains.

Both in the summer and winter seasons, the Adirondacks are visited by tens of thousands of tourists. The Adirondack Park, a forest preserve of New York State, occupies the central part of the mountains and covers over 2,000,000 acres. It is a region of remarkable scenic beauty and the second largest forest preserve in the United States. It was established in 1885 to be "forever reserved, maintained and cared for as ground open for the free use of all the people for their health and pleasure." Wild life is abundant, and in spite of the influx of tourists this is a region steeped in tradition. The largest industry is still lumber, and folklore enthusiasts find here a rich hunting ground for songs, especially among the lumberjacks who float their logs down the many mountain rivers to the wood-pulp factories.

Ahaggar Mountains

A remote, partly unexplored desert range. Location *Southern Algeria, in the central Sahara.* Height *Several peaks over 5,000 feet, rising to 9,850 feet in Tahat Peak.* Map 9, C3-4.

The mountains of Ahaggar (or Hoggar) rise 1,000 miles south of the Mediterranean, 1,000 miles east of the Atlantic and roughly the same distance north of the Bight of Benin. Surrounded by the most barren plains of the Sahara, yet rising to nearly 10,000 feet, the range is still noted for its inaccessibility and remoteness, which give it a romantic aura.

Only in the twentieth century was there any

real penetration into the area with the expansion of French influence and interest in North Africa. Even under French military domination, the Tuaregs, who live in the valleys from which the fantastic rock peaks and pinnacles of the group rise, were allowed to retain their ancient nomadic customs. Slavery has not yet been stamped out in the area.

French mountaineers have shown great interest in Ahaggar. From the nineteen-twenties onward – and increasingly during the last decade – they have attacked the bare rock peaks. From Tamanrasset, on the southern edge of the Ahaggar range, they have penetrated into and across the central, oval-shaped massif of the Koudia. This eroded platform of lava fields, some 155 miles in diameter and rarely dropping below 6,600 feet, presents a bizarre landscape of extinct volcanoes and pinnacles of naked rock, reminiscent of the Dolomite peaks.

"The Ahaggar is especially the desert of stones; of bare rocks or great plains of pebbles and gravel," wrote Gautier. "It is said that the camels of the country, perfectly at home in traversing the rough edges, are less at ease in the low country on the yielding sand of the dunes. It is an extremely striking thing, this preponderance of bare stone, swept and polished by the eternal wind and veneered by the desert patina in all shades of deep red, brown or black."

The mountaineers followed the army in the Ahaggar and during the last few years the archeologists have been adding their own quota of knowledge and speculation. Interest has been fastened on the rock drawings, paintings and carvings found in many parts of the range, some of them showing elephants, lions and giraffes and suggesting that in not so distant times the climate of the area may have been very different from that of today. The Ahaggar receives rather more rain than the surrounding desert and gives rise to several wadis, or intermittent rivers, among them the Oued Igharghar. Tamanrasset, on the trans-Saharan auto route, is the chief settlement.

Exploration is bound to become more extensive with the opening up of the Saharan oil wells and a great deal that is still unknown and shrouded in mystery is bound to be clarified – bringing also new challenges and opportunities to the mountaineer.

Aiguille du Midi

A rock needle. Location *Mont Blanc Massif, south-east France.* Height *12,608 feet.* Map *8, B8.*

The Aiguille du Midi, three miles north of Chamonix, is one of the many rock needles surrounding Mont Blanc. It has a funicular railway which takes tourists almost to the summit.

One of the most remarkable ascents of the precipitous peak was made in January, 1883,

A car of the Mont Blanc cable railway, near the summit of the Aiguille du Midi

when Mrs Aubrey LeBlond, author of *The High Alps in Winter; or, Mountaineering in Search of Health,* was sent to Chamonix to be cured of consumption. She had climbed Mont Blanc and the Grandes Jorasses and "enjoyed herself immensely." On January 15, 1883, she crossed the Col des Grands Montets with her guide, Edouard Coupelin, and four days later walked up to the Montenvers, intending to climb the Aiguille du Midi next day. Even in summer this ascent direct from the Montenvers would be a stiff day's work; but the gallant lady, whose doctors had recommended "the utmost caution," reached her goal in 12 hours, and was far from exhausted. Down in Chamonix her exploit was duly noted and a cannon was fired off in her honor. "While descending to Chamonix next morning we considered what more we could do to make the good people below open their eyes," she wrote high-spiritedly, and proceeded to make a whole series of first-class winter ascents.

In November, 1955, the Aiguille du Midi was the scene of a tragedy. Louis Lachenal, who, with Maurice Herzog, had been one of the conquerors of Annapurna and had lost all his toes in the ordeal, was ski-ing down from the peak. "He was unroped," wrote Sir Arnold Lunn, "even though he must have realized that the glaciers are never so perilous as in November, when the crevasses are masked but not securely bridged by powdery snow, which has not consolidated. Suddenly he broke through into a concealed crevasse, and, less lucky than on Annapurna, fell to his death. So perished one of the greatest of modern guides."

In August, 1961, the Aiguille was the scene of a disaster unique in Alpine history, when a French air force jet accidentally severed the traction cable of the famous Mont Blanc cable railway. Three cars fell some 400 feet on to a glacier on the Aiguille du Midi – killing their six occupants – and several more cars were trapped in mid-air. Ninety-one passengers spent the night suspended 10,000 feet above the "White Valley" until they were rescued next morning. Some of the rescuers climbed hand over hand along the suspension cable to fix ropes to the cars, so that they could be pulled to safety; other cars were lowered into a crevasse from which the passengers were taken by helicopter.

Aiguilles d'Arves

Three rock needles. Location *Dauphiné Alps, south-east France.* Height *11,513 feet (highest point).* Map *8, B9.* Climbed *Two unidentified chamois hunters (central peak), 1839.*

The three Aiguilles d'Arves – the Southern Aiguille (11,513 feet), the Northern Aiguille (10,926 feet) and the Central Aiguille (10,520 feet) – dominate the rolling sub-Alpine landscape between St Jean de Maurienne in the Arc valley and La Grave in the Romanche valley, not only by their height but by their commanding and impregnable aspect. "All three of the aiguilles *may* be accessible but they look as inaccessible as anything I have seen," wrote Edward Whymper in 1871 – a revealing comment from the man who had by that time succeeded in making the first ascent of the Matterhorn.

These three spectacular pinnacles were by no means as insuperable as their appearance suggested. The central peak had been climbed by two chamois hunters in 1839. Their unsubstantiated (and much doubted) story was confirmed in 1876 when a coin was found on the summit by a later explorer. The Southern Aiguille provides some difficulty and a *mauvais pas* (bad patch) which has become a prominent feature on the local postcards.

Standing high above the surrounding meadows, the Aiguilles d'Arves supply something more like a rock climb in the Highlands of Scotland than do most of the Alpine peaks. They also form one of the finest of all viewpoints from which the Dauphiné Alps can be seen at close quarters.

The Aiguille Verte

Aiguille Verte

A rock needle. Location *Mont Blanc Massif, southeast France, between the Argentière and Talèfre glaciers, overlooking Chamonix.* Height *13,540 feet.* Map *8, B8.* Climbed *Edward Whymper, 1865.*

The ascent of the Aiguille Verte (Green Needle) was, for Edward Whymper, a secondary time-killing exploit while he was preparing for the onslaught on the Matterhorn. Accompanied by Christian Almer and Franz Biener, he made a notable first ascent in July, 1865.

This fine peak was the second major summit in the Alps to be climbed by a dog – and the second human ascent was made to authenticate the first. T. S. Kennedy and the Rev. Charles Hudson had planned its conquest at Easter, 1865, but when they arrived in Chamonix on July 29 they learned that Whymper was already on the mountain; the next day he returned from his successful expedition. Whymper's guides, however, were Swiss, and the Chamonix men, being French and having made at least 20 attempts themselves, cast groundless doubt on his achievement. "So our expedition," wrote Kennedy, "was reduced to making the second ascent of the peak, partly to carry out an original intention, and partly to establish the truth of Mr Whymper's success by finding a rope which he had buried at the top."

Kennedy took with him his small black dog, who was "unhappy on snow" and may well have been carried at least part of the way in a rucksack. The party took a different route from Whymper's but the ascent went roughly as planned. Eventually, after a succession of jutting rocks, icy corners and, in Kennedy's phrase, "rousing of blood," the summit was reached. "And just as we all stood together to give a great cheer and to form a visible group against the sky," Kennedy wrote, "a gun, fired from the Flégère, announced our success to the valley of Chamonix."

Ailefroide

A mountain with a double summit. Location *Dauphiné Alps, southeast France.* Height *12,989 feet.* Map *8, B9.* Climbed *W. A. B. Coolidge and Christian Almer, 1870.*

The position of this great peak and even its existence as a separate mountain were still in doubt less than a century ago. One reason for confusion was its height, which is almost the same as that of the neighboring Pelvoux and only about 400 feet less than that of the Écrins, which it faces across the Glacier Noir. Another was its closeness to its neighbors and the difficulty of gaining a viewpoint from which the tangle of peaks could be clearly seen. The mountain, like a curiously large number of others in the Dauphiné Alps, has two summits, rising close together on the long ridge which sweeps round first westwards and then southwards from the Pelvoux itself.

In 1863 Francis Fox Tuckett, the experienced explorer of the district, was still arguing about its position with Edward Whymper; a few years later Whymper wrote that he was still uncertain of its exact height.

In 1870 the young American climber, W. A. B. Coolidge, with Christian Almer, the Swiss guide, camped out on the Glacier du Sélé, to the south of the peak, and on the following day they made the first ascent from their bivouac in little more than four hours. "Nothing could be easier than the ascent of the hitherto deemed inaccessible Ailefroide," commented the 19-year-old Coolidge.

Alaska Range

A gigantic massif, extending in an arc of about 400 miles, with southeast-flowing glaciers and many peaks over 10,000 feet. Location *Southern central Alaska.* Height *12,000 feet, rising to 20,270 feet in Mount McKinley.* Map *3, B6-C6.* Explored *W. A. Dickey; ascents made by Judge Wickersham, Pete Anderson,*

Billy Taylor, Archdeacon Hudson Stuck, Harry Karstens and others.

The Alaska Range forms a crescent south of Fairbanks and north of Cook Inlet, Kenai Peninsula and Prince William Sound. It is the northwest continuation of the Coast Mountains and is in turn continued by the Aleutian Range. It separates the coastal regions of southern Alaska from the tundra prairies of the interior, chiefly on the watershed between the Pacific Ocean and the Bering Sea. Its glaciers are the most extensive ice sheets of inland Alaska.

The intricate mountain complex of immense grandeur and beauty culminates in the majestic outline of Mount McKinley, the highest peak of North America. Other important peaks, lying to the west of Mount McKinley, are Mount Foraker (17,280 feet), Mount Hunter (14,960 feet), Mount Hayes (13,740 feet), Mount Silverthrone (13,130 feet), Mount Gerdine (12,600 feet), Mount Russell (11,500 feet) and Mount Dall (9,000 feet); while many summits are still unnamed. The range sweeps on to the east of Mount McKinley and east of McKinley Park station for 80-100 miles, where it is crossed by the old telegraph line from Valdez to Fairbanks. This part of the range is still little known and contains much unmapped country. Cathedral Peak (12,540 feet) and several other peaks over 12,000 feet are included in this wing of the Alaska Range, which continues as the Nutzotin Range. It is approached from the Mount McKinley Park station on the Alaska Railroad, which extends almost to Muldrow Glacier. It can also be reached by airplane from Fairbanks.

"The Alaskan mountains," wrote James Ramsey Ullman, "are in every sense Arctic mountains. Their rocky cores lie buried beneath enormous masses of ice and snow, and the glaciers that spill down from their slopes and fill the valleys between are far and away the largest in the world, outside of the polar icecaps." And J. Monroe Thorington stated: "The vast extent, great elevation, uncertain weather and proximity to the Arctic Circle make of the Alaskan mountains a territory of special technical problems to the mountaineer. Here, alone in North America, conditions demand equipment, time, and persistence not required in ordinary Alpine ascents. Although the conquest of these peaks has just begun, it is evident that they offer difficulties nearly equivalent to those of the Himalayas, and that the ascent of even a single major peak is a formidable undertaking."

It was in 1794 that George Vancouver, the English navigator, while surveying Cook Inlet, caught a first glimpse of Mount McKinley and Mount Foraker. Much of the Alaska Range has been explored and conquered since then, but there are still a great many challenging opportunities waiting here for the explorer and the mountaineer.

Alberta, Mount

Sixth highest peak of the Canadian Rocky Mountains. Location Western Alberta, near the British Columbia border. Height 11,874 feet. Map 3, F9. Climbed Japanese party, led by Yuko Maki, 1925.

Mount Alberta is situated in the Jasper National Park, 50 miles southeast of Jasper. The grim and forbidding summit faces the Columbia Icefield across the narrow gorge of Habel Creek, towering almost 8,000 feet above the Athabaska River. Its base was reached by way of Fortress Lake in 1901 by the German explorer, Jean Habd. Photographs of the peak created widespread interest among mountaineers and it was first ascended in 1925 by a party of Japanese accompanied by three professional guides. The next ascent was not made until 1948, and the mountain remains one of the most formidable in the Canadian Rocky Mountains, largely because of loose rock and falling stones.

Albula Alps

A range of summits intersected by a number of relatively

low passes. Location *Rhaetian Alps, eastern Switzerland.* Height *8,450–11,223 feet.* Map *8, E8.*

The Albula Range stretches from the Splügen Pass to the Flüela Pass, north and west of the Val Bregaglia and the Engadine. Its peaks over 10,000 feet include Piz Kesch (11,223 feet), Piz dellas Calderas (11,132 feet), Piz Platta (11,109 feet), Piz Julier (11,106 feet), Piz d'Err (11,093 feet), Piz d'Aela (10,959 feet), Cima da Flex (10,785 feet), Piz Uertsch (10,739 feet), Tinzenhorn (10,430 feet) and Piz Michel (10,378 feet). Of its principal passes the Fuorcla Calderas (Molins to Bevers) is the highest at 10,270 feet. The Albula Pass (Bergün to Ponte) at 7,595 feet rises above the Albula railway (finished in 1903), which uses more than 40 tunnels and crosses nearly two miles of bridges and viaducts.

The Albula Alps have neither the height nor the majesty of the Bernina, but form an admirable viewpoint for the higher range.

From the Pizzo Lunghino (9,121 **feet**) streams flow down to three seas: the Adriatic, the North Sea and the Mediterranean. The Piz Michel, the Tinzenhorn and the Piz d'Aela, which rise above Bergün to the north of the group, are three of the most important dolomitic mountains outside the Dolomites themselves. In summer the group provides a fine succession of viewpoints from which the Bernina and its peaks can be seen; in winter it is an ideal playground for the winter sports enthusiast.

Aletsch Glacier and Aletschhorn

The largest glacier in the Alps, comprising the Great Aletsch Glacier, the Upper Aletsch Glacier and the Middle Aletsch Glacier; and the second highest peak in the Bernese Oberland. Location *Southern central Switzerland, in the Bernese Oberland.* Height *Upper Aletsch Glacier, 8,672 feet; Aletschhorn, 13,774 feet.* Map *8, C8.* Climbed *Aletschhorn: Francis Fox Tuckett, 1859.*

On a June night in 1857, a party of Victorian mountaineers stood in the moonlight high among

The Aletschhorn

The Aletsch Glacier, with the Marjelensee
in the foreground

the great but only partially mapped glaciers of the Bernese Oberland.

"The position which we had now attained commands one of the most magnificent views in the whole range of the Alps," wrote the Rev. J. F. Hardy. "From it the spectator looks down upon a vast sea of ice, the confluence of three glacier streams which, uniting here, pour down their frozen waters along the mighty highway which we had trodden the day before. It is the Place de la Concorde of Nature; wherever you look there is a grand road and a lofty dome."

The name stuck, and today one may find on Swiss maps the words "Concordia Platz" where the three great glacier streams unite to form the Aletsch Glacier. Beside it are the new and old Concordia huts of the Swiss Alpine Club.

Fed by the great icefields which lie in the shallow basins whose northern wall is the Eiger-Mönch-Jungfrau-Mittaghorn-Aletschhorn ridge, the main Aletsch Glacier drops in a steady, majestic curve for ten miles, first south and then southwest, to end high above the upper Rhine valley. Though forming part of the Bernese Oberland, it is entirely in Canton Valais.

Noted since the Golden Age of Alpine exploration for the splendor of its views and the attraction of the peaks which surround its upper reaches, the glacier is also bordered by three of the most spectacularly placed mountain hotels in Switzerland.

These are the Belalp, high above the snout of the glacier, where Professor John Tyndall, the eminent scientist and mountaineer, spent his honeymoon and near which he built his own chalet, and those on the Eggishorn, 7,195 feet above the true left bank of the glacier. All were opened to serve the growing needs of the Victorian mountaineers and all have retained something of that tradition.

Near the Eggishorn lies the Marjelensee, a small lake bordering the Aletsch Glacier, from which minor icebergs sometimes detach themselves and float into the water. Facing the lake lies the tributary Middle Aletsch Glacier and above it rises the noble peak of the Aletschhorn, the second highest summit in the Bernese Oberland.

With its classic triangle of summit ridges, the attraction of its position between the main Oberland and Valais peaks, and its impressive nearer surroundings, the Aletschhorn had long been eyed with envy by mountaineers when Tuckett made the first ascent in 1859. The climb had all the traditional features of the night beneath the stars, the glacier walk, the crossing of the bergschrund (large crevasse) and the final struggle on the summit ridge. "Gradually the mass above us tapered away more and more," Tuckett wrote later, "and at length, after a stiff climb of three-quarters of an hour, and with the aid of rather more than 200 steps, we stood upon the summit exactly at 8.45 a.m. The effect was startling. A moment before, and nothing was visible but the snow-slope and the heels of the man in front, and now there was nothing above us but the sky, whilst all the world was at our feet."

Aleutian Range

A mountain range extending 600 miles northeast to southwest. The Aleutian Islands are partly submerged peaks of the range. Location Southwest Alaska. Height 5,000 feet, rising to 7,000 feet in Katmai Volcano. Map 3, A6-B6.

The Aleutian Range is the westernmost of the Alaskan ranges. It runs along the entire length of the Alaska Peninsula from the western end of the Alaska Range to the head of Cook Inlet and is then continued to the southwest by the Aleutian Islands themselves. It includes some of the world's largest volcanoes, notably the Katmai (7,000 feet) and the Veniaminof Crater. The composition of the range is largely volcanic, and evidence of volcanic activity is especially marked around Cook Inlet.

The Aleutian Range has been explored largely by American scientists and mountaineers, among whom H. Bradford Washburn, Walter A. Wood, Robert Bates and Dr Terris Moore have been the most prominent. During the Second World War, when some of the Aleutians were occupied by the Japanese and fighting continued for some time, a good deal of further exploration was made, this time for military purposes. Since the Second World War, aerial photography, helicopters and ski-planes have made the task of climbers safer, though not much less arduous.

Allegheny Mountains

Part of the Allegheny Plateau of the Appalachian Range, extending for more than 500 miles, with an escarpment of over 4,800 feet, including several generally parallel ridges. Location *Eastern United States, extending from northern central Pennsylvania into southwest Virginia and southern West Virginia.* Height *3,000–4,500 feet average.* Map *5, A4.* Explored *Early settlers in Colonial times.*

The name Alleghenies is usually applied to the ranges west of the Blue Ridge Mountains in Pennsylvania, Maryland, Virginia and West Virginia. The mountains form a complex of ranges and uplands, varying between 2,000 feet and 4,500 feet in height, composed of stratified rocks of the Silurian, Devonian and Carboniferous ages. The area is still for the most part a rugged near-wilderness belt with huge tracts of timber (mainly hardwood trees). There are deposits of bituminous coal, iron, petroleum, natural gas and clay.

The various sections of the escarpment are known as the Allegheny Front, Dans Mountain and Allegheny Mountain. The eastern edge of the Alleghenies overlooks the ridge-and-valley country of the Folded Appalachians, and on the western side the mountain belt merges with the rough country of the plateau region. The generally parallel ridges run northeast to southwest, and include Laurel Hill, Chestnut Ridge and Cheat, Negro, Rich and Shavers mountains. The highest peaks are Mount Davis (3,213 feet)

in Pennsylvania and Spruce Knob (4,860 feet) in West Virginia. The landscape around the latter is of great scenic beauty, as are the gorges cut through the mountains by the Potomac and New rivers.

Alps

Great mountain system of Europe with over 1,200 glaciers and several hundred peaks. Location *Southern central Europe, extending for more than 600 miles from the Gulf of Genoa to the low plains of Austria, over Italy, France, Switzerland, Austria and Yugoslavia.* Height *Rising to 15,781 feet (Mont Blanc).* Map *8.*

The Alps, Europe's most extensive mountain system, form a classic example of the range whose importance is due not only to its physical characteristics but also to its geographical position and the impact the mountains have had on human history.

Running in a series of parallel and crescent-shaped main groups for more than 600 miles, the system reaches more than 15,000 feet in the chain of Mont Blanc, and thus includes the highest mountains of Europe (excluding the Caucasus). Although many of them are small, its 1,200 glaciers are far more numerous than those of any other European range, and they are fed from snow-fields extending above a permanent snowline that varies in height from 8,000 to 9,500 feet according to situation.

Yet the importance of the Alps is mainly due to two other factors. These are the position of the range, astride the routes leading from the great European plains to the fertile valleys of Italy and the ancient magnet of Rome, and the fact that though lofty the Alps are marked by a series of geographical accidents which have enabled men to cross them with comparative ease from the earliest times – on foot, by horse and mule, by carriage, rail and car – while today many of the main air routes pass over them. The St Gotthard, the Great and Little St Bernard,

A party of climbers in the Alps

the Mont Cenis, the Simplon and the Brenner are only the more important of the passes. Hospices built along them and manned by various religious orders have provided board, lodging and succor for wayfarers since the early Middle Ages.

Thus the Alps have been crossed without undue difficulty by a long succession of travelers seeking Rome, intent on prayer or conquest; by armies, prelates, romantics, scientists and adventurers. All this has combined to give them an interest and importance out of proportion to their size and extent or even their beauty, impressive though this is. Hannibal and the elephants; Suvorov in his masterly campaigns above the St Gotthard; Paccard, Balmat and Saussure in their early assaults on Mont Blanc; Napoleon marching to the sound of the guns; and Whymper descending the sloping slabs of the Matterhorn to his own private appointment with destiny – these elements are the stuff not only of Alpine but also of universal history.

The precise extent and topographical division of the Alps has been the subject of endless argument, but there is little reason to question the judgment of W. A. B. Coolidge, the greatest of all Alpine historians, who placed the western boundary at the Col de Tende, where the Maritime Alps begin, and the eastern at the Radstädter Tauern at the farther end of the Tyrolean Alps. The mountain masses which curve in a gentle arc between these two depressions consist not of a single simple range but of numerous massifs, some of which are separated by deep valleys from the main watershed. They are usually divided topographically into the Western, the Central and the Eastern Alps, and although the boundaries of individual groups can still be disputed, the main divisions are clear.

In the west lie the low Maritime Alps (from the Col de Tenda to the Col de l'Argentière); the Cottian Alps (from the Col de l'Argentière to Mont Cenis and westwards to the Col du Galbier); the Dauphiné, spreading west and south, separated from the Cottians by the valley of the Durance; the Graian Alps (from Mont Cenis to the Little St Bernard Pass), split into the Western, Central and Eastern Graians, and forming in part the frontier between France and Italy; and finally the Pennine Alps (from the Little St Bernard to the Simplon Pass), the highest and most important group in the whole Alpine system. At the western extremity of the Pennines lies the Chain of Mont Blanc, followed to the east by the Central Pennines with their majestic peaks such as the Matterhorn, the Weisshorn and the Dent Blanche; then come the Eastern Pennines, which are dominated by Monte Rosa.

Of the Central Alps, the Bernese Oberland (from the Lake of Geneva to the Furka, the Reuss Valley and Lake Lucerne) lies to the north of the upper Rhône Valley and off the main watershed; it is the highest group. To the south and east of it, from the Simplon to the Splügen, and south of the Furka and Oberalp passes, lie the Lepontines; the Tödi Range extends from the Oberalp to the Klausen passes, while the Alps of northeast Switzerland spread north of the Klausen Pass. The Bernina Alps are enclosed between the Majola, the Reschen Scheideck and the Stelvio, lying south and east of the Val Bregaglia and the Engadine and north of the Valtellina; the Albula Range extends from the Splügen Pass to the Flüela Pass, north and west of the Val Bregaglia and the Engadine Pass; the Silvretta and Rhätikon group is bounded by the Flüela Pass, the Reschen Scheideck and the Arlberg Pass.

Beyond the Reschen Scheideck lie the Eastern Alps: the Alps of Bavaria (north of the Arlberg Pass, Innsbruck, the Pinzgau and the Enns Valley); the Alps of the Central Tyrol (from the Brenner Pass to the Radstädter Tauern Pass, north of the Drave Valley and south of the Pinzgau and the Enns Valley, including the Zillertal and Tauern ranges); the Ortler, Ötztal and Stubai ranges (from the Reschen Scheideck and the Stelvio to the Brenner Pass, south of the Inn Valley and north of the Tonale Pass); the Lombard Alps (from Lake Como to the Adige

Valley, south of the Valtellina, the Aprica and Tonale passes and including the Adamello, Presanella, Brenta and Bergamasque ranges); and finally the Dolomites, which run from the Brenner Pass to the Monte Croce Pass and south of the Pustertal, followed by the three small groups of the Julian, Carnic and Karawankas Alps, east of the Monte Croce Pass.

The Rhône and the Rhine both rise in the center of the system, their sources being only a few miles apart, and the long troughs which they follow separate the Bernese Oberland and the Tödi group respectively from the main chain. The Inn also has its source in the Alps, as do numerous tributaries of the Po, the drainage of the whole system being a complex one sending down waters to the North Sea, the Mediterranean, the Adriatic and the Black Sea.

Political control of the population – half Germanic and half of mixed French, Italian and Slav origin – has varied in the west with the fortunes of France and the House of Savoy; in the center with the struggle of the Swiss Confederation against both Austrians and Italians; and in the east with the growth and downfall of the House of Habsburg. Today control is shared by France and Italy in the west, by Switzerland and Italy in the center and by Italy and Austria in the east. The German Federal Republic contains a minor slice of the Bavarian, and Yugoslavia of the southeast Alps.

The history of the mountain system can be roughly divided into four periods. During the first, which ended in the mid-eighteenth century with the growth of the Romantic movement, passage through the Alps was made almost exclusively for purposes of war or pilgrimage. During the second, which began in the seventeen-sixties, largely under the stimulus of such Genevese as Saussure, the exploration of the Alps was extended from the lower glaciers to the world above the permanent snowline. With this growth of knowledge that came with scientific travel, there developed also a love of mountain exploration for its own sake, a love that had been

transformed, by the middle of the nineteenth century, into the rapidly expanding sport of mountaineering.

The period of concentrated Alpine exploration which followed, the "Golden Age" as it is sometimes called, extended from the mid-eighteen-fifties until Edward Whymper's first ascent of the Matterhorn in 1865. Yet "the playground of Europe" into which the Alps had now been transformed – in Leslie Stephen's happy phrase – continued for another two decades with only minor changes. The extension of railways into the mountain zone and the growth of the tourist trade which was thus made possible marked the end of this period during which the Alps had been, for better or worse, the playground of only a small group of specialists.

The Alps of the twentieth century have seen a vast proliferation of mountain railways, funiculars, ski-lifts and hotels; more recently, vast hydro-electric schemes have helped to transform the scene; while the growth of winter sports and winter mountaineering have radically affected the seasonal and economic basis of Alpine life. Even in the high Alps, the multiplication of huts, owned and run by mountaineering clubs, has made possible an organized mass enjoyment of these activities.

Today there are signs of a reaction. Efforts are being made by Swiss, Italian and French to safeguard the flora, the fauna and the scenery. Quite as significant is the fact that mountaineers in growing numbers are being driven to the more distant ranges of the world. It seems possible, in fact, that the Alps may be able to "carry" only a certain number of humans, as the lower slopes can of deer. If this is indeed so, the next few decades may see yet another phase in the relationship of Alps and men.

Altai Mountains

A major mountain system of central Asia. Location Central Asia, at the junction of the USSR (Russian SFSR and Kazakh SSR), China and Mongolia borders. Height *Average 8,000–10,000 feet, rising to 15,266 feet in the Tabun Bogdo knot.* Map *10, E4.* Explored *Karl von Ledebour (early nineteenth century), Sven Hedin and Sir Aurel Stein (early twentieth century).*

The Mongolian name for this mountain system is Altain-ula, the Mountains of Gold; the range of Altai (also spelled Altay) proper is also known as Ek-tagh, Mongolian Altai, Great Altai and Southern Altai. The two chief portions are the Great or Grand Altai (Ek-tagh) and the Gobi Altai. The Great Altai contains the highest summits with average elevations of 11,400 to 15,000 feet, culminating in the twin peak of Belukha (or Byelukha) in the Katun (or Katunskie-Belski) range which has an estimated height of 15,157 feet and lies within the USSR. This truly alpine section lies in the modern Soviet autonomous *oblast* (region) of Gorno-Altai and is extremely rugged and picturesque. The higher valleys are occupied by glaciers. The snowline varies from 6,000-7,000 feet on the northern to nearly 8,000 feet on the southern side of the range, whilst in the drier southeast section it rises to about 10,500 feet. There is much evidence of former more extensive glaciation in the form of old polished rocks and lake basins scattered through the alpine valleys.

In spite of the native name, there is no gold in the Altais, but there are deposits of silver, lead, zinc, mercury and occasionally copper, principally on the southwest (Kazakh) slopes. The silver mines at Leninogorsk and Zyryanovsk and the mercury mines at Chagan-Uzun are the most important.

All travelers have remarked on the fine forests and rich flora of the Altai Mountains. The Russian or Siberian cedar, apart from the value of its timber, is prized for the quality of its nut-like seeds; besides conifers there are also magnificent forests of birch, poplar and aspen. The flora of the surrounding steppe penetrates high into the mountain valleys and even to around 5,500 feet, where it mingles with purely alpine flora. The

rich alpine meadows have many species in common with the European Alps but in addition many peculiar and very beautiful Altaic species abound. The population consists of Turco-Altaic tribes who live by hunting, livestock and deer breeding. The great alpine range has received the attentions of an ever-increasing number of Soviet mountaineers in recent years; the first attempts on Belukha were made by Professor Sapozhnikoff in 1900 and by the Englishman Samuel Turner in 1903.

The Mongolian Altai starts in the Tabun Bogdo mountain knot and lies within the western Mongolian People's Republic. The Gobi Altai into which it merges consists of a series of parallel ranges rising to over 13,000 feet in the Ikhe Bogdo. It is extremely barren and not fully explored. One of the easternmost ranges of the Gobi Altai is the Gurban Saikhan, in the area of Dalan Dzadagad.

Altyn Tagh

Northern branch of the Kunlun system, separating Tibet from Chinese Turkestan and the Gobi Desert. Location *Southern Sinkiang province, China, along the southern edge of the Tarim basin and the Taklamakan Desert.* Height *Rising to 17,000 feet.* Map *10, D5-E5.* Discovered *Nicolai Prjevalsky, 1876.*

The Altyn Tagh is also called Astin Tagh and Ustun Tagh. Extending for over 500 miles westsouthwest and east-northeast, it is continued in the east by the Nan Shan. The eastward continuation of the range consists of four upper and lower ranges flanking the Tsaidam depression and a subsidiary chain flanking the upper range on the south.

A vivid description of the range was given by the Swede Sven Hedin, who started the second half of his 6,000-mile Asian journey here in December, 1900. His Mongolian guides had found with great difficulty the exit from the maze of the Akato Tagh, and by the last days of the year they were moving in the valleys between the parallel ranges of the Altyn. "We advanced for days in snowdrifts and the wind made our progress very difficult," Hedin wrote. "On New Year's Eve there was such a storm that we couldn't even light our stove. The century ended with an epoch-making hurricane. Under such circumstances riding is sheer torture. You fight in vain against the cold, you are barely able to keep in the saddle, sleep crawls over you, you grow dizzy and your limbs stiffen in the position which you have last taken. It was a great effort to dismount. New Year's Night was very cold and clear, the moon stood in the sky like an immense electric arclight. I was able to read the psalms and Bible texts which are sung on New Year's Eve in all the churches in Sweden . . ."

On New Year's Day Hedin and his small party caught a glimpse of the huge mass of the Anambaruin Ula. Here the River Anambaruin-gol burst through the Altyn Tagh range and entered the sandy desert where it became lost. It took them four days to cross the Anambaruin itself, which they found to be a continuation of the Altyn Tagh. On January 27, 1901, Hedin set out for the Gobi Desert through the valley which the Anambaruin River had carved into the range. He found many stone piles left by pilgrims who had crossed the Altyn Tagh; these primitive monuments had survived for centuries, as they were erected in sheltered spots where only erosion could destroy them.

On his return journey Hedin's party once again crossed the Altyn Tagh; the larger part of his caravan was lost on the high snow-fields and he succeeded in reaching his base camp with only two people and a single pony.

In 1906–08 Sir Aurel Stein led an archeological expedition into the same largely uncharted mountain ranges and published the results of his three years' work in *Ruins of Desert Cathay*. On his way to the Tarim basin he had to cross the Altyn Tagh. "To the south," he wrote, "my eyes roamed as far as the snow-capped range of the Altyn Tagh. For a moment I was delighted by the idea that from this spot I could feast my eyes

on the two great mountain chains of Central Asia. Somehow this lessened the feeling of oppressive dreariness which had overcome me in the solitude of the lifeless desert."

Amne Machin Mountains

Western spur of the Kunlun system. Location *Southeast Tsinghai province, China.* Height *Rising to 25,000 feet (approx.).* Map *10, E5–F6.*

The Amne (Amni) Machin Mountains (*Chi-shih Shan* is the Chinese name) form the western spur of the Kunlun system in the hairpin bend of the Yellow River; they rise to an estimated 25,000 feet 190 miles southwest of Sining.

". . . For a time during and after the last war," James Ramsey Ullman wrote, "there were recurrent reports of a summit even higher than Everest – a mysterious giant called Amni Machen, rising from the range of the same name in the remote wilderness of western China. Such grandiose claims for it have since been pretty well disproved but there is no question that it is a huge mountain – perhaps 23,000 feet or more in height."

There is little possibility of climbers from the Western world exploring the range or the towering peak in the near future; whether the Chinese themselves will explore them, or have indeed already done so, we cannot tell.

Andes

The main mountain system of South America, over 4,000 miles long, with ten peaks over 20,000 feet: the "backbone" of the continent. Location *Extending from Tierra del Fuego through Argentina, Chile, Bolivia, Peru, and on to the Caribbean coasts of Colombia and Venezuela, running parallel with the Pacific coast of South America.* Height *Average 10,000 feet, rising to over 22,000 feet.* Map *6, C2-11.*

The Andes form one of the two greatest mountain systems in the world. Three times as long as

The Central Railway of Peru, the highest rail crossing in the Andes

the Himalayas, which they rival in average height, they extend in an unbroken chain from the Caribbean Sea to the Strait of Magellan, rising to 22,835 feet in Aconcagua, the highest peak in the Americas.

Between central Colombia and southern Chile, a distance of 3,000 miles, there are no passes below 8,000 feet and most of the half-dozen railways (including the Transandine, completed in 1948, which crosses the Socompa Pass between Argentina and Chile) have to climb between 10,000 and 15,000 feet from the Pacific to cross the lofty western chain. In this long section surface transport across the Andes is all the more difficult because of two or more cordilleran ranges separated by deep troughs or by rugged and bleak plateaus.

It seems likely that the whole range was once glaciated; large glaciers still exist in the south, coming as low as 2,500 feet in southern Patagonia, though on the Western Cordillera the line of perpetual snow is 17,500 feet. Only three railways have so far been built right across the mountain zone, the Argentina-Chile Transandine, the Argentina Norte, linking Antofagasta and Bolivia, and the Central Railway (Lima-La Oroya) of Peru, which is the highest rail crossing in the Andes. In this extremely mountainous terrain, air transport, which has developed remarkably in recent years, has incomparable advantages.

As a mountain system the Andes begin in the south, in the Palmer Peninsula of Antarctica. For 1,500 miles north of the Strait of Magellan they consist of a single massive chain, never more than 200 miles wide, which continues throughout its entire length as the Western Cordillera. From the Bolivian border northwards, however, the Eastern Cordillera appears, doubling the width of the range and enclosing the Bolivian Altiplano (High Plateau) which contains Lake Titicaca, the relic of a much larger, earlier freshwater basin. The Eastern Cordillera continues, with some breaks traversed by the great headstreams of the Amazon, through Peru and Ecuador into southern Colombia, where the whole system divides into three cordilleran chains, the easternmost of which swings across into Venezuela. Ridges continue into the Isthmus of Panama, and appear to connect with the ranges of the Central American states, the Sierra Madre in Mexico and so with the Rocky Mountains, though geologists are not agreed on this point.

The Andes are composed of enormously thick beds of limestones, sandstones and slates, together with intrusive masses of granitic rocks, and vast quantities of lava ejected from the numerous huge volcanoes, active and extinct, that crown the Pacific Cordillera in serried lines. The continued volcanic activity and frequent earthquakes – such as the terrible devastation in Chile in 1959 – are evidence that the processes of uplift and mountain building are still in progress. These processes began millions of years ago (though late in geological time) when a broad sedimentary trough or geosyncline extended all along the present western borders of the continent, between the Guiana-Brazilian-Patagonian massifs to the east and a Pacific continental area to the west, represented by the present Coastal Range. A pincer movement from the west generated immense pressures between these continental masses, which squeezed the relatively soft sedimentary rocks out of the geosyncline to form the existing Andes. The general alignment of the Andes, with two major changes of direction, one near the Tropic and another south of the equator, follows very closely the western margins of the three ancient plateaus.

The intrusive mineral deposits have been of outstanding importance ever since the time of the Spanish conquest, when gold and silver were most eagerly sought. In modern times other, more widely distributed minerals have been exploited: copper ores at El Teniente and Chuquicamata in Chile and at Cerro de Pasco in Peru, where zinc and lead are also mined, the tin ores of Potosi and other centers in eastern Bolivia, and the platinum-bearing gravels of the Colombian Western Cordillera. Gold is now mined on a considerable scale only in the Central Cordillera, and though silver is produced in quantity, it is mainly a by-product of the mining of other minerals, such as copper.

The Andes are not only a physical but also a climatic barrier. From north of the equator to the Magellan Strait they effectively divide the continent into the Atlantic and the Pacific spheres of influence. In the south the Patagonian semi-desert is cut off from the almost constant rains that drench the Chilean side and, conversely, in the tropical zone the hot and humid regions of Amazonia and eastern Bolivia contrast with the extreme deserts of the Pacific slope and coastlands.

The Andes themselves are too cold in the south for habitation above 5,000 to 8,000 feet, but within the tropics, where they broaden to several hundred miles in a multiple mountain system enclosing high plateaus, they contain a number of areas of relatively dense population. Many of the people are Indians living on their sheep and llamas and crops of quinoa (a hardy native cereal), barley and potatoes (also natives of the high Andes). In three of the countries, Bolivia, Ecuador and Colombia, the majority of the inhabitants live up to and above 9,000 feet, where the capitals – La Paz, Quito and Bogotá respectively – are also situated.

The Altiplano of Bolivia with the adjacent mining zone of the Eastern Cordillera is the heart of that country. This plateau, 12,000 feet above sea level, is bleak and semi-arid, yet it has a considerable Indian and mestizo population; since the early period of Spanish rule, when Potosi was the largest town in the New World, it has dominated the border regions. Similarly in Ecuador, the inter-cordilleran plateau with its string of towns – Quito, Ambato, Riobamba and others – is more populous and of greater consequence in the life of the country than the humid equatorial lowlands on either side. In Colombia also, the slopes and plateau basins of the three cordilleran chains are most favored for settlement, not only because of their healthy climate but also because they afford highly suitable conditions for the cultivation of coffee (which provides over 80 per cent of Colombia's exports). Apart from two or three ports, almost all of the larger towns – Medellin, Cali and Manizales, as well as Bogotá, the capital – are situated well up in the Andean regions. The tropical Andes have always been the seats of power and population: the capital of the Inca empire, which extended from the equator to the Southern Tropic, was Cuzco, situated at over 8,000 feet in the Peruvian Andes.

It was anonymous prospectors and miners who first explored the Andes. The earliest mountaineering expedition was a Franco-Spanish one in 1736–44 which ascended Corazon (15,718 feet) and Pichincha (15,423 feet) in Ecuador. Alexander von Humboldt, the great German naturalist, and his companions attempted Chimborazo and Cotopaxi in 1802. Cotopaxi was ascended in 1872 by Wilhelm Reid and Chimborazo in 1880 by Edward Whymper, who later made many other Andean climbs.

The character of mountaineering in the Andes may be broadly placed between that of the Himalayas and the Alps. For climbers with experience of either, the Andes of Peru have perhaps the most to offer. There is far less red tape here than in the Himalayas; in most cases base camps can be reached from the road in a few days by mule. Coolie porterage is unknown and to arrange for mules and muleteers takes a long time; thus movement from one range to another is a slow process. Mountain porters are

so far restricted to the Cordillera Blanca in northern Peru and their climbing standard is not high.

Climbing routes in the Andes require in general a high standard of proficiency on snow and ice, which lie at remarkably steep angles. Few high peaks exhibit appreciable rock sections. Ridges are usually heavily fluted by avalanche and differential melting, and display exaggerated cornicing on their often fearfully narrow crests. Snow conditions vary sharply according to the direction in which the slope faces; south-facing snow is deep powder, capable of lying at a high angle, and extremely tiring to climb, since it melts too little in the day to freeze hard in the night. But once disturbed, it becomes firm after a night or so. North-facing snow is the opposite; good on the first night, routes are melted out in the daytime and need to be continually remade. Fixed-roping on snow and ice slopes on a long, hard climb may be taken as essential, as may the wearing of canvas overboots to prevent the leather of footwear from getting wet in the powdery snow, for the loss of insulation will cause frostbite. Nights are 12 hours long and extremely cold; a bivouac can kill.

Mountaineering in the Andes still has elements of exploration as well as of pure climbing, for large areas are still only imperfectly known.

Andorra

A tiny state, 191 square miles in area, with a population of about 6,000. Location *Eastern Pyrenees, between Spain and France.* Height *3,000 to 10,000 feet.* Map *7, C8.*

The mountain State of the Valleys of Andorra (the name is derived from the Biblical En-dor) is the largest in area and, with the exception of Vatican City, the smallest in population of the five miniature sovereign countries of Europe. It is the only survivor of the little Pyrenean Marcher States set up by Charlemagne and his son Louis the Pious to erect a wall of Christians as well as of mountains between their empire and the Moors. It consists of narrow valleys enclosed by high mountains and the passes leading to it are impassable in mid-winter.

Andorra is neither a monarchy nor a republic. In Catalan, the official language of the country, it describes itself as "Principat." Its joint overlords are the President of France and the Spanish Bishop of Urgel, who are styled its "co-Princes" and to whom a nominal annual tribute is paid.

Since the Second World War the advent of tourism on a massive scale has changed the face of Andorra's once primitive peasant villages. Its crude stone houses of simple, alpine austerity are tending to be displaced by modern hotels and places of entertainment, especially in the capital, Andorra la Vella, at the lower end of the main valley. However, once off the main road that passes through the country from the French frontier at the higher end to the Spanish frontier at the lower, the mountains are unspoiled and, in their rugged, desolate way, awe-inspiring.

Aniakchak

An active volcano, with crater six miles in diameter. Location *Southwest Alaska, on Alaska Peninsula, 40 miles north of Chignik.* Height *4,420 feet.* Map *3, A6.* Discovered *United States Geological Survey, 1922.*

Aniakchak has two claims to distinction. It was discovered on the computing table, and its 30 square miles of crater floor were found, when first explored, to provide the home for an astonishingly rich variety of flora and fauna.

It was only in 1922 that members of the United States Geological Survey, plotting survey readings, discovered that these revealed a circle of high points on the Alaska Peninsula that could only be the crater of a volcano, extinct or otherwise, and more than 4,000 feet high.

Explorers later followed the Aniakchak River upstream to what appeared to be a high mountain wall and finally entered the crater, more than six miles across. In its northwest segment they found a sheet of water later named Surprise Lake; in its northeast, the original vent of the volcano with 1,000-foot sides.

The lake, from which the Aniakchak River issued, contained both salmon and trout, while rabbits, foxes and brown bears were some of the animals found in the crater. Game-birds, eagles and ptarmigan were also noted and there were many varieties of flowers.

Annamese Cordillera

A range extending about 700 miles; largely wooded, of moderate height and traversed by short, narrow valleys. Location *Laos and Vietnam, running northwest to southeast along the coast.* Height *Rising to 10,500 feet in the Ngoc Ang.* Map *10, F8-9.*

The Annamese Cordillera is the main mountain range of Laos and Vietnam. It forms the divide between the Mekong River basin and the rivers – the Song-Ma and Song-Ca in the north and the Song-Ba, Don-Nai and Se-Bang-Khan in the south are the most important – draining into the South China Sea. The range of plateaus and wooded mountains runs north and south and declines on the coast to a narrow band of plain. The valleys which cut it transversely are short and narrow and through them run rivers which are mostly dry in the summer but turn into torrents during the rainy season between September and January.

The Tranninh Plateau is at the northern end of the range, in northern Laos. It runs with a width of 40 miles for 30 miles east of Luang Prabang. Its average altitude is 3,900-4,600 feet. Small streams run through the deep valleys cut into the sandstone and red clay hills, lined with oak and pine forests. The chief town of the district is Xiengkhouang. There are mineral deposits, especially gold, tin, tungsten and precious stones, and many hot springs.

The Annamese Cordillera is crossed in its lower central portion by the Mugia and Ailao passes; its highest point is in the southern massif. The drop to the coast is steep but the western slopes toward the Mekong are gentle. Here are the Moi Plateaus, a series of basaltic uplands which are part of central South Vietnam. From north to south they consist of the Kontum, Darlac, Langhiang and Djirling plateaus. Here the abundant rainfall and the red residual soil produce luxuriant jungle vegetation alternating with grassy plains and abundant big game. Tea, coffee and rubber plantations have been introduced by European (mostly French) colonists. The indigenous population are the primitive Moi tribes, who were expelled from the lowlands by the Annamese invasion. The main centers of the plateaus are Dalat, Djirling, Banmethuot, Pleiku and Kontum. Except in Dalat, European settlers did not arrive until 1924, when the first plantations were established. Roads were built to link them with the coast and with Saigon. In 1946 this part of the Annamese Cordillera was separated from Annam and became the territory of the Hill Peoples of South Indochina. It is now administered directly by the Vietnam government.

The Cordillera offers more attractions to the hunter, naturalist and anthropologist than to the mountaineer, but some of it is still unexplored and, if the international situation permits, it is a richly rewarding territory for unusual climbs, especially on the eastern side.

Annapurna

A 35-mile massif of the Himalayas, with northwest and western glaciers. Location *Central crest-zone of the Nepal Himalayas.* Height *Annapurna I: 26,492 feet; Annapurna II: 26,041 feet; Annapurna III: 24,858 feet; Annapurna IV: 24,688 feet.* Map *11, E5.* Climbed *Annapurna I: Maurice Herzog and companions, 1950; Annapurna IV: H. Biller, H. Steinmetz and J. Wellenkamp, 1955; Annapurna II and III: unclimbed.*

The Annapurna Himal (*himal* is the Sanskrit word for snow) stands east of the deep gorge cut by the Kali Gandaki through the Great Hima-laya. Its glaciers drain to the gorge; torrents from its southern flanks join the Seti Gandaki and the Marsyandi collects most of the drainage on the northern side. Annapurna I and II, the two highest peaks, stand at the western and eastern ends of the massif; Annapurna III and IV are between them. Their position and height were determined about 1850 from distant stations in India; not until 1925 were Indian surveyors permitted by the Nepal Government to enter the country and sketch the topography. Only after the Second World War was permission given to Europeans to visit the mountains.

In 1950 the British climber, H. W. Tilman, leader of the 1938 Everest expedition, took the first party of six to the "Goddess of the Harvests," as the Nepalese call the Annapurna. He chose Annapurna IV as his objective, but after three attempts the climb was abandoned at about 24,000 feet. A Japanese attempt in 1952 also failed; at last, on May 30, 1955, a German team succeeded. A second ascent was made by R. C. Evans and D. P. Davis in 1957.

However, the truly epic exploit of Annapurna was that of 1950, and it was a French achievement. Maurice Herzog, an engineer and mountaineer (who was later appointed by General de Gaulle to the post of Minister of Sport) took a team of nine with him: Louis Lachenal, Lionel Terray and Gaston Rébuffat, who were professional guides; Jean Couzy and Marcel Schatz, outstanding amateurs of the post-war mountaineering generation; Dr Jacques Oudot, physician, Marcel Ichac, photographer, and François de Noyelle (an attaché at the French Embassy in New Delhi), transport officer. There was also the usual complement of Sherpas (Nepalese mountain guides).

As the climbers made a circuit of the massif, they discovered that only the northwest face, an immense but not impossibly steep ramp of glacier and snow-slope, was a possible approach. They set up their base camp at the snout of the glacier and started their heartbreaking ordeal.

The first climbing camp was pitched on the

Maurice Herzog, severely frostbitten, being carried down Annapurna

fraction of the oxygen they needed. At last they saw a black patch, a final band of rock directly beneath the summit dome. As they approached, they saw a cleft splitting its center. On they toiled – until a blast of wind struck them coming from the *other* side of the mountain. Another few gasping steps and they stopped. Annapurna had been conquered – the first "eight-thousander" ever climbed by men; one of the giants measured not in feet but in meters.

On the summit Herzog planted a small French flag fastened to an ice-axe; Lachenal took a photograph. They could not leave either flag or axe up there as the wind would have blown it away. They started their descent after a few minutes. And now their real ordeal began. Herzog lost his gloves; hurrying ahead, he reached Camp 5 first. Lachenal, within a few steps of the camp, slipped and fell almost 300 feet. Terray rescued him, and for the next 24 hours he and Rébuffat did what they could for Herzog and the dazed, shocked Lachenal.

Next morning, as they started their descent, the storm burst in full fury. For hours they stumbled through white nothingness, numbed, blinded and lost. They decided that they would have to spend the night in the open. Just as they began to dig into the snow, Lachenal disappeared into a crevasse. Luckily it was not very deep and its floor was solid; but again it was a freezing night and they were buried by a mass of snow just before the dawn. Snowblind and frost-bitten, they gave themselves up for lost, but were found in the nick of time by Schatz. Even so, just above Camp 3 an avalanche almost swept Herzog, Rébuffat and two Sherpas to their death.

By the time the journey was over, Lachenal had lost all his toes and Herzog all his toes and fingers. It was a great victory at a heartbreaking price. This was the first mountain over 25,000 feet ever to be climbed to the summit and the achievement was yet greater in that it was climbed at the first attempt, without reconnaissance. Herzog and his companions had written an immortal chapter in the history of mountaineering.

lower glacier, about 2,000 feet above the base, the second near the head of the glacier and the third on the snow-slope beyond, more than 21,000 feet up. The principal danger was from the frequent avalanches, but by choosing their routes and camp sites carefully they managed to avoid them. The weather, fortunately, was favorable. Camp 4 was pitched on the only exposed rock on the side of the mountain, a long, curving arc of cliffs supporting the snowy dome of the summit.

Herzog and Lachenal moved on alone and set up a final camp at 24,300 feet on a precarious, slanting rib of rock which Herzog described as a "wrinkle in the snow." Here they spent a frosty, uncomfortable night. As they set out at dawn, Couzy and Schatz moved on to Camp 4 and Terray and Rébuffat from 4 to 5.

Step by step, hour after hour, the two men trudged up the tilt. The glare of the tropical sun almost blinded them; their heads seemed on fire yet the cold stiffened their clothing and bit at their fingers. They stopped again and again for breath, but the raw, bitter air gave them only a

Antisana

A large, snow-capped massif with an active crater. Location *Northern central Ecuador, 30 miles southeast of Quito.* Height *18,714 feet.* Map *6, B3.* Climbed *Edward Whymper, 1880.*

Antisana is one of the great, lumpy volcanoes of the Andes of Ecuador, still active, its crater emitting sulphurous gases. Alexander von Humboldt attempted to climb it and reached 17,000 feet, but it was Edward Whymper, the conqueror of the Matterhorn, who reached its summit during his South American climbing tour. Setting out from the Hacienda Antisana, one of the most elevated habitations in Ecuador (both the hacienda and the village of the same name are over 13,000 feet), Whymper met with what he described as the largest mudhole in the country, a four-foot booby trap in the middle of the track. Circumventing the obstacle, he made the ascent without trouble, finding complex glacier systems at about 16,000 feet. On the way down he fell into a crevasse but suffered no harm. He also had trouble with snow blindness but does not seem to have taken the natives' advice of applying slabs of freshly slaughtered vicuña meat to his eyes as a sure remedy.

Antisana has no special attractions for the climber but, seen from across the Chillo Basin or from the Hacienda Antisana, it is an impressive sight.

Apennines

A range 840 miles in length, 80 miles in average width, with rich mineral regions. Location *Running north and south through the entire length of Italy.* Height *Average 4,000 feet.* Map *7, D8-E9.*

In its geological history this mountain range is similar to the Alps, of which it forms a giant leg, stretching southwards from above the Gulf of Genoa, south of the River Po. Yet in almost all other ways the "backbone of Italy," as it is traditionally called, is totally different from the great range to the north.

The Apennines have no glaciers and no permanent snow – although in the Gran Sasso it may last for eight months of the year. Compared with the rock forms of the Alps, they have only pale examples in the Abruzzi and the marble mountains of Carrara and Seravezza. Their highest peaks are less than 10,000 feet.

The name "Apennines" seems to derive from the Celtic "pen" (mountain-height) which appears in the Pennine Chain of Britain and a number of Welsh names. The three main divisions are the North Apennines, extending from the Maritime Alps to the border of Tuscany; the Central Apennines, from Arezzo to the valley of the Pescara; the South Apennines, from the valley of the Pescara to Cape Spartivento; and the Insular Apennines or the Sicilian Range. The eastern slopes are extremely steep wherever they approach the coast; in central Italy and in some portions of upper and lower Italy the descent is gradual by way of plateaus and hills of moderate height down to extensive plains.

The Apennines form the watershed between the Mediterranean and the Adriatic. Steadily rising in height, the range reaches 9,560 feet in the Gran Sasso d'Italia, the rugged and truly mountainous area only some 20 miles inland from the east coast where Mussolini was held prisoner in 1943 and from which he was so dramatically rescued by Hitler's emissary, Otto Skorzeny. From the Abruzzi the Apennines bend slightly more south of east, their watershed approaching the west coast in the area of Naples, where Vesuvius – the only active volcano on the European mainland – smokes, and then following the coast into Calabria and Sicily.

The Apennines rank with Sardinia as the richest mineral region of Italy. The Tuscan hills and the Maremma district have valuable deposits of iron, copper, tin, mercury, lignite and borax. The most famous marble quarries in the world are at Carrara. At one time no less than 450 quarries were being worked between Genoa and Florence to provide statuary marble. There are many mineral springs. Forests are rare and vegetation extends to a height of 1,300 feet. Below this level the orange, citron, olive and palm, the agave, fig, myrtle, and vine grow far up the slopes; chestnut, oak and pine spread up to 3,000 feet and in some places even to 5,000 feet. Reforestation is making slow progress in the barren uplands. The southern division, especially the "toe," has suffered many earthquakes, the worst in 1783 and 1908. Extensive pastures and many hydro-electric plants are other features of the range, which is crossed by numerous roads and railways. Many ancient towns were built on the hills above the rivers, partly because of the seasonal floods and malaria of the plains below, and partly so that they could be more easily defended.

Appalachian Mountains

Long ridges divided into several major ranges, extending more than 1,600 miles. Location *Eastern North America, from the St Lawrence in Quebec to the Gulf Coast Plain in central Alabama, mainly between the Coastal and Interior plains.* Height *3,000 feet, rising to 6,684 feet at Mount Mitchell in the Black Mountains and 6,288 feet at Mount Washington in the White Mountains.* Map *5, A4.* Explored *American pioneers and settlers, eighteenth century.*

The Appalachians contain the major ranges (except the Adirondacks) east of the Mississippi, divided into three longitudinal bands: the Older Appalachians (with the highest peaks) on the east; the Folded or Newer Appalachians (including the Great Appalachian Valley) in the center; and the Appalachian Plateau (including the Catskill, Allegheny and Cumberland mountains) on the west. The Older Appalachians are composed of strongly-folded and metamorphosed Paleozoic rocks, with granitic and other igneous intrusions; in Canada this is represented by the Acadian uplands which include Shickshock and Notre Dame mountains and in the northeast

United States by the New England uplands, including the White Mountains (New Hampshire), the Green Mountains (Vermont), the Taconic Mountains (Vermont and Massachusetts) and the Berkshire Hills (Massachusetts). From this upland two prongs reach out across New York and New Jersey to the Blue Ridge in Pennsylvania, partly embracing the Triassic Lowland region. The Blue Ridge includes the highest peaks in the eastern United States.

The Folded or Newer Appalachians, west of the Older, include the Great Appalachian Valley, which is represented in the north by the St Lawrence and Lake Champlain lowlands and the Hudson River Valley. From the Hudson a chain of longitudinal valleys (of which the beautiful Shenandoah is the best-known) continue, to end in Alabama. West of the great valley are long, even-crested ridges which are classic examples of folded mountains. The westernmost part of the system is the Appalachian Plateau which begins in the north at the Mohawk River Valley of New York and extends to the vicinity of Birmingham, Alabama. This plateau is a rugged, westward-sloping region; its generally steep eastern escarpment overlooks the valleys of the Folded Appalachians. In the north it is known as the Allegheny Plateau; along the eastern margin in New York the Catskills rise; in Pennsylvania, West Virginia and Virginia the plateau is known as the Allegheny Mountains. The southwest end of the plateau and of the whole system is known as the Cumberland Plateau. The Appalachians have been glaciated only in the Canadian and New England portions and on the northern side of the Allegheny Plateau.

During the eighteenth century these stunted mountains formed a barrier between the plains of Virginia and the Carolinas and the fertile hills and bison herds of Kentucky and Ohio beyond. It was Daniel Boone (1734–1820) who led an armed band of colonists along the Wilderness Road from eastern Virginia through the Cumberland Gap, opening up vast new tracts and the road to the West. Many have followed him and today the whole massif has become cultivated and urbanized, though in the southern Appalachians (often called Appalachia) there are still remote settlements in the mountain valleys, inhabited by descendants of Scottish-Irish settlers of pre-Revolutionary and Revolutionary times, who have, to a certain extent, preserved the old ways of life. Their speech shows Elizabethan origins, and ancient ballads and handicrafts have survived in spite of the impact made by twentieth-century civilization.

The valuable mineral resources of the Appalachians include the great anthracite field of eastern Pennsylvania (which gave birth to the vast industrial complex of Pittsburgh), bituminous fields, petroleum and natural-gas fields (Pennsylvania and West Virginia) and iron ore (Alabama, the basis of the Birmingham steel industry). Salt, bauxite, fluxing stone, clay, talc, mica, cement and silica sand are also produced. The forests are still extensive, consisting mostly of mixed hardwoods, except for the conifers of New England and Canada. Hydro-electric development has produced the Tennessee River Authority project in the south with many reservoirs in the valleys, greatly stimulating the economy of the southern mountains.

The Appalachian Trail is a footpath extending from Maine to Georgia, running for the most part along the crest of the mountains. It was first proposed in 1921, and in 1922 construction started in the Bear Mountain section of New York. By 1935 over 2,000 miles had been completed and marked. Its southern terminus is at Mount Oglethorpe, Georgia, its northern end at Mount Katahdin, Maine. The path, used by hikers and campers, is maintained by various clubs, supervised by the Appalachian Trail Conference of Washington, D. C. The beauty of the Shenandoah and Great Smoky Mountains national parks as well as of the many national forests and resort areas make the Appalachians – especially in the south – one of the most popular vacation-grounds in the United States.

Arabian Mountains

A ridge of mountains along the western and southwestern coasts of Arabia. Location *Arabian Peninsula.* Height *Average 5,000 feet, rising to 12,000 feet.* Map *9, H4.*

From the Gulf of Aqaba a steep wall of barren sandstone extends south towards the Red Sea – the beginning of a great belt of highlands running down the side of Arabia, turning east a few miles north of Aden. The western half of the peninsula is an enormous plateau, broadest in the center (Nejd) but highest in the south. In the northwest the land rarely rises above 5,000 feet, except in places like the Jebel el Loz (8,458 feet), east of the Gulf of Aqaba, and in patches of volcanic (*Harra*) country.

C. M. Doughty wrote of "a sandstone platform mountain . . . overlaid, 2,000 square miles, to the brink, by a general effusion of lavas: then, beyond the volcanic crust, all around, we see a wasted border of undercliffs and needles of the sandstone rock, down to the low-lying plains. It seems thus that the lava floods have preserved the infirm underlying sand-rocks, whilst the old sandstone country was worn down and wasted by most slow decays . . ."

Certainly the great thickness of the lava floods points to the very ancient origins of the Harra. Streams of basalt appear in the walls of some dry watercourses. Many of the hills represent the slags and the powder cast up in one strong eruption. The earlier, overstreaming lavas are older than the present configuration of the land. It is amazing to see in a rainless country how the lava-basalt pan has been cleft and opened to a great depth in some valleys.

The greatest heights of the peninsula (up to 12,000 feet) are found in the mountains of Yemen. This is the area with the heaviest rainfall in the whole peninsula, and therefore more fertile than any other part of Arabia. The mountains once supported the ancient kingdom of Sheba on their eastern slopes – and perhaps the fabulous prosperity of Punt and Ophir as well.

The high land continues intermittently eastwards along the southern coast of the peninsula, rising to over 7,000 feet in the central Hadhramaut and coming to an end in the Jebel Qara in the Sultanate of Dhofar. The Jebel Qara is also relatively rich in vegetation and frankincense is an important crop. Here the seaward slopes of the mountains are covered with thick shrubs and trees, their summits are rolling yellow meadows and beyond the summits they slope northwards to a red sandstone steppe.

The Jebel Qara is separated by a flat, barren coastline of 450 miles from the mountain range, which is the eastern flank of the Arabian peninsula.

Oman consists largely of a tableland (Hajar) of dark limestone and granite, about 4,000 feet in height. The northeast and southwest edges of the plateau are indented by deep and often fertile wadis. In the center there is a ridge, 70 miles long and rising to 10,000 feet, by the name of the Jebel Akhdar (Green Mountains). The steppe vegetation is varied here and there by patches of small trees. The mountains have only slightly less rainfall than Yemen and there are numerous springs in the northeast. The water supply is carried lower down, where the sides of the Hajar

are terraced for the cultivation of apricots, figs, vines, cereals and coffee. Below these terraces the land slopes swiftly down through date palms to the Gulf of Oman.

Ararat

Highest portion of the Armenian plateau, a snow-capped volcanic cone. Location *Turkey, near the Turco-Iranian border, ten miles from Iran, 20 miles from the USSR.* Height *Great Ararat: 16,945 feet; Little Ararat: 12,877 feet.* Map *9, G1.* Climbed *F. Parrot, 1829 (first in modern times).*

Ararat's best claim to fame is its traditional association with the mountain upon which the Ark rested as related in Genesis viii 4. Legends about it have persisted since early times. On the slopes high above the Aras plain, Noah, after leaving the Ark, is reputed to have built his altar, offered burnt offerings and planted the first vine. Formerly surrounded by gardens and orchards, the Armenian convent of St James stood in an adjacent ravine, 2,300 feet above a village; 1,000 feet higher there was a chapel of St James. On July 2, 1840, an earthquake changed the form of the mountain, burying the convent, chapel,

Ararat (left), with the twin peak of Little Ararat

dwellings and gardens, together with the inhabitants, under an avalanche of rock and earth.

The snowy, conical peak of Ararat (with its "twin," the nearby Little Ararat) is a memorable sight from the upland plains and valleys surrounding it. Its face of lava, rubble, stones and snow rises some 14,500 feet above the Aras valley and its isolation when seen from this direction emphasizes its height and shape. The greater part of the mountain is treeless. To the northwest Ararat is linked by a col (6,900 feet) to a westward-stretching range of mountains, but its east face is gashed by a savage, rocky chasm which reaches up for several thousand feet. There is a small glacier near the summit. No crater exists and there has been no recorded eruption in historical times. The view from the top is very extensive, including the rugged peaks of Soviet Armenia across the Aras valley to the north and east, and on the south and west the wild plateau and mountain country bordering Lake Van.

Local legend used to assert that because of its sacred character, Ararat would never be conquered by man. But the first ascent in modern times was made without great difficulty by F. Parrot in 1829. There have been a number of mountaineering and archeological expeditions to the district since 1945 and unconfirmed reports in 1957 spoke of a "large ark's outlines" being sighted from the air by American reconnaissance planes. Nothing more was heard of these and no significant archeological discoveries have been made in the district.

Askja

A volcanic basin. Location *Eastern central Iceland, 60 miles southeast of Akureyri.* Height *4,754 feet.* Map *7, B2.*

Askja, a lava plain about four miles square, is surrounded by the Dyngjuföll hills and lies less than 20 miles north of the great icefield of Vatnajokull. Stretching away to the northeast is a barren region of dried-out lava covering about 1,400 square miles, called the Odadahraun. In the southeast corner of the basin lies Oskjuvatn, a lake 2½ by 1½ miles in extent and some 500 feet deep, which is the probable site of an explosion-crater. The basin, technically known as a *caldera*, is considered the first example of its kind in Europe.

In 1875 Askja erupted violently and much pumice and ash were ejected from a pit about 270 feet across. The ash laid waste 17 farms to the east in Jokudal; 24 hours later ash fell as far away as Stockholm. It is interesting to note that acid lava (known as rhyolite) rather than basic or basaltic lava was erupted from Askja – the only case of such lava in historical times. This lava is more viscous than the usual basic material and chills to a black glass known as obsidian or in Icelandic "raven flint." Though sometimes marked by a covering of pumice, these vitreous volcanic rocks are often of varied coloring and make attractive stones.

Askja is part of the short Dyngjuföll range. As a volcano it is still intermittently active.

Assiniboine, Mount

A spectacular, isolated pyramid. Location *Alberta-British Columbia border, Canadian Rocky Mountains.* Height *11,870 feet.* Map *3, G9.* Climbed *Sir James Outram, with the guides C. Bohren and C. Hasler, 1901.*

The name Assiniboine, which the mountain shares with a river, a town, a district and a national park, is derived from two Ojibway words, *assini* meaning a stone and the termination "to cook by roasting." There is also a sadly diminished tribe of Indians of Siouan stock known as "Stone-Cookers" after their method of cooking by dropping hot stones into a vessel of water.

Mount Assiniboine, sometimes called the "Matterhorn" of the Canadian Rockies, is the highest peak between the Canadian Pacific Railway and the International Boundary. G. M. Dawson of the Canadian Geological Survey saw

Athos, Mount

The easternmost of the three tongues of the Chalcidice peninsula, on the Aegean Sea. Location *Macedonia, Greece.* Height *6,670 feet.* Map *7, F9.*

The Greeks call Mount Athos *Hagion Oros* (Holy Mountain), for the mountain and its surroundings form an autonomous monastic district. A unique, exclusively male land, about 30 miles long and 10 miles across, it is dedicated to a way of life which has remained virtually unchanged for 1,000 years. Here are about 20 monastic establishments, 14 dependencies or *sketes* and many hermitages. All profess the Orthodox Christian faith, but many countries are represented. Greek, Russian, Serbian, Bulgarian and Rumanian monasteries form the community, which is governed by a Holy Assembly of 20 members elected annually by each monastery. In 1913 the International Conference of London proclaimed the independence and neutrality of Mount Athos, but since 1920 this theocratic republic has come under the sovereignty of Greece, while retaining considerable autonomy. The Rule of 1060 which forbade access to the mountain "to any woman, to any female, to any child, to any eunuch, to any smooth visage" is still in force.

The landscape is strikingly beautiful, but the chief interest of Athos lies in its way of life, its architecture, its relics and its treasures. Pillaged in the thirteenth century by the Latin conquerors of Constantinople, it has remained undisturbed since then by war or invasion.

From the outside the monasteries are like small, fortified towns. Inside there is usually an extensive courtyard with a number of domed churches in its center. Nearly all of them medieval foundations, the churches are richly decorated with frescoes. In the eastern part of each there is the ikonostasis, a carved and painted screen of holy pictures which divides the sanctuary from the main body of the church. In the sanctuary are stored the holy relics, including fragments of the Holy Church, of which every monastery

The monastery of Simon Petra on Mount Athos

it from afar in 1885 and named it. The first ascent was made by Sir James Outram with two guides who had come from Switzerland to be employed by the Canadian Pacific Railroad. Standing in a famous area, it is accessible from Banff, a two days' horseback journey bringing the visitor to its foot. There are many flowering meadows and lovely lakes – such as Magog – with cabin camps. Nearby are low passes of the watershed, such as White Man, Wonder, Assiniboine, Citadel and Simpson – the last named after Sir George Simpson, who crossed it in 1841, traveling westwards on the first overland journey around the world.

The Atlas Mountains, showing Djebel Toubkal (left)

possesses some, and many remains of saints and apostles, all set in precious reliquaries studded with jewels. To them the monks pray, and their healing powers are never doubted.

About 3,000 monks and a like number of lay brothers live on Athos. It has two forms of government – Idiorhythmic and Cenobian. The nine Idiorhythmic monasteries are ruled by an elected committee; the monks are free and have their own apartments. The Cenobians are ruled by an abbot who has absolute powers.

Athos has recently welcomed visitors (strictly male) and serves as one of the more unusual tourist attractions of Greece.

Atlas Mountains

An irregular mountain mass formed of several chains.
Location Northwest and North Africa, extending over
Morocco, Algeria and Tunisia. Height 3,000 to
10,000 feet, rising to 13,665 feet in the Djebel Toubkal.
Map 9, B2-C2. Explored Second half of the nineteenth
century.

Seen from the north, the Atlas Mountains form a magnificent skyline. Rising above the palm trees and minarets of Marrakesh, the rounded foothills lead to rank upon rank of mountains stretching across the horizon, each rising higher than the last, up to the jagged line of the highest peaks of all. Thousands of years ago they stood at the confines of the knowledge of Mediterranean man, for whom their valleys were inaccessible. The massive ranges were a barrier to the fabled lands of gold beyond. No wonder, then, that the Atlas figured so largely in the myths and legends of the ancients.

The High or Great Atlas is the highest and most continuous range, extending 400 miles southwest to northeast across Morocco, from Cape Guir towards the Algerian border. Some of the peaks are snow-capped. Northeast is the shorter Middle Atlas, which overlooks the Moroccan mesa towards the coast and extends northeast to the Taza corridor, rising to 10,794

feet in the Djebel Bou Naceur. Southwest of the High Atlas, the Anti-Atlas reaches the Atlantic at the Ifni enclave; it encloses the Sous lowland and is linked to the High Atlas by the volcanic Djebel Siroua (10,840 feet). In Algeria the three main divisions are the coastal Tell Atlas, the Saharan Atlas, overlooking the Sahara, and between these two chains the High Plateaus.

The Anti-Atlas is a wild and disordered landscape of broken plateaus ringed round by craters and strange peaks; farther east in the Djebel Sargho there are crags and jagged rocks among bare and arid plains. Walled villages stand beside the springs of the plateau and the oases of the plains. To the north, in the western and central High Atlas, narrow, steep-sided valleys drop down from the valley-heads and passes. A few rough, stone-walled, flat-roofed houses huddle together on the flatter ground. Lower down the slopes, the valleys widen out and the soil becomes more plentiful. Villages, alive with the sound of running streams, stand among meadows, walnut trees and poplars. Farther east in the High and Middle Atlas, forests, plateaus and gorges favor the semi-nomadic rather than the sedentary way of life. The Saharan Atlas between the High Plateaus and the Sahara consists of a broken chain traceable from the Moroccan border to Tunisia; in the Medjerda Valley it is reduced to isolated block mountains, terminating in Tunisia at the Cape Bon peninsula.

The Atlas has valuable mineral resources: tin along the Algerian-Tunisian border (Djebel Ouenza) and at Ait Amar in Morocco; manganese at Bou Arfa and in the Ourzazate area of Morocco; lead chiefly at Bou Beker (Morocco); molybdenum at Azegour (Morocco); zinc, copper, antimony and mercury in scattered deposits. At Tebessa (Algeria) there are extensive phosphate sources. The three main passes (all in Morocco) are crossed by roads leading from north to south. In Algeria there are railways linking Oran with Colomb-Béchar, Algiers with Djelfa and Constantine with Biskra; there is also a good network of roads.

The inaccessible ranges have long been strongholds of the independent and fiercely proud Berber tribes. Now and then a temporary empire has arisen under a strong ruler. Once, in the twelfth century, the scattered communities, their elected leaders and alliances were brought together and the Berbers swept across North Africa and Spain. The dynasty they established lasted a century.

The French and Spanish conquest of North Africa began in the second third of the nineteenth century; but not until the nineteenthirties did the French forces complete the "pacification" of the Moroccan Atlas, while in Algeria the tribes of the Aurès massif resisted for 40 years. In the Second World War there was little fighting in the Atlas. Today Morocco and Tunisia are independent sovereign states and French Algeria is on the threshold of achieving a similar status. In the final analysis, the people of the Atlas have never been conquered.

The Atlas Mountains, although close to Europe, are infrequently visited by mountaineers. In recent years, however, most of the high peaks of the Atlas have been climbed and much surveying has been carried out by the French.

Australian Alps

A chain of mountain ranges, forming the southern part of the Great Dividing Range. Location *Southeast Australia (Victoria and New South Wales).* Height *2,500 to 3,000 feet, rising to 7,305 feet in Mount Kosciusko.* Map *12, E7.*

The Great Dividing Range of Australia bears many local names, including that of Australian Alps. These extend about 200 miles southwest from the Australian Capital Territory to the Goulburn River in Victoria. Within the Australian Alps are the Muniong Range and the Bowen and Barry mountains. Sometimes the name of Australian Alps is applied also to the Blue Mountains, the New England Range, the Grampians and the Pyrenees of Australia.

The Australian Alps have the remarkable cliff-like outline which is the characteristic of Australian mountains. The plains are walled in with cliffs that are often well over 1,000 feet high, so steep that it is impossible to climb them; it is often possible to drop a stone direct from the top of a cliff on to the level ground 1,000 feet below.

The whole of the Australian Alps forms a plateau with an average height of 1,000-2,000 feet and many smaller tablelands ranging from 3,000-5,000 feet. The ranges are so densely covered with vegetation that in some places it is extremely difficult to penetrate them. There are about 15 peaks over 5,000 feet. Along the ranges grow the giant trees for which Victoria is still famous. The narrow valleys and gullies offer exquisite scenery; the rocky streams are overshadowed by groves of fern trees with the tall, smooth stems of white gum trees rising from them. There are over 8,000,000 acres of these forests still untouched by the inroads of the sheep farmer or by deforestation.

The Australian Alps are extremely popular with skiers and hikers. Naturalists also frequent them. The huge moths, called "bogongs," which the aborigines used to catch and grill when other food was scarce. have given their name to the second highest peak of the range, Mount Bogong (6,508 feet).

Balkan Mountains

Major mountain range of the Balkan Peninsula, subdivided into three sections. Location *Mainly in Bulgaria.* Height *3,000–4,000 feet, rising to 7,793 feet in Botev Peak.* Map *7, F8-G8.*

Extending 350 miles from the upper Timok River in the west, near the Bulgarian-Yugoslav border, to Cape Yemine on the Black Sea in the east, the Balkan Mountains are 12-30 miles wide. They form the major divide between the Danube and Maritsa rivers on the north and south. About 20 highway passes and three railway lines cross them and they are pierced by the Iskar River. Here, too, we find the northern limit of the Mediterranean climatic influence.

The mountains, though not high by Alpine standards, offer many attractive climbs. The fantastic sandstone formations near Belogradtchik provide "fancy climbing of a high order." The Vitosha in the Sofia district, where the highest peak is the Cherni-vrakh (7,506 feet), provides a most attractive view of the Bulgarian Alps. There are alpine meadows in the upper sections and conifers and deciduous forests on the slopes. Lignite, anthracite, graphite and metallic ores are mined, and there are a number of thermal and mineral springs.

There are three divisions of the Balkan Mountains: the Western Balkans, the Central Balkans and the Eastern Balkans. The first run for about 125 miles between the Timok River and Botevgrad Pass, rising to 7,113 feet at Midzhur Peak. Crossed by the Sveti Nikola and Petrokhan passes and by the Iskar River, their main peaks are the Berkovitsa, Chiporov, Murgash and Vratsa mountains and the main bases for exploring them are Belogradchik, Berkovitsa and Vratsa. The Central Balkans extend 125 miles between the Botevgrad and Vrantik passes, rising to 7,793 feet in the Botev Peak. It is traversed by several passes, including the Shipka, where a famous, gory, winter battle took place in the Balkan Wars, the Troyan, the Tvarditsa and the Zlatitsa; here the main peaks are Kalofer, Shipka, Troyan, Yelene and Yetropole, and the main towns Gabrovo, Teteven, Troyan and Yetropole. The Eastern Balkans are delimited by the Vratnik Pass and Cape Yermine of the Black Sea; their highest peak is the Bulgarka (3,875 feet), and they are crossed by the Kotel and Varbitsa passes. The main towns of this section are Omortag and Targovishte.

Bulgaria encourages tourism and Sofia, the capital, is an excellent center. The best season for the Balkan climber is from June to September and there are also a number of resorts available for winter sports.

Baltoro Glacier

A major glacier draining into the Braldo and Shigar tributaries of the Indus in Baltistan. Location *Karakoram mountain system, northern Kashmir.* Height *11,580 feet (at snout).* Map *11,* D3. Discovered *Colonel Godwin-Austen, 1861.*

The Baltoro is the main approach glacier to the highest mountains of the Karakoram. From Concordia at about 15,180 feet, to its snout near Paiju at 11,000 feet, a distance of 20 miles, most of its surface is covered by medial moraines, formed by rocks split by frost from the mountain walls, so that in the lower reaches little clear ice is seen. There are several tributary glaciers – Biange, Muztagh, Biale, Dunge, Trango and Uli Biaho – entering from the north, enclosed by precipitous walls but opening out in their upper reaches; they form approaches to the Baltoro Muztagh of the Great Karakoram. The watershed to the south is less well known.

Three component glaciers meet at Concordia and form the ice reservoirs and feeders of the main trunk: the Godwin-Austen, which joins from the skirts of K2 on the north; the Upper Baltoro, 16 miles long, entering from the southeast, with a vast collecting area from the Gasherbrum, Baltoro Kangri and Chogolisa groups; and the Vigne, which joins the upper Baltoro immediately above Concordia. These icy fastnesses have been an international mountain area for a century. Godwin-Austen discovered and first sketched it in 1861, showing that a pass led over the northern watershed to Chinese territory, about which he learned from the natives. Francis Younghusband was the first and only European to cross this pass for 40 years, at the end of his adventurous journey from Peking to India in 1867 – making the crossing without any technical alpine knowledge or equipment and with no guides.

The first detailed exploration and map were made in 1892 by Martin Conway, who brought back a large-scale plane-table sketch of all but the head of the Upper Baltoro. In 1909 the Italian expedition of the Duke of Abruzzi prepared a fine photogrammetric survey of the glaciers meeting at Concordia. Twenty years later the Duke of Spoleto's Italian expedition also resulted in a useful addition to geographical knowledge, particularly of the head of the Upper Baltoro, and of the northern tributary glaciers. In 1937 Eric Shipton's party only touched the lower reaches of the Baltoro, but made a new pass over the watershed at 18,650 feet, at the head of the Trango glacier.

In 1934 the Duke of Spoleto's Italian expedition, led by Professor G. O. Dyhrenfurth, climbed the head of the Upper Baltoro.

Many earlier and subsequent attempts to climb the peaks of the Great Karakoram involved crossing the Baltoro Glacier, which remains the main approach to the giants.

Banff National Park

Covers 2,560 square miles, with spectacular scenery, icefields and many mountain lakes. Location *Southwest Alberta, on the British Columbia border, in the Canadian Rocky Mountains.* Height *Includes many peaks over 10,000 feet.* Map *3, G9.* Established *1885, and subsequently enlarged.*

Banff National Park is 60 miles west of Calgary; it is 130 miles long and 30 miles wide. Within its limits are such peaks as Mounts Hector, Ball, Murchison, Patterson, Saskatchewan, St Bride, Sir Douglas, Temple, Willingdon and several others over 10,000 feet. Kicking Horse Pass is on its western boundary; in the north it borders on Jasper National Park and on the west on Yono and Kootenay national parks. It is crossed by the great Trans-Canada Highway. Within the park are the famous holiday resorts of Banff and Lake Louise and many sulphur and mineral springs.

Numerous peaks stand ranged around, from the highest, Mount Assiniboine, on the border with British Columbia, to Mount Norquary (on which there is a 7,000-foot ski-lift, the world's

highest) overshadowing the town of Banff itself.

For those who like to wake up and find a bear on the lawn, a chipmunk scratching at the tent flap, a beaver chopping down a tree or building a dam at the bottom of the garden, Banff National Park is an ideal place – but it offers every kind of vacation. Lake Louise, 5,670 feet high in the Rockies, is one of the most beautiful mountain-mirroring, glacier-fed lakes in the world with a deep blue-green sheen on its surface. There are luxury hotels and smaller establishments, cottages and camp-sites. Within a few dozen miles there is truly remote wilderness, inhabited by the Bighorn sheep, Rocky Mountain goats, grizzly bears, elks, cougars and coyotes.

Ponies, tents and guides are available for riders, hikers and climbers; there are canoes for river journeys (motor boats are restricted to the beautiful Lake Minnewanka, winding between its white-topped mountains, to prevent the wild life from being disturbed elsewhere). There is excellent fishing, golf and other sports.

But the real joy of Banff is its scenery. Perhaps nowhere else in North America is there such a subtle and varied combination of mountains, glaciers, lakes, rivers, forests and alpine meadows. Here the mountains rise from wide open valleys so that nowhere is one far from a superb view.

Beardmore Glacier

A huge Antarctic glacier, more than 110 miles long. Location *Between the South Polar plateau and Ross Shelf Ice, Antarctica.* Map *1, D3.* Discovered *Sir Ernest Shackleton, 1908.*

One of the world's largest known valley glaciers, the Beardmore is twice as large as the Malaspina in Alaska, which was the largest discovered until Shackleton explored the Beardmore. The latter is an immense stream of ice with great tributary glaciers and tumbled ice-falls which are, however, dwarfed by the hugeness of the main stream, as it stretches in places 40 miles from bank to bank.

The glacier is criss-crossed with crevasses and the crossings need to be made by a well-roped party. Most of the hazards, however, can be spotted by the strip of snow on the blue ice. Often too wide to jump across, the crevasses have to be negotiated gingerly by way of treacherous snow-bridges. "The Lord only knows how deep these vast chasms go down," Apsley Cherry-Garrard quotes from the diary of one of his companions. "They seem to extend into blue-black nothing-ness thousands of feet below."

It was the difficult journey down the Beard-more Glacier, combined with the unexpected cold on the trip down the Barrier, which defeated Captain Scott and his party on their return from the South Pole and led to their tragic end.

Beerenberg

One of the biggest volcanic cones in the world. Location *Jan Mayen, Arctic Ocean.* Height *8,347 feet.* Map *7, C1.* First climbed *J. M. Wordie and party, 1921.*

The Beerenberg, the white giant forming the bulk of the northeastern end of the island of Jan Mayen, is rarely seen despite its height because the island is off the normal shipping routes and usually wrapped in mist. On rare clear days the peak can be seen almost 100 miles away; but generally it looms suddenly and majestically out of the sea only when one's ship is relatively close to the island.

From the summit of the mountain about 15 glaciers flow down to the Arctic Ocean. The lip of this huge volcanic cone, which is almost 30 miles round the base, has broken away on one side. Below its high icefields, the largest glacier, the Weyprecht, tumbles down to end in blue ice pillars that "calve" as small icebergs directly into the surf. The upper reaches of the Beerenberg are practically devoid of animal life, but at 7,000 feet (1,500 feet above the snowline) moss and brilliant orange lichens cling to the rocks that project from the permanent snow.

The Beerenberg is a moderately easy climb. Since the first ascent it has been climbed on numerous occasions, repeatedly by the men who look after the Norwegian meteorological station below. The notorious uncertainties of the island's weather have prevented its ascent by several parties, for it is possible to start out on one of the rare brilliant days and then to find suddenly that visibility is limited to a few yards as the entire island is swathed in mist.

Ben Lawers

One of the principal mountains of the British Isles. Location *Western central Perthshire, Scotland.* Height *3,984 feet.* Map *7, B5.*

Ben Lawers is the culminating point of Breadal-bane, the barren mountainous district in the Grampians of northwest Perthshire, a district which extends between Strathearn and Loch Rannoch, about 35 miles long and 30 miles wide. But Ben Lawers itself is far from being barren; botanically, it is the most famous mountain in the British Isles, renowned for its unique assemblage of arctic and alpine plants, survivors of a flora which was widespread from after the Ice Age down to about 8,500 B.C., when it was forced to retreat as the climate got progressively warmer and forests began to cover the land again.

Among the beautiful and in many cases rare small plants which one can find growing here, clinging to rocky ledges among the cliffs, among the grass of sheltered slopes, beside the ice-cold springs and rills and the small hillside bogs near the summit, are various saxifrages with pink or golden flowers, boreal fleabane, alpine saussurea, rose root, alpine forget-me-not and several others, including the dwarf willow.

In summer the most rewarding localities for plants are the sloping sides of the corries where the soil is constantly enriched by earth movement caused by frost and snow, by silting from the mountain streamlets and by the descent of rock particles from above. For the rarest species one must go in spring, before grass and other vegetation has grown too high, and search the ledges of the cliff where there is every variety of habitat, from arid rock faces exposed fully to the sun, to sheltered pockets of rich soil and dark damp crevices, and a corresponding richness of flora; here growth is aided also by the inaccessibility of these sites to sheep, which tend to eliminate plants incapable of growing and reproducing under their grazing.

Why is Ben Lawers, no higher than many neighboring mountains, so rich in flora compared with them? The reason seems to lie in a combination of the nature of the rock – schists and quartzites which weather to produce rich, permeable soils constantly renewed by further break-

Ben Nevis, the highest peak in Great Britain

down of rock; of the climate, slightly drier than further west, and hence less likely to produce waterlogging and acidity; and of the altitude – for the mountain, though being constantly eroded, is still high for the region and still provides plenty of exposed rock surfaces for breakdown into new soil.

In addition to the botanist, the mountaineer will find a rich reward on Ben Lawers, from which there is a striking view of Loch Tay and the central Highlands of Scotland.

Ben Nevis

The highest peak in Great Britain, of volcanic rock, with a precipice of 1,450 feet on the northeast side. Location Southwest Inverness, Scotland. Height 4,406 feet. Map 7, B5.

The "Ben of Bens" offers far more to the mountaineer and the rock climber than its modest height (compared to the Alpine and Himalayan giants) would imply. "In winter conditions," writes J. E. Q. Barford, "Ben Nevis presents climbing problems as severe as or more severe than any usually encountered in the Alps with the additional handicap of limited daylight." J. R. Ullman compares it to Moby Dick if viewed from the west. "The snout" is the biggest cliff in Britain – a pile of volcanic rocks 2,000 feet thick and two miles long, made of alternating andesite, lavas and agglomerate.

The northeast face abounds in magnificent climbs; at its foot there is a well-equipped hut owned by the Scottish Mountaineering Club. "The north side of the mountain," wrote Thomas Wilkinson in 1824, "may be said to be hung with terrors. Perpendicular and projecting rocks, gulphy glens and awful precipices, gloomy and tremendous caverns, the vast repositories of snow from age to age; these, with blue mists gauzing the grey rocks of the mountains, and terrible cataracts thundering from Ben Nevis, made altogether a scene sublimely dreadful."

Three factors – its height, bulk and position close to the Atlantic seaboard – make the mountain meteorologically unique, and in 1877 the Scottish Meteorological Society considered taking readings on the summit. Four years later Clement L. Wragge offered to do so and subsequently made many hundreds of ascents for this purpose. An observatory was built on the summit in 1883, but it was closed in 1904.

Today you can walk up Ben Nevis along a specially constructed path which has seen ascents by motorcycles and wheelbarrows. There is an annual race on the track, zigzagging up the stony flank of the mountain, commemorating the solitary effort of William Swan, a hairdresser, who, in 1895, ran to the summit and back in 2 hours 41 minutes.

Bering Glacier

About 45 miles long, 20 miles wide, draining into Gulf of Alaska. Location St Elias Range, southern Alaska. Map 3, C6. Explored and named by Lieutenant H. W. Seton-Karr, 1886.

Part of the St Elias Range glacier system, west and northwest of Cape Yakataga, the "Great Bering Glacier" was named after the eighteenth century navigator Vitus Bering, who first sighted this part of the Alaskan coast in 1741. It is the second largest "piedmont" glacier in the subarctic regions, with only the Malaspina or Great Agassiz Glacier exceeding it in area.

H. Bradford Washburn, the American aerial photographer and mountaineer, made a survey of the region for the National Geographic Society in 1938. He described in detail the actual configuration of the glacier and the nature of its pronounced lobe-like outflow towards the coast; the most remarkable series of convolutions and contortions develop in the banded ice as it adjusts itself to the irregular movements and stresses within the body of the glacier, providing a perfect example of plastic deformation. Similar contorted ice-structure can be seen in the great Malaspina Glacier, 60 miles to the east of the Bering Glacier.

Bernese Oberland

A region of peaks, valleys, passes and glaciers, with 35 peaks over 10,000 feet, 63 over 4,500 feet and 34 passes. Location *Bern and Valais cantons, southwest Switzerland.* Height *Rising to 14,000 feet.* Map *8, B8-C8.*

The Bernese Oberland, also known as the Bernese Alps, lies north of the Pennine Alps, separated from them by the upper Rhône valley. Though the mountains are not quite so high as those of the Mont Blanc and Pennine chains, the Oberland has equal majesty of scenery and attractions for the mountaineer.

In the Wetterhorn it has the peak on which it is often claimed that the sport of mountaineering began. The Jungfrau railway takes the tourist to the highest hotel in Europe. The Aletsch Glacier is the longest in the Alps. For the historian the Bernese Alps have the peaks on whose slopes the Meyers and the Hugis, the early nineteenth-century explorers, laid the foundations of Swiss mountaineering.

With these and a multiplicity of other attractions, the Bernese Oberland draws as much attention from travelers, mountaineers and students as any region in the Alps. Its geographical limits are usually defined as extending from Lake Geneva and the bend of the Rhône at Martigny-Ville (west-southwest) to Grimsel Pass and Hasletal (east-northeast); its boundaries are the upper Rhône valley on the south and the lakes of Brienz and Thun in the north.

It is on the central, higher area of the Bernese Oberland that the interest of travelers has concentrated since the days when Grindelwald, "the Glacier Village," first began to attract eighteenth-century savants who studied the rude columns of ice which here thrust down from the upper snow-world to the meadows themselves.

Within a few miles rise the Finsteraarhorn, the highest peak in the Oberland, the Aletschhorn, Jungfrau, Mönch, Eiger and Schreckhorn, and the three peaks of the Wetterhorn. All played an important part in early mountain history and are now frequently and easily ascended each year by many climbers. Many, unlike the peaks of the Valais, were first explored largely by the Swiss.

Partly because of the early scientific interest in the Grindelwald glaciers, which could be visited more easily than others in the Alps, partly because of the accessibility from Bern, the Oberland attracted, during the nineteenth century, more tourist-seeking enterprise than any other part of the Alps. Grindelwald itself has been transformed into a typical visitors' resort. The Jungfrau railway gives easy access to the Jungfraujoch and the Aletsch Glacier alike – also to a great number of mountain climbs. At Rosenlaui there is an excellent mountain school run by the Swiss; and there are the Reichenbach Falls, the legendary place of Dr Moriarty's death-struggle with Conan Doyle's Sherlock Holmes.

But the wealth of tourist interest is less important than the basically fine features of the Oberland itself with its strongly-shaped peaks, its complex system of ridge and col, high enough to support snowfields, and its situation to the north of the main Alpine watershed where it catches the full force of bad weather and transmutes this into the snow and ice of the biggest glacier system lying entirely within Switzerland.

Bernina Alps

Easternmost section of the Central Alps. Location *Between the northeast Swiss Alps and the Albula Range, in Switzerland and Italy.* Height *Rising from 5,935 feet (Maloja Pass) to 13,304 feet (Piz Bernina).* Map *8, E8.* First climbed *Coaz of Switzerland, 1850 (Piz Bernina).*

Baedeker declared that the chain of the Bernina Alps was "scarcely inferior in grandeur to that of Monte Rosa." The high chain of snow peaks rises between the Val Bregaglia and the Upper Engadine in the north and the Valtellina in the south. The Piz Bernina itself, nearby Piz Palu, Monte della Disgrazia – the most prominent

A shepherd in the Bernina Alps

way back to Italy. Both the watershed and the international boundary are complicated, the latter following the main line of summits to the Piz Bernina and then turning south to enclose Poschiavo in a narrow Swiss enclave surrounded by Italian territory.

Of the Bernina summits wholly in Italy, Monte della Disgrazia (12,067 feet) is by far the finest, but many of the peaks have a character more impressive than their height would suggest. Their northern slopes have increasingly become the playground of the winter sports addict, while their easternmost stretches form part of a Swiss national park. Many of the peaks are remarkably accessible for their height, the Piz Languard above Pontresina being a typical example of the ascent which, even in Baedeker's day, was considered "justly a very favourite excursion, undertaken even by ladies."

Bhutan

A mountainous country between India and Tibet, still largely unmapped. Location Western Assam Himalayas, India. Height Rising to 24,780 feet in the Kula Kangri peak. Map 11, G5. First crossed by the Jesuit priests Stephen Cacella and John Cabral, 1626; later explored by Claude White, F. M. Bailey and others, subsequent to 1888. Most peaks still unclimbed.

The mountains of Bhutan, a protectorate under Indian authority since 1949, are part of the eastern or Assam Himalayas. They receive the full force of the Bay of Bengal branch of the southwest monsoon, over 120 inches of rain falling on the outer hills during the four months from June to September. This heavy rainfall causes dense tropical vegetation and has eroded the mountains into a different pattern from those in Nepal and farther west. The place of a geologically recent outer range is taken by the swampy, malarial tract known as the Duars (annexed by the British in 1866; part of it, known as the Dewangiri area, returned to Bhutan by India in 1949). In Bhutan the geological strike is from

peak in the western wing of the group – and Piz Languard, in the east, all underline this judgment.

Facing the Albula Alps across the shallow valleys to the north and the Bergamasque Alps across the deep trench of the Valtellina, the Bernina Alps are cut into their three sections by the Muretto and Bernina passes. The Bernina Pass (7,645 feet), crossed by the Bernina road and railway, leads from the Upper Engadine through Val Poschiavo into Italy. It is an ancient mountain crossing, for we know that Benvenuto Cellini passed through it (in winter, too) on his east to west; the mountains have been carved into great north-south ridges, separated by torrential rivers such as Amo, Raidak, Sankosh and Manas with their tributaries which sweep down from the snows of the Great Himalayas in parallel courses to the plains of India in Assam, where they join the Brahmaputra.

The "grain" of the country therefore runs from north to south, each valley having its administrative district headquarters – Paro, Tashi Chho (which contains the main lamasery of Bhutan), Punakha, Tongsa, Bumthang and Trashigong – which are sometimes completely isolated from one another, especially in winter. For the routes along the valleys are not easy, the paths are often destroyed or blocked by landslides and journeys from west to east by the route connecting these district centers entail a traverse of the successive intervening ridges which are densely forested and in places over 15,000 feet high.

Only in the north do the Great Himalayas consist of a continuous range from west to east, and this forms a boundary with Tibet. The range begins at the beautiful peak of Chomo Lhari (23,997 feet), sacred to the Tibetans. East of Chomo Lhari the Bhutan flanks of the Great Himalayas are almost entirely unexplored, though a few passes have been crossed by Europeans. There are many peaks of over 20,000 feet, though none of the first magnitude. Two groups over 24,000 feet stand on the range, one directly west of the difficult Mon La Kar Chung pass (17,422 feet) with summits of 24,740 and 24,660 feet; the other, Kula Kangri (24,780 feet), 15 miles northeast of it, just within Tibetan territory. The first European to cross the Mon La Kar Chung pass was Claude White in 1906.

The Bhutanese are of Tibetan stock and the religion of the vast majority is Buddhist, the Dukpa (Red Cap) sect of Lamaism. Strange to relate, almost the first crossing of the Himalayas by Europeans was made through this little-known land by the two Jesuit fathers, Stephen Cacella and John Cabral, in 1626, who took the route by the Raidak Valley, Paro Dzong and the Tan La to Shigatse on the Tsangpo in Tibet. In the second half of the eighteenth century Warren Hastings sent four missions by the same route, two of which reached Shigatse, mainly to investigate the possibilities of trade between Tibet and Bhutan and the East India Company. Apart from the scanty geographical information brought back by these travelers little was gleaned until 1864, when a small expedition entered the country and some hurried sketches were made by British officers. Even today our knowledge rests largely on reports and writings by White, F. M. Bailey, F. Williamson and other British political officers of Sikkim who, from 1888, made several official journeys to Punakha, the capital, and to some outlying districts. But the country has not yet been surveyed and the existing map is a compilation of route maps made in the course of such journeys and especially the travels of F. Ludlow and George Sherriff who, during the nineteen-thirties, added to our knowledge of central and northeastern Bhutan. Today, while not so exclusive as Nepal, Bhutan is open only to travelers who can secure special privileges.

Bighorn Mountains

A range extending 120 miles in a long curve, with many ancient Indian monuments. Location *Southern Montana and northern Wyoming, in the Rocky Mountains.* Height *8,000 feet, rising to 13,165 feet in Cloud Peak.* Map *4, D3-E3.* First explored *John Colter, 1807.*

The Bighorn Mountains rise just east of the Bighorn River in Montana and extend southeast into Wyoming along the eastern side of the Bighorn Basin. Varying in width between 30 and 50 miles, they consist of an uplift mainly of plateau-like character, from the higher parts of which the stratified beds have been removed by erosion, exposing the granites, and even these have been subject to considerable erosion. There are several small glaciers and the range is heavily forested throughout a good part of its upper reaches.

West of Sheridan, Wyoming, near the summit of Medicine Mountain (9,956 feet) stands the huge prehistoric shrine of the Medicine Wheel, 245 feet in circumference; its 28 radiating rock-spokes are believed to correspond with the 28 days of the lunar month. However, neither Cheyenne nor Crow nor any other of the Indian tribes whose ancient territories lie in this region have any record of these artifacts in their histories and the picture-writing far up on the cliffs nearby has not yet been translated.

Ruined fortifications, old mine workings and traces of iron tools show that the Spaniards had penetrated the Bighorn range; but no record remains of their explorations. The first white men known to have seen the range were the Chevalier de la Verendrye and his brother in 1738, and in 1792 sketches were made by Jesuit priests. After the Jesuit fathers, John Colter, the famous trapper and woodsman, passed through Prior Gap and wandered, lost, as far as Clark's Fork River. Other trappers and settlers followed not long after.

Today the Bighorns are familiar all over the world because they have served as a background to innumerable Western films. A high, bold mountain wall rising sharply from the rolling prairie, blue with haze or rugged and snow-capped, provides the scene of many of yesterday's famous real-life battles between white man and redskin. Even now the Bighorns are part of a West that is far from entirely tamed.

More than a dozen of the peaks tower above 9,000 feet, the lower ones swarthy with conifers beneath the permanent snowline of Cloud Peak (which has its own small glaciers). Glacial scouring has created a host of various-sized lakes along the slopes; numerous pretty streams and rivers wind their way down between banks hung with diamond willow, white hawthorn, black and red haws, wild gooseberries, currants and service berries, to the lower slopes where cattle graze and fields and orchards spread outwards from the tiny white homesteads with their giant red storage barns alongside.

In the mountains themselves dairying and flour-milling flourish; there is livestock grazing and irrigated agriculture in the foothills. The Bighorn National Forest in Wyoming forms part of the range and contains extensive stands of pine, fir and spruce. There is also some iron, copper and sub-bituminous coal mining.

Blue Mountains

The highest range in Jamaica, extending for 30 miles; dense forests and coffee plantations. Location *Eastern Jamaica, West Indies.* Height *3,000–4,000 feet, rising to 7,520 feet in Blue Mountain Peak.* Map *5, B10.*

The Blue Mountains form the most distinct part of the mountainous backbone running through Jamaica from east to west, throwing off a number of subsidiary ridges, mostly in a northwesterly or southeasterly direction. There are many cloud-capped peaks and numerous bifurcating branches. Five passes cross them at altitudes varying from 3,000 to 4,000 feet. After Blue Mountain Peak, the heights gradually decrease until the range merges into the hills of the western plateau.

The Blue Mountains are an extremely popular tourist area with dense vegetation and fine scenery, and they are beloved by naturalists and bird-watchers. Philip Gosse, writing in 1851 about the beautiful long-tailed humming-bird, remarked enthusiastically: "It seemed almost worth a voyage across the sea to behold so radiant a creature in all the wildness of its native freedom."

The purple velvet crest, emerald gorget, and long streaming black and purple tail plumes of this lustrous living gem (found only in Jamaica) flit and flutter all day among the flowers and shrubs of higher altitudes. It seems to love the tall, elegant *Hibiscus elatus*, a tree of startling rapidity of growth, much planted on the eroding hill-slopes. Newcastle and Mandeville, high up on Blue Mountain, are two of the most popular resorts.

Blue Ridge Mountains

A mountain range of moderate height and great beauty.
Location *Southern Pennsylvania and Georgia.* Height
*2,000–4,000 feet, rising to 5,964 feet in Grandfather
Mountain.* Map *5, A5.*

The Blue Ridge Mountains, forming the extreme
southwest part of the Older Appalachian Range,
bear many different names in their various sections. They begin in southern Pennsylvania and
run in a general northeast to southwest direction to Mount Oglethorpe in northern Georgia.
On the east they are bordered by the Piedmont
Valley and on the west by the Great Appalachian
Valley.

When they start near Carlisle, Pennsylvania,
they are known as South Mountain, a name they
keep in Pennsylvania and Maryland. This section runs 65 miles across Maryland and northern
Virginia, where the southern tip (here called
Short Hills) overlaps the Virginia section of the
Blue Ridge. Near Harpers Ferry (where John
Brown faced his moment of truth) the Potomac
River cuts through the range. South Mountain
range is lowest in the south, rising to 2,145 feet
in Quirauk Mountain, just south of the Maryland
stateline. In Maryland the range splits into two
prongs enclosing Middletown Valley; the eastern
prong is called Catoctin Mountain. Quartz,
manganese, iron-ore, sandstone, dolomite and
clay are some of the mining products here. The
battle of South Mountain, where McClellan defeated Lee's rear guard, was fought near Burkitts-
ville, Maryland, in the foothills on September 14,
1862.

The Shenandoah Valley is at the western base
of the Blue Ridge in Virginia. It marches on
across North Carolina, South Carolina and
Georgia. North of the Roanoke River it is
squeezed into a narrow linear ridge of 10-15
miles in width. South of the river the name is
sometimes applied to the entire eastern Appalachian chain but often it is restricted to the ridge-
like eastern front range of a complex mountain
zone which widens to about 70 miles in western
North Carolina and includes the Black Mountains. This is a spur of the Blue Ridge and the
highest range in the Appalachians, rising to
6,684 feet in Mount Mitchell, the highest point
east of the Mississippi. Its other peaks include
Balsam Cone (6,645 feet) and Cattail Peak
(6,593 feet), while the whole of the Black Mountains are included in the Pisgah National Forest.

The Unaka Mountains also include the Iron
Mountains and the Unicoi, Stone, Chilhowee,
Holston and Bald ranges. Most of the range is
covered by the national forests of Cherokee,
Pisgah and Nantahala. The name "Unaka" is
sometimes used to cover only the mountains in
the Unicoi-Carter counties of Tennessee and
Avery-Mitchell counties of North Carolina, between the Nolichucky and Doe rivers; the highest
elevation of this group is in Unaka Mountain
(5,258 feet) on the state line of Tennessee and
North Carolina.

The Blue Ridge proper (the eastern front
range) reaches its highest points in Georgia
(Brasstown Bald, 4,784 feet), Virginia (Mount
Rogers, 5,720 feet, in the Iron Mountains) and
South Carolina (Sassafras Mountain, 3,560 feet).
Stony Man (4,010 feet) and Hawks Bill (4,049
feet) are both in Virginia. Apart from the Potomac and the Roanoke, the James River has also
cut a transverse gap through the ridge; south of
the Roanoke the escarpment forms the east-west
drainage divide.

Superb scenery and many resorts have made
the Blue Ridge Mountains a most popular vacation and hiking area. In Virginia the Shenandoah
National Park is crossed by the famous Skyline
Drive, which was established in 1933 and connects with the Blue Ridge Parkway, continuing
to the Great Smoky Mountains. The Appalachian Trail follows much of the range. Trees are
mostly mixed hardwoods. In the remote Blue
Ridge valleys, especially in the south, the old
ways of American life and Elizabethan turns of
speech have survived in the midst of our atomic
age.

A peak of the Rocky Mountains in Banff National Pa

Bogdo Ola

A mountain massif, 150 miles across. Location *Eastern Tien Shan, Sinkiang Province, China.* Height *Average 13,000 feet, rising to 17,946 feet in the Turpanat-Tagh.* Map *10, D5.* Explored *Dr Grochen, 1903; Sven Hedin, 1930; and others.*

The Bodgo Ola (or Ulla), a mountain range sacred to the Kalmuck Mongols, is an eastern extension of the Tien Shan, from which it is separated by a wide gap between the Turfan Depression and Urumchi. It culminates in a lofty ridge, some two miles long, surmounted by three summits, the highest on the eastern end. Widely differing estimates have been made of the height of the mountain. Dr Grochen, the geologist of Merzbacher's Tien Shan expedition, who visited the range in 1903, put it at 21,300 feet, while according to the calculations of Sven Hedin's Sino-Swedish expedition it is only 18,000 feet. H. W. Tilman and Eric Shipton, who attempted to climb it in 1948, agree with this estimate.

The range forms the northern perimeter of the Turfan Depression, parts of whose floor are nearly 1,000 feet below sea level. The high peaks are heavily glaciated (on the north side of the range the snowline is at 9,500 feet) and the close proximity of this icy rampart to the torrid heat of the great hollow in the earth's surface probably accounts for the wind-storms that lash the southern flanks of the mountain, described by Shipton as "more violent than any I had experienced on Everest." The valleys on the southern side of the range are comparatively treeless but those in the northern foothills are densely forested, for the most part with conifers. In one of these there is an old Taoist monastery on the shore of Tien Shih (Heavenly Pool), a beautiful lake. Here, a bare 20 miles from the vast, barren steppes of Dzungaria, the scenery closely resembles many parts of the Swiss Alps. The upper valleys on both sides of the range are used as summer grazing grounds by Kazakh herdsmen, and have often served as strongholds for them.

Bonnet à l'Evêque

A sheer mountain with a flat summit. Location *Cap Haitien, Haiti.* Height *3,000 feet.* Map *5, C9.*

To the south of the little town of Cap Haitien lies a rugged range of forest-covered mountains. The highest peak is the Bonnet à l'Evêque (The Bishop's Hat) and even from 20 miles away the summit appears flat and ringed with precipices. In fact, it is the gigantic fortress of La Ferrière that one sees, the citadel built at immense cost of human life and suffering by Henri Christophe, the Black Emperor of Haiti, at the beginning of the nineteenth century, as a refuge and stronghold capable of garrisoning 10,000 men – in case the French, from whom Haiti had only just been freed, ever tried to recapture it. Vast cisterns still collect and contain enormous quantities of drinking water and in the magazines thousands of piled cannon balls moulder slowly away into rust.

Even today, though abandoned and neglected, it gives an overwhelming impression of impregnability. Its vast size, its position, resting like a crown on the mountain top, with the clouds just skimming the platforms or wreathing round its colossal walls, with its peaked prow of solid masonry jutting towards the only way of approach – La Ferrière is perhaps the most awe-inspiring castle in the world and one of its man-made wonders.

Henri Christophe was dethroned after a reign of only nine years but of astonishing achievement. When he became half-paralyzed he killed himself with a silver bullet. He is buried in the inner courtyard of the Citadel, in a small and simple tomb marked by a pyramid of cannon-balls.

Brenner Pass

The lowest Alpine pass, forming the divide between the Ötztal group of the Central Alps and the Zillertal group of the Eastern Alps. Location *Between Innsbruck, in Austria and Bolzano, in Italy.* Height *4,495 feet.*

e Brooks Range

Map 8, F7. Developed by the Romans, who replaced the grassy paths with a road.

The Brenner links the two cities at its northern and southern ends by means of the easy Sill and Inarco valleys. It has been in constant use since Roman times and can normally be traversed all the year round. Its approaches present few difficulties either for the road (opened in 1772) or the railway, which was completed by the Austrian Government in 1867, and it offers a genuine highway over the Alps. From 1772 to 1782, when the Col de Tenda road was opened, the Brenner was the only route by which travelers could at any time of the year cross the Alps without leaving their carriages. At the same time they passed the watershed between the Adriatic and the Black Sea.

Famous as the meeting-place of Hitler and Mussolini in 1940–42, the Brenner takes its name from the Breuni, conquered by Drusus after crossing the pass in an expedition recorded by Horace. In 1903 Murray's *Handbook to Northern Italy* called attention to "the long chain of castellated forts which crown the heights beneath which the road passes and which, though not older than the Middle Ages, doubtless occupy the sites of the hill-forts so formidable in the eyes of the Roman poet. . . These castles are usually so placed as to be visible from one another, or they are provided with isolated watch-towers from which a signal of fire by night or smoke by day could easily be discerned."

Historically, the Brenner has been the obvious invasion route from the northeast; it is believed that Attila poured his hordes across it into Italy in 452 A.D., followed 24 years later by Odoacer.

Brooks Range

The northernmost part of the Rocky Mountains. Location Northern Alaska, from the Chukchi Sea to the Yukon border, between the Yukon River and the Atlantic Ocean. Height Over 7,000 feet, rising to 9,239 feet in Mount Michelson. Map 3, C4-D4.

Everything associated with this great range is arctic. Caribou roam its uplands, pursued by wolves as large as can be found in North America, some "arctic white" and weighing 120 lbs and more. Its native inhabitants are Eskimos and Indians. The willows are stunted by the cold, and knee-high; lichens include the white and cream reindeer moss. From the snows and glaciers of the higher slopes rivers, ice-clad for much of the year, flow into ice-clad seas; the Porcupine into the fast, cold Yukon which, in turn, reaches the Bering Sea with its tributary, the Koyukuk; the Kobuk and Noatak into the icy sea encompassed by the coasts of Alaska and Siberia; the Colville across frozen muskeg into the Arctic Ocean.

Few white men have scaled the contorted ridges that rise to the pinnacles of Mount Michelson, visible from the little settlement of Arctic Village, or those culminating in the ice-clad Mount Doonerak. In the west, the Noatak River divides the Brooks Range into two tongues: the rugged Baird and De Long mountains, rising to 4,500 feet.

Once the only value of this vast range lay in its fur-bearing animals; the only form of transport through it was the canoe in summer and the dog-team and snow-shoe in winter. Since the Second World War, however, bush-planes have operated from airstrips and settlements at Wiseman, Arctic Village and Anaktuvik in the Endicott Mountains, home of a virile tribe of Eskimo hunters. Until the late nineteen-forties these had little lasting contact with the white man. There is much prospecting for minerals and oil, using the airstrip maintained near the Eskimo village of Umiat.

For the rest, the Brooks Range is remote even by Alaskan standards, its predominant sounds the clicking of caribou feet, the rattle of moose horns, the howl of wolf packs, and the hum of winds that sweep across the Arctic peaks from the ice-clad sea. Much of it is still inaccessible wilderness. The Brooks Range, in fact, knows no master.

Cairngorm Mountains

A rugged granite range. Location *Inverness, Banffshire and Aberdeenshire, Scotland.* Height *3,000 feet, rising to 4,296 feet in Ben Macdhui.* Map 7, B4.

Extending east to west between the upper Spey and Dee valleys, the Cairngorms are part of the largest high mountain area in Britain. They have several peaks of about 4,000 feet – among them Ben Macdhui (4,296 feet), Braeriach (4,248 feet), Cairntoul (4,241 feet), Cairngorm (4,084 feet), Ben Avon (3,843 feet) and Ben a'Bhuird (3,924 feet).

Height and isolation – for the Cairngorm plateau is cut by few low passes and fewer roads – and a situation on the northeast "bulge" of Scotland combine to give the group an arctic-alpine fauna and flora that is unique in the country, together with interesting meteorological conditions and the best ski-ing possibilities in the British Isles.

The Cairngorms, a spur of the Grampians, are bordered on the north by the River Spey and are deeply cut into by the Dee, which rises near their higher summits and then runs eastwards to isolate from the central Cairngorms the group which culminates in Lochnagar (3,768 feet).

Once known as the Monadh Ruadh, or red mountains, in contrast to the Monadh Liath, or gray mountains, which rise on the other side of the Spey, the Cairngorms are stony rather than craggy. They have given their name to "cairngorm," a yellow or brown quartz of which they contain deposits. At places their slopes break into fine granite cliffs; because of their remoteness, many have been exploited by the rock-climber only during the past two decades. The main problem of the walker is distance rather than difficulty of terrain; the traverse of the Larig Ghru, 30 miles from Aviemore on Speyside to Braemar on Deeside, has for long been among the most famous expeditions in Britain.

The Cairngorms can boast not only Balmoral, the royal home on the Dee built a century ago by Queen Victoria, but also Byron's "steep frowning glories of deep Lochnagar," one of Scotland's finest mountains, which provides some of the most severe climbing conditions in the country. There is also the Shelter Stone beside Ben Avon, many miles from nowhere, a useful and not uncomfortable gîte (bivouac) formed by a giant fallen block whose Visitors' Book it was once the fashion to sign on New Year's Eve.

There is also Britain's only mountain ghost, the Great Gray Man of Ben Macdhui. A traditional figure, reported privately by more than one climber, the Gray Man became famous in

A scene in the Cairngorm Mountains

1925 when Norman Collie, a respected member of the alpine world and a scientist of international repute, described an occasion when he had been followed by ghostly footsteps right to the top of the mountain. "When at last I reached the summit the footsteps did not stop but came nearer and nearer until they came right up to me. At that instant I was seized with an intolerable fright and I ran my hardest down the mountainside. No power on earth will ever take me up Ben Macdhui again."

Today, the Gray Man's territory forms part of Britain's largest nature reserve (some 40,000 acres), set up soon after the Second World War.

Cameroon Mountain

An isolated volcanic mass of about 800 square miles. Location *Cameroon, West Africa.* Height *13,350 feet.* Map *9, D6.* First climbed *Sir Richard Burton, 1861.*

The Cameroon massif is the highest point on the western side of Africa, with its southwest base washed by the Atlantic. It is the only great mountain of the continent lying close to the coast, and it presents a magnificent sight from any vantage point, but especially from the sea. It has only two distinct peaks – the Great Cameroon and Little Cameroon (5,820 feet), covered with dense forest from top to foot. To the local people the Great Cameroon is known as Mongo-ma-Loba, the Mountain of Thunder, while the whole upper region is usually called Mongo-mo-Ndemi, or Mountain of Greatness. The whole massif extends about 14 miles inland from the Gulf of Guinea; Victoria is at the southern foot, Buea on the southeast slope. Bananas, rubber and cacao are grown on the lower slopes.

In 1909 there was a violent eruption of the Great Cameroon and huge streams of lava were ejected. The last eruption took place in 1922.

The first woman to ascend "The Throne of Thunder" was the intrepid Mary Kingsley, the Victorian explorer, in 1893. Soaked through, her heavy skirt clinging to her legs, splashed with mud and nourished only by a cupful of sour claret drunk at dawn, she was deserted by her native porters and had to make the final ascent alone.

It took her six days to reach the summit, scrambling over the barren slopes and cliffs of jumbled black rock, dogged by violent storms and cloudbursts. The actual peak was one of the volcano's 70 known craters, consisting of a huge double cone, 1,000 feet across, 360 feet deep and divided by a steep wall. It was a desperate fight with a disappointing end to it. She found "a hurricane raging and a fog in full possession, and not ten yards' view to be had in any direction . . . verily I am no mountaineer, for there is in me no exultation but only a deep disgust because the weather has robbed me of my main object in coming here, namely to get a good view and an idea of the way the unexplored mountain range behind Calabar trends. I took my chance and it failed, so there's nothing to complain about."

Many have followed brave Mary Kingsley's footsteps but few have had her tenacity and her good-humored resignation to bad luck.

Cantabrian Mountains

A mountain range forming a wall between the sea and the great central plateau of Spain. Location *Bay of Biscay, northern Spain.* Height *Average 4,000–5,000 feet, rising to 8,678 feet in the Torre (or Peña) de Cerredo.* Map *7, A8.*

The Cantabrian Mountains or Cordillera Cantábrica extend about 300 miles from east to west from the Pyrenees along the Bay of Biscay to the Galician Mountains (which are sometimes considered a spur of the Cantabrians). Their northern slopes run steeply down to the sea; their southern slopes merge gradually into the sunbaked central massif. On the east they sink gradually before merging into the land which rises to the Pyrenees; on the west they peter out into the uplands of Galicia. Élysée Reclus, the French geographer, has suggested that they should be considered as the westernmost portion of the Pyrenees, a suggestion more usually applied only to the lower of the two parallel ranges which compose the whole group in most places.

The mountains traverse the Basque Provinces, Santander province and the Asturias. In the massif of the Picos de Europa they rise to their greatest height. Among other high peaks are the Peña Vieja (8,573 feet) and Peña Labra (7,136 feet). There are several parallel subsidiary ranges and spurs, among them the Sierra de Roñadoiro and the Leon Mountains.

Rich in iron and coal, the Cantabrians have been industrially exploited since ancient times and today their swift-flowing rivers are used to provide hydro-electric power for the towns along the Biscay coast. The prevailing wind comes off the sea and the moisture-laden air has helped to clothe the lower slopes with a rich vegetation of chestnuts, oaks, walnuts and vines.

High and crossed by few passes, the range is traversed by several railways and roads. The most spectacular is the railway using the Pass of Pajares on its way from Leon to Oviedo. In the 26 miles of twisted track which cover an actual distance of seven miles between Busdongo and Puente de los Fierros there are 58 tunnels.

The keynote of the range is wild, rugged magnificence; repeated, perhaps, in the character of the Asturian miners whose homeland is the craggy country between the mountains and the sea.

Cariboo Mountains

A range extending 200 miles, still incompletely surveyed. Location *Southern, central and eastern British Columbia.* Height *Rising to 11,750 feet (assumed) in Mount Titan.* Map *3, F8-9.* Explored *A. Carpe and R. T. Chamberlin, 1924.*

Extending between the upper North Thompson River and the northern apex of Fraser River, and running roughly parallel with the main range of the Rocky Mountains, the Cariboo Mountains are still something of a mystery. Between them and the Rockies lies the Rocky Mountain Trench in which the Fraser River runs. The height of the loftiest peak, Mount Sir Wilfred Launier or Mount Titan, is still not known precisely. The highest surveyed peak is Mount Spranger (9,920 feet).

The range extends for about 75 miles from north to south and is about 40 miles wide. A formidable barrier to the western outlet to Yellowhead Pass, it became important in the early surveys for the Canadian Pacific Railroad, but surveyors were never able to pierce the heart of these mountains. The central plateau opens eastwards and encloses the glacial sources of Canoe River. Large glaciers drain northwards, and the conjoined stream of Tête Creek and McLennan River enters the Fraser at the old fur-trading site of Tête Jaune Cache. There is a rudimentary trail on the western side of Tête Creek, leading to the glacier below the main peaks, several of which bear the names of Canadian premiers. The low valleys and heavy undergrowth make all approaches difficult. In the southeast part of the range are the Azure, Clearwater, Hobson and Murtle lakes enclosed within Wells Gray Provincial Park. The western foothills were the scene of the Cariboo gold rush of 1860. Within six years about $20,000,000 worth of gold was mined here; later the rich veins petered out and farming, stock-raising and hunting became the livelihood of the settlers. The Cariboo Road, built between 1862 and 1865 by the Royal Engineers at a cost of $250,000, extends from Yale at the head of the navigable part of the Fraser River via Ashcroft to Barkerville, a distance of about 500 miles. The trade centers are Prince George, Quesnel and Williams Lake.

The region was explored by Mahood in 1871 during surveys for the Canadian Pacific Railroad; Holway and Gilmour were the first mountaineers, in 1916. But there is still much to discover and many peaks to conquer in this wild, beautiful range.

Carmel, Mount

A short, rocky mountain ridge. Location *Northwest Israel.* Height *1,791 feet.* Map *9, G2.*

Mount Carmel extends 13 miles from the Plain of Jezreel to the Mediterranean at Haifa, forming the southern boundary of the Zebulun Valley. It ends in a magnificently wooded promontory marking the southern limit of the Bay of Acre in which the modern city of Haifa is situated. It is one of the most striking physical features of Israel and has long been an object of veneration.

Carmel – the word means garden or park – is a most important landmark in Biblical history. Here the prophet Elijah came face to face with King Ahab and received the challenge to face the "multitudinous priests of Baal and Ashtaroth," from which contest he emerged victorious. The place can still be identified, called "el-Mukrakah," the place of burning. There is a natural platform of naked rock, surrounded by a low wall with the sea just visible behind it; the great plain lies in front with Jezreel in the distance and Kishon just at the mountain foot. Nearby there is a well of water from which Elijah is supposed to have obtained the libation for the altar and the trench around it. Elisha, too, the minister and successor of Elijah, dwelled on Carmel. Pythagoras was said to have visited it; the Emperor Vespasian offered sacrifice here and it is still sacred to Christians, Jews and Moslems alike.

Carmel's numerous caves were inhabited by early Christian anchorites. Near the summit there still stands a monastery, originally founded in 1156. Not far away is a Bahaist garden shrine with the tombs of Bab ed Din and Abdul Baha, founders of this eclectic religion.

Christian pilgrimages to Carmel started in the fourth century – mainly because the early Fathers, especially St John Chrysostom, considered Elijah and his disciple Elisha as models of religious life. Elisha, latinized as Eliseus, gave his name to a monastery in the sixth century; in 1156 the Order of the Carmelites was established. Their rule (given them by the Patriarch Albert of Jerusalem and confirmed by Pope Honorius III in 1224) was at first one of extreme austerity, modelled upon the life led by Elijah. Silence, solitude, prayer, manual labor and study filled their days; they were allowed no meat except when ill and observed a long fast each year, from September 14 to Easter. The Saracens drove out the Carmelites in 1247 and they became wandering mendicants, known as White Friars, from the white cloak of their order.

In the Arab-Jewish war Carmel became, briefly, a battleground. But its beautiful gardens and villas have remained untouched and today the mountain stands sentinel over the main port of the young state of Israel.

Carpathian Mountains

A major mountain system connecting the Alps with the Balkan Mountains. Location *Czechoslovakia, Poland, Ukrainian SSR and Rumania.* Height *From 3,000 to 8,000 feet.* Map *7, F7.*

This important range forms one of the most striking mountain arcs of Europe, enclosing the great Hungarian plain with its sweep of over 900 miles and constituting a natural strategic and ethnic barrier between important national groups. It has played and still plays a dominant part in the political and economic history of the countries between the Baltic and the Adriatic. To the geologist the range presents a fascinating study for its complex and varied structure. Through outliers of the Eastern Alps in the Vienna basin, the Carpathians link the Alps to the Balkan Mountains, with which they merge in some lesser ranges in eastern Serbia. In all, the range extends from Bratislava on the Danube north through Slovakia, then east along the Czech-Polish border (where it attains its greatest width of about 160 miles) and southeast through the Ruthenian section of the Ukrainian SSR into Rumania. North of Ploesti and Bucharest it

turns abruptly west and forms the Transylvanian Alps as far as the Danube. Orographically the range continues even farther south into eastern Serbia and the Balkans.

The main Carpathian backbone forms an important watershed between the Dniester and Vistula rivers, which rise on its eastern slopes, and the Danube basin in the west and south. At the Dukla Pass, where the Hungarian plain projects most deeply into the range, the Carpathians narrow to barely 20 miles and thus offer an easy passage between the two densely populated basins. These mountains do not actually constitute such a formidable barrier as the Alps or the Pyrenees since they are cut by numerous low passes. Only three railway lines cross the Transylvanian Alps. Here bear, wolf and lynx still live in the "havas" or snowy fastnesses, and chamois abound, especially in the Tatra, where the highest summits are situated (in the High or Vysoke Tatra). This picturesquely alpine region of jagged peaks on the borders of Poland and Czechoslovakia is a popular district for mountaineering and winter sports, with many sanatoria for lung diseases.

Garlachovka (8,737 feet) is the highest peak of the Carpathians. To the south, in a lower parallel range, lie the Low Tatra (Nizske Tatry) whose highest peak is Dumbier (6,707 feet). By contrast, the Transylvanian Alps of the far southern Carpathians consist of a district of mainly flat-topped ridges and plateaus; but in the Fagaras massif they exceed 8,000 feet (Negoi, 8,361 feet).

With a snowline at around 8,500 feet, permanent snow-fields are found only in the Tatras and there are no glaciers. There is ample evidence, however, of their existence during the Glacial Epoch: cirques (natural amphitheaters) in high mountain valleys, many of them characteristically U-shaped, contain moraines and relict basins, now occupied by lakes (called "sea-eyes" or tarns) which were left by retreating glaciers. There is plentiful proof, too, of past glaciation in the Transylvanian Alps.

There are valuable oil fields on the outer

A peak in the Rumanian Carpathians

flanks of the mountains, as in the Prahova valley near Ploesti, Rumania, southeast of the Transylvanian Alps; and at Borislav (Ukrainian SSR) at the northern foot of the East Beskid Range. From the Hegyalja region flows a different and even more precious liquid – the famous Tokay wine.

Decisive historic battles were fought in the Carpathians during the early Turkish invasions of central Europe, and in modern times during the First and Second World Wars. In the early part of 1915 the 'Battle of the Carpathians" took place in the forested region extending from the Dukla Pass southeast to the old Rumanian border. These were ill-conceived, bloody and disastrous campaigns, waged between the Austrian and Russian armies and conducted in the depths of winter. In 1944 and 1945 the Red Army burst into central and western Europe through the Carpathian passes.

The Carpathians have always been the home of legend and folktale, a favorite playground of the Gothic and Romantic imagination from Mary Shelley's *Frankenstein* to Jules Verne's *Castle in the Carpathians* and Bram Stoker's *Dracula*. The folklore and folk-art of the range are varied and rich, and no political changes could suppress the sturdy individuality of the mountain people of the Tatras and the Transylvanian Alps.

Carrantuohill

The highest mountain in Ireland. Location *Central County Kerry, Eire.* Height *3,414 feet.* Map *7, A5.*

Carrantuohill ("inverted reaping-hook") is also spelled Carrauntuohil and Carrantual, and there are about nine other possible variants. It also boasts a summit cairn whose first stone was placed in position by Edward VII of England, when he visited Ireland as a youth of 16.

The ascent of the mountain is an easy exercise in good weather although a gully known as the Devil's Ladder has been described as "600 feet high and as vertical as makes no difference."

More usually, the ascent is described as a stroll – or pony-trot – followed by a walk uphill to the oval plateau of the summit, which measures some 130 feet by 60 feet.

In itself a tame enough peak, Carrantuohill provides a fine view, for it stands clear of attendant mountains and gives a vista as far as the Atlantic with the great trench of the Kenmare River on one side and the blue expanse of Dingle Bay on the other. As the highest point in Ireland, the mountain has inevitably become involved in record-breaking attempts. In 1934 it was climbed by a British naval officer who, in the three previous days, had for a wager ascended the highest summits of England, Wales and Scotland. The record was broken in 1937 when a party climbed Carrantuohill having ascended Scafell Pike, Snowdon and Ben Nevis in the previous 26 hours.

The mountain is the highest summit of the Macgillicuddy's Reeks, a fine 12-mile ridge which stretches west from the Gap of Dunloe, a few miles from Killarney, and rises to about 3,000 feet in a series of precipitous broken cliffs. The quality of the Reeks is due to a combination of form and atmosphere. Frequent mists, more than the danger of precipices, have for long encouraged the use of local guides for the various ascents that can be made.

Cascade Range

A mountain range of great variety including several volcanic peaks. Location *California, Oregon, Washington and British Columbia.* Height *Average 8,000 feet, rising to 14,408 feet in Mount Rainier.* Map *4, A2-B1.*

"Historically, these mountains have played a tremendous role in the making of the country," wrote James Ramsey Ullman, speaking of the three ranges of the Rocky Mountains, the Sierra Nevada and the Cascades. "There would be no American West, as we know it, without its peaks, canyons and passes and the great intervening plateaus."

Majestic Mount Hood, in the Cascade Range

The Cascades extend for more than 700 miles north from Lassen Peak in California, where they meet the Sierra Nevada, through Oregon and Washington to the Fraser River in British Columbia, whence they are continued by the Coast Mountains; they parallel the Pacific coast, running about 100 to 150 miles inland. The range was named after the great cascades of the Columbia River which occur where it canyons through the range by a pass 4,000 feet deep.

Many of its peaks are snow-covered and volcanic. Extensive glaciation has left many lakes, of which Lake Chelan is the largest; glaciers are found on the higher peaks. In the southern part of the range Crater Lake National Park occupies 250 square miles, lying in southwest Oregon. The circular Crater Lake is six miles across at an altitude of 6,614 feet with a 20-square-mile surface, and a depth of 1,983 feet, occupying an enormous pit which was originally the summit of a prehistoric volcano. Many-colored cliffs, 500 to 2,000 feet high, line the lake shore. There are breath-taking views from the rim road encircling the lake and from Cloudclap mountain (8,070 feet) on the eastern rim. The highest point among the volcanic peaks here is Mount Scott (8,938 feet) near the eastern boundary of the National Park. The lake was discovered in 1855 by prospectors; the park was established in 1902.

The chief resources of the Cascades are timber – cedar, fir and pine – and the rivers of their Pacific slope, which receives most of the rainfall, are used extensively for hydro-electric schemes. The drier slope in Washington is cut into several spurs, among them the Chelan, Entiat and Wenatchee ranges, separated by the Methow, Chelan, Entiat, Wenatchee and Yakima valleys, which are famous for their orchards. The principal routes are the Cascade Tunnel and the Snoqualmie Pass in Washington, the Columbia River gorge (which carries highways and rails along the Washington-Oregon line) and the Salt Creek Pass (5,128 feet) in Oregon. The British Columbia section contains no important mountains, but is rather a plateau dissected by numerous rivers; in other parts of the range, however, there are Mount Rainier, Mount Shasta, Mount Adams, Mount Hood, Mount Baker, Mount Jefferson and Mount St Helens, all towering, snow-capped volcanic cones of impressive stature.

The Cascades were discovered in 1792 by Vancouver and Broughton. They are a vast and popular tourist area which also offers challenging climbs for mountaineers, all the main peaks from Mount Rainier to Glacier Peak being frequently ascended.

Catskill Mountains

A rolling, wooded region with deep gorges and many waterfalls. Location *Greene, Ulster and Delaware counties, New York.* Height *3,000 feet, average.* Map *5, B3.* Settled *by the Dutch; Catskill Village founded by Derrick Tennis van Vechten, 1680.*

The Catskills are a low mountain group, part of the Allegheny Plateau, lying west of the Hudson River, in the southern part of New York. The peaks are generally isolated, with Slide Mountain (4,204 feet) and Hunter Mountain (4,025 feet) the highest. On the east the Catskills dip steeply to the Hudson, on the north they stretch as far as the Mohawk Valley where the Helderbergs form the northern escarpment of the plateau. Their characteristic features are the deep gorges known by their Dutch name of "cloves." Of these the Kaaterskill has three beautiful cascades. There are few lakes but many streams of which Neversink, Beaverkill and Willowemoc provide excellent fishing.

The Catskills are well wooded with oak, maple, ash, beech, pine, hickory, spruce, rhododendron and mountain laurel. The Catskill Aqueduct carries much of New York City's water supply 92 miles from the Ashokan Reservoir to Kensico in Westchester and Hillview Reservoir in Yonkers. The first section of the aqueduct was completed in 1917.

The Catskills have also given their name to a

geological formation, comprising a series of sandstones and shales of the upper Devonian system. These are shallow-water deposits, formed during the time when the marine sediments of the Hamilton, Portage and Chemung groups were deposited in deeper waters. The colors are usually brown, greenish, red and steel gray and the sandstone often splits into horizontal layers which are quarried for flagstones. Fossils are rare. The sediments are about 3,500 feet deep; their greatest thickness is 7,500 feet in the vicinity of Mauch Chunk, Pennsylvania.

One of the Catskills, the Dunderberg, was chosen by Washington Irving as the scene of his immortal *Rip Van Winkle*, which became part of American folklore. The Catskill Forest Preserve of 232,423 acres includes some of the range's most beautiful scenery and part of it is known as "Rip Van Winkle's country."

The Catskills attract the climber and the mountaineer less than hikers, fishermen and people on vacation. The summer climate is cool and many of New York's millions seek relaxation in the easily accessible mountain regions. There is also considerable winter sports activity.

Caucasus

A great mountain system divided into three ranges. Location *Southeast European USSR.* Height *6,000–9,000 feet average, rising to 18,481 feet in Mount Elbrus.* Map *10, A4.* Explored *British climbers in the second half of the nineteenth century.*

Here Prometheus was bound to the rock. Here the Argonauts sought the Golden Fleece. Here, for Herodotus, was the boundary of the Persian Empire, and here remained, almost to within living memory, the legend of a country of huge, mysterious peaks and great glaciers. This great mountain chain is, geographically speaking, the natural southern barrier between Europe and Asia.

The Greater Caucasus, bounded on the north by the plains of Russia and on the south by the Black Sea and the valleys of the Rion and Kur rivers, consists of a series of high parallel ridges. The glaciers are comparable in size to those of the Alps, though the permanent snowline is higher, varying from 9,000 feet at the western to 12,000 feet at the eastern end.

Douglas Freshfield, one of the greatest of English mountaineer-explorers, whose career spanned a full 50 years, wrote in 1896: "The central chain of the Caucasus, when studied in detail, recalls the features of the Pennine Alps. It consists of a number of short, parallel or curved horse-shoe ridges, crowned with rocky peaks and enclosing basins filled by the névés of great glaciers, the Maragom, the Dykhshu, the Bezingi, the Zanner and the Leksur. I name only a few of the greatest. In its double ridges, with vast frozen reservoirs between them, it resembles the group of Mont Blanc; it has lofty spurs like those of the Saasgrat and the Weisshorn. On either side of the main chain the succession is repeated with one important difference. On the north the schists come first, sometimes rising into peaks and ridges in a state of ruin most dangerous to climbers – a fact indelibly impressed on my memory – but more often worn to rolling downs, then the limestone range – writing-desk mountains that turn their steep fronts to the central snows; lastly, low cretaceous foothills that sink softly into the steppe."

The main peaks of this range were all first climbed by Englishmen – Elbrus (eastern, lower peak) and Kazbek by Douglas Freshfield in 1868; Elbrus (western peak) by F. Crauford Grove in 1874; Dykh-Tau by A. F. Mummery in 1888 – and throughout the nineteenth century they exercised a fascination for English climbers. In 1888–89 Koshtan-Tau, one of the Caucasian peaks, was the scene of a famous mountaineering tragedy. Two well-known British climbers, W. Donkin and H. Fox, set out with two Swiss guides in the summer of 1888 to try and reach its summit – and vanished without leaving a trace. There were rumours of kidnapping and murder by bandits; the matter developed into a minor international

dispute. Then, a year later, Freshfield and his climbing companion, Clinton Dent, went to the Caucasus to clear up the mystery. After weeks of searching and climbing, they found, high on a desolate ridge of the great peak, Donkin and Fox's last camp. Sleeping-bags, rucksacks and personal belongings were lying as if their owners had left them only a few hours before. It became clear that the lost men had been the victims of a mountaineering accident, not of foul play. No trace of the bodies was ever found; Donkin, Fox and their two guides must have died in some isolated spot and their corpses been destroyed by the weather or by wild animals.

Exploration of the Caucasus was made difficult until about a century ago by the persistent and largely futile attempts of the Russians to subdue the Caucasian tribes. At first most explorers kept well below the snowline and no major peak had been climbed, nor were reliable maps of the upper regions available, when Freshfield, Comyns Tucker and A. W. Moore made their successful foray into the area in 1868. A second party of Alpine Club members, Crauford Grove, Moore, Horace Walker and Frederick Gardiner, followed Freshfield in 1874 and made a number of ascents.

By the eighties the tide of exploration was

flowing fast, the Hungarian, Maurice de Déchy, making three expeditions, the British four and the famous Vittorio Sella undertaking two photographic journeys. In 1888 three British parties were at work in the Caucasus. Ushba, "the Matterhorn of the Caucasus," held out longest against assault, for although the lower, northern peak was climbed in 1888 by Cockin with the Swiss guide Ulrich Almer, the true summit was not conquered until 1903. The long series of British expeditions ended at the turn of the century and it was not until after the First World War that exploration of the Caucasus was begun once again – this time largely by German and Russian parties.

However, Caucasia, the long narrow area of which the Caucasus forms the rocky backbone, is not only a frontier region of considerable strategic importance but has the economically vital oil fields of Maikop and Baku at either end. The whole area has, therefore, been virtually inaccessible to foreign travelers since the end of the Second World War. Not until 1957 was Joyce Dunsheath allowed as the first foreign mountaineer to undertake some climbs. In 1958 a party of five under Sir John Hunt also made several ascents.

During the last decade the Caucasus has become one of the main training grounds for Soviet mountaineers and there are about 20 alpine training camps. Virtually all climbing is organized under the benevolent but all-enveloping auspices of the All-Union Alpine Section of the Ministry of Physical Culture and Sport.

Cayambe

An extinct volcano, craterless, with square, snow-capped top. Location *Northern central Ecuador.* Height *19,014 feet.* Map *6, B3.* First climbed *Edward Whymper, 1880.*

Edward Whymper, the conqueror of the Matterhorn, first saw Cayambe from the summit of Cotopaxi, some 60 miles away, its snow-sheathed plateaus glinting in the distance. Lying 40 miles northeast of Quito, Cayambe is almost exactly on the equator. It is also one of the loftiest peaks around Quito and, according to Whymper's account, one of the most rewarding and interesting to climb. Here one has the privilege of climbing on the highest point on the imaginary line around the center of the earth and also the experience of finding snow on the equator. Whymper established a snow camp for his climb and in the morning he and his companions found the spoor of a puma encircling their tent.

There is no longer a crater and the summit is formed of three domes, all covered by a single thick glacier – like a great rumpled blanket. This forms a ridge running north to south and the ice is likely to recede eventually to reveal rock aiguilles underlying the three hammocks of the glacier.

As in the case of most of the volcanic peaks of Ecuador, there has been little mountaineering activity since Whymper's day and interest in Cayambe has largely disappeared after the first ascent, more than 80 years ago. But it is a fine mountain to look upon and the sight of the sun catching the glacier of its summit is a temptation hard to resist.

Cévennes

A mountain chain 40 miles in extent: a range of rugged peaks and wooded valleys. Location *Southern France.* Height *3,000 feet, average.* Map *7, C8.*

"When I was a boy," wrote André Chamson, the noted French writer, member of the French Academy and himself a native of the Cévennes, "these hills, all this towering *Aigoual* peak, meant to me everything that other children demand from stories of adventure, warlike tales: the propinquity of a universe, heroic, legendary: and that first effort to justify existence, which with individuals, as with races, only the saga can effect."

Indeed, this mountain area of southern France,

extending over parts of three departments, swinging from the Montagne Noire to the Monts du Vivarais, has a heroic, legendary character. Here the *Camisards* (the Cévennes Protestants) rose against the might of Louis XIV and under Jean Cavalier, the baker's boy turned general, defied the greatest marshals of France for almost 20 years. Here the spirit of defiance, the strong religious conviction and the individual faith of non-conformism still survive and seem to be supported by the mountains and forests.

The narrow ridge of some 320 miles, with its numerous lofty plateaus and secondary ranges, which makes up the Cévennes in their broadest sense, forms part of the watershed between the Atlantic and the Mediterranean. The Cévennes lie along the southeast border of the central plateau of France, running across part of the Gard, Hérault and Lozère departments, from the Causse du Larzac to the Ardèche. They overlook the Rhône valley and the Languedoc coastal lowland. Their highest peaks are Mont Lozère (5,584 feet), and Mont Aigoual (5,141 feet). Mont Mézenc, in the Vivarais, rises to 5,755 feet. The Allier, Ardèche, Gard, Hérault, Loire, Lot and Tarn rivers all rise here. There are rich olive, mulberry and chestnut groves on the southeast slopes; the north has sheep pastures.

Chamson, who spent his childhood and youth among these wild and bewitching mountains, wrote evocatively: "There, amid our grass-tufts, the world around us seemed a source of perpetual wonder and delight... Facing us, in a single sweep, over half-a-mile high, the Aigoual climbs to the heavens, bearing aloft, above the chasms and the posy of Hort-de-Dieu, the tall Observatory tower. The mighty peak now opposite us, moment by moment, recaptures what the clouds manage to seize..."

The Cévennes have never been tamed by man, in spite of the mountain hotels, the motor roads, the industries of Alès. Their wild beauty can still inspire such writers as Chamson and – as during the Second World War – fighters for freedom in the tradition of Jean Cavalier.

Chimborazo

An extinct volcano, highest peak of the Ecuadorian Andes. Location *Central Ecuador.* Height *20,577 feet.* Map *6, B4.* First climbed *Edward Whymper, 1880.*

Rising several thousand feet above the snowline, Chimborazo is the highest of a series of extinct volcanoes that surmount the Western and the Eastern Cordilleras of Ecuador. Only from the Pacific side can its true proportions be realized. Set on a mountain chain that rarely falls below the 10,000-foot level, it loses nearly half of its true height when seen from the populous inter-cordilleran valley of Ecuador which skirts its eastern flanks. It is frequently visible from Quito.

Simón Bolívar called it "The Watchtower of the Universe" and it has been a famous landmark since the earliest days of the Spanish conquest. The district surrounding its base was well known to travelers and explorers of the Spanish Colonial period. Between 1736 and 1744 the first major scientific expedition to any high mountain range chose it for its target – a large, well-equipped party of geographers and naturalists, led by the Frenchmen Bouger and La Condamine, and the Spaniards Juan Jorge and Ulloa. As a result of their investigations Chimborazo ranked for almost three-quarters of a century as the highest mountain in the world – as neither the Himalayas nor the higher southern Andes were known.

Though the summit is no more than about 11,000 feet above the inter-Andean valley, the mountain has proved difficult to climb. Alexander von Humboldt, the German naturalist, and his companions attempted it in 1802 but were unsuccessful. However, the records published by various members of the party served to place Chimborazo among the most famous mountains of the world.

It was left to the great mountaineer, Edward Whymper, to reach the summit, making two ascents in 1880 and later giving a full account of his topographical observations. He found that whatever remained of a deformed crater was buried under a thick icecap crowning the upper 4,000-5,000 feet from which the summit ridges project, giving the mountain a rather irregular appearance. From this icecap large glaciers extend down the mountainsides, giving rise to streams – some of which become tributaries of the Guayas River on the Pacific side, while of the others, flowing eastwards into the inter-Andean valley, some eventually join the Amazon River system.

Chimborazo appears to be composed mainly of andesite lava, of similar composition to that found elsewhere in the Andes. The old lava streams on the flanks of the mountain consist of andesite, which also forms great vertical, jointed cliffs breaking the icecap towards the summit. As eruptions have long since ceased, any loose materials ejected by the volcano when it was active have been swept away by erosion. In its prime Chimborazo may well have been a considerably higher mountain, for the existing twin summits appear to be the reduced remains of a crater. In a later stage of volcanic activity violent explosions may have decapitated the mountain and destroyed the greater part of the crater. Alternatively, Chimborazo may have been extinct long enough for denudation to remove much of the upper cone.

The lower slopes of the mountain cover a large area. An eastern limb extends into the inhabited longitudinal valley, joining there with similar limbs of two other great extinct volcanoes, Sangay and Tanguahua, situated opposite across the valley in the Eastern Cordillera. North of this col lies Ambato and south of it Riobamba, both important towns, both of them nestling almost at the foot of Chimborazo, owing their rise to the fertility of the volcanic soils of these valleys.

Chiricahua Mountains

A range of rugged and spectacular beauty. Location *Southeast Arizona.* Height *Rising to 9,795 feet.*

Map *4, C6-D6.* First explored *American trappers and hunters in the first half of the nineteenth century.*

The Chiricahua Mountains lie in Cochise County, Arizona, north of Douglas, separated from the Dos Cabezas Mountains by the Apache Pass, one of the main routes of the wagon trains to California in the nineteenth century. The pass is 5,115 feet high.

The range, with two peaks rising almost to 10,000 feet (Flys and Chiricahua) and another of 8,100 feet (Cochise Head), forms part of the Coronado National Forest. This is a region long inhabited by the Apache Indians, who carried on a fierce war against the white settlers in the second half of the nineteenth century under their leaders Cochise, Geronimo and Massai.

The most spectacular part of the range is the Chiricahua National Monument, 70 miles from Douglas or Bisbee and 38 miles from Wilcox, a protected area of 16.4 square miles, established in 1924. The "Wonderland of Rocks" contains three canyons with gigantic monoliths of rhyolite, eroded by wind and water into many fantastic shapes. It is one of the few places in the world where lava flows have been eroded in sedimentary forms. Some of the canyon walls are 1,000 feet high. Arizona boasts some very striking rock formations: the "totem pole," 137 feet high and only a yard thick; the "mushroom;" "Thor's hammer;" "Punch and Judy;" and the balanced rock which weighs 652 tons and rests on a base of about 4 feet. One of the canyons contains natural caves with prehistoric paintings.

In the late nineteen-forties Bonita Canyon was added to the Chiricahua National Monument. There are camping areas, ranches and picnic grounds. Bonita Canyon has an eight-mile road leading to Massai Point, which offers a view of more than 100 miles to the east and across the Sulphur Springs Valley to the west.

Chomo Lhari

A great peak sacred to Buddhists. Location *Western*

Assam Himalayas, on the Bhutan-Tibet border.
Height *23,997 feet*. Map *11, G5*. First climbed
*Lt.-Col. F. Spencer Chapman and Sherpa Pasang
Dawa Lama, May 21, 1937.*

Chomo Lhari (also known as Chumalhari or
Jomolhari) is the great sentinel peak directly east
of the Tang La, the 15,200-foot pass which takes
the main trade route from India by way of
Sikkim and the Chumbi valley to Gyantse and
Lhasa. It is one of the three mountains most
sacred to the Tibetans and every year pilgrims
assemble at Phari Dsong, ten miles distant in a
direct line, and go in procession to the mountain
to pray for its protection. It has been known to
Europeans longer than almost any other Himalayan mountain under its present Tibetan name
or some variant of it, which, according to Charles
Bell, the Tibetan authority and writer, means
"the Mountain of the Goddess." It was seen by
the two Jesuit travelers, Stephen Cacella and
John Cabral, in 1627 when on their journey from
India to Shigatse in Tibet; it was included in
D'Anville's *Atlas of China*, published in Paris in
1735. Early estimates of its height, derived from
Chinese sources, were about 2,000 feet too high.
This is not surprising since from the Tibetan side
it gives an extraordinary impression of height
and inaccessibility, rising from the plain almost
sheer for nearly 9,000 feet.

Many Europeans have seen Chomo Lhari
since Cabral's day, but its exact position and
height were not determined until about 1883.
It became well known to members of Younghusband's mission to Lhasa in 1903–04 and to
those of the early Everest expeditions who crossed
the Tang La. But permission to explore it has
always been refused by the Tibetans.

It was climbed in May, 1937, by F. Spencer
Chapman and a Sherpa porter, Pasang Dawa
Lama. Chapman obtained permission from the
Bhutan Government to approach the mountain
from the south and after a thorough reconnaissance of the previously unexplored ridges and
valleys at the head of the Paro Chu, he chose

one of the southern ridges which meets the
southwest ridge of the peak some distance from
the summit. The party was very small, comprising only Chapman, C. E. Crawford and three
experienced Sherpa porters; the climb, arduous
in deep snow, was successful, though the exhausted Crawford had to return with two of the
porters, after reaching the camp at 20,000 feet.
The descent was difficult and nearly ended in
disaster. Pasang Dawa slipped out of his steps,
but was finally stopped by Chapman, to whom
he was roped, after both had been carried down
the mountain for about 400 feet. They were then
caught by bad weather; a blizzard reduced
visibility to zero and snow obliterated their upward tracks. After four nights spent on the
mountain, during the descent, Chapman brought
his frost-bitten and completely exhausted porter
to shelter in a yak-herd's hut and they returned
safely to Sikkim.

Since the Second World War no further
climbs have been made, and the detailed topography of the great mountain is still little known.
The Chinese occupation of Tibet has made
approach from that side impossible and permission to visit the mountain from Bhutan is
more difficult to obtain than ever.

Cho Oyu

Sixth highest peak in the world. Location *Northeast
Nepal Himalayas, on the Nepal-Tibet border.* Height
26,967 feet. Map *11, F5*. First climbed *Dr Herbert
Tichy, Joseph Joechler and Sherpa Pasang Dawa
Lama, October 19, 1954.*

Cho Oyu was first surveyed by the Mount
Everest Reconnaissance Expedition of 1921. It
became a familiar sight to the climbers on the
north face of Everest, the last peak in view to
sink beneath them as they struggled up towards
the Yellow Band. To the west of the mountain is
the Nangpa La, a glacier saddle 19,000 feet high,
which carries the main trade route between
Tibet and the Sherpa valley of Khumbu.

In 1952 Cho Oyu was attempted by an expedition led by Eric Shipton; the main purpose was to train a party for Everest in 1953. The previous year Shipton and Michael Ward had examined the south ridge from a distance and thought that it looked feasible. At the same time T. D. Bourdillon and W. H. Murray had seen the east face from just beyond Nangpa La and had reported that it seemed to offer an easy route to the summit. Closer examination of the south ridge showed it to be impracticable and the 1952 expedition was faced with a difficult decision. To reach the east face it was necessary to cross the Nangpa La and descend a short distance beyond, into territory which, although uninhabited and without an officially demarcated frontier, might reasonably be claimed as Tibetan. Tibet had recently been occupied by the Chinese Communist Army, and there was some risk that if the garrison commander in Tingri should hear about a British expedition crossing the pass, he would despatch troops to arrest them. Shipton therefore decided not to make a full-scale attempt but to try a "hit-and-run" approach with a lightly equipped, mobile party. The only serious mountaineering obstacle was an ice-cliff 250 feet high, formed by a glacier shelf running across the east face. The foot of this cliff, about 22,500 feet, was reached from Camp 2 by Bourdillon, Gregory, Secord, Hillary and Lowe. Though the cliff was by no means insuperable, it was thought that it would take several days to cut a way up and fix the ropes necessary to carry loads for establishing a camp within reach of the summit. As supplies were not available, it was decided to abandon the attempt.

In 1954 Cho Oyu was climbed by the east face by an Austrian expedition. The party was composed of Dr Herbert Tichy, Joseph Joechler and H. Heuberger. Their success was a splendid example of what can be achieved by a small, lightly equipped expedition. The climb was made in the autumn, an unusual time of year for such an enterprise. The party crossed the Nangpa La in late September and established Camp 1 at the foot of the east face and Camp 3 under the ice-cliff. Tichy, with Pasang and another Sherpa named Ajiba, found a comparatively easy route up this and pitched Camp 4 on the terrace above. Here they encountered an appalling storm. Their camp was wrecked by the force of the wind and they were compelled to descend at the height of the blizzard to Camp 3. During this ordeal Tichy's hands were so severely frostbitten that he became almost helpless. In spite of this, after a rest at Camp 1, he and his companions renewed the attempt in the middle of October. The bad weather persisted and at Camp 3 they slept in a snow cave which they had excavated. Camp 4 was re-established on October 18 and the following day Tichy, Joechler and Pasang reached the summit. Pasang had accomplished an amazing feat. While the climbers had been resting at Camp 1 he had been sent to Marlung for additional supplies. Returning, he left that village on October 17 and caught up with the party as they were leaving Camp 3 on the 18th. Thus in three days he climbed from 13,000 feet to the summit of Cho Oyu. The conquest of the mountain was achieved without oxygen equipment.

In the same month, Madame Claude Kogan, climbing with an Italian party, reached a height that was variously estimated as just above and just below 25,000 feet. At the lowest estimate, it remains the record height achieved by a woman in a mixed party of mountaineers. In October, 1959, Madame Kogan met her death on Cho Oyu while leading an all women's expedition.

Cirque de Gavarnie

A glacial corrie. Location *Hautes-Pyrenees, southwest France.* Height *5,740 feet.* Map *7, B8.*

Ever since travelers began to seek the picturesque and awful in mountains, the Cirque de Gavarnie, 45 miles south of Lourdes, has been a center of attraction. It lies at the end of a long, narrow valley down which rushes the Gave de Pau. About three miles from the village of Gavarnie

he Vajolet Towers in the Dolomites

the road threads through a jumble of house-sized rocks called, like other such mountain rock-falls, Chaos. This is almost equally celebrated in travelers' literature, and is the result of an earth tremor in the sixth century.

The Cirque is a natural *tour de force* which deserves all the admiring adjectives heaped on it. A great semicircular amphitheater, its series of terraces are relatively narrow ledges backed by a vertical cliff. The lowest bastion of cliff rises 1,200 feet sheer from the screes; to its left, on an almost unbroken eastern rock face which ends in the 10,681-foot peak of the Pic de Marbore, a slender 1,385-foot waterfall rushes out.

Out of sight of the village and of the Cirque, though visible on the approach up the valley or from vantage points on its flanks, is the Brèche de Roland. This is a strange, vertical-sided cleft, 9,200 feet up and about 300 feet across, in the tilted 300-foot cliff which forms the margin of the Cirque slightly to the west, between the rugged Marbore and the perfectly triangular Taillon (10,329 feet), whose resemblance to a pyramid is enhanced by its horizontal strata.

Though Roland's death is generally supposed to have taken place at Roncesvalles, much farther west, there is an account by Archbishop Turpin which tells how, having defeated Marsines, the Saracen king, at Roncesvalles, Roland – with no help forthcoming from his uncle Charlemagne – retreated to Gavarnie and here felt himself dying from his wounds. Finding it unbearable that Durendal, his famous sword, should fall into other hands, whether of friend or foe, Roland with his last breath drove it into the cliff where, splitting the rock apart, it shattered into fragments. In such a way did the Brèche get its name. Today it is a target for the climber and an entry for the hardy into Spain where one may stand poised on the frontier, between the northern chill of the French side and the southern warmth of the Spanish.

Coast Ranges of America

A mountain belt consisting of several ranges and uplands. Location *Western North America, from Alaska to Mexico.* Height *Varying from 2,000 feet to 19,850 feet (Mount Logan).* Map 4, A3-4.

The Coast Ranges start in the northwest with the uplands of Kodiak Island (over 5,000 feet) and are continued to the east and southeast by the Kenai Mountains. These extend about 150 miles along the southeast side of the Kenai Peninsula, sloping steeply to the Gulf of Alaska. This northernmost part of the Coast Ranges is still largely unsurveyed and has several glacier fields.

The next section is composed of the Chugach Mountains, which run in a crescent of 300 miles between Turnagain Arm and Cap Yakataga, north of Prince William Sound and south of the Alaska Range. Their highest peak is Mount Marcus Baker (13,250 feet). The Chugach National Forest of 7,500 square miles is on the southern slope of the range. Established in 1907, it includes much virgin forest, mainly western hemlock and Sitka spruce. It also includes several offshore islands.

After the Saint Elias Mountains, the Coast Ranges run south along the coast of southern Alaska and British Columbia. Here the mountains are partly submerged, their peaks rising from the sea as the Alexander Archipelago and Queen Charlotte and Vancouver islands. This island-mountain range is separated by the Inside Passage from the Coast Mountains until it reappears on the mainland as the Olympic Mountains, rising to 7,954 feet in Mount Olympus. The system continues south as generally low mountains (2,000-4,000 feet) along the Washington and Oregon coasts to the Klamath Mountains on the Oregon-California line. In California the ridges run from northwest to southeast, forming a 50-mile-wide belt between the Central Valley and a narrow coastal strip for most of the length of the state. This section includes the Diablo Range (up to 3,400 feet), the Santa Lucia Range (up to 5,844 feet), the San Rafael Mountains (up to 6,596 feet) and

Mount Pinos (8,831 feet), 40 miles south of Bakersfield. South of the San Rafael Mountains – at the western end of the transverse belt linking the Coast Ranges with the Sierra Nevada – there is a gap in the ranges. It is sometimes held that the Coast Ranges end here but another view is that they continue through southern California and include the low Santa Ynez, Santa Monica, Santa Ana and Laguna mountains and the high San Gabriel, San Bernardino and San Jacinto mountains (over 10,000 feet), which lie north and east of the city of Los Angeles. If we accept the second view, the Coast Ranges continue into the uplands of western Lower California. The southernmost portions are also called Los Angeles ranges in the vicinity of the city and Peninsular Ranges farther south.

From San Francisco up to Alaska there is abundant rainfall in the ranges and they support valuable forests – mainly conifers. Water power is extensively developed all along the mountains from northern California to southern British Columbia. South of San Francisco the climate is drier and the forests are restricted to higher altitudes, but there is much valuable agricultural land in the valleys.

Although the Coast Ranges are often confused with the Coast *Mountains* of British Columbia, the two systems are clearly distinct. The Coast Mountains are the continuation of the Sierra Nevada and the Cascade Range; they are, in turn, continued by the great Alaska and Aleutian ranges. The Coast Ranges are represented by the offshore islands in Canada. A series of lowlands, the Pacific troughs (the Central Valley in California, the Willamette valley in Oregon, the Puget Sound lowlands in Washington, the Inside Passage in British Columbia and Alaska, the deep valleys between the two mountain belts in Alaska and finally Cook Inlet and Shelikof Strait), separate the Coast Ranges from the Coast Mountains along their entire length. In the south the Coast Ranges consist mainly of geologically recent sedimentary rocks which are still far from being settled (hence the frequent Cali-

fornian earthquakes); some portions are formed by igneous intrusions and areas of igneous and metamorphic formation; farther north are ranges of both sedimentary and igneous origin. The ranges in the far northwest contain active craters. Glaciation and sinking of the northern Pacific coast have produced the island form of the range in British Columbia and southern Alaska. The Coast Mountains have undergone intensive glaciation and their northwest continuation (containing the highest peaks in North America) abounds in active volcanoes.

Cockpit Country

A rugged upland area covering about 200 square miles. Location *Western central Jamaica.* Height *Rising to about 2,700 feet, average 1,000–1,750 feet.* Map *5, B10.*

On the map of Jamaica, southeast of Montego Bay, is an area marked "The Cockpit Country" with "Land (or District) of Look Behind" and "Me no sen you no come" on its southern side – but otherwise remarkably bare of place-names for so populous an island. West and south are Maroon Town and Accompong, recalling the Maroon wars of eighteenth-century Jamaica, conducted against slaves who, freed from their Spanish masters, had taken to the hills and been joined by runaways from British plantations. It is a wild and uninhabited, moist but well-drained, rugged and tree-covered tropical karst-land consisting of a succession of innumerable conical hills and more or less circular pits. These are sometimes joined into glens, mostly 300-500 feet deep and as much across, with cliff-like or steeply sloping sides – more fitted to be the arenas of rocs than of game-cocks. It was in allusion to cock-fighting that, some time before 1738, they were metaphorically named "The Cockpits."

"From the difficulties presented by the uneven surface, the loose fragmentary limestone, the steepness of the declivities and acclivities, the absence of soil or water. . . it remains under the shadow of the virgin forests of a 'terra incognita'," wrote the geologist, J. G. Sawkins, in 1866.

Although now superficially surveyed by aerial photography, visited by adventurous botanists and geologists and traversed by the paths of woodcutters, its investigation still demands considerable physical endurance. To penetrate deeply into the uncharted wilderness means carrying food, water and equipment for several days up and down twisting, slippery tracks, avoiding the treacherous crevasses and holes into which the high tropical rainfall has eroded the rock, cutting a way through dense vegetation, climbing precipitous slopes and suffering the onslaughts of countless mosquitoes and blood-sucking flies, while the sun directly overhead makes the windless air uncomfortably hot for such continuous exertion. Though the rainfall is heavy – probably about 100 inches a year – it drains almost immediately into deep underground reservoirs and caves (one of which extends for three miles) and any explorer who is unfortunate enough not to find a spring may have to depend for water upon the leaf-tanks of the bromeliad plants in which the mosquitoes breed.

Human interference is beginning to change even this wild region. On the edge of the Cockpit Country, particularly at Accompong, live the Western Maroons, descendants of the runaway Negroes who in 1739 – after some 80 years of guerilla warfare against the island's British planters and cattle-raisers – made an honorable peace with Governor Edward Trelawny under which they became privileged, self-governing free peasants on an island of slavery. No one knows the Cockpit Country better than they do. They have cleared the bottoms of many nearby pits to plant bananas, yams and colocasias. For timber they go much farther afield and their felling of the big trees is undoubtedly changing little by little the flora of even the remote Cockpits.

Cocuy, Sierra Nevada de

The highest massif in the Cordillera Oriental. Location *Boyacá department, central Colombia.* Height *Rising to 18,021 feet.* Map *6, C3.*

The Sierra Nevada de Cocuy, extending 15 miles from north to south, is the natural continuation into Colombia of the Venezuelan Andes; the two form the northern hook at the beginning of the whole backbone of the Andes. The Cocuy range itself consists of two parallel lines of snow-covered mountains; the eastern, the "picos orientales," is the lower.

The region was first visited by a Swiss party in 1929, who ascended, among others, the highest peak, Alto Ricuba (18,021 feet). A large number of later expeditions were made by the Swiss up to 1946 and an Italian party climbed in the range in 1953. In 1957 a Cambridge expedition repeated the ascent of Alto Ricuba and made three first ascents of other peaks. The botanists found many new plants; the flora of the Cocuy is particularly rich and varied, in marked contrast to the fauna. The local Indians – many of whom still practice polygamy – employed some of these plants for medicinal purposes.

The position of the range, with hot plains and steamy jungle all around, makes for poor weather and visibility is usually bad. This accounts for the difficulty of route-finding and survey and for the time it has taken climbers to get to know the topography. The lush vegetation and dank cloudy weather invite comparison between the Sierra Nevada de Cocuy and the Ruwenzori in Africa, for appearing unattractive at first sight while possessing an indefinable allure that makes the difficulties worth while.

Colorado Plateau

A vast arid upland containing spectacular mountain scenery. Location *Arizona, Utah, Colorado and New Mexico.* Height *5,000–11,000 feet.* Map *4, C5-D5.*

Bounded on the east by the southern Rocky Mountains and the valley of the Rio Grande, and on the west by the Great Basin, the Colorado Plateau is one of the least populated and most inaccessible regions of the United States. Deep canyons and high plateaus have made railway construction impossible over most of it and there are few roads. Yet it is one of the most striking and beautiful areas of the whole continent.

Those finding themselves on the lip of the Grand Canyon see level plains all around, miles and miles of flat uplands, ringed only in the distance by lines of flat-topped hills. Farther still, are the great mountains surrounding the plateau. And in the midst of all this – the great, sheer-sided, waterworn cleft, 6,250 feet (well over a mile) deep in places and 5-18 miles wide. Standing on the edge, one looks down as if from an airplane upon ranges of mountains 5,000 feet high, rising from the floor of the canyon.

The Grand Canyon, Colorado

Along these multicolored slopes, piled layer upon layer, step upon step, the eye traverses one of the most spectacular and complete geological series known, with rocks ranging in age over a period of 1,750,000,000 years, from the Archaean of the deepest zones to the Pleistocene era. And far down one may catch a glint of water – the Colorado River which has carved this whole astonishing gorge out of the living rock.

The history of this extraordinary plateau began 100,000,000 years ago, in Cretaceous times, when this region and its surrounding mountains were lifted high above the sea. In the center was a great alluvial plain with lakes and winding rivers – and along the swampy shores of those lakes and rivers lived immense reptiles. There was the Brontosaurus (the "Thunder Lizard") 67 feet long; the Diplodocus, largest of all reptiles, 90 feet long (but with a brain weighing only 15 ounces); the floundering Stegosaurus, with a two-and-a-half-ounce brain, and many others; herbivores, browsing on the aquatic vegetation, or ferocious carnivores tearing each other to pieces. This was the Age of Reptiles, and as the mountains wore down and the lakes silted up, the remains of these great beasts were covered in sediments which hardened into rocks, preserving them for future ages.

In the middle of the Tertiary era, perhaps 50,000,000 years ago (by which times mammals had come on the scene and the great reptiles had vanished), the land was uplifted again; then slowly, over the succeeding epochs, worn down once more by wind, weather and what by now was quite recognizably the Colorado River until a low-lying level plain had been produced, bordered to the north by the buttes and mesas of the old plateau and to the south by extensive lava plains.

Within the last 5,000,000 years came the last uplift, of some 7,000-10,000 feet, beginning a new cycle of erosion which, geologically speaking, has today scarcely begun.

In all these earth movements the level lie of the plateau and its beds of rock has been little disturbed. Like beds of masonry, the various strata lie one above the other in horizontal layers which, varying greatly in resistance to erosion, produced when eroded away the step-like profile so characteristic of the region. The topmost layer of all, that of the plateau around the canyon, is a great terrace of a particularly resistant limestone, from which the overlaying beds have been worn away.

Nor is the Grand Canyon the only marvel of this region. Brilliantly colored strata carved by erosion into fantastic shapes are also to be seen in Bryce Canyon National Park, Zion National Park, Cedar Breaks National Monument (Utah); the Painted Desert, Meteor Crater and Petrified Forest (Arizona). The Rainbow Bridge National Monument (Utah) is the largest known natural bridge; the Mesa Verde National Park (Colorado) and the Canyon de Chelly National Monument (Arizona) preserve ancient cliff dwellings. In northeast Arizona, southern Utah and northwest New Mexico are the vast, dry, colorful lands of the "Navajo country" with Hopi and Navajo Indian reservations. To the west lie the Great Basin, Boulder Dam and Death Valley, while to the south is a desolate, blasted region of hundreds of volcanic cones, of great black lava flows and unexpectedly beautiful canyons like Walnut and Oak Creek.

This plateau area is a world of its own, a world in which long ago men lived and built fantastic cliff-dwellings.

Now it is deserted, save for a few Indians and a few white settlers; but thousands of tourists visit the region each year, and so powerful is its evocation that it is unforgettable to all who have seen it.

Columbia, Mount

A snow-clad peak with glaciers. Location *Rocky Mountains, on the Alberta-British Columbia border.* Height *12,294 feet.* Map *3, F9.* First climbed *Sir James Outram and the guide C. Kaufmann, 1902.*

Situated on the Alberta-British Columbia border, snow-clad Mount Columbia rears above the western end of the Columbia Icefield, which comprises about 110 square miles, much of it above 10,000 feet. The icefield forms a tri-oceanic divide, the Saskatchewan, Athabaska and Columbia glaciers being important sources of their rivers. The mountain was discovered in 1897 by J. N. Collie, who sighted it from the Freshfield area and thought it might be the legendary Mount Brown of David Douglas and his fur traders. Collie viewed it and the icefield at close range in the following year when he achieved the first ascent of Mount Athabaska.

"A new world was spread at our feet," he wrote. "To the westward stretched a vast icefield probably never before seen by human eye, and surrounded by entirely unknown, unnamed and unclimbed peaks... From this great snowfield rose solemnly, like 'lonely sea-stacks in mid-ocean,' two magnificent peaks which we imagined to be 13,000-14,000 feet high, keeping guard over those unknown western fields of ice."

Since Sir James Outram first climbed it, Mount Columbia has been ascended by various routes. Approach to the mountain once required almost a week of pack-train travel, but the Lake Louise-Jasper highway now brings one to the Icefield Chalet near Sumapta Pass and the Athabaska Glacier, whence the ascent can be made.

Cook, Mount

A mountain with three peaks, the highest in New Zealand. Location *Southern Alps, western central South Island, New Zealand.* Height *12,349 feet.* Map *12, H8.* First climbed *T. C. Fyfe, G. Graham and J. M. Clark, 1894.*

Mount Cook was named after the great English navigator of the eighteenth century, Captain James Cook; its height was determined by measurement from shipboard during survey-cruises between 1847 and 1850. Its native name, *Aorangi,*

means "a big white cloud" – a word which the Maoris apply to any cloud, whether capping a mountain or not.

Mount Cook towers over 8,000 feet above a network of glacier-filled valleys in the heart of the range; it is situated just off the Main Divide, on a branch or spur that runs southwards between the great Tasman Glacier, almost 18 miles in length and the longest in New Zealand, and the Hooker Glacier on the western side. The mountain actually consists of three peaks: High, Middle and Low; the last two have elevations of 12,173 feet and 11,787 feet respectively. The whole forms a most impressive ice-bound crest, whether viewed from near or far and from whatever direction.

After a number of attempts by New Zealanders and visiting British climbers, the first successful ascent was made on Christmas Day, 1894, by a New Zealand party, whose hazardous route from the west has subsequently been avoided for the most part. A more favored route from the west lies up a very rotten rock buttress, consisting of slaty greywacks, the prevailing rock formation. Half a dozen or more ascents by alternative routes to the three different summits have been made in later years, as well as traverses of all the peaks in the course of one excursion.

Because of its isolated position near the Tasman Sea, the Cook range receives heavy precipitation and experiences sudden and violent storms, making conditions difficult and frequently dangerous for climbing. Indeed, some seasons go by with no ascent of Cook itself being made; it was not, in fact, until the 1955-56 season that the hundredth ascent of the High Peak was completed. Deaths by avalanche or other causes have from time to time occurred; a tragic occasion was the disaster that killed the noted English climber S. L. King and two New Zealand guides in 1914, during their descent by the Linda Glacier on the eastern side of the mountain. To his memory the King Memorial Hut was erected at about 7,000 feet on the southern spur of Mount Haast, from which many parties nowadays set out for Mount Cook, Mount Tasman and other peaks. There are now many other huts, and a hotel, accessible by road from the east coast, is conveniently situated as a base for mountaineers and tourists. There is ski-ing on the Ball Glacier; and from a flying-field near the hotel flights can readily be made over the peaks and glaciers. In 1952 the Mount Cook National Park was set up, comprising 151,000 acres on the southeast side of the Main Divide. Within the park there are many varieties of indigenous alpine flora of which the shepherd's or mountain lily (really a buttercup) and the giant daisy are outstanding.

Córdoba, Sierra de

A pampean mountain range. Location *Argentina.* Height *6,500–9,450 feet.* Map *6, D7-8.*

"The Sierra de Córdoba, an outlying range in the center of Argentina," wrote Dr Philipp Borchers, "is only of interest to anyone who lives in Córdoba."

Nevertheless, this range, situated largely in western Córdoba province with outliers in San Luis, Santiago del Estero and Tucumán provinces, has a definite interest for the less ambitious mountaineer and, above all, for the tourist. It extends 300 miles from north to south and covers about 11,500 square miles. There are three parallel ridges running north to south. The Sierra Chica extends 55 miles south from Deán Funes, rising to about 6,000 feet. The Sierra Grande runs 40 miles north to south, west of Alta Gracia, and rises to 7,645 feet in the Cerro Gigante, which has large granite quarries. The Sierra de Comenchingones is about 50 miles long, running on the San Luis-Córdoba border with the 7,237-foot Cerro Oveja as its highest peak. The Sierra de Guasapampa extends 45 miles and rises to about 4,500 feet. Finally the Sierra de Pocho, running 40 miles north of Villa Dolores, rises to 4,800 feet with a pampean tableland to the east of it.

Geologically older than the Andes, the Sierra de Córdoba is drained by the Primero, Segundo, Tercero and Quarto rivers. The Sierra's mineral deposits are mostly marble and lime. There are many popular resorts in the range.

Cotopaxi

Probably the world's highest active volcano. Location *Andes, northern central Ecuador.* Height *19,344 feet.* Map *6, B4.* First climbed *Dr Wilhelm Reiss and A. M. Escobar, 1872.*

Cotopaxi is situated in the Eastern Cordillera, about 35 miles south of Quito. Although within 50 miles of the equator, it is normally snow-capped, the snowline ranging between 15,000 feet on the eastern and 16,000 feet on the western slopes. Because it is exposed on the east to the moisture-saturated tropical air rising from the Amazon lowlands, it is frequently veiled in clouds and mists, but when visible from the inhabited inter-cordilleran high valley to the west, its perfect form is apparent. It is an almost symmetrical cone, rising some 10,000 feet from the surrounding plateau country, strewn with ash and boulders ejected in the frequent eruptions. Edward Whymper, who scaled it in 1880 and was the first to describe it in detail, commented: "Cotopaxi is an ideal volcano. . . It is not one of the provoking sort, exploding in paroxysms, and going to sleep immediately afterwards. It is in a state of perpetual activity and has been so ever since it had a place in history. There are loftier mountains that have been volcanoes yielding greater quantities of lava but the summit of Cotopaxi, so far as is known, has the greatest elevation. . . of all volcanoes that are in working order."

The onset of a violent eruption of Cotopaxi is generally heralded by a dense column of ash-laden steam, resembling smoke, which rises from the crater and drifts away on the upper winds, sometimes for great distances. The eruption of 1877, for instance, caused complete darkness at

8 a.m. in Quito and some of the fine ash actually fell on steamers 200 miles away in the Pacific. The surrounding plateau and the slopes up to the snowline are covered with mud, loose ash and rock fragments, and are therefore uninhabited, but the western valleys, leading down to the populous inter-cordilleran corridor, are fully settled. The villages in these valleys, though miles away from the mountain, are liable to suffer from the deluges, caused by the melting of great quantities of ice and snow by lava and steam during eruptions, which sweep down masses of debris in the swollen torrents. Similar, probably more violent, floods occur on the eastern flanks of Cotopaxi but these soon lose themselves in the dense, uninhabited forests of the Oriente, on their way to the Amazon.

Though Cotopaxi sometimes discharges lava from its crater, which is generally filled with boiling water in contact with incandescent matter, it seems to be reaching the later phases of volcanic activity. Its energy is now derived more from the explosive force of large quantities of imprisoned steam of plutonic (deep-seated) origin than from the extrusive force of molten rock. Its open crater acts in a way as a safety valve through which superheated steam is being more or less continuously discharged – sometimes, as in the repeated eruptions, with greater than usual energy. In many older volcanoes whose craters were sealed with solidified lava, the pent-up force of superheated steam developed such tremendous explosive power that the upper portions of the mountains – or almost whole mountains – were blown to pieces. Cotopaxi (as Whymper maintained) owes the preservation of its symmetrical form to its crater vent, which has saved it from the fate of many of its older fellows.

The earliest recorded eruptions took place in 1532 and 1533. The most important and violent

The summit of Cotopaxi

were those of 1744, 1746, 1768 and 1803. In 1744 the "thunder of Cotopaxi" was heard 500 miles away; in 1768 ash covered all lesser vegetation as far as Riobamba. In 1802 Alexander von Humboldt made an unsuccessful attempt to scale the cone; he declared that it was an impossible task. A year later he heard the noise 160 miles away in the port of Guayaquil "day and night like continued discharges of a battery." Jean-Baptiste Boussingault made another unsuccessful attempt to climb the great volcano in 1831; M. Wagner failed twice in 1858. But in 1872 Dr Wilhelm Reiss, with A. M. Escobar, succeeded in reaching the top. He was followed by Dr A. Stübel in 1873, T. Wolf in 1877 and M. von Thielmann in 1878. Whymper, during his Andean tour, was the fifth to reach the summit and the first to explore the area thoroughly. Cotopaxi has not been climbed often in recent years and has remained one of the more spectacular and difficult ascents in the Andes.

Cottian Alps

A wild, craggy mountain system. Location *Western Alps, on the Franco-Italian border.* Height *Rising from 9,410 feet to 12,602 feet in Monte Viso.* Map *8, B10-C9.*

The Cottian Alps extend along the frontier of France and Italy, from the Col de l'Argentière to the Mont Cenis and westwards to the Col du Galibier, between the Maritime and Dauphiné Alps. The peaks over 10,000 feet include Monte Viso (12,602 feet), Viso di Vallante (12,048 feet), Aiguille de Scolette (11,500 feet), Aiguille de Chambeyron (11,155 feet), Grand Rubren (11,142 feet), Brec de Chambeyron (11,116 feet) and others. Among the chief passes the Col Sommeiller (Bardonnèche to Bramans, 9,718 feet) and the Col de la Traversette (Crissolo to Abries, beneath a pass tunnel made in 1478–80, 9,679 feet) are the highest among 20 others.

The Cottians only occasionally rise above 11,000 feet and have only a few small glaciers.

Argument has been raging for centuries as to which pass of the Cottian Alps Hannibal used for his historic crossing. Today opinion seems to be largely agreed on the Col de la Traversette. Many of the other crossings, free from permanent snow, have been forced more than once by large bodies of men; several of the battles between France and the House of Savoy were fought here and the Cottians might well be called "the cockpit of the Alps." They have great beauty and still offer interesting and rewarding climbs and a number of easy crossings for the motorist.

Craters of the Moon

48,280 acres of spectacular volcanic craters and cones. Location *Southeast central Idaho.* Height *20–600 feet.* Map *4, C3.*

The Craters of the Moon form a National Monument, established in 1924, of 73.7 square miles, 20 miles from the town of Arco, at the foot of the White Knob Mountains.

The area contains more volcanic features than any other of similar size in the United States. It is also the most recent example of fissure eruption in America; the last eruptions probably occurred within the last 1,000 years.

For many miles around the craters there are streams of black lava, with hundreds of cinder cones, varying in height from 20 feet to 600 feet. The newer lava is in the northern part of the area. The southern part is the older and here the lava is covered sparsely with stunted pines, grass and wild flowers.

There are 35 or more craters, some nearly half a mile across and hundreds of feet deep. The lava tunnels and caves are equally remarkable. Many of them are 30 feet in diameter and several hundred feet long, containing many fantastic lava formations colored chiefly in blues and reds. The volcanic pits found all over the monument are often filled with springs of fresh water with a temperature of 34°, even when the air is 90°.

Crillon, Mount

A mountain with two important glaciers. Location *Fairweather Range, southeast Alaska.* Height *12,725 feet.* Map *3, D7.* First climbed *Dartmouth College expedition, 1934.*

Though Mount Crillon was named by the eminent French navigator the Comte de la Perouse, who sailed along this exposed and spectacular coast in 1786, following a voyage by Captain James Cook in 1778, it was not until the Harvard University and Dartmouth College Alaskan expeditions between 1932 and 1934 that the district was first surveyed in detail.

Lying 100 miles west-northwest of Juneau, in the Glacier Bay National Monument, this forbidding peak is of interest mainly for the twin North and South Crillon glaciers. These drain the western slopes, debouching into the glacial Crillon Lake. The South Crillon Glacier's complex motion was the subject of a special study. The expeditions found that, where the glacier terminated in ice-cliffs in Crillon Lake, the larger tributary of clean ice was being squeezed against and over the smaller tributary, becoming repeatedly faulted in the process and giving an unusual superimposed relationship. The glacial movements were uneven and jerky and became considerably slower during periods of bad weather, when the whole ice-mass was much less plastic. The expeditions took seismic soundings and found that the average thickness of the ice was about 885 feet.

Cristóbal Colón, Pico

Highest peak of the Sierra Nevada de Santa Marta. Location *Magdalena department, northern Colombia.* Height *18,950 feet.* Map *6, C2.*

Cristóbal Colón is a name only recently given to the culminating point of the Sierra Nevada de Santa Marta. This is a small, wedge-shaped range in the extreme north of Colombia, close to the

Lava field, with cinder cone in the background, Craters of the Moon

Atlantic, unconnected with the main chain of the Andes. The highest summits, some of them still unclimbed, are capped with permanent snow. Towards the north these mountains fall steeply to the Caribbean. Up to a height of over 3,000 feet they are covered with virgin forests of truly tropical luxuriance. The southern slopes are the more favorable for climbing. This curiously isolated group of peaks, many miles to the north of the true Andean chain, is sometimes seen from the Caribbean and confused with the mother range.

The Nevada de Santa Marta was first investigated in 1898 by the Frenchman, De Brettes. In 1923 A. F. R. Wollaston observed that the range might well be not intimately related to the Andean mountain formation but rather a part of the system which was responsible for the formation of the Caribbean islands. The range is roughly triangular in shape, and its axis is east to west.

It was not until 1939 that a small American party, led by Walter A. Wood, penetrated the intervening wilderness and scaled several of the higher summits, among them the Pico Cristóbal Colón (which was then called Central Peak). They found, however, that a German party had already achieved the first ascent, a few weeks earlier. Wood and his party found, to their surprise, that many of the peaks were more than 18,000 feet high, an altitude which ranks them among the tallest coastal mountains in the world. Wood's party made the first ascent of East Peak, now Pico Simón Bolívar, a very short distance away from Cristóbal Colón and only a few dozen feet lower. The expedition remarked on the evidence shown on the mountain of particularly recent ice recession. The peak and the range may easily be approached either from across the Rio Magdalena from Barranquilla or direct from Santa Marta, where the great patriot, Simón Bolívar, died. A few subsequent expeditions have visited the range but it is still imperfectly known and should prove a rewarding objective for climbers of the future.

Cuillin Hills

Several ridges with ragged summits. Location *Southern part of the Isle of Skye, Inverness, Scotland.* Height *About 2,500 feet, rising to 3,309 feet.* Map 7, B4.

For mountaineers, the Cuillin (or Coolin) Hills still retain much of the attraction they had in Victorian days when their narrow gabbro ridge, shattered at places into genuine rock climbs, could claim the only virgin summits of the British Isles. They retain it, moreover, in spite of the fact that much of their remoteness and technical difficulty have disappeared.

The Black Cuillin of Skye (the Red Cuillin, geologically different, topographically less important, and of little mountaineering interest, form a minor range across Glen Sligachan) run in one main and many subsidiary ridges for some eight miles in a southern corner of Skye. The highest peak in the Black Cuillin, Sgur Alasdair (3,309 feet), lies a short distance off the main ridge. The coarse gabbro of which the group is formed has been weathered into a series of rugged summits which rise almost from sea level, carry virtually no vegetation and are characterised by a multiplicity of steep rock-faces, slabs, arêtes and gullies, which today form the playground of the rock climber.

Four things combine to make the Black Cuillin unique. Many of the summits can be reached only by genuine rock climbing, a fact which severely limits the number of human beings one is likely to meet upon them. The peaks have a true mountain character – the difficulty is sometimes not that of following the route but of finding it. The curious quality of the gabbro, which at times clings to the climber almost as sternly as he clings to it, enables routes of surprising steepness to be ascended with relative ease; while the traverse of the ridge itself, involving some 10,000 feet of ascent and descent, is possibly the finest single expedition which can be carried out in Britain. The Inaccessible Pinnacle, a rocky finger thrusting upwards from the

The pinnacle ridge of Sgur nan Gillean,
in the Cuillin Hills

ridge, Sgur nan Gillean with its pinnacle ridge, and the great face of Sgur Sgumain with its unique promontory of the Chioch, discovered through Norman Collie's photography in 1899, are but three of the features which make the Black Cuillin essentially a range of mountaineers' mountains.

Cuzco Cordilleras

A mountainous district with several high ranges. Location *Southern and south central Peru.* Height *17,000–19,000 feet.* Map *6, C5.*

Cuzco (or Cusco) is the name of a large department in central Peru, a region immensely rich in historical associations and natural beauty. The ancient Inca city of Cuzco is the principal city of the department.

Here the Andes split into several high ranges. The Cordillera de Carabaya is a continuation of the Nudo de Apolobamba, running about 190 miles northwest, rising to 19,193 feet at the Nudo de Quenamari. Parallel to it, on the western side, runs the Cordillera de Vilcanota, lying east of the city of Cuzco; it extends southwest for about 130 miles to the Carabaya and rises to 17,988 feet at the Nudo de Vilcanota on the border of Puno department. Here, at the northern end of the Altiplano, the Cordillera Oriental and Cordillera Occidental meet. Towards the north the Andes spread out into three ranges, the Cordilleras Oriental, Central and Occidental. Still another Andean range in the Cuzco area is the Cordillera

Vilcabamba, which extends about 160 miles northwest from a point north of Cuzco, rising to 20,551 feet in the Cerro Salcantay. The Cordillera de Carabaya and the Cordillera de Vilcanota are connected by the Cordillera de Asungate, which is a northwest spur of the Carabaya, extending from the area of Macusani for 100 miles, rising to 20,187 feet in the Asungate peak.

The Cuzco province is drained by the Apurimac and Urubamba rivers, two Amazon tributaries. The climate is tropical in the northern forests, temperate in the settled uplands and cool in the high sierras. Gold, silver, copper, iron, tungsten, marble, lead, salt and coal are mined and there is intensive agriculture, mainly wheat, corn, sugar cane, cacao, coffee and rubber.

Here the lover of mountains can combine climbing with the exploration of one of the oldest civilizations in the world. All around Cuzco the ancient agricultural terraces which stretch high up the surrounding mountains – the remains of an extensive system of roads, temples, walls, bridges and vast fortresses, all built of gigantic, beautifully fitted stones – testify to the former existence of a population far greater and richer than today's. This was the population of the old Inca Empire, with its benevolent monarch, its intensive cultivation of the soil, its monumental architecture and its worship of the Sun God of which the city of Cuzco was the capital before its conquest by the Spaniards under Pizarro. There are still old Inca streets, Inca water conduits, the remains of palaces, and everywhere walls – walls more beautifully made than anywhere else in the world – but even so it is hard to picture the ancient city, for most of its buildings were dismantled by the Spaniards and the stones used in the construction of their own works, such as the great seventeenth-century baroque cathedral, with its famous high altar covered with silver.

Daryal Gorge

A deep gorge cut by the Terek River. Location *Central Greater Caucasus, northern Georgian S S R.* Depth *5,900 feet.* Map *10, A4.*

The Daryal (or Dariel) Gorge has been identified with some certainty as the Caspian or Iberian Gates of classical times, the noted and central point from which distances were reckoned, called Caspiae Portae or Pylae.

The gorge runs for eight miles among vertical walls of rock which rise almost 6,000 feet. The Georgian annals mention it under the names of Ralani, Dargani and Darialani; the Persians and Arabs knew it as the Gate of the Alans; Strabo, the historian, called it Porta Caucasia or Portae Caspiae (a name also bestowed on the "gate" or pass beside the Caspian Sea at Derbent) while the Tartars called it Darioly. As it is the only available passage across the Caucasus, it has been fortified since time immemorial – at least since 150 B.C. – and today is part of the Georgian Military Road. Overlooked by Mount Kazbek, it is 70 miles north of Tiflis.

Lermontov, the Russian writer, immortalized it in poetry after spending several months at Darial, a Russian fort which stood at the northern end of the gorge, at an altitude of 4,746 feet.

Dauphiné Alps

Western offshoot of the Cottian Alps. Location *Southeast France.* Height *From 4,953 to 13,462 feet.* Map *8, B9-10.*

The Dauphiné Alps rise between the Cottian and Graian Alps, running west and south from the Col du Galibier. With 24 peaks over 10,000 feet and about two dozen important passes, this was the last main massif of the Alps to be surveyed, explored or climbed. For a long time the Dauphiné possessed a reputation for inaccessibility that only slowly dissolved during the last third of the nineteenth century. And only in recent years has it become a popular climbing ground with experts and the scene of some of the most difficult and sensational ascents ever made.

In this isolated backwater, far off the main trans-Alpine routes that had already brought prosperity to many other parts of the range, the explorers of the eighteen-sixties found to their surprise a mountain world only partially mapped. There was already talk of "the Alps being worked out," yet here, almost untouched by human foot, were four peaks above 13,000 feet, 17 peaks above 12,000 feet, 14 passes above 10,000 feet and more than 100 glaciers. Moreover, the savage grandeur of the upper valleys, the rocky outlines of the peaks and the wild confusion of rock-rib and hanging glacier which these peaks presented, overawed the early adventurers into the Dauphiné as they have overawed many men since.

The stately mass of the Pointe des Écrins (13,461 feet) is the highest of these summits, followed by the two highest peaks of the Meije (13,081 feet and 13,025 feet) whose serrated ridge rises as a great wall between the Romanche and the Veneon valleys, bounded on the north by the Brèche de la Meije (10,827 feet), a high col somewhat reminiscent of the Brèche de Roland in the Pyrenees. The Ailefroide (12,989 feet), Mount Pelvoux (12,973 feet) and Les Bans (11,979 feet) are but three of the other magnificent peaks of the Dauphiné, the term once applied to the highest central area, but increasingly used to include such outlying groups as the Aiguilles d'Arves and the Grande Chartreuse.

Exploration of the Dauphiné was hampered by the primitive conditions and the lack of adequate maps and general information. In 1839 James David Forbes, the Scottish scientist and mountaineer, became the first Briton to visit La Berarde, though General Bourcet had already surveyed the district in 1749–54. It was largely from this hamlet that, during the eighteen-sixties, the exploration of the group was carried out by such pioneers as William Mathews, Francis Fox Tuckett, Professor T. G. Bonney and – during a famous journey in 1864 – Edward Whymper and A. W. Moore.

From 1870, W. A. B. Coolidge, "the young American who climbed with his aunt and his dog," began his own systematic exploration of the Dauphiné and it was largely due to his energetic demands for less austere conditions that the *Société des Touristes du Dauphiné* was created – an organization which opened good mountain inns and correlated and published information.

Development still comes slightly later in the Dauphiné than elsewhere in the Alps. The Meije, for instance, was among the last of the Alpine peaks to be conquered. This is due not only to geographical conditions but to a traditional local aversion to what the French call *la vulgarisation de la montagne*.

Demavend

A dormant volcano with a narrow summit. Location *Elburz Mountains, Iran.* Height *18,600 feet.* Map *9, H1.* First climbed *W. T. Thomson, 1837.*

The seasoned traveler in Iran is so used to seeing gaunt, rugged precipices, jagged peaks and bare deserts, that the sight of Demavend is a relief and surprise to the eye. Visible from many miles away, though it is surrounded on every side by the peaks and ridges of the Elburz, its superior height and singular outline compel attention. It is as prominent a feature in northern Iran (only 45 miles northeast of the capital, Teheran) as is the well-known Fujiyama in Japan. Many travelers say that its snowy-white cone is the most beautiful sight of the country and the one they treasure most. A small and picturesque town bearing the name of Demavend is beautifully situated on the southern slopes and is much used as a summer resort by the people of Teheran. There has been no eruption of the mountain in historical times and it is now regarded as virtually extinct though some hot springs are found on its lower slopes. At the summit there is a crater, some 200 yards across, with a profusion of yellow sulphurous rocks and pumice stones. Snow covers the crater and upper slopes in winter and spring; in sheltered hollows snow may remain all the year. On most days of the year the summit can be seen from Teheran and, when the air is clear, from faraway Kashan to the south of the great salt desert.

It is not surprising that such a prominent mountain should figure in Iranian legend. The great tenth-century Persian poet, Firdausi, relates in his epic *Shahnama* how the tyrant Zohak is overthrown by the young Feridun and imprisoned in chains to die in a cavern on the slopes of Demavend. Local legend asserts that his groans may still be heard. On these slopes lived the heroes, Jemshid and Rustem. Another legend associated Demavend with the Ark, claiming that it rested here, and not on Ararat.

Demavend has been frequently climbed since W. T. Thomson's first ascent. Traditionally, the Persians were opposed to the conquest of the mountain. The climb is long, but not difficult or dangerous. Loose stones and small ribs of rock have to be clambered over; at higher levels, if the ascent is made in early summer, expanses of snow must be crossed to the crater at the top. Because of its great height and isolation, the view from Demavend is very extensive, a vast panorama of mountains, valleys and deserts, covering

Demavend, the highest peak of the Elburz Mountains

many hundreds of square miles. All around are other peaks of the Elburz range, sweeping down in the north to the humid Caspian plain and in the south descending to the deserts of central Iran.

Dent Blanche

One of the noblest Alpine peaks. Location *Pennine Alps, southern Switzerland.* Height *14,304 feet.* Map *8, C8.* First climbed *T. S. Kennedy, W. Wigram and Jean-Baptiste Croz, 1862.*

The Dent Blanche is one of the noblest peaks in the Alps. It was the scene, towards the end of the nineteenth century, of a remarkable feat of endurance illustrating the efforts a man can make if his life depends on them.

T. S. Kennedy, W. Wigram and Jean-Baptiste Croz – brother of Michel Croz, who died on the Matterhorn – had reached the summit in 1862 by the southwest face and the south arête. Many other ascents followed and although the peak's reputation was retained – "often one of the most difficult and dangerous mountains in the Alps," wrote W. A. B. Coolidge more than 30 years later – it presented no insuperable difficulties to such a man as Owen Glynne Jones, one of the finest British rock climbers, who attempted the ascent in 1899.

Jones, F. W. Hill and three guides – Furrer, Zurbriggen and Vuignier – set out on August 28, 1899. Rain and snow had made conditions difficult. High on the ridge Furrer, who was leading, called for help. Zurbriggen placed an ice-axe under his feet. Standing on this, Furrer reached up for higher holds; Jones, the third man on the rope, also came to give aid. As Furrer pulled himself up, he slipped back on the men below. All three toppled down the slope, instantly pulling the third guide from his holds. As Hill waited for the inevitable tug to destruction, the rope, caught perhaps in a cleft of rock, broke behind the third guide.

The accident, which cost Jones and the guides their lives, happened a few hundred feet below the summit. Hill, unable to descend alone, continued upwards, reached the top and found to his dismay that two climbers whom he had seen on the ordinary route had gained the summit and had disappeared. As he started to descend he ran into mist and snow and had to spend a day and a half sheltering in a rocky cleft. It took him another day to get down when the weather cleared and he was on his own, without supplies or blankets, for over 50 hours before he made his way down to the valley.

On August 11, 1882, J. Stafford Anderson and G. P. Baker, with the guides Ulrich Almer and Aloys Pollinger, made the first ascent of the famous Viereselsgrat ridge of the Dent Blanche. Another famous climber who conquered the redoubtable mountain was Baron Emmanuel Boileau de Castelnau, making the ascent before he was 20. The first winter ascent was made in 1911 by Professor F. F. Roget of Geneva and Marcel Kurz, pioneers of ski mountaineering. It was not until 1927 that the first ascent of the north ridge was made by Ivor Richards and his wife, Dorothy Pilley, with the guides Joseph and Antoine Georges.

Dent du Midi

A mountain with several peaks. Location *Western Alps, southwest Switzerland.* Height *10,695 feet (highest peak).* Map *8, C8.* First climbed *Clément, curé of the Val d'Illiez, 1874.*

"The Parthenon of the Alps" is only one of the proud phrases used to describe this most beautiful mountain, which appears to close the long trough of the Rhône Valley when seen from the eastern end of Lake Geneva. Its summit is formed of a rocky ridge which rises into a number of individual pinnacles. The most important are the Haute Cîme (the highest at 10,695 feet), the Cîme de l'Est or Dent Noire (10,433 feet), the Cathédrale (10,387 feet), the Dent Jaune (10,456 feet), Les Doigts (10,538 feet) and the

Forteresse (10,381 feet), the lowest of them. The highest peak is also the easiest to climb; the most difficult was not conquered until the eighteen-nineties.

Émile Javelle, the French mountaineer-school-master, who had the peak almost constantly in his sight during his two-year tenure at Vevey, was the mountain's greatest admirer and made its ascent – which he claimed could be done in at least 20 different ways – many scores of times. He acknowledged it "a mania" but he claimed that in this group there existed "a field of learned, curious and picturesque observation vast enough to occupy a lifetime and that, in order to attain a complete knowledge of the seven peaks, the glaciers, the moraines, the gorges and the valleys, it would be necessary to spend many days on the spot."

Devils Tower

A tower-shaped rock of volcanic origin. Location *Northeast Wyoming.* Height *865 feet from base.* Map *4, E3.*

This spectacular, fantastic work of nature was the first of the United States National Monuments to be established (1906). The igneous rock tower has a base of about 1,000 feet in diameter. Its Indian name is Malo Tepee. Not only is it a remarkable physiographic feature but its geology has been much debated. It is now generally regarded as a volcanic neck or plug which was intruded into the surrounding sedimentary strata. These have remained perfectly horizontal and unaffected in the vicinity, showing that the molten magma made its way upward without bending or otherwise disturbing the surrounding rocks. But the resistant, intrusive rock has survived erosive action in marked degree compared with the softer sedimentary rocks. Very slow cooling within the enclosing sedimentary rocks was responsible for the remarkably regular columnar jointing that is so striking a characteristic of the tower.

The National Monument occupies 1,193 acres. The tower itself rises from a rock platform situated about 600 feet above the Belle Fourche River. The top is estimated to cover one and a half acres and has a growth of sagebrush and cactus. The sides are beautifully symmetrical and are supported by many fluted columns. In certain lights the many subdued shades have an awe-inspiring effect, and the Indians attributed to it supernatural powers.

The Devils Tower is one of the most famous rock climbs in America. In spite of its apparent impregnability, it has been frequently climbed – even, by using pitons, on its sheerest north and west faces. During a "Mountaineers' Week" in 1956, 81 ascents were made.

Dhaulagiri

A short section of the Himalayas with several summits. Location *Northern central Nepal.* Height *26,795 feet.* Map *11, E5.* First climbed *Max Eiselin and party, May 1960.*

The Dhaulagiri Himal lies between the Thali Bheri (the headwaters of the Bheri tributary of the Gogra) and the deep gash in the range carved by the Kali Gandaki river. Four of its summits – I (26,795 feet), II (25,429 feet), III (25,271 feet) and IV (25,064 feet), numbered from east to west, rise above 25,000 feet. Dhaulagiri V (24,885 feet) is between III and IV. At the western end of the Himal (snow range) stand Churen (24,158 feet) and Putha Hiunchuli (23,750 feet). Dhaulagiri I is the western sentinel of the Kali Gandaki gorge, as Annapurna I is the eastern. It is very difficult to approach from the east, where the precipitous northeast and south-east ridges are formidable barriers. These meet at a rock shoulder some distance east of the summit at a high altitude. The long southwest ridge is also extremely difficult; the south face was described by a member of the Swiss expedition of 1953 as the most horrifying he had ever seen.

The Devils Tower, from the west

Dhaulagiri – "White Mountain" – has several claims to fame. It was the first mountain in the Himalayas – in fact, anywhere – found to exceed anything in height in the Andes; for nearly 30 years it maintained its claim as the highest in the world until humbled first by Kanchenjunga, then by Everest, Makalu and K2.

Robert Colebrooks, Surveyor-General of Bengal, was the first to recognize the great height of Dhaulagiri in 1802; it was he who sent his young lieutenant, W. S. Webb, to explore the Ganges sources in 1808. Webb took the first observations and in 1809 checked them from four different survey stations. European geographers ridiculed his results – yet his height of 26,882 feet for Dhaulagiri I was only 87 feet more than the official height today, after 150 years.

The treaty after the Nepal war of 1814–16 closed the country to Europeans for over a century and prevented surveyors and explorers from learning the topography of the mountain. Maps were based on native reports and rough route traverses made by amateur native explorers. Only in 1925 was the Survey of India permitted to send a party of native surveyors to sketch the approach valleys and none of these were trained or equipped as mountaineers. It is not surprising therefore that in 1950 Maurice Herzog and his party were misled into making their reconnaissance from the most difficult side, the Kali Gandaki gorge. They decided that it was too formidable to hold out hope of success and turned their attention to Annapurna.

An exhaustive reconnaissance was made of the mountain before the monsoon in May, 1953, by a strong party of Swiss climbers led by Bernhard Lauterberg. They approached it from the southwest by a tributary of the Mayangdi Khola which joins the Kali Gandaki far below the gorge; by this tributary they reached its glacier source below the north face of Dhaulagiri I. After several attempts the climb was abandoned at about 25,000 feet because of the lack of suitable high camp sites. An Argentinian party led by 26-year-old Francisco Ibanez tried the Swiss route in 1954 with no previous Himalayan experience. They reached much the same height as their predecessors; but most of the 11 climbers were badly frostbitten and Ibanez, worn out by his sufferings, died of pneumonia two days after his arrival at the hospital in Katmandu. He had lost all his toes from frostbite.

Knowledge of the other high peaks of the group rests on the reconnaissance in 1954 by J. O. M. Roberts and George Lorimer. They chose the post-monsoon period and examined the northern flanks from the Barbung Khola or upper Thuli Beri. Roberts, with the Sherpa Ang Nyima, climbed Putha Hiunchuli (23,750 feet), a fine performance in November when the days are short and the nights very cold at these great altitudes.

At last, on May 13, 1960, Dhaulagiri itself was conquered. The Swiss expedition was led by Max Eiselin, a sports writer, and its 11 members included a Swiss postal worker, a Polish doctor, a Swiss and an Austrian student and a Polish author. They were the first climbers to use a plane (a Pilatus Porter) in an attempt on a Himalayan peak. The aircraft landed baggage at 16,000 feet on a snowfield after a series of mishaps which almost led to the abandonment of the expedition. Six of the climbers reached the summit.

Dinaric Alps

A bleak mountain chain along the east coast of the Adriatic. Location *Yugoslavia, Albania and Italy (Trieste).* Height *Average 5,000 feet with several peaks over 8,000 feet.* Map *7, E8.*

The Dinaric Alps are linked to the main Alpine system through the Julian Alps, while they themselves form the connection between the Alps and the Balkan Mountains. The range extends southeast for about 400 miles, from the Isonzo and Sava rivers in the north to Drin River in the south, bounded on the east by the Kolubara, Ibar and Sitnica rivers.

A number of peaks near the ancient city of Split (known also as Spalato, a city that has grown entirely within and around the ancient palace of the Emperor Diocletian) are over 6,000 feet. In central Bosnia, west of Sarajevo, the mountains consist of an elevated block or horst of ancient schists thrust up among the Triassic limestones. Here the Dinara Planina, as the Yugoslavs call the mountains, are mostly forested. Tobacco and maize grow on the low levels, wheat and oats on the slopes and flax and hemp at somewhat higher levels. Near Tuzla there are important salt deposits.

In Montenegro, the formerly independent pocket-kingdom, now one of the federal republics, the mountains are covered with forests: pines grow as high as 6,000 feet with beeches and oaks on the slopes below. There are many underground rivers, especially in Herzegovina. Farther north are the rather bare plateaus of Lika and Velebit, which drop abruptly by a steep scarp to the plain of Karlovel behind Zara, the former Italian enclave.

Dalmatia is almost wholly isolated from the rest of Yugoslavia by the sparsely wooded, elevated Karst region, the most inhospitable barrier in Europe. This limestone plateau, rising to 1,946 feet, extends 50 miles between the lower Isonzo River and the Kvarner gulf. It is characterized by a sink (karst) topography interspersed with abrupt ridges and funnel-like caves. There is a large underground stream, the Reka, and several smaller ones. The Karst was denuded in historical times by the Turks, who used the forests for ship-building; rainfall decreased rapidly and the bleak, arid range came into being.

There are many ruined fortresses in the Dinaric Alps, built in chains as a defence line against the Turks. A new railway has been built, following roughly the Korana River valley, which often disappears into deep, narrow ravines. In the mountains are the Plitvice Lakes, 16 turquoise-colored tarns, descending from the plateau in terrace formation, connected by many waterfalls. The surrounding woods have been turned into a

The Velebit Mountains in the Dinaric Alps

national park. From Drnis the country is desolate and the mountains are drab and barren without grass or trees. In summer this Zagora district is very hot and in winter bitterly cold, torn by the Adriatic "bura" (bora) wind.

Distaghil

A major peak of the Great Karakoram. Location *Northern Kashmir.* Height *I 25,868 feet; II 25,250 feet.* Map *11, C3.* First climbed *Diether Marchant and Gunther Starker, June 1960.*

The twin peaks of Distaghil stand on the boundary between the feudal states of Hunza and Nagar (Nagir) in the Gilgit Agency of Kashmir. The southern slopes feed the Kunyang tributary glacier of the Hispar; from the northern flank the Malungutti glacier descends, reaching and sometimes blocking the Shimshal valley.

The mountain was discovered in 1892 by Sir George Cockerill, then a young officer in the Intelligence Branch of the British Agency at Gilgit. "A great double-headed mountain," he described it, "extraordinarily bold and massive, which the natives call Malungi Diaz. The two peaks, whose altitude can scarcely be less than 24,000 feet, are connected by a ridge, in height hardly inferior. For grandeur of form and prominence of position there is no feature in the whole Shimshal valley more striking than this magnificent mountain."

There has been some argument about the name Distaghil. Some suggested that "Malungi Diaz" was really a corruption of the glacier's name "Malungutti Yaz" and did not refer to the mountain. In the end Distaghil Sar was officially adopted by the Survey of India.

The position and height were fixed in 1913 by Kenneth Mason, when correlating the Indian and Russian surveys. The Malungutti approaches were first surveyed in 1925. Mrs Jenny Visser-Hooft who, with her husband, led this expedition, thus described the view: "Above the peaks which formed the background of the

glacier, the clouds had partly drifted away, suddenly revealing a vision of ethereal beauty – a great snow mountain of incredible height. It looked so unearthly, so sublime, wreathed by the veils of mist, so translucent in its rose and golden glory of the setting sun, that we could hardly believe it was a real mountain."

Distaghil was eventually climbed on June 9, 1960, by the Austrian Karakoram Expedition, without the use of oxygen. The summit was reached by Diether Marchant and Gunther Starker, two members of the party which had left Gilgit, in Kashmir, on May 6; probably the shortest time ever taken to climb a peak of this height.

Dolomites

A mountain group with comparatively low peaks. Location *Eastern Alps, northern Italy.* Height *9,000 feet, rising to 10,965 feet.* Map *8, F8.*

The compact area of the Eastern Alps known as the Dolomites is equipped with admirable high level roads, such as the Dolomite Road from Bolzano in the west to Cortina in the east (one of the chief holiday towns of the area) and the branch road which passes under the great limestone walls to reach the Passo di Sella in a panoramic theater between the Sasso Lungo and the Gruppo di Sello. There are many villages which have become Alpine suburbs of the great cities of Europe, lovely lakes and well-organized tourist attractions.

Yet few mountain areas are so bizarre. Few mountains are so ideally, so fantastically mountainous, as if, indeed, they were made to the mountaineer's pattern. They have attracted artists and poets alike; they are said to have inspired the painters and architects of Venice – a city from which they are often visible as a distant cloud-capped boundary wall with a jagged edge.

Their first peculiarity is their limestone. They are called Dolomites from dolomite, the mineral in their rock. Both the mineral and the mountain area owe their names to the eighteenth-century French geologist, Déodat de Gratet, Marquis de Dolomien, who observed that the rock of these mountains, unlike softer limestones, was hardly affected by cold, dilute hydrochloric acid.

The hard rock has weathered less into heavy, thick masses of more or less regular outline than into natural versions of architectural form, echoing architecture of every kind from Gothic to Indian. Peaks rise like jagged Gothic pinnacles (the Sasso Lungo) and lofty Gothic spires (the Cima della Madonna), or they resemble Indian temples (the Tre Cime di Lavaredo). They build roof on roof, table on table (the Sasso di Pordoi), they shoot upwards in splendid verticals (the Tofana di Rozes, above Cortina d'Ampezzo); crags outline themselves against the deep blue sky in strong, slender towers (the Vajolet Towers). The variety of shape is surprising, endless and spectacular; so are the colors at sunrise and sunset.

The rather lumpy mass of Marmolada, the highest peak of the Dolomites, rises only to 10,965 feet. Other major peaks (Antelao, 10,705

A typical Alpine village in the Dolomites

feet; Le Tofane, 10,640 feet) are about the same height – so there is no gigantism in this Alpine area. The snow melts away early. Rocks rise up gleaming and crystalline among the flower meadows and the screes. They vary in color through gray, yellow, black and red, though a rosy gray predominates – a sparkling surface, at times almost white, which reflects all lights and colors from cloud to sky; though the peaks, crags and towers are at their most exciting when half in and half out of shifting cloud. The upper world of the Dolomites is markedly dry and silent. After the snow disappears in May and early June the streams vanish as well; the magnesian limestone begins to feel the strength of a sun which belongs rather to Italy than to the north.

The population is divided between Austrians and Italians. The Austrians along the route from the Brenner Pass and around Bolzano have a legend of the peaks of what they call the Rosengarten and the Italians Catinaccio. According to the legend this fine section of great walls and keels and crests between Bolzano and the Val di Fassa belonged to Laurin, King of the Dwarfs, and formed a superlative garden. Laurin involved himself in war over the theft of a wife from the world of the humans below the summits. His magic failed, he and his dwarfs were killed, and his great Rose Garden was reduced to jagged rocks.

Climbing in the Dolomites is an exciting challenge. Generally the limestone cliffs are smooth, while the dolomite is full of holes, resembling a petrified sponge. Although many of the peaks are easy, climbing is chiefly on steep faces, vertical chimneys and giddy pinnacles; it is often extremely difficult and has a cult of its own. The exhilarating breeze from the glaciers is missing; the Dolomites are dry, parched and thirsty.

The alpine flora of the Dolomites compensates richly, though, for their high-summer dryness. In the early weeks of June slopes of spring gentian, of starry soldanella and large sulphur anemones, with clumps of mezereon in damper gullies, are only a preliminary to the full blaze.

Some of the most sensational rock climbing of recent years has been accomplished upon the precipices, chimneys and dizzy pinnacles of this colorful and enchanting section of the Alps.

Donner Pass

A highway pass in the Sierra Nevada. Location, *Eastern California.* Height *7,135 feet.* Map *4, B3.*

Motorists driving across the Donner Pass (which is about 35 miles west-southwest of Reno, Nevada) or passengers traveling by rail through the Norden Tunnel under the pass rarely pause to think of the tragedy that was played out on the shores of nearby Donner Lake.

The Donner party (which consisted of two families named Donner and several others) was a wagon-train of early emigrants who set out across the plains for California in 1846. South of the Great Salt Lake they took a new short-cut and were so delayed that they were blocked by the unusually early snows in the Sierra Nevada. They camped out on the lake shore and during the terrible winter of privation 36 out of the 81 died of starvation. Rescue parties from California finally brought out the survivors in the spring of 1847. They had survived by eating their dead.

Several writers were inspired by this grim episode – among them Bret Harte, whose *Gabriel Conroy* was based on the Donner tragedy and Vardis Fisher, whose *The Mothers* is a striking and imaginative reconstruction.

Today the glacial lake is a summer and winter resort, lying 13 miles northwest of beautiful Lake Tahoe. A simple monument commemorates the fate of the pioneers who perished here during a terrible winter more than a century ago.

Drakensberg

The main mountain range of South Africa. Location *South Africa and Basutoland.* Height *Rising to over 11,000 feet.* Map *9, F11-G10.*

The Drakensberg Mountains, the highest in South Africa

The lost continent of Gondwanaland, supposed to have extended in Jurassic times from South America to Australia, survives in part in the great African plateau. Its most striking remnant is the vast triangular block of mountains that now occupies Basutoland, and whose eastern ramparts are called the Drakensberg. The ridge, extending 700 miles from the Tropic of Capricorn in eastern Transvaal to southern Cape Province, dominates a huge area of Natal – a blue, misty wall that forms the province's western boundary. One of the Union's main watersheds, it contains the source of the Orange River, flowing into the Atlantic, and of its tributaries.

The name originates in the legend of a cave-dwelling dragon. The dragon has disappeared – though as late as 1877 an old Dutch farmer and his son were reported in a Bloemfontein newspaper as having seen it in flight – but the caves remain. The lower layers of the range, classified as Cave Sandstone, sheltered South Africa's first inhabitants, the Bushmen, who left some astonishing wall-paintings in them. They show an amazing skill and have had considerable influence on contemporary South African art.

Above the Cave Sandstone the mountains are capped for 300 miles of their length by a layer of basaltic lava up to 4,500 feet thick. The top of this layer is the highest land in South Africa and the source of three major rivers. The lava tends to fracture in straight lines and the weathering of centuries has produced a fantastic conglomeration of rugged blocks and pinnacles. Some, like the Devil's Tooth, stand isolated from the main wall. The Zulus call the range Khuahlamba, the Barrier of Pointing Spears.

The general direction of the range is southwest to northeast. At the easternmost point of Basutoland, however, it bends sharply to the northwest, continuing in this direction for some 60 miles before reverting to its northeasterly course. In this 60-mile stretch the most spectacular scenery and all the major peaks are to be found. It was only in 1951 that Thabantshonyana was established as the highest (11,425 feet). Others are Giant's Castle (10,868 feet), Champagne Castle (11,075 feet), Cathkin Peak (10,438 feet) and Mont-aux-Sources (10,822 feet). Only a few heights have been trigonometrically fixed, but it is unlikely that any higher peaks will be revealed.

Climbing in the Drakensberg is a challenging and difficult undertaking. Large portions are almost unknown to the mountaineer because of the difficulty of access and lack of transport facilities. But there are countless new climbs and magnificent scenery, including scores of virgin peaks, awaiting the climber with initiative. He can vary his ascents from simple scrambles in the Mont-aux-Sources area to summits of extreme difficulty like the pinnacle of the Devil's Tooth.

From the main wall several outliers reach towards the sea and the pattern of the eastern face is one of deep, picturesque river valleys with crenellated walls of rock at their heads. These bastions cover a retreat, however, for the mountain mass is receding westwards under the onslaught of wind and water at the comparatively rapid rate of four feet every thousand years.

The Drakensberg range is frequently covered with snow in winter and exercises a considerable influence over the climate of the interior. People in the Transvaal automatically mutter "snow on the Berg" as they turn up their coat collars. The higher peaks command magnificent vistas of Natal, but many climbers, expecting a similar vista on the western side, have been disappointed, as the upper surface of the mountain block appears to shelve gradually away. Some miles farther to the west, however, Basutoland is again a tumbled wilderness of mountains, deeply intersected by river valleys; waterfalls are not uncommon and the highest, where the Maletsunyane River plunges 630 feet, is four times the height of Niagara from the plateau rim. Roads are few (the pastoral Basuto traverse their hills on horseback) and only the Sani Pass, which crosses the main wall of the Drakensberg into Natal, is capable of bearing vehicular traffic.

Écrins

Highest peak of the Massif du Pelvoux and of the Dauphiné Alps. Location *Southeast France.* Height *13,461 feet.* Map *8, B9.* First climbed *Edward Whymper and A. W. Moore with the guides Christian Almer and Michel Croz, 1864.*

Much hidden by the surrounding peaks, the Écrins – variously "Barre des Écrins," "Les Écrins," "Pic" or "Pointe des Écrins" – presents the climber who at last approaches its upper slopes with noble features which have few parallels in the whole of the Alpine chain. To the north these slopes rise from a glacier setting into a steepening pyramid, between 700 and 800 feet high, habitually plastered with snow and ice and topped by narrow, bristly and disintegrating ridges. To the east they present a fine rock wall.

The separate existence of this impressive mountain was confirmed only in 1862 during the explorations of the British mountaineer, Francis Fox Tuckett, and at least three attempts were made on it before the success of Edward Whymper's party two years later. Its members ascended by the northeast ridge and descended by the northwest, taking part as they came down in an incident which became a bone of contention between Victorian mountaineers.

This incident was "Almer's Leap" – the passage of a huge gap in the summit ridge necessitating a perilous jump by the leading guide; a feat later illustrated as the frontispiece of Whymper's classic *Scrambles Amongst the Alps* and described by him in great detail. Years later it was claimed by W. A. B. Coolidge that the whole incident had taken place only in Whymper's imagination and that the gap did not exist. Coolidge resigned from the Alpine Club when its members refused to take his side; Whymper printed 4,300 copies of the long correspondence involved. Later par-

ties found no trace of the gap – but in fairness to Whymper it must be added that rock-features on such a ridge change with time. Exaggeration, rather than deceit, was probably responsible.

Fourteen ascents of the Écrins were made by various routes on the north face of the mountain before the southern precipices were successfully scaled by Henry Duhamel and the two Gaspards, the La Berarde guides, in 1880. In 1925, Albert Plossie, the young president of the Students Club of Grenoble, made the first ascent with skis of the lower summit of the Écrins – accompanied by R. Michelet – and also of the Dome de Neige des Écrins.

Today the ascent of the Écrins is a popular climb and its traverse one of the classic routes of the district, well served by huts of the French Alpine Club.

Egmont, Mount

An extinct volcano, shaped like a symmetrical cone. Location *North Island, New Zealand.* Height *8,260 feet.* Map *12, J8.* Discovered *Captain James Cook, 1770.*

Mount Egmont, so named by Captain Cook

Mount Egmont, which has been called "the Fujiyama of New Zealand"

Part of the famous north wall of the Eiger

and called by the Maoris Taranaki, is the most beautiful of New Zealand's active or quiescent volcanoes. It is the center of the Egmont National Park.

When Captain Cook first saw it the whole lower part of the mountain was densely wooded, and it remained so until the end of the nineteenth century. Rising from the sea, it was both a landmark and a challenge to explorers.

Early in the twentieth century there was a ferocious and deliberate destruction of its forests, almost to the limits of tree growth. The trees were not even cut and used but simply burned away; grass seed was sown between the stumps and around the charred trunks. Most tales of such forest destruction end tragically, but, quite exceptionally, Mount Egmont's deforestation did not lead to serious soil erosion, for the sowing was followed by grazing and occasional reploughing and topdressing. Today this is one of the most productive dairy farming areas in the world.

Higher up one can still find forest in the National Park. Then comes an open stretch, with great dark sheets of lava and basalt. Crowning it all is the shining snow-field of the summit, from which there is a view north and south over the two Taranaki Bights of the Tasman Sea, the lush pastures of the lower slopes and the pleasant towns of New Plymouth, Stratford and Hawera.

The ascent of Mount Egmont affords little scope for alpine work – but the mountain has by far the longest casualty list of any peak in New Zealand.

Eiger

A peak with a towering rock wall. Location *Bernese Oberland, southern central Switzerland.* Height *13,036 feet.* Map *8, C1.* First climbed *Charles Barrington, 1858.*

A blunt thumb of a peak, catching on its rosy whorls the fiercest storms that come, the Eiger is the easternmost of the trinity that includes the Jungfrau and the Mönch, part of the set-piece view from distant Bern and nearby Wengen. It has, in the Eigerwand, one of the few rock walls that have given rise to as many headlines as the Matterhorn, a bill-board of a mountain face that kills its devotees where the telescopes of the tourist world can be trained on them with the minimum of inconvenience.

With a characteristic name ("The Ogre"), the mountain has a genius for the bizarre and the unexpected that began when Charles Barrington (who had never before visited the Alps and who led his guides to the summit when they preferred to turn back) made the first ascent.

The Eiger consists of a truncated pyramid from which a snow ridge runs south, a longer rock and snow ridge runs west, and the fine pinnacled Mittelegi ridge runs east. Barrington climbed the broken flank into which the western edge merges. The other "normal" routes were followed later, the Mittelegi arête finally being ascended by Yuko Maki, the Japanese climber, with the help of three Grindelwald guides.

Between the east and west ridges lies the north wall, freezing and disintegrating, sunless and vertical, rising 5,250 feet above the scree, the target of that new race of mountaineers, "the north face men." Its western half, the Eigerwand, one of the most fearsome rock walls in the world, was first tackled in 1935 by two young Germans from Munich who perished after three days on the face. Some admired their courage; others, like Colonel Strutt, the President of the Alpine Club, thought that this was one of the "flagrant examples of the neglect of every sane principle in the attempt to gain cheap notoriety."

The following year two Germans and two Austrians, hoping for the Olympic Gold Medal from the Nazi Government, made another attempt. After four days on the great face, beleaguered by storms, one fell, one was strangled by the rope and one died of exhaustion; the fourth, roping down on the fifth day after the most gallant rescue efforts made by volunteer professional guides, died within 15 feet of safety. Three days later the local authorities in Inter-laken put the Eigerwand "out of bounds," a futile measure that was promptly ignored.

In 1937 Germans, Austrians, Italians and a Swiss woman all camped at the foot of the Eigerwand in the hope of good weather. The Germans spent five days on the face, covered their retreat with caches of food, turned back and survived. Only in 1938, after two Italians had died on the Eigerwand, was the great face finally scaled – by Heinrich Harrer and F. Kasparek from Vienna, L. Vorg (who had retreated safely the previous year) and A. Heckmaier, a Bavarian guide.

Many others have followed them since; yet there are still the dangers of the climber falling off the mountain and of exposure to bad weather.

In the summer of 1957 even the Eigerwand surpassed itself when two Germans and two Italians tackled the face. After the party had been marooned for seven days, only one man lived. Swiss, French, Italian and German amateurs helped in rescue work; so did a Polish military unit. A German Red Cross squad drove across Europe with winching equipment plus thousands of feet of rope. At last a German guide, instructed via transmitters farther down the mountain, was lowered 1,000 feet from the summit and returned carrying the survivor on his back.

In March, 1961, the first winter ascent of the notorious north face was achieved by four climbers – Toni Hiebeler, editor of a Munich mountaineering magazine, Anton Kinshofer, a carpenter, Andreas Mannhardt, a sawmill hand, and Walter Almberger, a miner. The first three were German, Almberger Austrian. They spent six nights on the mountain in bitter cold; at one time they were thought to be lost and rescue parties were organized. But they returned safely by way of the Kleine Scheidegg.

The climbers were feted and rewarded with gold medals, which they returned, however, a few weeks later, after being accused of using the mountain railway up to a considerable height and thus of not making the climb from scratch. At first they denied the charge, but later they admitted it. Although their achievement was not any the less daring for this, its impact was somewhat modified.

Elbrus, Mount

Twin conical volcanic peaks. Location *Caucasus, northwest Georgia.* Height *I 18,481 feet; II 18,356 feet.* Map *7, J7.* First climbed *Douglas Freshfield, A. W. Moore and C. C. Tucker, 1868 (lower peak); F. Crauford Grove, F. Gardiner, Horace Walker and Peter Knubel, 1874 (higher peak).*

Mount Elbrus is the highest peak in Europe. Geographers today speak of the Caucasus mountains as the physical boundary between Asia and Europe; the position of Elbrus on the northern side of the watershed places it in Europe. Since it is higher than Mont Blanc, its title as the mountain-monarch of Europe is clearly justified.

Elbrus stands 12 miles north of the main range of the central Greater Caucasus and 40 miles south-southwest of Kislovodsk. Its glaciers give rise to the Baksan, Kuban and Malka rivers. Its volcanic origin can be seen from its smooth, regularly inclined slopes and rounded summits. It has a perpetual icecap swept by constant gales and from it 22 vast glaciers descend, covering an area of 56 square miles. The snowline is at 10,500 feet on the southern slope, 11,500 feet on the northern side.

After the ascents of the Freshfield party in 1868 and the Grove party in 1874, a Hungarian climber, Maurice de Déchy, made the next climb in 1884. Carl Egger, one of the first men to explore distant ranges on ski, made the first ski ascent with G. Miescher just before the outbreak of the First World War, on July 28, 1914.

The conquest of the mountain, which had been famous for centuries under its ancient name, Strobilus, as the legendary prison of Prometheus, was a significant event in the history of mountaineering and it marked the opening of the era of serious climbing on a world-wide scale. War and revolution interrupted mountaineering for many years, but more recently it has been greatly encouraged in the Soviet Union and organized parties of young men and women make the ascent every year. In 1956, 400 mountaineers climbed it *en masse* to mark the four hund-edth anniversary of the reunion of Kabarda, the Autonomous Soviet Socialist Republic which covers the northern slopes of the central Greater Caucasus, with Russia. In 1957 Joyce Dunsheath became the first foreign mountaineer to obtain permission to climb in the Caucasus for more than 20 years and the first British woman to reach the summit.

Today Intourist is running conducted tours to Elbrus. One leaves the train at Kislovodsk, a famous watering-place, travels by car to Vierkhny-Baksan in the Baksan valley and then covers 15 miles on foot (or horse) to a summer camp at the junction of the Terskol and Asau rivers. The climb to the summit is made from the curious metal structure known as the "Refuge of Eleven" at 13,650 feet. There are no technical difficulties to be encountered in a normal summer ascent and the summit can be reached in eight hours, but owing to its elevation and the force of the elements the climb is always an arduous one. On the summit the climber is rewarded by magnificent views over the whole Caucasus range, a panorama unsurpassed outside the Himalayas. The eye travels from Kazbek in the east over the giants of Koshtan-Tau, Dykh-Tau, Shkhara and Ushba to the western summits and the Black Sea, a distance of over 200 miles. The lower snow-fields provide excellent ski-slopes for beginner and expert alike.

Elburz Mountains

A major mountain range separating the Caspian Sea from the central Iranian plateau. Location *Northern Iran.* Height *9,000 feet average, rising to 18,600 feet in Demavend.* Map *9, H1-J1.*

This great range extends for 600 miles in a narrow series of steep parallel ranges in the form of a shallow crescent, along the southern border of the Caspian coastal provinces of Gilan and Mazanderan in Iran. The abrupt face of the Elburz rises like a great wall of rock only a few miles from the streets of Teheran, the Iranian capital. The sight is perhaps most imposing in spring and early summer, when the flowers are blooming in the gardens and the gleaming snow-clad summits are clearly etched against a glorious blue sky.

It is a mountain chain of steep and rocky slopes, forbidding precipices, sinuous ridges and high, alp-like summits, many of which are higher than Mont Blanc, the highest being Demavend. The Firuzkuh or Gaduk pass, some distance east of Demavend, carries the only rail route across the Elburz; other passes, crossed by roads, link Teheran with Chalus (via the Kandavan pass) and Kasvin with Resht (via the Sefid Rud gap).

One of the most interesting features of the Elburz is the contrast between its northern and southern slopes. The northern have a heavier snowfall and rainfall than the southern, and this climatic division is also emphasized by the contrast in vegetation. On the lower slopes, below 8,000 feet, luxuriant forests sweep down to the Caspian coastal plain, but across the watershed to the south there are few trees. The tangle of forest and patches of cultivation, the oaks, beeches, maples and other trees, the rich undergrowth and the many orchards of the Caspian-facing slopes form a striking contrast to the stark, barren emptiness of the slopes merging with the desert. Even the types of houses are different, the mud-brick dwellings found in most Iranian villages giving place to houses of stone and timber.

The Elburz Mountains have played an important part in Iranian history and legend. Armies have tramped over their passes, and rebel groups have sought refuge in the "Hara-bere-Zaiti," the High Mountain. Alexander the Great crossed the range after his defeat of the Persian monarch, Darius III, in the fourth century B.C. In medieval times the mountains gave shelter to a dissident religious sect which had its stronghold in the forbidding and almost impenetrable Alamut valley; here they built fortresses and their chief, the "Old Man of the Mountain," held undisputed sway over them. This sect, known as the Assassins, terrorized its enemies, carrying out murderous sorties when under the influence of the drug hashish (which gave it its name). It maintained its power for nearly two centuries but was finally destroyed by the Mongol invader, Hulagu Khan, in 1256.

The higher ranges of the Elburz are snow-capped for the greater part of the year and some, not exposed to the refracted heat of the arid deserts, are rarely without snow. Large areas are inaccessible and though the mountains were explored and described in the nineteenth century, they are rarely visited by mountaineers today.

Elgon, Mount

A huge extinct volcanic cone. Location *Uganda-Kenya border.* Height *14,178 feet.* Map *9, G6.* First climbed *Kmunke and Stigler, 1911.*

Elgon gets its name from the Elgonyi, a tribe akin to the Gallas, who formerly lived in huge caves in the cliffs along the southern edge of the great mountain. Its lower slopes, precipitous in the north, west and south, gentle on the east, are densely covered with bamboo forests; above is an extraordinary vegetation of tree-sized heather, groundsel and lobelias. The crater is five miles across and almost 2,000 feet deep.

Elgon, which the local Bantu call Masawa, has long been extinct. The crater is now occupied by a large marsh from which, through a deep cleft, flows the headstream of Lake Rudolf.

"From a distance," wrote Patrick M. Synge in 1937, "the mountain looks like a great somnambulant whale, with a long flat back. . . There is now no permanent snow on Elgon but hailstorms are not infrequent and sometimes the white crystals lie on the ground for some hours. It freezes practically every night. . . Formerly the icecaps extended several thousand feet lower than today... Around the crater is a great expanse of high moorland... not unvisited by the Africans as are the similar zones on the other high equatorial mountains we visited..."

Elgon was first explored in 1883 by Joseph Thomson, who discovered the cave-dwellings on the south face. In 1890 it was crossed from north to south and its crater was reached by F. J. Jackson and Ernest Gedge. The first journey around its 150-mile circumference was made by C. W. Hobley in 1896.

"It must be recorded," Synge continued, "as a very easy and comfortable mountain to climb ...The Wanderobo people graze their cattle over it and a path has long existed through the crater between Kenya and Uganda. The mountain does not seem to be in any way a place of fear or veneration... On the Kenya side of Elgon trout have been introduced into several of the rivers and there is good fishing..."

Coffee is grown on the slopes and the south side is very densely inhabited.

Erebus and Terror

Two volcanic peaks. Location *Ross Island, Ross Sea, Antarctica.* Height *Erebus 13,202 feet; Terror 10,750 feet.* Map *1, C2.* First climbed *T. W. E. David and party, 1908.*

It was on January 28, 1841, that the expedition of Captain James Clark Ross, R. N., sailing towards the South Magnetic Pole, sighted the two great Antarctic volcanoes. "We were startled by the most unexpected discovery," wrote R. M. M'Cormick, a member of the expedition, "in this vast region of glaciation, of a stupendous volcanic mountain in a high state of activity... As we made a nearer approach... this apparent snowdrift resolved itself into a dense column of black smoke, intermingled with flashes of red flame emerging from a magnificent volcanic vent, so near the South Pole, and in the very center of a mighty mountain range encased in eternal ice and snow..."

Not far from it, separated only by a saddle of ice-clad land on its east, "arose a sister mountain... but now extinct, though having the same general outline, which also doubtless belched forth at no very distant period its volumes of smoke and flame."

The first mountain was named Erebus, the second Terror, after the two ships of the Ross expedition – tiny vessels, the Erebus being 370 and the Terror 340 tons. Sir James Ross and his frail ships explored the area and M'Cormick had several good looks at the newly discovered volcanoes. "Mount Erebus presented a splendid spectacle," he wrote, "sending upwards a tall, dense column of smoke, tinted red on the right side, and extending out in that direction in an oblique line of pale red along the sky, a smaller vent appearing on the first small eminence to the right of the crater..."

Erebus was climbed by a small party of the Shackleton South Polar Expedition of 1907–09. They were rewarded by the amazing sight of its huge crater – a boiling, steaming cauldron rising from the icefields of the coldest region in the world.

Erzgebirge

A mountain range rich in ores. Location *Czechoslovak-German border.* Height *2,000–3,000 feet, rising to 4,080 feet.* Map *7, D6-E6.*

The Erzgebirge – Ore Mountains, or Krusne Hory, as the Czechs call them – extend for 100 miles between the Fichtelgebirge on the south-southwest and the Elbe on the north-northeast between Czechoslovakia and the German Democratic Republic (East Germany). In Czechoslovakia the highest peak is Klinovec Mountain (4,080 feet), in Germany the Fichtelberg (3,983 feet).

For many centuries this range has been one of the richest mining districts in Europe. Silver and iron were mined here from the fourteenth to the nineteenth centuries, especially around Jachy-

Mount Etna in eruptio

mov. Today the emphasis has changed to tungsten, lead, tin, bismuth, arsenic, antimony, sulphur and – the most important – uranium. The chief mining areas are Annaberg, Freiberg and Schneeberg. Since 1945 Russian aid and demand have opened up the uranium-ore deposits centered round Aue and Jachymov.

With a dense population, the Erzgebirge is also an important industrial area, especially for textiles and metal-working. There are extensive forests and, therefore, the lumbering and timber industries are also important, while at high altitudes oats, potatoes and rye are grown. With all the mineral wealth there are also numerous mineral springs, around which famous watering-places have grown up such as Carlsbad (Karlovy Vary) and Teplice in Czechoslovakia, Brambach and Oberschlema in Germany.

The wooded slopes drop steeply in the south towards the valley of the Eger, where (at Most and Sokolov) lignite is mined. To the north they merge gradually into the highly industrialized foothills, where Chemnitz, Plauen, Zwickau and Oelsnitz-Lugau are the principal centers. There is also a long tradition of cottage industries such as embroidery and toy making.

Because of their riches, the Erzgebirge have often been fought over. In 1938, Hitler seized the Czech part of the range; in 1945, when the Russian occupation armies arrived (the American forces having been withdrawn), it was returned to the Czechoslovak People's Republic, after which most of the German population were expelled.

The Erzgebirge offer easy and pleasant excursions to the undemanding mountaineer. But today they are not accessible to the Western world, mainly because of the uranium mines, which are heavily guarded and placed in a semi-military zone.

Ethiopian Mountains

A complex of mountain groups, mainly composed of volcanic rocks. Location *Covering most of Ethiopia.*

Height *5,500–8,000 feet, rising to over 15,000 feet.* Map *9, G5.*

Bordered on the east, west and south by arid, unfriendly desert, extending in the north to the southwest shores of the Red Sea, the mountains of Ethiopia form a geographical unit which enabled an ancient civilization, though perpetually under the strain of internal struggles, to preserve its independence and integrity for over 2,000 years. The modern state of Ethiopia (excluding Eritrea) has an area of about 350,000 square miles, of which roughly 300,000 are mountainous with a mean elevation of some 6,000 feet. The outer escarpments of the mountain area present a forbidding aspect of sheer cliffs or steep terraces several thousand feet high, broken here and there by precipitous river gorges filled with dense tropical vegetation. Beyond this natural barrier is a vast hilly plateau with here and there groups of mountains of alpine appearance, the highest sometimes capped with snow.

The region is divided sharply into two groups of highlands by the Great Rift Valley running southwest from the Red Sea along the valley of the Awash River and through a line of smaller lakes to Lake Rudolf in northern Kenya. The main Ethiopian massif, 400 miles wide, lies north and west of the Rift Valley, rising to over 15,000 feet in the Simen Mountains some 350 miles west of the southern entrance to the Red Sea. The highest peak is Ras Dashan (15,158 feet). Other important peaks are Mount Guna (13,800 feet), in the middle of the northern part of the massif, and Mount Kollo (14,000 feet), closer to the eastern escarpment. In the south, Mount Gughe reaches 13,700 feet. Beyond the Rift Valley to the southwest is a narrower plateau composed of the Arussi Mountains with an eastward extension, the Chercher Hills, reaching out to the base of the Somali peninsula.

The structure of the Ethiopian massif can be seen in the sides of the deep stream-worn canyons which carve the tableland into irregularly-shaped blocks. Covering the whole is a layer of volcanic rock which is as much as 6,000 feet deep in Shoa, the region around Addis Ababa. Below are levels of limestone and sandstone and, in some places, notably the Tigre region in the north, streams have worn down to the underlying crystalline rocks, which date from the earliest (Archaean) division of geological time.

The southeast highlands are also chiefly composed of volcanic rocks; volcanic activity has probably taken place in this region within the last few centuries. On the lower plateau (Ogaden), southeast of the Arussi Mountains, the ancient basement rocks are exposed and have weathered to produce poor sandy soils, contrasting with the relatively fertile lands of the volcanic regions.

The fertile plateau country between 5,500 and 8,000 feet is known to the Ethiopians as *woina dega* and here, in a healthy and temperate climate, with generous rains in the wet season from June to September, cereal and vegetable crops are grown with considerable success as well as vines, coffee and aromatic plants. Here, too, are the main centers of population, although visitors to cities at such an altitude experience some difficulty because of the rarefaction of the air.

Many parts of the Ethiopian mountains remain unexplored. The first Europeans to visit the country – Portuguese adventurers and missionaries in the fifteenth and sixteenth centuries – seldom survived to describe their travels. Those who did – and their successors in later centuries – were rarely permitted to travel extensively. James Bruce, a Scotsman, is credited with the discovery, in 1773, of the source of the Blue Nile in Lake Tana, a vast sheet of water lying in a depression high on the northern plateau.

Traditional mistrust of the foreigner, together with bad communications, have hampered the exploitation of the mineral wealth of the mountains, though Emperor Haile Selassie took some steps to remedy this. Gold is obtained both from streams and rock deposits, while copper, lead, platinum, magnesium, iron and aluminium ores are also present. Traces of radioactivity in some of the hot springs on the mountains seem to indicate uranium deposits, and there has been prospecting for oil on the Ogaden plateau.

The natural vegetation of the plateau is rich in small flowers and grasses, as well as small trees such as the acacia, and the Australian eucalyptus was recently introduced to compensate for extensive deforestation. On the slopes of the higher peaks junipers and the cactus-like euphorbia extend even above the mountain pastureland used for grazing the short-horned cattle which were introduced from India more than 1,000 years ago.

Among the many kinds of animals native to the country are numerous varieties of antelope, including the nyala southeast of the Rift Valley, while the lesser cats, hyenas, monkeys and (in the Simen Mountains) the ibex are all found. Eagles, vultures and other predatory birds are common. But it is perhaps indicative of the gradual opening up of the Ethiopian mountains that game protection laws have recently had to be introduced where in previous centuries Nature was more than able to protect her own.

Etna

An active volcano in the shape of a truncated cone. Location *Catania province, eastern Sicily.* Height *10,750 feet.* Map 7, E10.

The highest active volcano in Europe lies 18 miles north-northwest of the Sicilian city of Catania. It consists of an inner cone with a main crater, and an outer truncated cone over 9,000 feet in height with over 200 subsidiary cones on its side, formed by lateral eruptions. The southeast slope is cleft by the large, precipitous Valle del Bove, over three miles wide, with walls 2,000-4,000 feet high. To the northwest, at 9,652 feet, lies the observatory, which is approached by a motor-road (completed in 1935) from Nicolosi, the usual starting-point for the ascent.

Etna's 90-mile base, which is marked by the Alcantara River on the north and by the Simeto on the west and south, is encircled by a railway. Four vegetation zones are distinguished: subtropical (up to 1,640 feet), producing citrus fruit, figs and olives; temperate (to 4,260 feet) with vineyards and tree crops (almonds, apples, hazel nuts and pears); the forest zone (to 6,880 feet) with birch, chestnut and pine woods and cereal crops; and the desert zone of lava and ashes, covered with snow for three-quarters of the year. The fertile lower slopes are among the most densely populated in the world, especially in the triangle of Acireale-Catania-Nicolosi.

The first recorded climber of Etna was Empedocles, the Greek philosopher, though the legend that he committed suicide by throwing himself into the crater has been discounted by historical research. It was a mountain often climbed for pleasure and observation – the Emperor Hadrian made one of the early ascents. There have been innumerable legends attached to *Aitne*, as the Greeks called it (from *aitho*, to burn). Here Zeus crushed the giant Typhon; here was the workshop of Hephaestus and the Cyclopes. Other Latin writers (Lucretius and Lucilius among them) sought explanations in natural causes for the Burning Mountain.

Over 260 eruptions of Etna have been recorded. Thucydides mentions eruptions in the eighth and fifth centuries B.C.; Livy speaks of others in 125, 121 and 43 B.C. Catania was overwhelmed by lava and ashes in 1169 A.D., and there were many other serious outbursts in 1669, 1830, 1852, 1865, 1879, 1886, 1892, 1899 and March 1910. The most recent occurred in 1928 and 1947.

Europa, Picos de

The highest massif of the Cantabrian Mountains. Location Northern Spain. Height 7,000 feet, rising to 8,687 feet. Map 7, A8. First climbed Fontan de Negrin, 1907 (highest peak).

The massif of the Picos de Europa extends about 30 miles from east to west between New Castile, the Asturias and Leon. Its peaks include the Torre (or Peña) de Cerredo (8,687 feet), the Peña Vieja (8,573 feet) and the Torre de Lambrión (8,586 feet).

Fontan de Negrin, the first man to scale the 1,600-foot sheer wall of the Narango de Bulnes (8,385 feet) described the massif eloquently: "Glaciers, névés, towers, pinnacles, gorges, precipices, rocks, huge chasms, chaos itself – all this we gazed upon. . . as well as the occasional shooting butt and the chamois which stood watching as though on little rock plinths, or passed in small groups across the distant valley which lay at a profound depth below, silent and otherwise deserted. Some of the summits were lost in the clouds, others rose above them, while all around us there hung empty space, isolated as we were by the huge precipices of this enchanted peak which had until now remained virgin through the centuries."

The whole group between the Sella and Deva rivers forms the culminating stretch of the Cantabrian Mountains, and much of it is even today a region of relatively unspoiled mountain wilderness. These are the really difficult mountains of Spain; even the Pyrenees have nothing to beat them as a group. The rocks are more of the Karwendel than the Dolomite type and resemble most closely the southeast limestone Alps. There is no water in the upper corries, but plenty of snow.

Much of the western portion of the Picos, including the Pico Santa de Castilla (8,400 feet), forms a National Park. In the east the valleys have been spoiled by mining. It is in the central area, once a hunting preserve of the Kings of Spain, that there rise the highest peaks, all of them providing more exciting mountaineering problems than is usual in Spain.

Everest, Mount

The highest mountain in the world. Location Northeast Nepal Himalayas, on the Nepal-Tibet border. Height 29,002 feet (also estimated at 29,145 feet).

Map *11, F5*. First climbed *Sir Edmund Hillary and Sherpa Tenzing Norkay, May 29, 1953*.

In 1852 the Bengali Chief Computer rushed into the office of Sir Andrew Waugh, the Surveyor-General of India, and panted, breathless with excitement: "Sir, I have discovered the highest mountain in the world."

Thus Chimborazo and other peaks lost their claim to supremacy and Mount Everest – named after Sir Andrew's predecessor, Sir George Everest – came into its own. Until then Everest was known as Peak XV to surveyors, while the local name was Chomo Langma, "Goddess Mother of the Snows." It is revered by the followers of Buddha and two monasteries – the Rogbuk in Tibet and the Thyangboche in Nepal – have been deliberately built in such a manner that the monks may contemplate the peak.

The exact height of Everest has long been a matter of controversy. The first computation gave a main altitude of 29,002 feet, from a number of survey readings taken from distant viewpoints. A different computation arrived at 29,145 feet, and this height is currently accepted: whatever the exact figure, it is certain that there is no higher mountain above sea level. There were unsubstantiated claims for a giant peak discovered by an airman during the Second World War while flying over the mountains on the Burma-China border, but these were found to be mistaken.

The first discovery of Everest's pre-eminence among mountains was naturally followed by the desire to explore and climb it. But though the project was discussed for many years, it was found equally impracticable, on political and religious grounds, to approach the mountain from the north through Tibet or from the south through Nepal. It was not until after the First World War that permission was at last granted by the Dalai Lama and in 1921 a reconnaissance expedition was jointly sponsored by the Royal Geographical Society and the Alpine Club, under the leadership of Colonel C. K. Howard-Bury. This group

provided valuable information not only regarding the route – they indicated the way to the top along the North Ridge – but also about the effects of high altitude and, most particularly, about the weather.

In 1922 another expedition was launched in which two members, George Finch and Geoffrey Bruce, reached a height of over 27,000 feet, using oxygen. In 1924 a third expedition made history when Colonel E. F. Norton, who had taken over the leadership when Brigadier C. G. Bruce fell ill, climbed to 28,140 feet without oxygen. A few days later George Leigh Mallory and Andrew Irvine, making a further attempt, disappeared for ever high on the mountain. Speculation as to the fate of these gallant men has never ceased. The geologist, N. E. Odell, was the last man to see them; he climbed twice to Camp 6 and beyond it alone, until forced to retire at the end of his strength and in the certainty that his friends had perished.

Other British expeditions followed in 1933, 1935, 1936 and 1938, always by the same route, as Nepal remained closed to foreigners. Although Norton's feat was twice repeated, the final 800 feet remained unconquered.

At last, in 1949, Nepal opened her frontier; Tibet, under Communist pressure, closed hers. A small Anglo-American reconnaissance led by Dr Charles Houston and H. W. Tilman in 1950 reported unfavorably on the prospects of the southern approaches but in 1951 Eric Shipton, a veteran of several pre-war expeditions, penetrated farther to the edge of an inner recess high on the southwest flank of the mountain, known from earlier years as the West Cwm; it was the prelude to the final triumph.

In 1952 two attempts were made by Swiss expeditions following the route suggested by Shipton. The first was led by Dr Edouard Wyss-Dunant and Rene Dittert with seven others; the Sherpas led by Tenzing Norkay. During their two assaults a height of about 28,000 feet was reached by a guide, Raymond Lambert and Tenzing. In 1953 Colonel (now Sir) John Hunt

The summit ridge of Mount Evere

followed in the footsteps of the Swiss. His party included George Band, Thomas Bourdillon, Dr Thomas Evans, Alfred Gregory, Edmund (now Sir Edmund) Hillary, George Lowe, Wilfrid Noyce, Dr Griffith Pugh, Thomas Stobart, Dr Michael Ward, Michael Westmacott, Major Charles Wyll and Tenzing the Sherpa. All their names must be recorded, for the conquest of the highest mountain in the world was just as much the result of team-work as of individual achievements.

On May 29, 1953, Edmund Hillary, the New Zealander, and Sherpa Tenzing stood at last on earth's ultimate height.

Finsteraarhorn

Highest peak of the Bernese Oberland. Location *Southern central Switzerland.* Height *14,032 feet.* Map *8, D8.* First climbed *Three Swiss guides, 1812.*

A steep-sided pyramid, rising amid the central tangle of the Oberland glaciers, the Finsteraarhorn was perhaps the most difficult rock peak to be tackled in the early nineteenth century.

Controversy existed for many years regarding the first ascent of the Finsteraarhorn. In 1812, two sons of J. R. Meyer – who had made the first ascent of the Jungfrau the previous year – visited the Oberland. Frustrated at first by bad weather in their attempts to climb the Finsteraarhorn, known to be the highest peak in the area, one of the sons subsequently set out for the mountain from the Grimsel Hospice with four guides. They bivouacked, at the height of about 11,000 feet, on the Gemslucke or Rothornsattel, a depression on the southeastern ridge of the Finsteraarhorn. The following morning, the party tackled the mountain and reached a minor summit; here Meyer, exhausted by his efforts, remained with one of the guides while the other three continued to the summit. The exploit, a most remarkable one for its time, was described in a book the following year, but in such a garbled way that the ascent was questioned, and it was not until 1852 that Dr Meyer's own account finally showed the story to be correct.

Other ascents followed, but it was not until 1857 that the Rev. J. F. Hardy, E. S. Kennedy, B. St. J. Mathews and W. Mathews made the first British ascent by the easier northwest arête, which had been discovered in 1829 by Swiss guides. Characteristically, Kennedy was accompanied up to the summit ridge by his page. It was on this climb that the idea of forming an Alpine Club was first mooted. This ultimately led to the establishment of the famous mountaineering society of that name.

In July, 1904, Gustav Hasler and his guide, Fritz Amatter, were the first to climb the northeast wall of the Finsteraarhorn. The second ascent (and the first guideless one) was made in August, 1906, by V. A. Fynn (whom Sir Arnold Lunn described as "that superb American climber") and the Swiss climber A. Brüderlin. A quarter of a century passed before this formidable face was again climbed – this time by the most famous of all American lady climbers, Miss Miriam O'Brien (Mrs Underhill), with Adolf and Fritz Rubi of Grindelwald.

The first ascent on skis was made by the Anglo-Dutch mountaineer, Dr Henry Hoek, in 1901. Eight years later Professor F. F. Roget, Arnold Lunn and the guides, Gyger, Schmidt and Adolf of Kandersteg made the first end-to-end traverse of the central Bernese Oberland and the Finsteraarhorn on skis.

This beautiful, towering peak offers a rich reward to the mountaineer. Professor John Tyndall, who climbed it in 1858, wrote this striking account of the view from "the monarch of the Bernese Alps": "The various shapes of the mountains, some grand, some beautiful, bathed in yellow sunshine, or lying black and riven under the frown of impervious cumuli; the pure white peaks, cornices, bosses and amphitheaters; the blue ice rifts, the stratified snow-precipices, the glaciers issuing from the hollows of the eternal hills, and stretching like frozen serpents through the sinuous valleys; the lower cloud field – itself an empire of vaporous hills – shining with dazzling whiteness, while here and there grim summits, brown by nature, and black by contrast, pierce through it like volcanic islands through a shining sea. . . the weird strange sound of the wind surging with the full deep boom of the distant sea against the precipice behind, or rising to higher cadences as it forces itself through the crannies of the weatherworn rocks; all conspire to render the scene from the Finsteraarhorn sublime. . ."

Flinders Ranges

A mountain range about 400 miles long. Location *Southern Australia.* Height *2,000 feet, rising to 3,900 feet.* Map *12, D6.*

On all sides of the Flinders Ranges, except on the south, stretch vast saline or brackish lakes: Lake Gregory, Lake Blanche, Lake Callabonna, Lake Frome and many others. Below them, and for 600,000 square miles to north and east, lies the world's greatest artesian basin. Some of the bore holes go down 5,000 feet to tap the underground strata, which are full of pure, fresh, gushing water, bringing it to the surface for homes and farms. In the desolate far north of the ranges – here called the Gammon Range – a mysterious booming sound can sometimes be heard emanating from the heart of the mountains. According to the aborigines it is Arkaroo, the Great Snake. In a time of great drought he once drank Lake Frome dry and its water has given him indigestion, causing him ever since to groan and belch. Geologists say the sound is caused by rock falls.

Geologically, this is a most curious region. Lignite, copper, lead ore, uranium (there is a small mine at Mount Painter), talc and ocher are found. But the formations themselves are also exciting. The folding of the range, which appears to be fairly recent, was a very complex process, with pressure from every side. It resulted in an extraordinary system of domes and basins, the basins (or "pounds" as they are known locally) being huge natural amphitheaters encircled by tier after tier of rocky ledges. In the heart of the range is the most famous, Wilpena Pound, an isolated, oval-shaped plateau, some 12 miles long and 5 miles wide, rising from a mass of lower hills. All round it is rimmed by a steep, serrated ridge of hard quartzite, reaching a summit height of 3,900 feet in St Mary's Peak, the highest point in the ranges, to the southeast; in the center it is hollow, like a vast volcanic lake. On the summit of the range near Orroroo, farther south, a bore penetrated 591 feet of river gravels without reaching bed rock; here are the uplifted relics of a vast river system, probably rivalling the present-day Murray River, which once drained southeast Australia and entered the sea near the head of St Vincent's Gulf, north of Adelaide.

Fujiyama

The highest mountain in Japan; an extinct volcano. Location *Shizuoka prefecture, central Honshu, Japan.* Height *12,389 feet.* Map *10, J5.*

Fuji-No-Yama is only one of the many names given to the most famous mountain of Japan, sacred since ancient times. It is also called Mount Fuji or Fuji San and has been addressed by innumerable different poetic appellations throughout the centuries. Lafcadio Hearn made the long and exhausting climb to the summit in 1897. Of the view he wrote: ". . . The view for 100 leagues. . . and the light of the far faint dreamy world – and the fairy vapors of morning – and the marvelous wreathings of cloud: all this, and only this, consoles me for the labor and the pain. . . Other pilgrims, earlier climbers – poised upon the highest crag, with faces turned to the tremendous East – are clapping their hands in Shinto prayers, saluting the mighty Day. . . The immense poetry of the moment enters into me with a thrill. I know that the colossal vision before me has already become a memory ineffaceable – a memory of which no luminous detail can fade till the hour when thought itself must fade, and the dust of these eyes be mingled with the dust of the myriad million eyes that also have looked in ages forgotten before my birth, from the summit supreme of Fuji to the Rising of the Sun.''

Sixty years later a plane-load of writers, traveling to the P.E.N. Congress in Tokyo, saw Fujiyama from 20,000 feet as their plane dipped over Tokyo Bay and the foam-girt islands. One of them wrote: ''Six o'clock in the morning and on the left Fujiyama swims into our ken, filling three of the portholes like a three-part Japanese screen. The snow-capped upper part is bathed in an incredible golden pink; the forests on the slopes, reaching dark tongues towards the crater, are gradually lighting up in golden-green. It is totally unbelievable, yet warmly and singingly familiar. It remains in sight for fully 15 minutes in spite of our speed. It seems that the mountain is moving and we are standing still, suspended in the blue air. I can understand the worship of beauty that is embodied in Fujiyama – the poetry and painting it inspired. And also the humbleness of all those inspired by it who could never do justice to such beauty.''

The last eruption of Fujiyama was in 1707. The great holy mountain of the Shinto religion was closed to women until the Meiji Restoration in 1868 and even now all-male parties are more frequent than mixed ones. The upper reaches are still preserved for religious contemplation and exercise, although summer and winter sports take place on the foothills, and the five lakes at the base (which is 65 miles in circumference) are the object of many excursions from Tokyo, only 55 miles away.

Gasherbrums

Four remote peaks in the Karakoram. Location *Northern Kashmir.* Height *I 26,470 feet; II 26,360 feet; III 26,090 feet; IV 26,000 feet.* Map *11, D3.* First climbed *Gasherbrum I, Peter Schoening and I. Kauffman, 1958; Gasherbrum II, Austrian expedition led by Fritz Moravéc, 1956; Gasherbrum IV, Walter Bonatti and Carlo Mauri, 1958. Gasherbrum III, unclimbed.*

The four Gasherbrums are on the great ridge enclosing the Upper Baltoro Glacier on the north and separating the feeders of this glacier from the Gasherbrum and Urdok glaciers which drain into the Skaksgam. The last three of the peaks are on a line running almost due east-west. Gasherbrum I is about three miles southeast of Gasherbrum II. Remote and inaccessible to any but experienced mountaineers, they were first fixed for position and height by observations from distant survey stations during the triangulation of Kashmir in 1857–59. They appear in the old records as K5, K4, K3a and K3 respectively. Gasherbrum IV, the westernmost, has a steep western arête connecting it with the southern end of the "Broad Group" ridge, a long southern buttress ridge, precipitous and rocky, and an

Fujiyama, Japan's highest mountain

ice-clad north face. Its eastern ridge falls steeply for 2,000 feet to a col and rises again as the western arête of Gasherbrum III which is connected by a high ridge to Gasherbrum II. Both of them have steep rock and ice-ribbed south faces. Between Gasherbrum II and I there is a marked notch in the ridge at 21,580 feet. The ridge divide between the drainage to the Baltoro and that to the Skaksgam continues southeast for about seven miles to a col at the extreme head of the Baltoro Glacier.

On Sir William Martin Conway's map of his 1892 Karakoram explorations Gasherbrum I appeared as "Hidden Peak" because from the main trunk of the Baltoro glacier it is hidden by the others and by a southern outlier of IV; but the name has never been officially accepted, since the great peak is conspicuous from the south, east and north. It was first seen from the Urdok glacier on its northern side by Colonel Younghusband on his second journey to the Skaksgam in 1889, when searching for the Saltoro pass. It was seen again by the Duke of Abruzzi in 1909 from the Baltoro, but the southern approaches were not well mapped until the Duke of Spoleto's expedition in 1929. In this year, too, the northern side of the group was sketched from a distance by Ardito Desio; though it was only in 1935 that Khan Sahib Afras Gul and Muhammad Akram, mountain surveyors with much experience in India, completed the cartography of the northern glaciers.

The first serious attempt to climb Gasherbrum I was made in 1934 by an international expedition led by Professor G. O. Dyhrenfurth. He was badly served by his Balti porters and by the weather and failed to get very far along the southeast ridge. However, reconnaissance made by members of his party helped the French expedition which made a second attempt in 1936. It was sponsored by the French Alpine Club and its leader was H. de Ségogne, whose team comprised 11 Europeans and 35 Sherpas brought from Darjeeling. They chose for their main attempt a rock and ice ridge leading from the southwest to the foot of the final pyramid, which had been examined and tried by two members of Dyhrenfurth's 1934 party. Progress was steady in a month's fine weather to Camp 6 at about 23,000 feet and ropes had been fixed on all the most difficult pitches of the climb. At this critical stage the weather broke and for ten days and nights there was continuous snowfall. The climbers could move neither up nor down; supplies were exhausted and they had to return.

Victory came at last on July 5, 1958, when an American expedition, led by Peter Schoening and I. Kauffmann, reached the summit. They used the southeast ridge route.

Gasherbrum II was climbed by the Austrian Karakoram expedition of 1956, led by Fritz Moravéc. Three members of the expedition – S. Larch, Moravéc and H. Willerpart – reached the summit, which Moravéc described as a plateau of névé crowned by rock-teeth ten feet high. They left behind them a German and English record of the climb in an empty film case and a medallion of the Holy Virgin, both wrapped in a large Austrian flag, and built a cairn.

Gasherbrum IV was conquered in 1958 by an Italian expedition led by Riccardo Cassin; the summit was reached by two members of the expedition – Walter Bonatti and Carlo Mauri – on August 6.

Gauri Sankar

Highest peak of the Rowaling Himal. Location *Northeast Nepal Himalayas, Nepal-Tibet border.* Height *23,440 feet.* Map *11,F5.*

The Rowaling Himal is the part of the Himalayas which drains southwards into the Tamba Kosi. A sacred mountain of the Nepalese, its accepted name is Sanskrit for "the Goddess and her Consort," a name attached to the peak by pilgrims to the neighboring shrines. The mountain is also one of the three holiest to the Tibetans, who know it as Trashi Tsering. Its position and height were first fixed from distant stations by the Survey of India in about 1850 and listed as Peak XX. It was considered of little importance until in 1855 the German explorer, Hermann Schlagintweit, visited Kaulia in Nepal. He misidentified the mountain as Everest at a time when the geographers were searching for the correct name, either Nepalese or Tibetan, for the recently discovered highest mountain in the world. Fortunately Schlagintweit's panoramic drawings were so accurate that it was easy to prove that his Gauri Sankar, so prominent from Kaulia, was identical with Peak XX and *not* with Peak XV – the name by which Everest was officially known until 1865. In 1903 Lord Curzon, then Viceroy of India, obtained permission from Nepal for Captain H. Wood to take further observations from Kaulia. These proved conclusively that Schlagintweit had been mistaken and that Gauri Sankar was 36 miles distant from Everest.

Another 18 years passed before anything became known of the great peak's approaches. In 1921 Major H. T. Morshead, on the first Everest expedition, reconnoitered the approach valleys from the Tibetan side. During the reconnaissance survey of Nepal, between 1925 and 1927, the southern approaches were also sketched, but there are still no accurate maps of the Rowaling Himal.

In November, 1959, the Japanese made an attempt on Gauri Sankar. At one time it was thought that 32 members of the expedition which included the three well-known Japanese mountaineers Hideki Kato, Moriaki Oke and Mituji Oishi and several high-altitude native porters were lost on the northern slopes of the mountain, or had strayed into Tibetan territory.

Aircraft and climbing parties were sent out to search for them. After strenuous and difficult efforts, they were found alive on the north face where they had been trapped by snow conditions. Later they returned to Katmandu and reported that they had also been hindered by armed Tibetan raiders who posed as frontier guards.

The reconnaissance of the Japanese expedition confirmed the theory that Gauri Sankar cannot be scaled from the south – and it still remains unconquered.

Ghats

Two mountain systems, running roughly parallel to the Bay of Bengal and the Arabian Sea coasts. Location *Peninsular India, on the edge of the Deccan Plateau.* Height *Average 3,000–5,000 feet.* Map *11, C8-9 and D9.*

The word *Ghats* means stairs leading down to a river, like those used by the Hindu pilgrims at Benares and Muttra. At a certain period the word was applied to the passes crossing these low mountains, forming the eastern and western edges of the Deccan Plateau and finally to the two ranges themselves, the Eastern and Western Ghats, which have a stairlike appearance in places.

The Eastern Ghats run for about 875 miles southwest, south and south-southwest from the Mahanadi River. They cross southern Orissa, northeast and central Madras, southeast Hyderabad and Mysore to join the Western Ghats in the Nilgiri Hills. The disconnected hills have an average height of 2,000 feet, rising at the northern and southern ends to peaks of 4,000 to 5,000 feet; Dodabetta (8,640 feet) in the Nilgiris is the highest.

The main southern outliers of the Eastern Ghats are the Javadi Hills, Shevaroy Hills and Chalk Hills. At the foot of the range there is a low, very fertile coastal plain, varying from 30 to 100 miles in width, which is watered by the deltas of the Cauvery, Godavari, Kistna, Palar and Penner rivers; these break through the Ghats from the west to flow to the Bay of Bengal. Several smaller rivers rise in the Eastern Ghats and flow eastwards. The rainfall is fairly heavy, especially in the northern section; forests are sparse but have valuable teakwood, red sandalwood and sas trees. Some of the remote hill areas – such as the Malliahs in Orissa – are still inhabited by primitive tribes. Large hydro-electric works are being built in connection with dams on the Godavari and Machkund rivers.

The Western Ghats, extending about 1,000 miles, generally north-northwest to south-southeast, in an almost continuous chain from the Tapti River valley on the north to Cape Comorin, the southern tip of India, form a countryside of jagged spikes of bare red hills rising above the jungle. It was here that, in 1803, Arthur Wellesley finally destroyed the Mahratta confederacy in one of his most brilliant campaigns, after breaking the power of the Moguls.

From its northern limit near Nandurbar in northern Bombay the range runs south-southwest to a point east of the city of Bombay; then it continues south-southeast, crossing Bombay, western Mysore, Coorg and western Madras, meeting the Eastern Ghats in the Nilgiri Hills. Just south of the Nilgiris the 20-mile-wide Palghat Gap cuts through the Ghats; but they rise again in the Anaimalai and Cardamom Hills, along the border of Madras and Travancore-Cochin, and terminate about ten miles north of Cape Comorin. A northeast spur is formed by the Ajanta Hills, famous for their caves, which contain frescoes and sculptures illustrating Buddhist legends.

Between the Western Ghats and the Arabian Hills there is a coastal strip, varying from 10 to 30 miles in width, broken in places by the rugged spurs of the range, which almost reach the sea. In the northern section (which has a general altitude of 3,000 feet) the Ghats rise to 5,400 feet in Kalsubai Peak. South of Mahabaleshwar (4,719 feet) there is a dip in the heights, but south of the Mysore border there are peaks of from 5,000 to 7,000 feet. The Wynaad section culminates in Camel's Hump (7,673 feet); in Travancore the highest point is Anai Mudi (8,841 feet).

The Western Ghats are the main watershed of peninsular India. Many large rivers – the Bhima, the Cauvery, the Godavari, the Kistna and the Tungabhadra among others – rise here, flowing eastwards across the Deccan Plateau into the Bay of Bengal. From the steep western face numerous short streams drain into the Arabian Sea.

The Ghats have considerable climatic interest. The Western Ghats deprive the southwest monsoon of its moisture and have an average rainfall almost double that of the Eastern Ghats in the hills; the Deccan Plateau and southern Madras have considerably less. The slopes are covered with thickets of tropical evergreen and deciduous forests; in the Nilgiris and the Anaimalais there are large tracts of bamboo, teak, blackwood, sandalwood and ebony. In the southern sections tea, coffee, cardamom, cinchona, pepper and rubber are grown on large estates. Elephants, bison and tigers are plentiful. Three railway lines cross the Ghats but travel across them is still something of an adventure to the driver (not to mention the hiker). There are three hydro-electric plants in Kolara (Bombay province), one in Mysore (Jog) and one in Travancore (Munnar works) which also has a large irrigation reservoir in Periyar Lake. There are several popular hill resorts in the Western Ghats but Poona, the ancient Mahratta capital, is the only city of any importance. It has a new university and an air of vanished glory mingling with the martial atmosphere of the new India, for it is the headquarters of the Southern Command of the Indian Army as it was once one of the most important army bases of the vanished British Raj.

Glacier National Park - Canada

One of the oldest national parks of Canada, containing mountains, forests and glaciers. Location *Southeast British Columbia.* Height *Highest peaks rising to over 10,000 feet.* Map *3, G9.*

The Glacier National Park, established in 1886, with an area of 521 square miles, lies in the heart of the Selkirk Mountains. This range extends about 200 miles from the Canada-United States border, with a breadth of about 80 miles, bounded by the great northern bend of the Columbia River. The Park is served by the Canadian Pacific Railway; there are no motor roads.

Many of the highest mountains of the Selkirk range are included in the park area. They include: Mount Rogers (10,525 feet, 40 miles northeast of Revelstoke), Mount Bonney (10,194 feet, 30 miles east-northeast of the same town), Mount Dawson (11,123 feet, about five miles from Mount Bonney) and Grand Mountain (10,842 feet, 35 miles southeast of Revelstoke).

The scenery is wild and magnificent. Below the snowline, especially on the western side, the slopes are densely wooded. The upper valleys are filled with glaciers, of which the Illecillewaet, near Glacier House on the Canadian Pacific Railway, is the largest, being nearly ten square miles in area and falling more than 3,500 feet from the névé. The snowfall is extremely heavy, sometimes exceeding 49 feet in a single winter, and the heavy rainfall has created the huge forests.

Nearby are the Nakimu Caves, a series of beautiful caverns formed by the Cougar Creek and first surveyed in 1905–06. The railroad crosses the Park at Rogers Pass, which was discovered in 1883. There are extensive trails throughout the area, radiating from Glacier Station.

Glacier National Park - United States

A glacier-carved mountain and forest region. Location *Northwest Montana. Height 3,000–10,000 feet. Map 4, D1.*

The Glacier National Park of Montana, some 1,500 square miles in area, is bounded on the west by the Flathead River, on the southwest by its Middle Fork and on the north by the Canadian border, which separates it from the adjoining Waterton Lakes National Park in Alberta.

The Park's mountain peaks rise serrated and sheer. Their height is especially impressive from the east, for though they are not the highest of the Rockies, they rise suddenly from the Montana plains. The highest peak is Mount Cleveland (10,448 feet) near the Alberta border; Going-to-the-Sun Mountain (9,604 feet) is also within its limits.

The distinctive character and beauty of Glacier National Park is the result of the geological phenomenon known as the Lewis Overthrust. Millions of years ago this region was beneath the sea. Great layers of sand, silt and lime accumulated on the ocean floor, then were compressed and gradually changed to sandstone, shale and limestone. The movements of the earth and heat brought other changes; volcanic action forced molten lava into cracks in the rock and between the layers. Then the land began to rise and the sea withdrew. Here and there the earth's crust, of varying thickness, buckled and split. In this area the pressure must have been especially great; in a displacement along one fault a huge mass of rock was pushed up, then forced northeastwards for 15-18 miles, pushing the older rocks that once formed the ocean bed on to the newer rocks. Later, erosion and glaciation wore down the top layers of this overthrust, so that on top of the peaks one sees colorful older rocks, rich in fossils of clams and oyster shells and remains of fish and other marine life.

During the period of uplift and faulting, newly formed streams cut deeper and deeper into the mountain mass, forming deep, narrow canyons, sharp ridges and peaks. Then came the glaciers, forming large icefields, which slowly but invincibly moved down into and through the stream valleys, gouging out the basins in which today some 200 mountain lakes are bedded, and giving the valleys their present U-shape. The lakes in Glacier National Park include McDonald (ten miles long and one mile wide, with an altitude of 3,154 feet), near the western boundary; Waterton (11 miles long and half-a-mile wide, with an altitude of 4,196 feet), on the Alberta border; St Mary Lake (nine-and-a-half miles long and one mile wide, with an altitude of 3,154 feet) in Glacier county and the highest, Iceberg Lake, at 6,000 feet. Streams plunge hundreds of feet down smaller side valleys with numerous waterfalls.

There are about 60 glaciers; the largest is Blackfoot (ten square miles, about 7,500 feet up) southwest of St Mary Lake and near Mount Jackson (10,033 feet).

After the main glaciers disappeared, soil formed and vegetation took root. Now there are extensive forests with about 30 species of trees, most of them evergreens; there are colorful wild flowers of many varieties and at various elevations. The forests teem with mountain goats, moose, elks, mules and white-tailed deer; in addition there are grizzly and black bears, coyotes, martens, minks, otters, cougars, badgers, wolverines and beavers.

Going-to-the-Sun Mountain in
Glacier National Park, Montana

The Park lies astride the Continental Divide (which here follows the Lewis Range). A road famous for the grandeur of its scenery crosses it at Logan Pass (6,664 feet). The Park was established in 1910, and for many years was completely without roads. The Going-to-the-Sun Highway was begun in 1921 and finished in 1933; it provides easy access to motorists for a large part of the area. But most of the Glacier Park remains a rugged wilderness, only to be explored along 1,000 miles of trail.

Gosainthan

A mountain massif in the Himalayas. Location *Nepal-Tibet border.* Height *26,291 feet.* Map *11, F5.* Explored *H. W. Tilman and party, 1949.*

"The great massifs of Gosainthan. . . are quite unknown to us," wrote Dr T. G. Longstaff in 1951, and the last decade has brought no change in this respect. Gosainthan still keeps its secrets unconquered.

The Trisuli Gandaki River breaks through the Great Himalayas near the old Nepalese frontier fort of Rasua Garhi, about 40 miles north of Katmandu and 15 miles south of the Tibetan town of Kyirong. An important trade route, difficult at certain seasons, passes through the breach cut by the river. Gosainthan – a Sanskrit name meaning "the Place of the Saint" – stands on the northern crest-zone of the Great Himalayas about 30 miles east-northeast of Rasua Garhi, and has long been identified with the Tibetan mountain Shisha Pangma. This was believed to be within Tibetan territory.

As Peak XXIII, its position and height were fixed from the distant south in about 1850. Both Main Singh, first of the "pundit explorers" who passed through the Rasua Garhi gap in 1865, and the Indian surveyors in 1925 showed it north of the Nepal boundary. Towards the end of the Second World War two Germans, Peter Aufschnaiter and Heinrich Harrer, who had escaped from the internment camp at Dehra Dun, were detained for several months at Kyirong by the Tibetan authorities. Aufschnaiter's sketch-map of the Tibetan frontier indicated that the boundary watershed was probably farther north than had hitherto been suspected. The problem was settled in 1949 by H. W. Tilman, who led a party to the Langtang Khola. The large left-bank tributary of the Trisuli Gandaki was found to be entirely within Nepalese territory and to be hemmed in on the north by the Langtang Himal, which culminates at Gosainthan. Though no close reconnaissance of the peak was made and the party was not equipped to climb it, it is almost certain that it marks the present boundary between the two countries.

Graian Alps

Northern division of the Western Alps. Location Franco-Italian border, between the Cottian Alps and the Little St Bernard Pass. Height 7,000 feet, rising to 13,324 feet. Map 8, B9-C9.

The Graian Alps extend in an arc from Mont Cenis to the Little St Bernard Pass. They are usually divided into the Central, the Western (or French) and the Eastern (or Italian) Graian Alps. Besides many glaciers, they contain 55 peaks over 10,000 feet and many passes, ranging from the Col de la Grande Rousse (from the Rhèmes Valley to the Val de Grisanche) at 11,483 feet to the Col de la Madeleine (La Chambre to Moûtiers Tarentaise) at 6,509 feet. Just north of the Mont Blanc group, this important massif is bounded by the valleys of the Isère and Arc rivers.

The highest and most famous peak of the Graian Alps is the beautiful Gran Paradiso (13,324 feet), which rises above the town of Cogne. It is the only summit in the Alps whose first ascent was repeated by its conqueror the following day – solely for the sake of the view. It was in September, 1860, that John Jermyn Cowell made the ascent – after a fruitless attempt to discover the legendary Mont Iseran.

"No high mountain in the whole region of the Western Alps has remained in undeserved obscurity so long as the Gran Paradiso," Cowell claimed with some truth. Lack of communications and the fact that the Graians were beyond the range of the established mountaineering centers were the main reasons for this.

Cowell, together with his friend, John Dundas, and the guide Michel Payot, found the going easier than they had expected. They were, however, driven from the summit by mist and intense cold, taking only eight minutes to dash down a summit arête that had taken them two hours to ascend.

The following morning Cowell set out for the summit once more and reached it with Payot in five hours. "To please Payot," he wrote, "I counted carefully the number of steps that he had cut the day before. The grand total was 1,275, a score of which he was not a little proud, it being, he said, the greatest number that had ever been accomplished by a Chamonix man in one day."

Cowell was rewarded by a magnificent view. "It was a strange and exciting sensation – that of being alone on this little spot, lifted so high in the air above all surrounding peaks, and with no visible surface or support below. Looking over the dim mist at my feet, I felt as if perched on the very topmost pinnacle of the universe."

The first winter traverse of the Gran Paradiso was made in 1925 by Count Aldo Bonacossa, the outstanding Italian ski pioneer, and his wife, also a leading European ski mountaineer. She earned another title during the Second World War – the proud one of "Mother of the Partisans."

Grand Combin

A high peak near the Italian border. Location Pennine Alps, southwest Switzerland. Height 14,164 feet. Map 8, C8.

Rising as a great snowy mass crowned by two separate peaks, the Grand Combin is the cul-

The Grand Combin, in the Pennine Alps

minating point of the ridge which runs first northeast and then north from the Vélan and divides the Val d'Entremont from the Val de Bagnes. It therefore lies well to the north of the main Alpine watershed which here forms the frontier between Switzerland and Italy.

The mountain is most frequently approached by the Glacier de Corbassière, above which the Combin rises like a white face, not too steeply inclined, surmounted by the Aiguille du Croissant and the Graffeneire.

William Mathews, who was one of the founders of the Alpine Club, was determined to ascend the Combin from the moment when he first saw it in 1854. It proved a frustrating and bewildering exploit. In 1856 he climbed the Combin de Corbassière, the considerably lower peak to the north of the Corbassière glacier, believing it to be the

Grand Combin. Then, the following year, he set out once again from the Val de Bagnes and this time arrived on the higher slopes of the mountain.

"We were standing at the vertex of a great triangle of rock which forms the principal part of the eastern face of the mountain," he wrote later. "Before us was a dazzling cone of frozen snow of extreme steepness, rising from far below on either side and terminating in a very acute point some 200 feet above our heads."

Mathews and his companions, Simond and Felley, made a horizontal traverse of the snow-field, forcing a passage along a steep and very thin knife-edge ridge to gain the summit. They drank to their success and shouted with delight – only to discover later that they had reached the lower of the two summit points and that even this had been ascended by a local man exactly a month earlier.

The first winter ascent of the Grand Combin was made by Marcel Kurz. Sir Arnold Lunn, who later made such an ascent, using skis, re-called with delight "the bellying surges of black cloud breaking on the ice-fretted bastions of the Combin and disintegrating into long feathery streamers of icy particles. . ."

The Petit Combin is three miles north-north-west of its "big brother," and is more than 2,000 feet lower.

Grandes Jorasses

A peak of the Mont Blanc massif. Location *Franco-Italian border.* Height *13,799 feet.* Map *8, C8.* First climbed *Horace Walker, Melchior Anderegg, Johann Jaun and Julien Grange, June 30, 1868.*

Even in the range of Mont Blanc, packed with set-pieces of mountain scenery, the Grandes Jorasses presents an exceptional sight, combining strength with grace. For nearly a century moun-taineers have been drawn to it both by its beauty and by the challenge which it offers.

The peak towers up direct from the surface of the Leschaux Glacier as a 4,000-foot rock wall, a north face rising to the rocky ridge which here forms the frontier between France and Italy. To the south, the slopes are less steep (though steep enough). On the west lies the Col des Grandes Jorasses; on the east, the Col des Hirondelles, named by the English writer and mountaineer, Leslie Stephen, who described in moving prose how he found a number of dead swallows on the Col. "There were no swallows," one of his guides wrote later, "the whole thing was a joke."

Edward Whymper was the first to reach the ridge, in 1865. He had ascended from the south, mainly with the intention of gaining a good view of the nearby Aiguille Verte, and found himself on the western and lower summit. Horace Walker climbed the eastern or true summit, with three guides, on June 30, 1868.

Both Whymper and Walker used routes on the south face of the mountain, for here – a rare case in the Alps – the main ridge leading down east and west to the two cols was more hazar-dous. Both of these, steep, difficult and dangerous, held out for many decades – the western until 1911 when it was climbed by Geoffrey Winthrop Young, and the eastern (*descended* by Young in 1911 after he had made a second ascent of the peak) until it was climbed in 1927.

Last of all came the conquest of the north face, 4,000 feet of vertiginous rock which took its turn as "the last great problem of the Alps" and col-lected its due list of victims. Richard Haringer, a German climber, was killed in an attempt in 1934. On June 28–29, 1935, two Munich climb-ers, Martin Meier and Rudolf Peters, made the first ascent. On July 1, an Italian party consisting of G. Gervasutti and R. Chabod, and a Genevese party consisting of Raymond Lambert and Loulou Boulaz, repeated the ascent without realizing that the Germans had reached the summit. Lambert was later to play an important part in the Swiss attempt on Everest. Mlle Boulaz was not only a brilliant mountaineer but a fine skier. These three parties had climbed the north face up to the Pointe Croz, which is not the highest point. The first direct ascent of the

Gauri Sankar (left) in the Himalay

north face to Pointe Walker, the highest peak, was accomplished on August 4-6, 1938, by an Italian party, consisting of R. Cassin, G. Esposito and U. Tizzoni. The climb is still considered one of the most formidable in the Alps.

Great Dividing Range

A series of ranges and plateaus with many subdivisions. Location Roughly parallel with the east and southeast coasts of Australia. Height 4,000 feet, rising to 7,305 feet in Mount Kosciusko. Map 12, E4-F6.

The Great Dividing Range is a misnomer. This great series of ranges and plateaus and elevated depressions is strung for about 2,000 miles along the eastern Australian seaboard, but it is not continuous. Nowadays it is generally called simply "The Great Divide." In Australia there are no lofty "young" mountains due to the sharp, relatively recent folding that produced the Alps, Andes and Himalayas. What the Great Divide lacks in height, however, it makes up, along its enormous length, in picturesque variety. The Southern Alps have extensive snowfields. North of these, but not continuous with them, is the Blue Plateau, the so-called Blue Mountains, running parallel with the Pacific coast behind Sydney. Blue Mountains is another misnomer; they are in fact a warped and elevated crust of rough sandstone, rising to about 4,000 feet, deeply dissected into steep-sided, timbered canyons of misty beauty. In these valleys within 50 miles of Sydney you find clear sunny pools in which the duckbilled platypus swims. North of the Blue Mountains begins the first of a series of lush mountain rain forests, extending in a broken chain right up to Cape York, east of the Gulf of Carpentaria. In these picturesque "big scrubs" live regent and golden bower-birds, rifle birds of paradise, incubator-birds and, in North Queensland, tree-kangaroos. The Macpherson and Bollender Ker ranges, the former below Brisbane, the latter in tropical Queensland, are surmounted by moss-forest and giant beech trees.

On the latter range grows a white rhododendron, a southern representative of a family that has migrated south from Asia.

Dozens of rivers are born in the Great Dividing Range. Many run east into the Pacific Ocean, while others flow inland, peter out and are lost. From the top end of the Divide rivers run north into the great, muddy Gulf of Carpentaria. From the south, others find their way into the sea by way of the Murray River at the very bottom of the continent.

Great St Bernard Pass

An Alpine pass between Martigny-Ville and Aosta. Location Italo-Swiss border, southwest Pennine Alps. Height 8,110 feet. Map 8, C8.

Known to pre-Roman travelers, and a thoroughfare across the Alps since the early Middle Ages, the Great St Bernard is famous throughout the civilized world for its Hospice, its dogs and the mortuary where the bodies of unlucky travelers were once preserved for inspection. It is also reknowned as the passage through which Napoleon marched with 40,000 men on his way to the plains of Italy and the victory of Marengo (1800).

In spite of its height, the Great St Bernard has for more than 1,000 years been part of the road to Rome taken both by prelates (such as Sigeric, Archbishop of Canterbury, who crossed it in 990) and potentates (such as Bernard, the uncle of Charlemagne, who crossed it in 773, and Frederick Barbarossa who did the same in 1162). In the days that preceded mountain travel for its own sake, the passage of the St Bernard was a frightening experience. For example, the Canterbury monk, Master John de Bremble, wrote of the place: "I have been on the mount of Jove; on the one hand looking up to the heavens of the mountains, on the other shuddering at the hell of the valleys, feeling myself so much nearer to heaven that I was sure that my prayer would be heard. 'Lord,' I said,

Himalayas, Mount Everest in the foreground

'restore me to my brethren, that I may tell them that they come not to this place of torture.'"

The road from Martigny to Aosta, completed in 1805, rises past Bourg St Pierre until the massive stone Hospice is seen standing in the gap between the minor peaks of the Chenalette and the Mont Mort. Originally built at Bourg St Pierre, the Hospice was moved to the summit pass late in the ninth century and re-established there after the depredations of the Saracens less than a century later. From 1215 onwards the Augustinian monks have obeyed the commands laid down by St Bernard of Menthon, the founder of the Hospice, and provided simple board and lodging for travelers, while their dogs, a cross between a Newfoundland and the Pyrenean mountain dog, have been used to find and rescue those overcome by the weather.

The museum attached to the Hospice contains gifts from travelers aided by the monks, as well as relics from the Roman temple to Jupiter which once stood near the summit of the pass. Until modern times the scene of greatest interest at the Hospice was that of the Morgue, where the dead bodies of lost travelers were deposited. Near the Hospice is a second building, now used as an hotel, to which during the summer months the monks direct all those except pilgrims, walkers or the needy who may require accommodation.

The mean temperature at the pass (meteorological records have been kept since 1817) is almost 3° below freezing.

The Italian side of the pass is both steeper and more attractive than that on the north (the frontier runs through the center of the little lake by the Hospice).

Great Smoky Mountains

A heavily forested mountain range. Location *Western North Carolina and eastern Tennessee.* Height *6,000 feet, average.* Map *4, J5-6.* Explored *Thomas L. Clingman and Arnold Guyot, mid-nineteenth century.*

The Smokies are the home of the original mountain people of whom Horace Kephart, a university librarian and an authority on woodcraft and camping, wrote his famous *Our Southern Highlanders* in 1913. Kephart painted a vivid picture of the sturdy, independent mountain folk who have preserved so much of their ancient customs and speech. "When one dines in a cabin back in the hills," he wrote, "he will taste some strange dishes that go by still stranger names. Beans dried in the pod, then boiled 'hull and all' are called leather-breeches (this is not slang, but the regular name). Green beans in the pod are called snaps; when shelled they are shuck-beans. The old Germans taught their Scots and English neighbors the merits of scrapple, but here it is known as poor-do... Your hostess, proferring apple sauce, will ask, 'Do you love saas?'... It is well for a traveler to be forewarned that the word love is commonly used here in the sense of like or relish... Evening, in the mountains, begins at noon instead of at sunset. Spell is used in the sense of while ('a good spell afterward') and soon for early ('a soon start in the morning')... A mountaineer does not throw a stone; he 'flings a rock.'... When a man is tired he likely will call it worried; if in a hurry, he is in a swivvet; if nervous, he has the all-overs; if declining in health, he is on the down-go..."

The homeland of this colorful speech is part of the Appalachian system which is sometimes considered as belonging to the Unaka Mountains. The Great Smokies stretch from Asheville and Knoxville, and are the western escarpment of the Appalachians, merging on the east into the Blue Ridge escarpment. They take their name from the deep blue haze which is characteristic of the region. The Great Smoky Mountains National Park has an area of 789.3 square miles and was established in 1930. The crest of the main range forms the North Carolina-Tennessee state line here, zigzagging for 71 miles; the area of the park is about 427 square miles in North Carolina and 361 square miles in Tennessee.

The main peaks of the Great Smokies include

The Great Smoky Mountains

hiking paths along the crest of the range or through the wooded valleys.

Green Mountains

A low range of great beauty. Location *Mainly in Vermont, extending from Massachusetts to Quebec.* Height *Average 2,000–3,000 feet.* Map *5, B2-3.*

The Green Mountains with their gentle slopes represent one of the most popular and charming features of New England. They are part of the Appalachian system and they extend from near Long Island Sound, through the western part of Connecticut and Massachusetts and into Vermont and Canada; but only in Vermont, through the center of which state they run, are they called Green Mountains – indeed, Vermont is known as the Green Mountain State. It was here that Ethan Allen and the Green Mountain Boys successfully defied the New York authorities in the seventeen-seventies. In Massachusetts and Connecticut the mountains are variously known as the Berkshire Hills, Taconic Mountains, and Hoosac Mountains.

This is one of the oldest ranges in North America. Erosion and weathering have polished the peaks until in many places they have become low, rounded hills. The highest peaks are in Vermont – Mount Mansfield (4,393 feet), Killington Peak (4,241 feet), Camel's Hump (4,088 feet), Lincoln Mountain (4,078 feet) and Jay Peak (4,018 feet).

The Missiquoi, Lamoille and Winooski rivers divide the range from east to west; they are short streams but they supply abundant water-power. The range forms the divide between the basin of the Connecticut River on the east and the Lake Champlain and Hudson River basin on the west. There are many smaller streams and fertile valleys; the mountain slopes are covered with evergreens, hardwood trees and sugar maple. Their varied beauty has led to the establishment of many resorts both for summer and winter sports. Granite, marble and slate exist in large

Clingmans Dome (6,642 feet), the highest point in Tennessee, 35 miles southeast of Knoxville; Mount Guyot (6,621 feet), 40 miles east-south-east of Knoxville, on the Tennessee-North Carolina line; Mount Le Conte (6,593 feet), which is six miles southeast of Gatlinburg with a popular tourist lodge; Mount Collins (6,188 feet); and Mount Kephart (6,100 feet). The Smokies have almost 130 different tree species in the practically unbroken forests, half of them of virgin growth. The spectacular displays of mountain laurel, rhododendron and wild flowers attract the botanist; the varied and plentiful animal life the hunter; the 600 miles of streams the angler. The headquarters of the park are at Gatlinburg. There are still many typical mountain communities and a Cherokee Indian reservation close by. The Great Smoky Mountains are dotted with lodges, camping grounds and hotels, and the Appalachian Trail is only one of many quantities and are quarried extensively, and there are also deposits of copper and manganese. The Green Mountain National Forest includes large areas of the range; the 260-mile "Long Trail" snakes along the full length of the range and is in part identical with the Appalachian Trail.

Grossglockner

The highest peak in Austria. Location *Hohe Tauern, Austria.* Height *12,460 feet.* Map *8, G7.* First climbed *The Bishop of Gurk and party, 1799–1800.*

This rocky summit, the highest point on the long ridge of the Hohe Tauern, which stretches east from the Brenner Pass, has an impressive outline. It stands imposingly at the head of the Moll valley in Carinthia and is a popular tourist peak, nowadays easily ascended either from Heiligenblut or from Kals.

It was a familiar sight to the inhabitants of Gurk, including Count Franz Altgraf von Salm-Reifferscheif-Krantheim who became Bishop of Gurk in 1783. In 1799 two local peasants climbed high on the mountain and decided that it could be conquered, and the bishop began to organize the first ascent. He was adventurous enough to attack a great peak but too little of an ascetic to risk unnecessary discomfort, so he postponed the climb until a wooden hut could be built on the southern flanks of the mountain. In August, 1799, a small party established themselves in the hut and a few days later the bishop and his party set out. Eleven amateurs, including Sigismund von Hohenwart, a botanist who later became Bishop of Linz, Bishop Salm's court chaplain, 19 guides, porters and carpenters (and the bishop's chef) made up the retinue.

The summit was reached without undue difficulty, a great iron cross was planted and, as the watchers in the valley fired a salute of cannon, the bottles were broached and the toast of the Grossglockner was drunk. Only then was it discovered that the party had reached but the lower of the two peaks forming the mountain.

The error was rectified the following year when Bishop Salm conducted another party to the highest peak where both an iron cross and a tree were planted. However, he himself did not then traverse the narrow snow-ridge to the true summit, though he did so two years later.

The conquest of the Grossglockner at the end of the eighteenth century was a significant milestone in the story of the Eastern Alps. In addition, it had the distinction of being the first Alpine summit to be conquered by a bishop.

Guadarrama, Sierra de

A mountain range extending about 120 miles. Location *Central Spain.* Height *5,250 feet average.* Map *7, A9-B8.*

The Sierra de Guadarrama dominates Madrid and the province of Segovia. Northwest of the capital, it rises from the central plateau and runs northeast, roughly between the Tagus and Douro (Duero) rivers, separating Old Castile from New Castile. These are the Montes Carpetani of the ancients, the sentinel and protector of Madrid. They send northerly gales to the shivering upland city and cause intense cold, but they also render the atmosphere unusually dry by intercepting the moisture of the northwest winds which prevail in the summer.

The rugged, frequently snow-capped range rises to 7,972 feet in the Peñalara peak, which stands on the border of Madrid and Segovia provinces, 11 miles from Segovia. Near its top there is a megalithic monument.

The range is crossed by several passes, among them the Guadarrama and the Navacerrada, which link Madrid with Segovia. The Navacerrada is 5,905 feet high and runs at the southern foot of the Peñalara on the old Madrid-Segovia road. Not far from it stands the royal Guadarrama hospital, where there is a favorite ski resort for the Madrileños.

The Sierra de Guadarrama is to a large extent covered by forests and yields fine timber. Within the range there are several resorts, sanatoriums and ski-ing châlets, and the Peñalara Club has built several huts for mountaineers.

Harz Mountains

A largely deforested mountain range, extending 60 miles. Location Central Germany. Height Rising to 3,747 feet in the Brocken. Map 7, D6.

Before the Second World War it was claimed that if you sat long enough on the top of the Brocken, the highest peak of the Harz Mountains, you would see every living German.

Today it is a different story, for while much of the Harz lies in West Germany, the Brocken and its ugly summit buildings lie a mile or so east of *die grüne Grenze* – the green frontier of pine forests along which runs the line separating West from East Germany.

The Harz, stretching between the Leine and Elbe rivers, and 20 miles wide in places, forms Germany's northernmost mountain group. The range is divided into the Upper Harz on the northwest and the Lower Harz on the southeast, but except for the natural differences due to altitude, they form a single unit. The lower slopes of this undulating country, cut through in places by minor craggy gorges resembling those of the Ardennes, are thickly wooded despite considerable depredation under the Nazis, with pine and fir to the north and beech, oak, elm and birch to the south. The higher slopes, rising in gentle curves from the forests, reach 3,000 feet in many places; they are whale-backed ridges and knolls, gray and forbidding rather than green and inviting.

From the earliest times the Harz has been prolific both in fauna and legends. The last bear was killed in 1705 and the last lynx in 1817, but deer, foxes and badgers are still numerous.

Here paganism yielded later to Christianity than in other parts of Germany and the part the Brocken has played in German legends of witchcraft and evil was underlined, not created, when Goethe took Faust to the summit of the Brocken for the revels of Walpurgis Night which have been traditionally associated with this site since the sixteenth century. As late as 1933 Harry Price, the British psychical researcher, and C. E. M. Joad solemnly tried to turn a goat into a handsome young man, following ancient cabbalistic rites – and though they failed, quite a few people had expected that they would succeed.

Goethe himself visited the Brocken in 1777 and the visit is commemorated by a memorial plaque. With its views across the heart of central Germany, ranging from the Teutoburgerwald in the north to the hills of Thuringia in the south, the bare expanse of the summit, eight miles west of Wernigerode, was a tourist attraction from the days of the Romantic Revival. Today the peak, which has given its name to the "Brocken specter" – an optical illusion in which the shadows of the spectators, greatly magnified, are projected on the mists about the summit of the mountain opposite – is reached by a railway and two roads and is crowned by a hotel, a station and an observation tower.

For centuries the Harz was of great industrial importance to the administrations of Prussia, Brunswick and Anhalt, which controlled it before the rise of modern Germany, for its mineral wealth was considerable. Lead, gold, copper, silver and iron have all been worked here, many of the mines using water-power from the numerous small streams which rise in the area. Intensive uranium prospecting began after the last war.

Strategically the Harz forms a commanding hub of the country; some of the last minor actions of the Second World War were fought among its forests. American troops encircled the whole area and advanced with the British to meet the Russians on the Elbe, but German resistance continued for some time afterwards in the Harz itself. Later, American and British troops were withdrawn from their positions to the zonal frontiers which had been agreed beforehand (incidentally giving the Russians a major bridgehead across the Elbe and the observation post of the Brocken itself).

Hekla

An active volcano with numerous craters. Location *Southern Iceland.* Height *4,747 feet.* Map *7, A2.*

Arngrimus Jonas, the seventeenth-century geographer, was highly incensed at the slanders about his native Iceland spread by his colleagues Munster, Frisius and Ziegler, and set out in his *Navigations* to refute their statements about Hekla and the other Icelandic volcanoes. "Whosoever they be that have ascribed unto Hecla perpetuall belching out of flames, they are farre besides the marke: insomuch that as often as it hath bene enflamed, our countreymen have recorded it in their yerely Chronicles for a rare accident: namely in the yeeres of Christ 1104, 1157, 1222, 1300, 1341, 1362, and 1389: For from that yeere we never heard of the burning of this mountaine untill the yeere 1558, which was the last breaking foorth of fire in that mountaine. . ."

Jonas (or Jonnsson) firmly denied that Hekla was one of the main entrances of hell or that people vanished into it when they were called by specters. Yet the Icelandic sagas and legends themselves are full of references to this wild and fearsome "gateway to Hell from which night and day came the gnashing of teeth and the groaning of the damned." The lost souls, they said, could be seen whirling above the crater, escorted by vultures. Some even placed here the Castle of Brunhilde, encircled by the eternal fires of flowing lava which the weakling King Gunther, escorted by the redoubtable Siegfried, had to brave to reach the bride he sought.

The Rev. Frederick Metcalf, who explored Iceland in 1860, found the grim volcano forbidding enough even without legendary specters. "About the cone, vapor was issuing at intervals from the black sand," he wrote, "while in the crater itself, some hundred fathoms below, were gaping ice-holes, and great masses of snow side by side with sulphureous steam jets. I can bear witness that the poet who used Hekla as an illustration of blowing hot and cold in a breath,

An eruption of Mount Hekla

was quite true to facts."

Since 1104, 21 eruptions have been recorded. That of 1300 rent the mountain from top to bottom in a tremendous explosion (the rent is today a deep and rugged valley). A major eruption in 1766 caused great loss of life. The 1947 eruption consisted of a violent series of explosions which tossed lava high into the air.

Helicon

A mountain group famous in classical legend. Location *Boeotia, eastern central Greece.* Height *5,736 feet* (*highest peak*). Map *7, F9.*

Almost opposite the city of Corinth, some 40 miles away across the Gulf, the mountain range of Helicon runs up to its highest peak in the western section of the mountains, which is known as Palaivouna, while the eastern section is called Zagora. For a number of reasons this was believed by the Greeks to be the abode of the Muses; Mount Parnassus lies close at hand, the highest and most imposing peak in the area, and the site of Helicon between Lake Copais (now drained) and the Gulf of Corinth is one of exceptional beauty, a fitting home for the goddesses of the arts. The mountain, whose eastern slopes are fertile, was credited with the possession of many healing herbs and it was said that no snakes were ever to be found on it.

In recent years French archeologists have excavated most of the classical site – the temple of the Muses which was set in a sacred grove still marked by the two famous fountains, Hippocrene and Aganippe. Classical legend proclaimed that Hippocrene ("Fountain of the Horse") was created by the stamping of the winged horse Pegasus. The fountain is still surrounded by an ancient wall and the water is pure and cold.

On a summer day, with the cool north wind blowing, the view from Helicon over the Gulf of Corinth makes one realize the genius of the Greeks in choosing it as a shrine to the Muses. To the northwest lies Parnassus; south is the city of Corinth with its ancient hill of the Acropolis behind it; eastwards lies the narrow neck of the Corinthian isthmus with all the Aegean Sea beyond. The poet Hesiod lived nearby at Ascra, a fact which added to the mountain's fame in ancient times.

Hermon, Mount

A snow-capped mountain massif; highest point in the Anti-Lebanon range. Location *Syria-Lebanon border.* Height *Rising to 9,232 feet.* Map *9, G2.*

Mount Hermon impresses by its bulk and isolation rather than by the more usual and dramatic mountain features of precipices and pointed peaks. It rises southwest of the main Anti-Lebanon range and part of the Syria-Lebanon border follows the line of its summit. The crest, which is about 20 miles long and rises at least 5,000 feet above the surrounding countryside, has three peaks of almost equal height only a few hundred yards apart. On the southernmost summit are the ruins of an ancient temple (called Qasr

Antar) to which St Jerome referred when he visited Syria in the fourth century. The surface of the top is composed of shingle and is devoid of vegetation. Snow covers the higher slopes in winter, spring and early summer. The Syrians know it as Jebel al Shaykh ("Grayhaired Mountain") or Jebel al Thalj ("Mountain of Snow"). Limestone prevails at the top, basalt at the lower levels. Fragments of white limestone litter the surface, especially in the southwest ravines, which fall steeply to the Jordan valley. The isolation of Hermon accounts probably for the presence of a variety of wild game, wolves (now uncommon), foxes, the Syrian bear and several birds of prey, including eagles, buzzards, kites and falcons. The western and southwest slopes are better watered than the eastern, and here are orchards, vineyards and scattered groups of oak trees.

The Old Testament frequently mentions Hermon both as a landmark and as a holy mountain. In Deuteronomy and Joshua it is referred to as forming part of the frontier between different groups of peoples; in the Psalms, God is praised for creating Hermon; and in the Song of Solomon there is a reference to the wild beasts found on its slopes. Some writers assert that this mountain was the scene of the Transfiguration of Christ. The ruins of many ancient temples built round the mountain attest its importance as a shrine; though most of these date from Graeco-Roman times, they are probably successors of earlier buildings erected on the same site. The earliest temples were dedicated to Baal, the Sun God, and Hermon's summit was considered as the seat of the deity. Sacrifices were made here until about the fifth century A.D. In the Middle Ages Christian and Arab armies swept round its flanks; early in the eleventh century it gave shelter to the dissident Islamic sect of the Druses, many of whom have continued to live in the region until the present day.

Hermon is not a difficult mountain to climb. It can be ascended either from Hasbeiya and Rasheiya on the west or from Arni in the east. It is a full day's walk to the summit and back;

many travelers have preferred to camp on the mountain and see the sunrise from the summit. The view from the top is very fine; it extends west to the Mediterranean, south to Mount Carmel, east and southeast to the plains round Damascus (25 miles away) and the Jebel Druse, and north to the Anti-Lebanon range and the Baalbek valley.

Himalayas

A great mountain system of Asia, containing the highest peaks in the world. Location *Northwest Pakistan, Kashmir, northern India, southern Tibet, Nepal, Sikkim and Bhutan.* Height *20,000 feet average (Great Himalayas); 7,000–15,000 feet (Lesser Himalayas); 2,000–5,000 feet (Outer Himalayas).* Map *11.*

Infinitely complicated, the Himalayas (or Himalaya, a Sanskrit word meaning Abode of Snow) run in a 1,500-mile shallow crescent between the great bend of the Indus in the west and that of the Brahmaputra in the east, bordered by the high plateau of Central Asia and the alluvial plains of the Indian subcontinent; they form a belt 100–150 miles wide. On the south they rise up from a series of parallel foothills which themselves stand out above the plains of India; on the north they drop sharply to the plateau of Tibet, of which they form the high, protruding rim. Geographically they are divided into four sections: the Punjab Himalayas, between the Indus and Sutlej rivers; the Kumaun Himalayas, between the Sutlej and Kali (Sarda) rivers; the Nepal Himalayas, between the Kali and Tista rivers, and the Assam Himalayas, between the Tista and Brahmaputra rivers. In the north they seldom fall below 18,000 feet, while towards the east they reach their highest point in Mount Everest. More than 30 peaks exceed 25,000 feet; a dozen rise to more than 26,000 feet. The Himalayas are sometimes considered to be structurally related to the Hindu Kush and Baluchistan ranges in the west and to the mountains of Sikang (China)

and western Burma in the east. In the far northwest, beyond the Indus bend, yet part of the Himalayan complex, rise the Karakoram, containing K2 (the second highest peak in the world) and the longest glaciers outside the Polar regions. The Indus separates the Himalayas not only from the Karakoram but also from the Ladakh and Kailas ranges, while the upper Brahmaputra forms a dividing line between the great range and the Kailas and Nyenchen Tanglha mountains.

Stretching almost as far as the distance between Moscow and London, the three longitudinal zones of the ranges are the Great Himalayas, perpetually snow-clad, with a height of about 20,000 feet, containing Mount Everest, Kanchenjunga, Makalu, Dhaulagiri, Nanga Parbat, Nanda Devi and Namcha Barwa; the Lesser Himalayas, which sometimes merge with the main range and enclose the valleys of Kashmir and Nepal; and the Outer Himalayas, consisting mainly of the Siwalik Range.

For historical and geographical reasons the exploration and conquest of the Himalayas began with the British, and British influence persisted even after the states of the vast sub-continent won their independence after the Second World War. The work of the Indian Survey which first mapped the highest peaks; the relative ease with which Indian Army officers could utilize their leave for climbs above the snowline; British preoccupation with Mount Everest for half a century; the chance that brought British air force officers and men to Kashmir towards the end of the last war – all these have helped to give Himalayan exploration an almost predominantly British background. Of course, mountaineers from many other nations – Americans, Swiss, Austrians, French, Germans, Japanese, more recently Russians and Chinese – have taken part in the great mountaineering adventures in the region.

Many of the native states, especially Tibet, for long excluded or severely restricted the entry of white men. This, allied to the constant fear of

Supposed footprint of the "Abominable Snowman," approximately twelve inches in length

stage of the major surveys and mapping of peaks. Among the many pioneers must be recorded the names of W. W. Graham, Sir Martin Conway, A. F. Mummery, Douglas W. Freshfield, and Dr Tom G. Longstaff together with Colonel Francis Younghusband and General C. G. Bruce.

The Second World War was to have a profound influence on Himalayan exploration. New materials, light-weight equipment, improved methods of using oxygen, all developed as a by-product of the war, greatly aided the post-war expeditions.

Today much of the Himalayas has been explored, mapped and climbed – but there are still many peaks to be ascended, many areas to be opened up to the mountaineer and the natural scientist, and the great mountain range still provides almost weekly reports of courage and endurance.

One problem as yet unsolved concerns the yeti, or "Abominable Snowman," the mysterious creature said to live above the snowline. Firmly believed in by the Nepalese, the Snowman has been dismissed by various authorities as being a bear, an ape, or simply a myth. But many expeditions have brought back tantalising reports of an unidentified animal heard, or seen briefly in the distance, and unexplained footprints – if they really are footprints – have been photographed. At least one expedition has been to the Himalayas for the sole purpose of solving the mystery – but a mystery it remains.

Russia, gave to much early Himalayan exploration a secret and quasi-military air.

This limiting of access to the great peaks gave a political air to the most innocent climbing expedition; this, in turn, led during the first half of the twentieth century to the preoccupation of certain countries with specific peaks. For a long time Britain was the only country allowed to send an expedition to Everest. The Italians concentrated on K2 and the Karakoram, while Nanga Parbat became for many years almost a German preserve.

Each portion of the Himalayas has its own tale of exploration to tell. Towards the end of the nineteenth century the development of serious mountaineering coincided with the significant

Hindu Kush

An important mountain system of Central Asia. Location *Northeast Afghanistan.* Height *Rising to 25,000 feet.* Map *10, B6.*

The Hindu Kush extends southwest for about 400 miles from the magnificent "Pamir Knot," the hub of great radiating ranges at the western end of the Karakoram, to central Afghanistan, near the Bamian Valley. It bars the way between Central Asia and the northern plains of the

Travelers in the Hindu Kush

Indian sub-continent. The eastern section, on the Afghanistan-Pakistan border, rivals the Karakoram in both the height of its peaks and the size of its glaciers. It is here that the Tirich Mir (25,263 feet), the highest peak, rises. In the western section the Hindu Kush is split into several outliers which cover most of central Afghanistan. These include the Band-i-Turkestan, the Hazarajat ranges, Koh-i-Baba, the Paropamisus Mountains, the Safed Koh and the Siah Koh. Within Afghanistan, the Hindu Kush forms the natural divide between Badakshan, Kataghan and Afghan Turkestan on the north and Nuristan and the Kabul and Jalalabad valleys in the south.

Forming, as it does, a barrier, the Hindu Kush is chiefly notable for the occasions upon which it has been crossed. By 1000 B.C. or earlier, the Aryan tribes had passed through to settle in the plains of the Indus and the Ganges, to produce what we know as Hindu civilization. Among innumerable pockets of different races and languages left in high and remote valleys by successive tides of invasion, the Dards, surprisingly European in appearance, were known to Sanskrit literature and to the geographers of Alexander the Great, who considered the Hindu Kush as a distant extension of the Caucasus. This is perhaps less far-fetched than might at first appear, if it is remembered that Dr Tom G. Longstaff, the great climber, was constantly reminded of the Caucasus in traveling among the mountains and glaciers of the eastern Hindu Kush. Even today direct descent from Alexander is a usual claim among the isolated aristocracy of Gilgit and the neighboring valleys. In songs and sayings folk-memories lightly bridge great chasms of time. A mysterious stone circle may be pointed out as "the work of Kafirs," embracing in one word all those who preceded the enlightenment of the Prophet. In the foothills of the Hindu Kush Buddhism left its records for the archeologist, for it was among the hills of the north-west corner of the Indian sub-continent that this great religion gathered its strength for proselytizing High Asia.

Both Alexander and Timur the Barlas Turk (Tamerlaine) are believed to have used the same pass, the Khawak. Other passes are the Baroghil, Dorah, and, near the western end, the Shikari Pass (used by the Kabul-Mazar-i-Sharif highway). But the watershed was never itself a frontier until modern times; and then only in the high eastern section, when the Russian advance to the Pamirs in the eighteen-eighties caused this to be demarcated as a "neutral" strip of Afghanistan. The country itself came into being politically as a buffer state where formerly Persian and Indian empires had washed against each other among a jetsam of unassimilable peoples. The founder of the Mogul dynasty in India, Baber – descendant of Timur and of the Mongol Genghiz Khan – was master of both sides of the Hindu Kush as King of Kabul before he invaded the Indian plains in 1526.

Today, in Pakistan's corner of the Hindu Kush, hitherto inaccessible places in the Swat valley are being developed for the more adventurous tourists. Pakistani climbers and mountain troops attack the formidable peaks and Pakistani pilots fly their planes through the dizzy gorges above the narrow strips of habitation.

Huascarán

An extinct volcano; the highest point in Peru. Location *Cordillera Blanca, western central Peru.* Height *22,205 feet.* Map *6, B5.* First climbed *Miss Annie S. Peck, 1908.*

In the north of Peru, running parallel with the coastline, lies perhaps the most spectacular range of peaks in the whole Andean chain, the Cordillera Blanca. Queen of a vast realm of snow- and ice-covered mountains which make this Cordillera a mountaineer's paradise is the twin-peaked Huascarán.

Although its ascent presents few technical difficulties, the altitude and distance involved make an attempt on the mountain a serious undertaking: it was long considered a great prize and even today, after several parties have reached its highest point, to have climbed it is a feat of which one may justly be proud.

From a ship traveling along the Pacific coast the massive form of the mountain can be seen white and shining far away beyond the mist and the green and brown of the foothills; it may be seen from the plaza of Yungay with the evening light waning on its massive folds of snow, or from the air, at dawn, towering above its satellites from a sea of clouds, like a rock reef rising from a gray lagoon.

Huascarán holds an interesting place in mountaineering history as one of the few major peaks in the world to be first ascended by a woman. It was Miss Annie S. Peck, a remarkable, tireless lady from Providence, Rhode Island, and an ardent feminist, who for most of the year taught Latin at Smith College and Purdue University and during the rest of the year went after the big mountains among the ranges of Europe and Central and South America. In 1904 Miss Peck reached a height of 20,500 feet on Illampu (Mount Sorata) in Bolivia. In 1908, when she was over 50, she visited the Andes again and this time fought her way successfully to the northern of Huascarán's formidable twin peaks. A natural gift for exaggeration displayed in her account led many to dispute the validity of her claim to the first ascent. A German party which reached the summit in 1932 claimed the prize as theirs, but history has been inclined to give Miss Peck the benefit of the doubt.

The south summit, which is the higher, has been ascended several times since the Second World War by American expeditions and others, most of which required two mountain camps. The route leads first to the saddle between the twin dome and then straight up.

The mountain may be reached from Lima via the Santa valley and the town of Yungay. From Yungay the way leads south of the Quebrada Yanganuco. Problems of access are minimal; porters with climbing experience who can also act as guides are now available.

Ida Mountains

A mountain range of volcanic origin. Location *Northwest Turkey*. Height *Rising to 5,797 feet in Mount Gargarus*. Map 7, G9.

The Ida Mountains or, as the Turks call them, the Kaz Dagi, run from north to south across the northwest peninsula of Asia Minor, just northwest of Edremit (Adramyttium) and south of the Kucuk Menderes (Scamander) River, the Meander of Homeric times, which drains the center of the Trojan plain. The site of ancient Troy lies to the northwest, on the Aegean Sea. Volcanic in origin, the Ida range has a number of hot springs which join the Menderes in the foothills. The range is about 40 miles long, the foothills running down from the main mass almost into the Hellespont. In many places its sides, in spite of centuries of deforestation, are still thick with pines; the plane, the ilex and the valonia oak grow on the western slopes. The mountains are visible from a great distance, for the air is crystal clear, especially in the summer when the *inbat*, or northerly wind, blows strongly from dawn to dusk. In the blue and cloudless sky the peak of Mount Gargarus still dominates the ruins of the city of Troy.

In ancient times Mount Ida was dedicated to the worship of Cybele, the Great Mother goddess of the ancient Phrygians. Here, according to legend, Paris gave his judgment in favor of Aphrodite, thus beginning the chain of events which led to the Trojan War.

Illimani

A peak of the Andes. Location *Cordillera de La Paz, western Bolivia*. Height *21,185 feet*. Map 6, D6. First climbed *Sir William Martin Conway, 1898*.

Illimani, the sentinel mountain of La Paz, the capital city of Bolivia, is on the great Altiplano, the core of the Andes. Here the range reaches its greatest breadth, spreading over an area of more

than 75,000 square miles. The plateau is one of the highest inhabited districts in the world. The peaks encircling it on the north, called the Cordillera Real or the Cordillera de La Paz, are far better known to mountaineers than are those to the south, and of them Illimani is the most famous.

When Sir William Martin Conway arrived in South America in 1898, his aim was to climb Illampu (Mount Sorata) and Illimani, at either end of the Cordillera Real. He crossed the cordilleras and then traveled across Lake Titicaca, the vast expanse of water nearly 13,000 feet above the sea, where, in his own words, he "wondered whether he was suffering from sea sickness or mountain sickness or both. . ."

Conway had trouble with the native porters, who deserted him when they came to steep rocks on the way to the high camp on Illimani, leaving only an old man and a boy of 16 with him. These two he induced to climb the more difficult pitches by holding out small silver coins for them to climb for; but when they came to ice, they refused to go on. Conway's two guides, Antoine Maquignaz and Louis Pelissier, had to carry very heavy loads on the last part of the climb to the camp. But next day, after a gruelling morning, they reached their goal and, as Conway put it, "I was, as it were, awakened from a dream by hearing Maquignaz invite me to take the lead and be first upon the summit."

It was not until 1950 that a group of climbers who had conquered both summits (the northern one for the first time) discovered that the latter was some hundred feet higher – so that Conway had actually made the first ascent of the lower peak.

Between these two dates there was a political incident connected with Illimani. In 1938 a group of three young Nazis had climbed the peak and planted a Swastika flag on it – though they maintained that they had really hoisted a Bolivian *and* a German flag. However, the members of the Andine Club at La Paz suspected the truth and confirmed their suspicions by a look through the big Observatory telescope of the Bolivian capital. They saw that the three German climbers had planted a strong pole and on it "a Swastika flag machine-sewn above the three Bolivian stripes, red, gold and green." They took a photograph of the party giving the Nazi salute and published it in a La Paz newspaper.

In 1940 E.S.G. de la Motte, a member of the British Alpine Club, persuaded a young Bolivian skier to accompany him in an attempt to climb Illimani and remove the flag. They reached the top, a nearly level ridge about 50 yards long, after two days hard climbing. De la Motte and his young companion removed it and descended safely "with the flag carefully folded and stowed in the rucksack."

Japanese Alps

A mountain group divided by rivers into three sections. Location *Honshu island, Japan.* Height *Rising to over 10,000 feet.* Map *10, J4.*

The Japanese Alps form the eastern boundary of the provinces of Hida and Etchin on the island of Honshu (or Hondo). They include or have in their immediate vicinity the highest peaks of Japan after Fujiyama, 15 of them over 10,000 feet. The highest point is Hodaka or Hotaka (10,527 feet) with On-take (10,450 feet) the second highest.

This jumbled massif constitutes the most imposing collection of mountains in the country. The ridge runs due north and south for about 140 miles and has a width of 60 miles; rivers divide it into northern, central and southern sectors. Only two of the mountains – Norikura and Tateyama – show clear traces of volcanic origin; the prevailing rock is granite. The lower flanks are covered with forests of beech, oak and coniferous trees.

The skilled mountaineer finds challenging climbs in many of the summits of the Japanese Alps, though none of the peaks is as difficult as many in the European Alps. Several – such as On-take – are climbed regularly each year by thousands of pilgrims, for their summits are considered sacred, the home of the gods. On the summit of On-take there are eight large and several small craters; here also may be seen displays of trance and "divine possession" by adepts in the "occult sciences."

The Rev. Murray Walton found the view from the summit of Hodaka especially striking. "The jagged edge," he wrote, "continues away to the south, rising and falling as it crosses peak after peak, but what is most impressive is the long sweep culminating in Mae-Hodaka itself. From this aspect it looked even grander than Yari, and might well be called the Matterhorn of Japan."

The Japanese Alps provided scope for much mountaineering activity before and after the Second World War for both Western visitors and the Japanese themselves. Several members of the imperial family, including the late Prince Chichibu, have been devoted followers of the sport. This has created a mountaineering fashion, followed by marked trails, huts and the organization of trained guides. It is in the Japanese Alps that the universal climber's invocation was born, addressed to the ancestral gods: "May our five senses be pure and may the weather on the honourable mountain be fine."

Jostedalsbre

The largest icefield (340 square miles) on the European mainland. Location *Western Norway.* Height *Rising to 6,700 feet.* Map *7, D4.*

This icefield (*bre*) can be regarded as a relic of a much greater ice-sheet which covered Scandinavia during the last glacial epoch. It lies throughout at a high level and the ice-sheet is believed to be over 1,000 feet thick in parts. The main icefield sends down a number of steep glacier lobes into the surrounding valleys in which there are numerous lakes, themselves the drainage relics of the former extended glaciers. The valleys are among the grandest and wildest to be found in Norway; they dissect the land deeply as they extend to Sogne Fjord, Nord Fjord and Stor Fjord. Those areas of the field between 3,000 and 6,000 feet which are now free of ice are notable for their barrenness. Great stretches of smooth, rounded old land-forms, scored and polished by earlier ice action, scattered often with boulders and gravel, supporting very little grass, moss or lichens, and interspersed with many lakes – such is the high, ice-free field of much of this part of Norway.

The Jostedalsbre itself has always constituted a great natural barrier to communication between the surrounding districts; but there exist certain standard routes across its undulating ice surface – such as the one between Jostedal on the east and Loen or Strynsvatn at the head of Nord Fjord. These traverses are not to be undertaken lightly, except by hardy walkers and mountaineers, and fine weather is essential. The descent by the outlet glaciers, which are often crevassed, may be difficult in some cases and especially dangerous in fog.

W. Cecil Slingsby made a pioneer crossing of the Jostedalsbre, accompanied by the Norwegian schoolmaster, Johannes Vigdal. His account gives some indication of the dangers and difficulties of such a traverse: "Immediately in front of us were two narrow towers of ice 25 to 30 feet high and about 12 feet apart; the lower one was perched on the top of the cliff, and each seemed ready to fall at any moment. Between these we had to go; there was no other way. The passage through was only about 20 yards, but what terrible yards! Vigdal said he dared not go, but though I thought of his wife and children, I said sternly, 'We must go, come on, don't waste a moment.' We had to go astraddle along a sharp ridge of ice, and climb up and down very steep ice with the dread towers and huge icicles overhanging us. Once the rope got round a knob; the agony of the few seconds we spent in disentangling it was intense. In fact I never had such anxious moments as during the five minutes we spent between these icy walls. . ."

Jotunheim Mountains

The highest mountain massif in Scandinavia. Location *Southern central Norway.* Height *Average 6,000 feet, rising to 8,097 feet.* Map 7, *D4.* First explored *Bathasar Matthias Keilhau, the geologist, in the eighteen-twenties.*

Jotunheim ("Home of Giants"), or Jotun Fjelde, the great mountainous region of southern Norway, lies between Gudbrandsdal on the east and Jostedalsbre and the head of Sogne Fjord on the west. Here are the highest mountains of the Scandinavian peninsula – Galdhoppigen (8,097 feet), 80 miles northwest of Lillehammer; Glittertind (8,048 feet), Skagastolstind (7,887 feet) and Knutshulstind (7,680 feet). Steinbusjo, Bygdin and Vinsteren lakes are on the southern slopes of the massif. The upper parts of the valleys have a characteristic form, not ending in lofty mountain walls but comparatively low and level, bearing lakes.

The crescent-shaped chain of hard volcanic rock-masses extends about 120 miles north of the head of the 100-mile-long Sogne Fjord. The sharpness of peaks like Galdhoppigen and the magnificent Horunger, southwest of the main group, is accentuated by the deep narrow valleys which lie between them. There are several glaciers and many of the peaks are deeply scored by their movement. In the southwest the second highest waterfall of Europe, Vettisfoss, falls 900 feet from the edge of the mountains into an inlet of Sogne Fjord.

In the Old Norse myths Jotunheim was the land of the giants, encircling the sea; the end of the world – Ragnarok, the Twilight of the Gods – was supposed to come when the giants emerged from Jotunheim and crossed the great sea to Midgard, the world of men. The name was attached to this region in the early nineteenth century and although the only legendary significance of the mountains lies in their borrowed name, they have repeatedly stimulated the Norwegian literary imagination, notably to provide Ibsen with a romantic, troll-haunted background for the exploits of Peer Gynt.

W. Cecil Slingsby, the "Father of Norwegian Mountaineering" first saw Skagastolstind in 1872 and resolved "to make it my own." He made three attempts on the mountain – one with his sister – until in 1876 he reached the summit, though his two Norwegian companions deserted him 508 feet from the summit. "I climbed the rest," Slingsby wrote, "all rock and very tough, quite alone. I certainly should not have attempted rocks such as those when alone upon any other mountain but Skagastolstind; but it was the particular peak on which I had concentrated my energies and that solitary climb I shall always look back upon with a feeling of veneration, as it formed an event in my life which can never be forgotten."

Skrlatica, in the Julian Alps

Julian Alps

A mountain group within the Eastern Alps. Location *Northwest Yugoslavia and northeast Italy.* Height *Averaging 8,000 feet, rising to 9,395 feet.* Map *8, H8.*

The Julian Alps extend southeast from the Carnic Alps at Tarvisio to the Ljubljana area; they are bounded on the north by the Karawanken Range, on the northwest by the Fella River and Camporosso Pass and on the east by the upper Sava River. The Predil Pass, which leads from Villach via Tarvis and Flitsch to Gorizia, at a height of 3,813 feet, divides the Julian Alps into two subgroups. The range constitutes part of the watershed between the Adriatic and the Black Sea. The Julian Alps, are, in effect, the result of the Alps' final struggle to remain a mountain range before they give up the effort and peter out in the plains of Hungary.

Their western part is pleasant but at first undistinguished sub-Alpine country. Only when the limestone suddenly sweeps up into the massive bulk of Triglav, their highest point (9,395 feet), is there a final display of mountain majesty. With one huge face almost two miles wide and some 3,000 feet high, the peak is truly spectacular. The surroundings are rich in flowers. Other peaks include the Jof del Montasio, Skrlatica, Mount Mangart, Jalovec, Mount Canin and Krn. Among the high intermontane valleys the Planica, Trenta, Vrata, Kot and Krma are the most important. Though less massive, these mountains and valleys are rugged and sometimes almost dolomitic in their jagged outlines. There are tourist resorts on the Bled and Bohinj lakes.

Triglav was first ascended in 1778; it presents no special difficulty and for nearly a century the normal route to the summit has been festooned with all manner of artificial aids.

Jungfrau

A great Alpine peak with the highest point reached by railway in Europe. Location *Bernese Oberland, southern central Switzerland.* Height *13,653 feet.* Map *8, C8.* First climbed *the Meyer brothers of Aarau, 1811.*

There are few sights in the world to compare with

the sudden revelation of the Jungfrau that can be gained from the neighborhood of Wengen or from Interlaken.

"The Jungfrau, covered with an eternal shroud of snow, now appears in all its majesty," wrote Karl Baedeker nearly a century ago about the justly-named "Queen of the Bernese Oberland." "Its proportions are so gigantic that the traveler is bewildered in his vain attempts to compute them; distance is annihilated by their vastness. The summits and higher peaks are covered with snow of dazzling whiteness; the lower and less precipitous slopes also present a boundless expanse of snow and glaciers."

This is still the impression created by the shimmering white north face of the "Virgin" that forms such a setpiece of the Oberland. Neither Guyer-Zeller's railway, boring up through its $4\frac{3}{4}$-mile tunnel to the Jungfraujoch (11,412 feet), nor the station and hotel built into this high col some 2,000 feet below the summit can destroy the majesty of the natural scene.

The Jungfrau, with its eastern neighbor, the Mönch, forms the northern rim of the huge snow basin which slopes away to the south and feeds the Aletsch Glacier. It was from this side that the mountain was first climbed by the Meyer brothers, who reached the Rothal-Sattel due

The Jungfrau

south of the summit and then climbed the long, steep snow- and ice-slope which led up from it. In 1812 Gottlieb Meyer repeated the feat. Both ascents were made from the eastern or Valais side, the foot of which was reached in 1828 over the Mönchjoch by six peasants from Grindelwald. In 1841 Professor J. D. Forbes, with the three scientists, Agassiz, Desor and Duchatelier, made the fourth ascent by the 1812 route. It was not until 1865 that Sir George Young and the Rev. H. B. George succeeded in making the far more difficult ascent from the western or Interlaken side.

Today the Rothal-Sattel is most frequently reached from the comforts of the Berghaus, the hotel built into the rocks of the Jungfraujoch at the upper terminus of the railway which was constructed between 1896 and 1912. Lines from Grindelwald and Lauterbrunnen meet at the Little Scheidegg, 6,770 feet up, on a northern spur thrust out by the Jungfrau, and from here the line mounts to the Eigergletscher station before entering the tunnel which brings it to the Jungfraujoch station. Built into the Sphinx, a minor ridge above, and joined to the railway station and hotel by tunnels and a lift, lie a meteorological station and an observatory.

Jura

A mountain range of parallel folded ridges. Location *Franco-Swiss border.* Height *2,000–3,000 feet, rising to 5,652 feet.* Map *8, B7.*

This long stretch of upland country, whose limestone formation has given the Jurassic period its name, consists of a massive rectangle some 160 miles by 40, more plateau than range. Extending from the Rhône River gorge in the south to the Rhine near Basel in the northeast, it is cut by several deep transverse gorges known locally as "cluses" which are a feature of the pleasant, pine-forested scenery. These were created by the vast internal forces which helped raise the Jura to their average height of between 2,000 and 3,000

feet. There are rivers, often disappearing underground, and numerous caves. Geologically, the Jura belong to the Alpine system.

A certain cragginess marks much of the Jura scenery, while the ridges rise to Mont Tendre (5,520 feet) in Switzerland and to the Crêt de la Neige (5,652 feet) in France. Other peaks include Mont Reculet (5,643 feet) in France and Mont Dole (5,513 feet) in Switzerland. Switzerland has the lion's share of the Jura, although the northern, French, slopes are the more important topographically, particularly in the east, where they overlook the Belfort Gap, a nodal point of military strategy in Western Europe.

The chief passes of the Jura are the Col de la Faucille (4,340 feet) and the "cluse" of Pontarlier. The steep eastern slopes overlook the lakes of Geneva, Neuchâtel and Biel and the Aar River valley. The Doubs, Loue and Ain rivers, which rise in the Jura, drain longitudinal valleys on the French side; on the northwest and west the uplands are bounded by the Doubs and Saône river valleys. Moderation is the characteristic of the scenery, and its rocky outcrops attract but do not terrify. Rivers provide just the right amount of sport and there is a nice modicum of spectacle and places of historic interest.

Pastoral and forest industries predominate; but the Jura are also the home of the famous Swiss watch-making industry; an industry initially based on home labor, demanding even now little heavy machinery – a clean industry well fitted to the country of attractive small towns that the Jura has contrived to remain. Le Locle and La Chaux-de-Fonds are the main watch-making centers. The former claims priority in the foundation of the industry by Daniel-Jean Richard in 1705. Today the town boasts a technical school and the headquarters of the Chamber of the Swiss Watch and Clock Industry.

K2

The second highest mountain in the world. Location *Karakoram, northern Kashmir.* Height *28,250 feet.*

Map *11, D3*. First climbed *Achille Compagnoni and Lino Lacedelli, 1954.*

K2's position, some 70 miles northwest of Skardu in Kashmir, was first fixed in 1858, following work by officers of the Topographical Survey of India, who subsequently found that the summit designated K2 in their records was, in fact, the second highest in the world. Three years later Col. Henry Haversham Godwin-Austen reconnoitered its approaches and sketched a few of its details from a spur of Masherbrum. The peak is often called Mount Godwin Austen after him, but this name has never been officially adopted, and K2, which seems to have caught the imagination of climbers, is the more usual designation. The local name is Chogori or Dapsang. It was for long considered to be unclimbable – not only because of its enormous height but because it towered 12,000 feet above its glaciers in a sheer, unbroken pyramid of rock and ice. Its ridges were little better than cliffs; its faces bristled with precipices and overhangs; along its entire sweep there seemed to be no single spot level enough to hold even the smallest camp.

Lord Conway of Allington climbed up the great glaciers in 1892 but was content to look at K2 from a distance, describing "the majesty of K2 . . . almost too brilliant for the eye to rest upon in its mantle of sunlit white. It was clear from base to summit, a broad and heavy mass, four-faced and four-ridged like the Great Pyramid, inaccessible by any route that we could see, and, as was afterwards proved, impregnable also on the other side. . . Here for me the glory of this transcendent scenery culminated." Dr and Mrs William Hunter Workman also confined their climbing to lesser peaks between 1899 and 1908. The first real attempt was made in 1902 by a mixed party of English, Swiss and Austrian climbers, who were forced to turn back at 21,000 feet from the northeast spur. The Duke of Abruzzi organized an elaborate expedition in 1909 with the express purpose of conquering the great peak. He made two attempts; the first ended at 20,000 feet on the southeast ridge, the second at about 21,800 feet on the northwest. The Duke, too, had to admit defeat.

There was a second Italian expedition 20 years later. A further attempt was made in 1934 by Dyhrenfurth and his party, and this was followed by three expeditions from the American Alpine Club in 1938, 1939 and 1953. The 1938 party was led by Dr Charles Houston with Richard Burdsall, Robert Bates, William House and Paul Petzold as his companions. They reached almost 25,000 feet, but lack of supplies and the danger of storms stopped them under the 2,500-foot summit-pyramid. They made one last try which carried them to almost 26,000 feet – but then they had to turn back. The second American expedition was led by Fritz Wiessner, accompanied by Jack Durrance, Dudley Wolfe, Eaton Cromwell, Chappell Cranmer and George Sheldon, with a British transport officer, nine Sherpas and a large group of local coolies. Two men – Wiessner and the Sherpa Pasang Lama – made the final assault; but only 750 feet below the summit Pasang Lama refused to go on and Wiessner had to turn back. A second attempt was also frustrated, and during the descent four members of the party died of exposure.

In 1953 Houston led the third American expedition with Bates as second in command; George Bell, Robert Craig, Arthur Gilkey, Dee Molenaar and Peter Schoening, all younger men and outstanding climbers, completed the American party. Their British liaison officer was Captain Anthony Streather, himself an experienced mountaineer. But this well-equipped and well-prepared expedition was defeated by the weather. Gilkey was stricken by thrombo-phlebitis; during the descent several of the party fell (though luckily their ropes held) and Gilkey, helplessly strapped to a stretcher, was swept away by an avalanche.

Victory came at last in 1954. The Italian expedition, led by Ardito Desio, professor of geology at Milan University, was one of the largest and best-equipped in Himalayan history. More

K2 (photograph by Vittorio Sella, 1

than 500 porters helped the 11 climbers and six scientists to move towards the base of the mountain. But even this did not ensure a smooth journey. Many of the porters deserted; Mario Puchez, a professional guide and one of the best climbers, died of pneumonia. Storms raged for 40 days.

Camp 8 was set up at a height of 25,000 feet. Then Achille Compagnoni and Lino Lacedelli, the chosen "summit team," pitched a single tent at 26,600 feet from which to make a final attempt. The weather remained fine, but they had to struggle through deep snow with serious danger of avalanches and made slow, painful progress. Then, at 800 feet below the summit, their oxygen supply ran out. Still they fought on, and when at last they reached the final height they fell, gasping and choking, into the snow. They recovered to break the Italian and Pakistani flags from an ice-axe on the highest point, took photographs and for half an hour enjoyed the superb view from the summit.

The descent was scarcely less perilous; almost all of it was made in darkness. Once they were caught in an avalanche and almost carried away. Later one of them fell for 30 feet down a wall of ice. But at last they reached Camp 8 and their companions.

Kailas

An unclimbed holy mountain. Location *Southwest Tibet, in the Kailas Range.* Height *22,028 feet.* Map *11, E4.* Explored *Col. R. C. Wilson, 1926.*

Kailas, famous in Sanskrit literature as the Paradise of Siva and Parvati, is a trans-Himalayan mountain immediately north of the two lakes, Rakas Tal and Manasarowar – or, as the Tibetans call them, Langak Tso and Mapham Tso. Manasarowar, at about 14,950 feet, and Rakas Tal, 50 feet lower, are separated by an isthmus cut through by a dry watercourse which occasionally takes an overflow from one to the other. Mountain and lakes are sacred to both Tibetans and Hindus, because the four rivers, Indus,

Sutlej, Ganges (Humla Karnali) and Tsangpo (the Tibetan Brahmaputra) all rise within 40 miles of them; Hindus, in fact, incorrectly assert that the Ganges has a source in the lake itself – as indeed, it may once have had, in the distant past.

Kailas appears in the Mahabharata writings of the Hindus as Kailasa; it is known to Tibetans as Kang-rim-poche and is holier to them than either Gauri Sankar or Chomo Lhari. Sven Hedin, the Swedish explorer, regarded it as the most famous mountain in the world. It first appeared on d'Anville's map of Tibet, part of his great Atlas of China (published in 1735), and was probably seen by the Portuguese Jesuits who founded a Christian Church at Tsaparang near the headwaters of the Sutlej in 1626. D'Anville's name for it was Kontaisse; Klaproth in 1828 showed it as Gang-dis-ri. Sarat Chandra Das' Tibetan dictionary gave it as Tisre; these are all corruptions of an old Tibetan name.

No European explorers reached the lakes before William Moorcroft in 1812 but Richard and Henry Strachey, who visited them about 1846, were the first to describe the physical geography. Pundit Main Singh sketched the topography in 1866; Major C. H. D. Ryder fixed the mountain's position and height on his journey from Lhasa to Simla after the Younghusband Mission to Tibet in 1904. Ryder's party mapped the sources of all the rivers which rise in the Manasarowar region. Other travelers who visited it included C. A. Sherring, a deputy commissioner, with Dr T. G. Longstaff in 1905; Sherring described Kailas and the pilgrimage attached to the mountain.

Old men and women, Buddhist and Hindu, attain "great merit" by making a circuit of Kailas, over high passes – the highest of which is over 18,000 feet – a distance of 25 miles, in three days. The most fanatical pilgrims carry out their circuit by prostrating themselves, stretching out their arms and making a mark with metal-tipped gloves, rising, walking to the mark and prostrating themselves again. This takes three weeks and the exhausted pilgrims are often known to sleep in their tracks.

Hugh Ruttledge, his wife and Col. R. C. Wilson, while on a mission to Tibet in 1926, were the first Europeans to complete the *parikarma* or sacred circuit. Though no attempt has been made to climb Kailas (and permission to do so would probably never be given), Wilson examined the south, southwest and west faces of the mountain. He considered that an ascent by the east ridge was the most practicable. No detailed survey of the mountain has yet been made.

Kamet

A major peak of the Himalayas. Location *Kaskar Range, northern Uttar Pradesh, India.* Height *25,447 feet.* Map *11, D5.* First climbed *Frank S. Smythe, Eric Shipton and Sherpa Lewa, 1931.*

Kamet was the first of the Himalayan giants over 25,000 feet to be climbed. It is in the Central Himalayas but lies well to the north of the main axis of the range and does not receive the full force of the monsoon. The surrounding country is barren and its valleys lack the dense forest found farther south. Because it was situated in British India, it was accessible to Western travelers and more attempts had been made on it before it was eventually climbed than on any other Himalayan peak. The first of these was made as long ago as 1855 by the redoubtable pioneers, Adolf and Robert Schlagintweit, while they were engaged in a magnetic survey of the area. Approaching the mountain from the north, they reached a height of 22,250 feet – a remarkable performance considering that this was before many Alpine mountains had been climbed. Nearly half a century passed before another serious attempt was made on a major Himalayan peak.

The next reconnaissance was made in 1907 by Dr T. G. Longstaff, C. G. Bruce and A. L. Mumm, with two Italian guides. They approached the mountain first by way of the East Kamet Glacier and later from the west. Bad weather made their reconnaissances inconclusive but they decided that the western side offered the best hope of success. In 1911 and 1913 attempts were made on this side by A. M. Slingsby.

Though on both occasions he was accompanied only by a local man, untrained in mountaineering, he reached an altitude of 23,000 feet on a subsidiary peak known as Abi Gamin.

C. F. Meade made three attacks on Kamet and eventually discovered a practicable route to the summit. In 1910, accompanied by two alpine guides, he made his approach from the Khairam Glacier on the west but, partly because of bad weather, did not make much headway. In 1912, with four alpine guides, he followed Slingsby's route and also reached 23,000 feet. Later that year he went round to the east, where he found that there was, after all, a promising line of attack from the East Kamet Glacier. In the following year he returned with the French guide, Pierre Blanc, and succeeded in reaching a col (now called Meade's Col), 23,500 feet high, between Abi Gamin and Kamet. This attempt was repeated in 1920 by A. M. Kellas and H. T. Morshead, who also reached Meade's Col.

In 1931 Kamet was climbed by an expedition composed of six British climbers, F. S. Smythe (leader), E. B. Beauman, R. L. Holdsworth, R. Greene, E. St J. Birnie and Eric Shipton, with eight Sherpas, following Meade's route. Base camp was established on June 8th. The chief mountaineering obstacle was a 1,000-foot wall of rock and ice above Camp 3 (20,700 feet) which took six days to surmount. Camp 5 was established below Meade's Col at 23,200 feet on June 20th, and the following day the summit was reached by Smythe, Shipton, Holdsworth and Sherpa Lewa – first to set foot on the summit – at 4.30 p.m. The climb from Camp 5 took 8½ hours, nearly half of which had been spent on the last 500 feet. Lewa's feet were severely frostbitten. Two days later the summit was again reached by Birnie, Greene and a Bhotia porter named Kesar Singh. In 1955 Kamet was climbed again by an Indian expedition led by N. D. Jayal.

Kanchenjunga

The third highest mountain in the world. Location
*Singalila Range, eastern Nepal Himalayas, Nepal-
Sikkim border. Height 28,146 feet. Map 11,F5.
First climbed George Band and Joe Brown, 1955.*

Kanchenjunga (formerly known as Kinchin-
junga and sometimes spelled Kangchenjunga) is
unique in one particular: it is the only peak
whose topmost few feet have been kept inviolate
solely to spare religious feelings – the successful
British expedition of 1955 having stopped within
seven feet of the actual summit.

The peak rises on the frontiers of Nepal and
Sikkim as a mass of narrow ice-clad ridges whose
length and difficulty more than compensate for
the comparative ease with which they can be
approached. It is some 105 miles northwest of
Darjeeling, and its main features can be discerned
in some detail from about 50 miles away during
good weather. It is the culmination of a huge
massif from which there fall some of the largest
avalanches in the world.

The southern approaches of the great mountain were explored by Sir Joseph Hooker, the
botanist, in 1848. Other expeditions followed
until, in 1883, W. W. Graham made his climbs
on Kabru and other nearby peaks, the first purely
mountaineering ventures in the district. In 1899
Douglas Freshfield set out from Darjeeling with
the photographer Vittorio Sella and a few other
companions, making a leisurely circuit of the
whole mountain; they were the first Westerners
to look upon it from any but the southern side.
It took seven weeks and was a dangerous, exhausting journey; but his investigation was so
thorough that Freshfield's Circuit remains a
classic model for mountain exploration. He
thought, however, that Kanchenjunga was
"guarded by the Demon of Inaccessibility."

The first disastrous attempt to climb "The Five
Treasures of the Snow," as the local people call
it, was made in 1905 when Swiss, French and
British mountaineers pitched camp more than
20,000 feet up on the southwest face. But their
luck gave out and four members of the party
were killed by an avalanche.

For more than 20 years no further attempts
were made on the mountain although the surrounding peaks were investigated, notably by the
tireless Dr A. M. Kellas in the early twentieth
century and by C. G. Crawford and Harold
Raeburn in 1920. Three attempts were then
made in quick succession. In May, 1929, E. F.
Farmer, a young American climber from New
Rochelle, New York, set out accompanied by a
few porters. His companions soon gave up but
Farmer continued alone. He was never seen
again. Paul Bauer of Munich led another expedition in the same year, composed of the most
brilliant German climbers of the time. Their
"feats without parallel" as the British *Alpine
Journal* described them, came to naught even
though they had invented quite new techniques
of mountaineering, boring shafts through towers
and cornices or hacking them away entirely when
they could not surmount them by ordinary step-
cutting. The weather turned against them and
they survived only by extraordinary skill and
courage. Professor G. O. Dyhrenfurth and his

*George Band climbing near the summit
of Kanchenjunga*

companions set out in the spring of 1930; they made an international expedition from half the countries of Western Europe. But Dyhrenfurth and his men fared even worse than their immediate predecessors. An immense avalanche crashed down and it was only by a miracle that the whole expedition was not wiped out. Even so, Chettan, one of the outstanding Sherpa porters, was caught beneath a crumbling ice-wall and crushed to death.

In mid-July, 1931, Bauer and his fellow Bavarians returned to the attack. Once again they were frustrated. Hermann Schaller, one of the strongest members of the party, and a porter were killed and when Hans Hartmann and Dr Karl Wien pushed up to the very summit of the northeast spur at a height of 26,220 feet – higher than any man had ever gone before except on Everest – they found that the last slope was impassable; a steep wall of ice and snow; to venture on to it would have meant certain death. Sadly they turned back within sight of their goal.

No further close reconnaissance of the mountain was made until 1951, when a British party inspected the southwest face which had been prospected in 1905. The same group made a detailed reconnaissance of the face in 1953 and 1954. Next year a small British party went out under Charles Evans to climb the mountain. Although they were to attack the Nepalese flank, the Sikkimese – as they learned when about to leave London – strongly objected to the attempt since they regarded the mountain as sacred.

Eventually Evans and the Sikkimese authorities arrived at a compromise. The party would climb only far enough to ensure that a route to the actual summit was possible; and they would, in any case, not set foot upon the summit itself.

When George Band and Joe Brown (a rock climber of almost startling ability) came close to the summit, they found their way barred by a smooth nose of rock.

"When we reached it," George Band said later, "we went round the corner, up a little gully and there – in front of us – the wall was vertical, ending in a slight overhang, but seamed by a series of vertical cracks. Brown chose one of these cracks, and by a very fine feat got up to the top, having turned the oxygen valve full on for the tremendous effort required. We still had no idea of how far we had to go, and so I was extremely surprised when from that position Brown turned round and shouted out: 'George, we're there!' When I in turn climbed up and joined him, there in front of us, 20 feet away and five feet higher than the ground on which we stood, was the summit, a gently sloping cone of snow. We had come as far as we were allowed."

Karakoram

A great mountain system comprising four ranges. Location *Northern Kashmir, near the Afghanistan border.* Height *Average 18,000 feet, rising to 28,250 feet in K2.* Map *11, D3-4.*

The Karakoram (or Karakorum) extends about 300 miles from the Afghanistan border southeast to the main bend of the Shyok Range. It is the most heavily glaciated region outside sub-polar latitudes and contains some of the highest peaks and longest glaciers in the world.

The main range, called Great Karakoram or Muztagh-Karakoram, extends for about 280 miles and for much of its length is the main divide between the drainage to the Indus and Indian Ocean on the south and to the Yarkand River and the deserts of Central Asia on the north. Except where the Hunza River cuts a deep gorge near its western end the range rarely falls below 18,000 feet; and on it and the Lesser Karakoram ranges there are no fewer than 19 measured peaks above 25,000 feet, including K2, the second highest in the world at 28,250 feet. In this vast ice-world descend long glaciers – the Siachen, 47 miles long, the Baltoro and Batura, each 36 miles, and the combined Hispar-Biafo, a 76-mile ice passage, connected by the Hispar pass.

The Aghil-Karakoram Range runs laterally

from the China border southeast to the head-waters of the Kara Kash River; it consists of a series of ranges connected by high tablelands with an average altitude of 20,350 feet. On the northwest it is continued by the Muztagh Ata Range. Another lateral range, the Kailas-Kara-koram, runs parallel with the main range for about 200 miles from the Hunza River bend southeast to the main bend of the Shyok River.

It contains four groups extending northwest to southeast: Rakaposhi, Haramosh, Masherbrum and Saltoro, which are considered sub-ranges. The average altitude of the Kailas-Karakoram is 18,000-19,700 feet; on the southeast are the Chang Chenmo and Pangong extension ranges.

Finally the Ladakh Range stretches from the mouth of the Shyok River to Tibet. It extends for about 230 miles, running parallel with the right

A moraine lake in the Karakoram
(photograph by Vittorio Sella, 1909)

bank of the Indus and rising to a crest-line of 20,000 feet. The Deosai Mountains in the western part of the Punjab Himalayas are regarded as its trans-Indus extension.

Except for the main valleys – the Hunza valley and its tributaries Shimshal and Chapursan on the west, Shigar and Nubra in the center and east and other secluded approach valleys from the Indus and Shyok on the south – almost the whole area of the Karakoram is uninhabited. Travel is still difficult, especially from July to September, when the rivers rise with the melting ice and snow. In winter the traveler can keep to valley floors, but in the summer months he may often be forced to follow paths built in pegs and props driven into the gorge walls or to cross the flooded rivers on slender bridges of rope and twigs, or on rafts of hide. Of the two main routes to Central Asia the western follows the Hunza gorge and crosses either the Mintaka (15,450 feet) or Kilik (15,600 feet) passes to the Pamirs and Soviet Asia; the eastern, from Kashmir and Ladakh, takes the Nubra valley to Panamil, crossing the Great Karakoram by the Saser pass (17,480 feet) and then the Karakoram pass (18,605 feet) to Yarkand and Kashgar. Between these two routes, passable at favorable seasons for pack animals but dangerous in blizzards, there have long been reports of a few difficult routes across the main ranges, used by hardy Hunza raiders from the west or by occasional travelers in times of political disturbance.

Because the Karakoram is beyond the Punjab Himalayas, the southwesterly monsoon from June to September is far less active than farther east in the Nepal Himalayas. In the "rain-shadowed" valleys, deep in the range, the average annual precipitation is less than ten inches, but the mountains and passes get much more, both from western disturbances in late winter and spring and from occasional monsoon incursions in July and August. Yet these are probably the best months for high mountaineering, though one must be prepared for spells of bad weather and local storms on the heights when for a week or

ten days all progress is impossible. In fine weather the winds at high altitude are normally from the west.

The Karakoram was first visited by adventurous European travelers during the first half of the nineteenth century. They included Alexander Gardner, William Moorcroft, G. T. Vigne, Richard and Henry Strachey, Dr Thomas Thomson and Alexander Cunningham. Then came the surveyors from India: Captain T. G. Montgomerie (1856), Col. Henry Haversham Godwin-Austen (the first to explore the great southern glaciers Chogo Lungma, Kiafo, Panmah and Baltoro in 1861), and their principal assistants, Beverley, Brownlow, Shelverton, Ryall and Johnson, who shared with them the pioneer observations and exploration.

The trans-Asian journey of Col. Francis Younghusband from Peking to India in 1887, when he crossed the unknown Muztagh pass over the Great Karakoram, was a landmark in travel in the great range. A British Agency was established at Gilgit by Algernon Durand, and Younghusband made two more journeys. The tribesmen were pacified after the Hunza-Nagir campaign in 1891. The following year George Cockerill of the Gilgit garrison explored the Hunza valleys and discovered the great pinnacled glaciers which descend the northern flanks of the main range and the double-headed Distaghil, highest peak west of the K2 group. In the summer of that year Sir William Martin Conway led, for the first time, a large party of Europeans into the ice-locked wilderness. The purpose of the party was exploration rather than pure mountaineering, but they included among their exploits the ascent of Pioneer Peak.

During the next two decades there was much activity in various sections of the range. Douglas Freshfield made his adventurous circuit of Kanchenjunga. Dr and Mrs William Hunter Workman, a remarkable American couple who became mountaineers in advanced middle age and made no less than six major Himalayan expeditions between 1899 and 1912, also explored the

Karakoram and adjoining ranges. Dr Workman made his highest ascent on Pyramid Peak at the age of 56 and Mrs Workman, at 47, set a world's climbing record for women at 23,000 feet which stood unchallenged for 28 years.

In 1909 Dr T. G. Longstaff crossed the almost legendary Saltoro pass to the Siachen glacier, discovering its great length and the mountain groups at its head. Two Italian expeditions led by the Duke of Abruzzi to K2 in 1909 and by De Filippi to Rimo glacier in 1913–14 also added a great deal to geographical and physiological knowledge at high altitudes. In the inter-war period Kenneth Mason in 1926, Ardito Desio of the Duke of Spoleto's expedition in 1929, Khan Sahib Afraz Gul in 1935, and, above all, Eric Shipton and Michael Spender in 1937, completed the exploration and survey of the northern flanks and glaciers of the range. During this period the detailed reconnaissance of routes to the highest summits also began.

Since the Second World War, K2, Gasherbrum I, II and IV, Broad Peak and Rakaposhi have all been conquered. But there are still many unclimbed peaks in the Karakoram.

Katmai Volcano

A subarctic volcano in Katmai National Monument. Location *Southern Alaska, near the head of the Alaska Peninsula.* Height *7,000 feet.* Map *3, B6.* First explored *Expedition led by Dr Robert F. Griggs, 1915–16.*

Katmai stands 100 miles west-northwest of Kodiak. Its crater is eight miles in circumference and 3,700 feet deep. Within the crater there is a lake with a small island; the walls are glacier-covered.

Up to July 6, 1912, the volcano rose above a beautiful, unnamed valley which was 15 miles long and four miles wide, stretching away to the northwest, its floor and sides covered with poplar, birch and spruce, roamed by moose and bear. Katmai was serene among its glacier-clad volcanic neighbors. Then, at 1 p.m., without warning, it exploded in one of the greatest eruptions of historical times. In three days the mountain was reduced to a jagged stump, its heart a huge crater, and the beautiful nameless valley, showered with incandescent sand, its floor rent with sulphuric fissures, had become the Valley of Ten Thousand Smokes. Nearby Kodiak Island was showered with ash. To the natives and the few white people living in the villages of Katmai and Kodiak the eruption was a time of terror; for three years no white man set eyes on the cause of their fear.

In 1915 Dr Robert F. Griggs, leader of the first of a series of the American National Geographic Society expeditions to Katmai, made his way with difficulty to the base of the shattered mountain. He saw a once-great peak destroyed. The next year, during further reconnaissance, he rounded a hill to behold what he described as one of the most amazing visions ever beheld by man – a dead valley from which spouted tens of thousands of jets of live steam and smoke.

Two years later, on September 24, 1918, mountain, valley and their environs were set aside by decree of President Woodrow Wilson as a national park. The Katmai National Monument occupies 4,214.9 square miles and is bounded by the Shelikof Strait, 100 miles west-northwest of Kodiak. The volcanic region, which is slowly cooling, includes many wooded valleys, desolate volcanic areas and glacier-covered mountains. For many years the region remained utterly remote. Today the park may be reached by air from Anchorage and the settlements of Kodiak Island, the Alaska Peninsula and Bristol Bay. Many American fishermen visit the holiday camps on its rivers and lakes. But there are very few visitors, either by bush plane or by canoe up the swift rapids of the Naknek River, to the valley that Katmai killed.

The Valley of Ten Thousand Smokes is slowly coming to green life again. Surrounded by a large crater ring is a dome of lava 1,200 feet across and 200 feet high, the lava plug in

the throat of Novarupta, a new volcano risen from the valley floor. Vapor curls from fumaroles and through the hot sand. But the "smokes" have dwindled; there are not more than 100 left. Here and there, stunted fire weed, tufts of grass, sedge and creeping willow maintain a slender hold in the sand; even some of the hot fumaroles are ringed with the blue-green of lowly algae and mosses, evidence that life is slowly returning to the devastated valley.

Kazbek, Mount

The second highest peak of the Caucasus, an extinct volcano. Location Central Greater Caucasus, northern Georgia. Height 16,541 feet. Map 10, A4. First climbed Douglas Freshfield, A. W. Moore and C. C. Tucker, 1868.

Among the great peaks of the 900-mile-long Caucasus chain, Kazbek (or Kasbek) is second

187

only to Elbrus. Certainly it is the most beautiful among them and the one that has most deeply impressed itself on the imagination of Caucasian and other peoples from the very earliest times – not to mention modern Russian poets such as Lermontov. Here, according to the tradition of the Ingush people, is the throne of the irascible snowstorm goddess whose seven sons are the stars of the Great Bear.

Mount Kazbek is approached from Tiflis by the Georgian Military Road, which first follows the valley of the river Aragwa, then that of the upper reaches of the Terek. Between Kazbek and the watershed dividing Asia from Europe is the somber pass of Daryal.

After Mtzkhet, the ancient capital of Georgia, the mountain and river scenery is rich and beautiful but between Pasanaur and Kazbek it becomes more and more forbidding; yet it can offer lovely, unforgettable sights. There is a mountainside some seven miles east of the peak, by Kazbek village and near the source of the Terek, which, at the right moment in spring, is covered with honey-colored azaleas and faced on the other side of the ravine by one of the watch-towers of Queen Tamara. No one who has seen Kazbek can wonder that this supremely beautiful and elusive peak of "the frosty Caucasus" is to the Georgians and other mountain races, in song and folklore, what Ararat is to the Armenians and Fujiyama to the Japanese. The Georgians call it Mkinvari, the Ice Mountain; the Ossetes, Christ's Peak, and on its summit, according to legend, is the tent of the Patriarch Abraham, in which the Child Jesus lies asleep in a cradle supported by an invisible hand.

Since it was first climbed almost a century ago, Kazbek has become a popular target for Russian and other mountaineers, and its environs have become a tourist and sports area.

Kenya, Mount

The second highest mountain in Africa, an extinct volcano. Location *Central Kenya.* Height *17,040 feet.*

Map *9, G6.* First climbed *Sir Harold Mackinder, Cesar Ollier and Joseph Brocherei, 1899.*

Rising boldly above the East African plateau, 70 miles north-northeast of Nairobi, Mount Kenya stands in the middle of a 300-square-mile national park which begins above 11,000 feet. Its base is 40 miles in diameter; most of the crater has been eroded, leaving a central core of rocky peaks. It has twin summits, called Batian and Nelion after local Masai notables by the first man to climb the mountains; these are only 40 yards apart and there is a mere 200-foot drop between them. The base is 40 miles in diameter; a scenic road runs around it from Fort Hall at the southern foot; Nanyuki, at the northwest side, is the chief base for ascents and is connected to Nairobi by railway. Fifteen glaciers are found above the 14,000-foot level; between 5,000 and 12,000 feet there are forests of camphor, cedar and bamboo.

It was on December 3, 1849, that the German missionary Dr Johann L. Krapf, gazing northwards from Kitui, an African hamlet in the Wa-Kamba district, saw snow on the equator – snow on the flanks of an unnamed mountain mass, rising into the blue sky. Local legend had spoken about it for a long time but it had never been accepted in Europe. "It appeared to me like a gigantic wall, on whose summit I observed two immense towers, or horns, as you might call them," the missionary recorded in his journal that night, but his story was disbelieved for years.

Half a century passed before the mountain was first climbed by the geographer Sir Harold Mackinder and his two alpine guides. It was an astonishing feat, for they not only encountered great climbing difficulties but were constantly harassed by the savage, hostile tribes of the region. It was, as James Ramsey Ullman remarks, probably the only major mountaineering party in history that had to fight men as well as nature on its way to its goal.

Thirty years later, in 1929, Eric Shipton repeated the ascent with P. Wyn Harris and also climbed the slightly lower Nelion. To ascend, as these two did, the long, difficult west ridge of Batian, the higher summit, continue over the twin summit, Nelion, and descend the southeast face in one day was a very fine feat of skilled and sound mountaineering. In 1930 Shipton and H. W. Tilman made the first ascent of Midget Peak, by far the most difficult aiguille in the range, and narrowly escaped death on the descent. The first ascent of Batian by a woman was made in 1938 by Miss Una Cameron. Since then it has been scaled on several occasions – but only by highly skilled climbers though there was one extraordinary exception to this rule. During the Second World War three Italian prisoners in a camp at the foot of the mountain slipped away, climbed to the summit and returned – all undetected. They did it out of boredom and a desire for adventure; but it would appear from the title of the book one of them, Felice Benuzzi, wrote later that it was "No picnic on Mount Kenya."

Kerinchi, Mount

The highest peak of the Barisan Range. Location *Western Sumatra, Indonesia.* Height *12,467 feet.* Map *10, F10.*

Mount Kerinchi (formerly known as Indrapura Peak and also spelled Kerintji, Kurinchi and Koerintji) is the highest mountain in Sumatra and the culmination of the Barisan Range. This volcanic range extends about 1,000 miles, almost the whole length of the island, parallel with the west coast. The central part of the range is known as the Padang Highlands and valuable coal deposits are mined here.

Kerinchi itself is something of a mystery mountain. Not many white people have climbed its upper slopes where the tumbling, turbulent Si Oel Ok has its source among the boulders before rushing down to meet the great Batang Hari at the foot of the mountain. Until 1904 the Kubu tribes of this area were independent of the Dutch, waging a fierce guerilla warfare from

their fastnesses. Even today, as citizens of the Republic of Indonesia, they are notably wild, almost legendary figures to the other peoples of Sumatra. The mountain is difficult of access and by no means completely explored. About 80 miles from Padang, in the western central part of the island, Kerinchi is notable both for its immense pine trees (*Pinus merkusii*), which grow in unexpected splendor on the higher slopes, and for the herds of serow (*Capricornis sumatraensis*), wild and shy animals of the ibex family. They roam the high grassy slopes below the huge, vertical-walled volcano, which continuously emits rolling clouds of sulphurous smoke.

Khingan Mountains

A range extending about 700 miles with several subranges. Location *Western Manchuria.* Height *Average 2,000–3,000 feet, rising to 5,670 feet.* Map *10, G3.* Explored *V. A. Obruchev, G. N. Potanin, early nineteenth century.*

The Khingan or Great Khingan Mountains lie at the eastern edge of the Mongolian plateau, forming the western limit of the central Mongolian plain. They extend from the great Amur River bend to the area of Tolun, where they merge with the Yin mountain system. At Kalgan they are crossed by the highway from Urga to Peking. As a border ridge they are of great orographical importance, constituting both a climatic boundary and the western limits of the Manchurian flora. The very gentle western slope rises from a base of 3,000 to 3,500 feet; the highest peak is Shihwei (5,670 feet), lying 70 miles north-northwest of Solun. The eastern slope drops very steeply to the plains of Manchuria, which have an altitude of only 1,500-2,000 feet. On this stretch there are some subordinate ridges, parallel with the main range and separated from it by longitudinal valleys, forming two different terraces and giving to the whole system a width of 80-100 miles. There are many volcanic formations in the main range and its

A camel train in the Khyber Pass

southeast slopes. Actual volcanic activity was last observed in the years 1720–21. The range is densely forested and forms the divide between the Argun and Nonni rivers; it is crossed by the Chinese Eastern railway. It is still one of the more backward areas of Manchuria and is populated mainly by tribes of nomadic hunters.

The Lesser Khingan or Little Khingan Mountains are a continuation of the Ilkuri Mountains, themselves a northeast offshoot of the Great Khingans, to the southeast. They form the watershed between the Amur and Sungari rivers and rise to 4,665 feet 80 miles northwest of Kiamusze. They are continued beyond the Amur in the USSR by the Bureya Range, whose southern section is also called Lesser Khingan.

Khyber Pass

A famous defile, about 30 miles long, now a strategic military road. Location Safed Koh Range, between Afghanistan and Pakistan. Height Rising to about 3,500 feet. Map 11, B3.

Nine miles to the west of Peshawar, capital of the North-West Frontier Province, with its famous bazaars, rise the walls of the Fort of Jamrud, for many years headquarters of the Afghan

Rifles, guarding the entrance to the Khyber Pass. Three miles farther on, across the stony plain, the pass itself begins.

At first the road follows the bed of a ravine, between parched, rugged, rock-strewn hills of shale and limestone, then skirts a narrow plateau before, halfway along its length, it reaches the fort of Ali Masjid. After this comes the wildest country. The road descends by winding hairpin bends to the Ali Masjid River, then follows its bank. At its narrowest the pass shrinks to only 15 feet in width, whilst on either side sheer cliffs rise to between 600 and 1,000 feet and beyond them are mountains 3,000 feet high. After three more miles, and still climbing steadily, the path widens, until high above can be seen the hamlets and 60 towers of the Zakka Khel Afridis. Then comes a broad plateau region three miles wide and some seven miles long; at the far end, 3,370 feet up, stands the fort of Landi Kotal. Beyond lies Afghanistan.

Through this pass, the traditional gateway from Persia and Turkestan to the rich plains of India, have come successive invasions; Greeks, Tartars, Mongols, Moguls came pouring through, before spreading out to loot and conquer the rich lands beyond. This way came Genghis Khan, Tamerlaine, Mahmud of Ghazni (whose empire, in the eleventh century, extended from the Tigris to the Ganges), Nadir Shah, Ahmed Shah, Baber, Humayun and perhaps even Alexander the Great.

A perfect setting for ambushes, inhabited by tribes such as the Afridis, constitutionally inclined to banditry, its history is one long record of bloody massacres. In modern times the most famous slaughter connected with it – that at the end of the first Afghan War of 1838-42 when the British Army was withdrawing after the capture of Kabul – took place, in fact, in the Jagdalik Pass, a few miles to the northwest. Despite the truce, the Afghans fell on the 690 British, 3,810 Indian soldiers and 12,000 camp followers, killing or capturing all but one – Dr William Brydon alone escaping to tell the tale. During the British rule in India three Afghan wars (1838-42, 1878-80 and 1919) were largely fought around the possession of the Khyber Pass. So grim has been its reputation that until very recently it was avoided if possible by traders even in peace time. Even invading armies have preferred to take the longer roads into India through Baluchistan or Kashmir.

Kilauea and Mauna Loa

Two active volcanoes. Location *Southern central Hawaii.* Height *Kilauea: 4,090 feet*; *Mauna Loa: 13,675 feet.* Map *2, F10.*

Mauna Loa rises on "Big Island," in the midst of Hawaii's National Park. An active volcano, its main features are Kilauea, the immense crater sunk in the southeast flank of the enormous cone; Halemaumau, the fiery pit inside Kilauea itself, and, on its summit, Mokuaweoweo, another huge active crater.

Kilauea itself is a "shield" volcano, with walls 200-800 feet high, built up by the solidifying of successive overflows of very liquid basaltic lava. The active vent in Kilauea's crater floor is Halemaumau, a vast cauldron with almost vertical walls, 3,700 feet in diameter and 1,300 feet deep, inside which the liquid lava rises and falls as it enters or ebbs away through channels in the floor. The floor itself is occasionally completely exposed; sometimes it is crusted over, but generally it presents a magnificent, pyrotechnic display, especially at night. Flaring, leaping fountains of fire burst through the dull red glowing surface, affording a glimpse of the mighty forces imprisoned in the volcano.

In 1934 Professor T. A. Jagger made a recording of an eruption from the very edge of the vent. As the volcanic activity is confined to the huge bowl and the eruptions are not of an explosive character, there is no danger to spectators at Kilauea's fiery demonstrations – and they take advantage of this. "A thousand people," wrote Professor Jagger "are standing there...

The line of motionless white faces. . . like a concourse of fire-worshippers. Sulphur from the volcanoes is in their nostrils. At the bottom is a pool of blood-red molten slag. Through it come bursting fountains, making slow outward surges of fiery melt. Away from the fountains radiate bright zigzag lines. They are brilliant orange cracks eternally splitting the dark crust. Farther out in the lake is a tremendous fountain shooting 300 feet up in huge ropy flings which slop down on to the surface of the lake. . .''

When caught by a strong wind, the jets of molten lava are drawn out into long threads like fine-spun glass, known as Pele's Hair – for Halemaumau, Everlasting House, is in Hawaiian legend the home of that ill-tempered, unpredictable, terrible yet not wholly unloved goddess whose ''passions were as turbulent as the lake of fire in her crater home.''

Mokuaweoweo is on the summit of Mauna Loa, and occupies an area of 3.7 square miles. Its greatest recorded eruption was in 1880–81 when the lava flow was 50 miles long.

Kilimanjaro

The highest mountain in Africa. Location *Northeast Tanganyika, near the Kenya border.* Height *19,565 feet.* Map *9, G7.* First climbed *Dr Hans Meyer, 1889.*

The dust of the Amboseli Reserve, 3,000 feet above sea level in Kenya, is legendary. There is no escaping it – it will filter through the most tightly closed car window and even into vacuum flasks. It can make life very unpleasant, yet it is worth enduring for the sake of the marvelous wild life – elephants, giraffes, zebras, cheetahs, rhinoceroses, lions, antelopes and ostriches. Mirages are common: lakes and trees floating in the sky, water that looks tantalizingly real. The greatest spectacle, however, is Kilimanjaro – a mountain that has inspired many a traveler and writer including Ernest Hemingway.

To Hemingway the snows of Kilimanjaro became a symbol around which he spun one of his most striking stories. Other writers have noted down the wonderful repose suggested by the smooth, simple dome of ice and the halo-like effect given by the long lines of snow extending down the deep erosion gullies that score the cone. After the dusty plains it is sheer joy to ascend to a comfortable hotel high up on the slopes, sit before a crackling log fire or stretch out on the terrace to gaze at the immense landscape spread out below. From the arid scrub-lands one climbs into a forest zone at about 6,500 feet, cultivated here and there by the once fierce, warlike Chaga tribe, and a few white men. Then, above 9,500 feet, one enters the alpine zone of flower-dotted grassland which continues with decreasing luxuriance up to about 15,000 feet.

The ascent is not difficult. Kilimanjaro – the ''Mountain of Cold Devils'' – was discovered by two missionaries, Johannes Rebmann and Ludwig Krapf, in 1848. Krapf achieved safety in a region of notoriously hostile natives by means of his umbrella, which he would point at them and suddenly open. The news, however, especially of the discovery of snow so near the equator in Africa, was not believed until many years later. The symmetrical, snow-capped Kibo, the higher peak, was first climbed by Dr Hans Meyer in 1889, the lower, irregular Mawenzi (17,300 feet) in 1912. At the summit there is a crater 6,000 feet wide and 600 feet deep; the icecap is 200 feet thick. A saddle ridge 5,000 feet below carries one to Mawenzi, seven miles to the east – a precipitous, jagged older cone, stripped bare of its ash and cinders by erosion. Moshi, at the southern foot of the mountain, is the chief trade center and base for ascent.

Kinabalu, Mount

The highest mountain in Borneo. Location *North Borneo.* Height *13,455 feet.* Map *10, H9.*

Kinabalu lies in the southern Crocker Mountains, which extend 40 miles south-southwest from Marudu Bay, near the west coast of the island. It rises gently at first from a level plain, 35 miles east-northeast of Jesselton and about 70 miles from the island's northernmost tip, and then shoots up from a talus slope of rock fragments in a great bare, flat-topped block, surrounded on all sides by granite cliffs and precipices thousands of feet high, scarred here and there by gullies. The summit consists of a noble terrace half a mile in length, its sides sloping at an angle of 30°, edged on all sides by jagged, irregular rocks and rising, in one or two places, into sharp pointed peaks a few hundred feet higher.

The lower slopes are farmed to about 2,000 feet; above lie jungle, scrub and bare rocks. Above 4,000 feet the fauna and flora of Kinabalu show a marked resemblance to those of the Himalayas, suggesting that this and some other mountains of Malaya and Borneo were formerly much more closely connected with that mountain system. A water-shrew in particular is elsewhere known only from Sikkim, Assam and the Kachin Hills of northern Burma, while the forest is full of magnificent rhododendrons, magnolias and bamboos. The most interesting plants of Kinabalu, however, are typically Indonesian – among them the extraordinary carniverous pitcher plants which trap, drown and digest insects, and even mice and small rats.

Among the detached rocks and in the crevices of the summit grows a small moss on which, the Indians declare, the spirits of their ancestors feed. The mountain is feared as a haunt of spirits by the neighboring tribesmen, who always try to discourage would-be climbers – while a certain grass, they say, feeds the ghostly buffaloes that follow their dead masters to the other world.

Klamath Mountains

A mountain range of moderate height and great beauty. Location *Northern California and southwest Oregon.* Height *Rising to 9,000 feet.* Map *4, A3-B3.*

The Klamath Mountains, named after the dominant Indian tribe of the district – today one of the richest in the United States – form a mountain knot connecting the Coast Ranges of Oregon on the north with those of California in the west and south; and meeting the Cascade Range at the northern end of the Central Valley of California. They begin in the foothills south of the Willamette Valley (Oregon) and their southern extensions end along the western side of the Central Valley. Topographically, therefore, they separate southern Oregon from northern California.

The Klamaths are made up of several sub-ranges, which run from north to south: the Rogue River Range in Oregon is the northernmost. Then follow the Siskiyou Mountains, with Mount Ashland (7,530 feet), Dutchman Peak (7,411 feet) and Siskiyou Peak (7,147 feet) as the chief elevations. The Siskiyous contain the Oregon Caves National Monument, 49 miles from Grants Pass, with a striking mountain of marble and several miles of trail traversing fine stands of virgin forest; the area of the park is 480 acres. The Siskiyou Mountains are famous for large-scale lumbering (fir, pine and spruce) and as hunting and fishing preserves. Equally famous are the pears grown in the Rogue River valley.

The other sub-ranges include Scott Mountains, Salmon Mountains, Trinity Mountains and South Fork Range (the farthest to the southwest and sometimes considered part of the Coast Ranges), the Bullychoop and Yolla Bolly or Yallo Bally mountains. The highest peaks of the Klamaths are Mount Eddy (9,038 feet) about 15 miles southwest of Mount Shasta and Thompson Peak (8,936 feet). The beautiful Salmon-Trinity (or Trinity) Alps region covers the border between Trinity and Siskiyou counties in California and has been set apart as a wilderness preserve. The Conquille, Rogue, Klamath and Trinity rivers drain the range. There are many evergreen forests, and considerable dairying and fruit-growing communities, notably along the Rogue River and in other valleys.

Klamath county, in which part of the range

lies, has 114 lakes and over 1,000 streams. Here lives the white pelican, protected by law. One of the largest stands of pine timber in the Western States surrounds the town of Klamath Falls. The Klamath Indian Reservation, 51 miles long and 45 miles wide, is a modern settlement where few of the old Indian customs are practised. The Klamath Indians hold large tracts of timberland and are extremely prosperous.

Kosciusko, Mount

The highest mountain in Australia. Location *Southeast New South Wales, Australia.* Height *7,305 feet.* Map *12, E7.* Discovered *Sir Paul Strzelecki, 1840.*

Named by its discoverer after the most famous of Polish patriots, Mount Kosciusko is 240 miles southwest of Sydney and 96 miles south of Canberra in the Muniong Range of the Australian Alps, in the extreme southeast corner of Australia. It is only 12 hours by rail from Sydney and even nearer to Melbourne, which has made it the most popular resort of eastern Australia. Its chain of miniature snow-fields – each about 200 yards long and five feet thick – remain even in midsummer on the sheltered eastern slopes. They are reminders of the fact that only 10,000 years ago glaciers covered the mountain: no large ice-sheet, at least in recent times, but a number of individual valley glaciers. At their former heads the amphitheater-like cirques cut by them are now mostly occupied by small, circular rocky lakes, popular for swimming and fishing in summer and stocked with imported English and Canadian trout.

Between the rocky gullies and crevasses are wide, boggy plains. Here odd, half-familiar alpine plants grow: yellow and white buttercups, forget-me-nots, shrubby, heath-like swamp epacrids and the curious compositae, whose flowers and stems are covered in woolly hairs which protect them from winter frost and summer sun. Below 5,500 feet there are large patches of snow gum trees, then extensive forests and scrub. It is a carefully protected catchment area, for the 1,200-mile-long Murray, chief river of a drought-ridden continent, rises here. Since 1949 a series of hydro-electric stations has been built to utilize the water as a source of power.

Kunlun

One of the great mountain systems of Asia with several ranges and branches. Location *China, between the Himalayas and Tien Shan, Central Asia.* Height *Rising to 25,340 feet.* Map *10, D5-6.* Explored *Sven Hedin, Sir Aurel Stein and others, late nineteenth and early twentieth centuries.*

The Kunlun is the great mountain system dividing northern Tibet from western China. It ranges from the northern buttress of the Tibetan plateau, where it merges into the Aghil mountains, to the Tsaidam Swamp and the sources of the Yangtse, extending for about 1,000 miles. It drops abruptly to the Tarim basin of Sinkiang province; it is separated from the Karakoram by the Yarkand River at the Pamir mountain knot and in central Tsinghai province branches into the complex ranges of western central China.

Like the Himalayas which buttress the Tibetan plateau on the south, the Kunlun is composed of parallel mountain folds with two crest-zones of high, snow-clad peaks; the glaciers and troughs between these are drained through defiles cut in the outer folds. In the west the crest-zones are compressed and close to each other; here they are known as the northern and southern Kunlun. They begin to diverge into separate ranges at about longitude 82°; the northern forms the Altyn Tagh (or Astyn Tagh), the southern the Arka Tagh. These, as they extend east-northeast and east, enclose the Tsaidam swamps, and the Altyn Tagh becomes the Nan Shan. The Arka Tagh eventually breaks up into separate divergent ranges such as the Amne Machin Mountains and the Bayan Kara Shan of China. The highest peak of the Kunlun so far measured is the old E61 (25,340 feet), now known by its Turki name of Ulugh Muztagh (ice-mountain) – not to be confused with Muztagh Ata in the Pamirs. It is possible, though not very likely, that other peaks in the east may reach as high.

Unlike the Himalayas, the Kunlun are unaffected by the southwest monsoon of the Indian Ocean; though much farther north, the snowline is higher and the glaciers smaller. The piedmont oases – Khotan (4,490 feet), Kerya (4,460 feet) and Charchan (3,170 feet) – are higher than the Indo-Gangetic plain at the foot of the Himalayas. The rivers of the west, Karakash, Turungkash, Kerya and Charchan, reach the line of oases but their waters are evaporated or lost in the sands of Taklamakan or in Lop Nor, some probably being returned to the mountains as snow early in the year. Only in the extreme east are the mountains affected by moisture-laden winds from the China seas.

Exploration of these remote mountains has been extremely difficult and arduous. Early travelers from western Tibet were concerned with survival in a land of brackish water and no supplies. The successful travelers have been those who, after long journeys into Chinese territory, have examined the mountains from the north or east. The most important scientific explorers were Sven Hedin and Sir Aurel Stein, who practically re-discovered the Kunlun. Sir Aurel Stein in particular, with the Indian surveyors Ram Singh, Lal Singh and Afraz Gul Khan, surveyed the northern Kunlun and Altyn Tagh from the Karakash River to Tunhwang at the western end of the Nan Shan of China – on his three Central Asian journeys (1900–01, 1906–08 and 1913–15) – though nowhere, except south of Khotan, did they cross the whole width of the ranges. For 200 miles, the Arka Tagh is still practically unknown; Sven Hedin explored its south end in the trough between it and the Koho-shili range. No peaks of the Kunlun have been climbed by Westerners. The approaches to the Ulugh Muztagh have been described by Sir Aurel Stein, but W. H. Johnson was mistaken in his claim to have climbed it in 1865. Today, of course, the range is completely closed to Europeans.

Lake District

A region of lakes and mountains, known for its beauty. Location *Northern Lancashire, western Westmorland and southern Cumberland, northwest England.* Height *Rising to 3,210 feet in Scafell Pike.* Map *7, B5.*

A knot of rough mountain country with its masses radiating from the Scafell area, the Lake District contains the highest peaks in England, including four of more than 3,000 feet (Scafell Pike, 3,210 feet; Scafell, 3,162 feet; Helvellyn, 3,118 feet, and Skiddaw, 3,054 feet), while many of its valleys enclose long narrow meres or lakes. These include Windermere, 11 miles long, Coniston Water, Ullswater, Derwentwater, Buttermere, Grasmere, Thirlmere, Crummock Water and Wastwater. Only some 30 miles from north to south and 25 miles from east to west, the Lake District can be crossed on foot in a day in any direction. Largely owing to its radial structure, which ensures that any road crossing its center must climb at least 1,600 feet, most valleys leading to the highest ground lack through routes for vehicles.

The scenery of the Lake District is the result of a complex geological history involving three major marine and three major land phases; only after the last of these did the Ice Age start inexorably to carve the details of today's scene from the high nodal mountain mass which remained. The outcome is a landscape with more diversity concentrated in a limited area than perhaps any other in the world, and from each different geological base there has come an individual outline, plant-life and economic history.

The result is a collection of intimate landscape-cameos, each acting as foil to its predecessor and successor. By any standard they are cameos rather than pictures – but even so, there was enough dramatic beauty here to attract the

Scafell (left) and Scafell Pike (center), in the Lake District

pioneers of the Romantic Revolution. They, in turn, prepared the way for the enthusiasm of the "Lake Poets." Wordsworth, born at Cockermouth on the fringe of the Lake District, was the first of many. Southey and Coleridge lived and worked here; Ruskin came here in old age to live at Brantwood. Keats, Shelley, Arnold ,Tennyons

and many others also came to find inspiration in the beauties of the Lake District landscape.

In 1951, 866 square miles of the Lake District were designated as a national park. Much of the area is now either owned or administered by the National Trust, including 3,000 acres on the upper slopes of 12 central mountains bought in 1923 as a war memorial by the Fell and Rock Climbing Club of the English Lake District.

Fell-walking and rock climbing have been practised for many years – a center for the latter being Scafell Pike, the highest summit in England. Lying in Cumberland, between Eskdale and Wasdale, the Pike forms the swelling center of the broad ridge which runs from Scafell itself to Great End in the north before bending round, horseshoe fashion, to form the line of summits that run from Esk Pike to Crinkle Crags.

Between Scafell Pike and Scafell lies Broad Stand, a precipice which provides a challenging problem for the rock climber. The first passage of it was probably made by Coleridge early in the nineteenth century; by 1837 it was well known to local people. Parallel routes up the line of rock were made by later scramblers and attention soon turned to the great line of cliffs which drops to the north of Scafell. Here a multitude of rock climbs have been worked out since the sport of British cragsmanship was founded in the eighteen-eighties – Moss Ghyll, Deep Ghyll, Collier's Climb, Botterill's Slab and many others.

Lassen Peak

The only active volcano in the United States. Location *Cascade Range, northern California.* Height *10,453 feet.* Map *4, A3.* Discovered *Luis Argüello, about 1821.*

Lassen Peak

Though Mount Lassen or Lassen Peak – named after Peter Lassen, a pioneer and guide of the Far West – has not erupted since 1921, it is still regarded as an active volcano. Set in the National Park of the same name which was established in 1916 with an area of 161.6 square miles, it rises at the southern end of the Cascade Range, north of the Sierra Nevada.

For a period of about 200 years Lassen Peak was quiescent; then, in the spring of 1914, it started a series of comparatively small eruptions.

Since the close of its most vigorous activity in 1915, it has remained relatively quiet, although there are many hot springs as proof of its internal heat and from time to time it still emits querulous puffs of steam.

Mill Creek breaks through the south side of the crater, south of the Peak, forming a deep canyon. In addition to Lassen Peak and Cinder Cone (6,913 feet) there are several other volcanic cones in the park, including Prospect Peak (8,342 feet) and Mount Harkness (8,039 feet). From the summit of these peaks and from Brokeoff Mountain (9,232 feet) trails lead to smaller volcanic peaks and fantastic lava fields, to old and new fumaroles, hot springs, mud volcanoes, boiling lakes and other striking volcanic features. The cones, easily climbed and studied, have remained nearly perfect.

There is a magnificent skyline on the western edge of the park, culminating on the north in pink-toned lava crags which rise to a height of over 8,500 feet and tower over 3,300 feet above the older lava flows forming their base. The central cone of the crags rises to a height of two thirds of a mile above the crater; its base is about a mile in diameter.

The southern half of the park contains six distinct areas where the active manifestations of volcanic forces can be observed. The highly colored earth, the smell of sulphur, the roar of live steam rushing under pressure from the vents, the gurgling mud pots and the noise of fumaroles, steamers and small geysers create a weird and impressive atmosphere.

In the eastern part of the park there are dozens of lakes and streams with rainbow and brown trout. Lassen Park is also a popular winter sports area from December until early summer. A two-and-a-half mile trail leads to the top of the volcano.

Laurentian Mountains

A long, wooded range, rich in minerals. Location *Southern Quebec.* Height *Rising to over 3,800 feet.* Map 5, A2-B1.

The Canadians proudly speak of the Laurentians, or Laurentides, as the oldest mountains in the world, and certainly these hills, scoured by the glaciers of the Ice Age, are probably the oldest on the North American continent. At the same time, with the adjoining Laurentian Plateau or Canadian Shield they form one of the most attractive and popular holiday areas of Canada and the most concentrated source of timber and other natural resources.

The Laurentians run northeast from the Ottawa River along the northern edge of the great St Lawrence valley. North of Quebec and south of Lake St John, they include the Laurentides National Park, established in 1895, which has an area of 4,000 square miles and is 80 miles long and 60 miles wide. The park also contains 1,600 of the Laurentides' countless lakes (estimated at about 70,000) and the range rises here to 3,800 feet. Another National Park within the range is the Montagne Tremblant, northwest of Montreal, with Mont Tremblant (3,150 feet) in its center. Just south of the Laurentides Park, northeast of Quebec, the Laurentians reach their culmination at 3,905 feet.

The Laurentian Plateau or peneplain is hummocky in character; as seen from the higher points in the area the skyline is nearly level. The lakes either lie in basins etched in the rock surface by glacial action or are bounded by the irregularly distributed drift which more or less covers the surface of the underlying rocks. Near the mouth of the Saguenay River the Laurentians form a steep escarpment above the St Lawrence River which constitutes the watershed between Hudson Bay and the St Lawrence.

The range is close enough to Montreal and Quebec to attract many thousands of skiers, swimmers and vacationers in both winter and summer. Those who want to go farther afield can explore the entire Laurentian Plateau, which covers over half of Canada in the shape of a vast horseshoe. Its southern boundary roughly follows the Labrador Coast, around Hudson Bay, across Quebec and Ontario, through Winnipeg, Great Slave and Great Bear lakes right up to the Arctic near the mouth of the Mackenzie River; on the south it extends into the United States. Its many thousands of lakes and extensive marshes are remnants of the continental glacier of the Pleistocene age. Its forest resources (mostly conifers) are probably the greatest in the world – so are its hydro-electric potentials and mineral deposits. While the Laurentians are highly developed for agriculture, industry and tourism, the Laurentian Plateau is still only sparsely dotted with mining towns, lumber camps and fur trading posts.

Lebanon Mountains

A short, steep mountain range. Location *Lebanon, close to the Mediterranean coast.* Height *Rising to 10,131 feet in the Qurnet es Sauda.* Map *9, G2.*

The Lebanon range extends about 100 miles north-northeast to south-southwest – almost the whole length of the country. Its name means the "White One." In the arid Middle East it is not surprising that the range should have derived its name from its snows – though another theory ascribes it to the white chalk and limestone characteristic of much of the range. Running north and south, it rises on one side with splendid vigor from the Mediterranean. In places there is barely space for beach or coastal road between the mountains and the sea. To the east, facing the deserts and the Anti-Lebanon mountains, the range falls away with similar dramatic abruptness, dropping in steep steps 1,000 feet at a time to the alluvial plain of the Bekaa valley. Where ravines wind into the mountainsides, villages cling to the rock face. Orchards seem to hang over the abysses. A voice that floats across a mountain torrent is often three hours away by mule track. Laden camels still tread fastidiously across the snowbound passes. At the same time the slopes above Bcharreh have seen in recent years the development of the best ski-ing in the Middle East, and many summer resorts have sprung up near the rapidly growing capital, Beirut.

Though the highest summit rises little over 10,000 feet, the Lebanon range has played an important role in myth, history and contemporary politics. At Afka the Adonis River springs ice-cold from the mountain flank and here, where Astarte first saw her lover, the slain god is commemorated by a great sanctuary, and anemones, reddened by his blood, cover the hillsides in spring. The Romans who raised, eastward in the Bekaa, the immense temple of Baalbek (on the site of earlier temples) regarded *Mons Libanus* as an inexhaustible timber yard. Of the cedar forests which they knew, only two or three small groups of trees remain.

Set between sea and desert, the range has always been a natural retreat and fortress and as such is closely linked with two important religious sects of the Middle East: the Maronites and the Druses. The Lebanon has been a Maronite stronghold since the seventh century and geographical factors have assured the survival of this Christian sect – owing allegiance to Rome but electing its own Patriarch – among the mountain peasantry. The rugged hills at the southern end of the massif for nearly 1,000 years offered a similar retreat to the Druses, worshippers of the heretical Muslim caliph, El Hakim.

Lenin Peak

The second highest mountain of the USSR, with a huge adjoining glacier. Location *Trans-Alai Range, Kirghiz-Tadszhik SSR border, USSR.* Height *23,382 feet.* Map *10, C5.* First climbed *W. Rickmer Rickmers and party, 1928.*

Lenin Peak was originally called Mount Kaufmann, after Constantine Petrovich Kaufmann, the famous conqueror and Governor-General of Russian Turkestan from 1867 until his death at Tashkent in 1882. The mountain was said to have been actually discovered by A. D. Fedchenko in 1871 and the immense glacier in the neighborhood is still named after him.

For several years Lenin Peak was thought to be the highest mountain in the USSR until 1932–33 when Stalin Peak (in the Pamir-Alai mountains, 24,590 feet) was discovered to be higher by over 1,000 feet. The north face of Lenin Peak sweeps upwards in great precipices 12,000 feet above the Alai valley.

The Russo-German Alai-Pamir expedition of 1928, led by W. Rickmer Rickmers, although essentially a scientific enterprise, included three expert German climbers, Eugen Allwein, Karl Wien and Erwin Schneider. After assiduous reconnaissance they made an eventual approach from the west by the Saukdara Glacier (about 20 miles long) to a high saddle at 17,000 feet on the southeast side of the peak. Thence they forced a difficult route upwards to achieve the first ascent on September 25, 1928. The second ascent, from the east face, was not made until 1934 by a Russian party, consisting of V. Abalakov (leader), E. Lukeen and N. Chernukla. Since then the Russians have reported six ascents by their parties; in 1955 one was made by a combined Sino-Soviet expedition.

Much of the pioneer exploratory and scientific work in the region was carried out by several expeditions of Rickmers from the border of Chinese Turkestan westward into the Trans-Alai.

Lepontine Alps

A major group of the Central Alps. Location *Swiss-Italian border, mostly in Ticino and Grison cantons, Switzerland.* Height *Varying from 3,004 feet to 11,683 feet.* Map *8, D8.*

Rising south of the upper Rhine and Rhône valleys, the Lepontine Alps are bounded on the west by the Simplon Pass and on the east by the Splügen Pass, lying south of the Furka and Oberalp passes. The long, curving ridge of summits of the Lepontines is of great geographical importance, forming the nodal point of the whole Alpine range.

Cutting deep into the group runs the Val Leventina from which the range takes its name, and at its head lies the St Gotthard. Slightly to the west of the pass rises the Wyttenwasserstock (10,119 feet); from its flanks emerge streams

flowing to the North Sea via the Rhine, to the Adriatic via the Tosa and the Ticino and to the Mediterranean via the Rhône.

The highest peak is Monte Leone (11,683 feet), at the extreme western end of the Lepontines, standing almost immediately above the Simplon tunnel. The average height of the summit ridges is less than suggested by their fine appearance when seen across the upper Rhône from the middle slopes of the Bernese Oberland. The Rheinwaldhorn (11,173 feet), and the Güferhorn (11,103 feet) are the highest peaks after Monte Leone.

From the Simplon to the Gries Pass the Swiss-Italian border follows the line of the Lepontine summits, which form the main Alpine watershed. Here, however, it bends sharply south, allowing to Switzerland the whole of the Ticino, south of the Alps, before turning northwards again to the Splügen. The Lepontines include the Adula and St Gotthard groups; in addition to the Simplon, the St Gotthard, Lukmanier and San Bernardino, they are crossed by 26 other passes at heights varying from 10,105 to 6,289 feet.

For mountaineers the most outstanding peaks are Monte Leone, Pizzo Rotondo (10,483 feet) and the Rheinwaldhorn, though most of the others also offer rewarding climbs.

Lhotse

The fourth highest mountain in the world. Location *Tibet-Nepal border, in southern Mount Everest massif.* Height *27,890 feet.* Map *11, F5.* First climbed *Ernst Reiss and Fritz Luchsinger, 1956.*

Lhotse Peak – or E1, as it was long known from its Indian Survey appellation – was for many years thought to be one of the peaks of Everest. It was only gradually that the mystery of the towering peak was dispelled; even today some writers identify it as the south peak of Everest.

Up to 1953 no attempt was made to climb it. The vast 25,000-foot ridge that joins it to Everest was explored by H. W. Tilman's party, who considered climbing Everest by the south wall of the Lhotse-Nuptse (a second satellite-peak) ridge, but the "monstrous precipices" on this southern side soon proved to be unassailable. Eric Shipton's party of 1951, which included Tom Bourdillon, W. H. Murray and Edmund Hillary, had reached a vantage point 20,000 feet high on Everest and had a good view of the west face of Lhotse and the high saddle (known as South Col) which joined it to the highest peak in the world. The second Swiss expedition of 1952 established its Camp 5 at the foot of the western face of Lhotse and climbed South Col; but the weather forced it to retire. The 1952 British expedition, led by Col. Sir John Hunt, also used the Lhotse Glacier and the west face of Lhotse in attempting Everest.

It was not until Everest had been conquered in 1953, however, that serious attention was

Lhotse, with a cairn of Buddhist prayer stones in the foreground

turned to its great southern neighbor, and three more years passed before the Swiss Foundation for Alpine Research organized an expedition under the general direction of Ernst Feuz to repeat the ascent of Everest and to climb Lhotse, which, by then, was the highest unscaled mountain left in the world.

The leader of the expedition was Albert Eggler, with Wolfgang Diehl as his deputy. In the beginning the Swiss climbers were dogged by setbacks; several of them, including Diehl and the Sirdar Pasang Dawa Lama, fell ill; the latter had to be carried back to Namche Bazaar by ten Sherpas and Dr Eduard Leuthold, the physician of the party. But in spite of these difficulties and a fall of fresh snow which made the assault on Lhotse doubly difficult, on May 18 Ernst Reiss and Fritz Luchsinger made the first ascent of the peak. It was the first Eight Thousander (as the tallest peaks, measured in meters, not in feet, are called) which any Swiss climbers had conquered.

Reiss was the only member of the expedition who had Himalayan experience, having been a participant in the 1952 Everest attempt. He and Luchsinger climbed slowly to the foot of the Lhotse couloir and were lucky to find good snow, for the couloir varies in steepness from 45° to 60° and at one point it is little more than a foot in breadth. They were lucky too to have a strong wind at their backs, but even so their oxygen-masks and glasses were soon crusted in ice.

A steep slope of green rock and a final snow funnel led them to the narrow ice-ridge of the summit, five and a half hours after setting out. The wind had risen and on the descent they had to edge their way down, fully roped, almost foot by foot. Soon after they reached their camp, a storm burst upon them and raged all night. Next day they joined their party, slightly frostbitten – but a few days later they both took part in the successful Swiss assault on Everest itself.

Little St Bernard Pass

An Alpine pass between the Mont Blanc massif and the Graian Alps. Location Savoie department, southeast France. Height 7,178 feet. Map 8, C9.

The lowest gap in the main Alpine chain between the Mont Cenis and the Simplon, the Little St Bernard links Bourg St Maurice in the Tarentaise (France) with the valley of Aosta (Italy). It forms the commonly accepted boundary between the Graian and the Pennine Alps and although traversed by a road it can be crossed by walkers, on the old mule-path, with more pleasure than might be expected.

Julius Caesar used it on his last visit from Gaul to Rome and Roman officials traveled by it for several centuries. Throughout the Middle Ages it was overshadowed in popularity by its higher, but in some ways more convenient, neighboring passes. It was only in 1871 that the present road replaced the ancient mule-track.

The traveler mounting the long serpentine zig-zags which leave the road from Bourg St Maurice, in the neighborhood of Seez, eventually reaches a high grassy plateau, three miles by one, bordered by minor peaks and containing not only the frontier but a cluster of historical relics which include the remains of a prehistoric stone circle as well as the famous Hospice.

The Hospice, founded in the tenth century by St Bernard de Menthon, a nobleman of the district, for the use of pilgrims traveling to Rome, was from the fifteenth century served by the Augustinian canons of the Great St Bernard. About 1750 it was handed over to the military and religious order of St Maurice and St Lazarus. It was damaged in the Second World War.

Near the Hospice lie the remains of the stone circle, dubbed the Cirque d'Annibal during the period when it was thought, erroneously, that Hannibal made his entry into Italy by this pass. Nearby, also, is the Colonne Joux, a 20-foot emblem of Cipollino marble, allegedly of Celtic origin and crowned today by the statue of St Bernard.

An undistinguished pass in itself, the Little St Bernard does enable the traveler to enjoy, within an easy day's march, the rich contrast between the rather austere landscape of Savoy and the wooded ravines, the precipices and the deep blue colors of the south that lie before him during the descent into Italy.

Livingstone Mountains

A belt of highlands. Location *Southern Tanganyika.* Height *Rising to 7,000 feet.* Map *9, G7-8.*

The Livingstone Mountains were named after David Livingstone, the great Scottish missionary, who was one of the first white men to explore Tanganyika. They form the eastern border of the Lake Nyasa rift valley, rising at the northern end of the lake. In some parts these highlands have the character of a plateau rather than that of a true mountain range. But they form a comparatively narrow belt of country falling away rather steeply to both east and west. The northern end is clearly marked by an escarpment descending to the Ruaha valley, the northeast branch of the main rift valley. On the south the Livingstone range ends in the deep valley of the Ruhuhu River (flowing southeast and southwest to Lake Nyasa), the first definite break in the highlands on the east shore of Lake Nyasa.

Geologically, the range shows on the side of the lake a zone of gneiss in a series of valleys and ridges, generally parallel to its axis. Nearest the lake is Mount Jamimbi or Chamembe, rising to 7,870 feet: that is, 6,200 feet above Lake Nyasa, falling almost sheer to the lake, the same steep slope continuing underwater. Towards the south the range is only 20 miles wide, but to the north it opens to twice the expanse, broken by the depression of Buanyi. North and east of Buanyi table-topped mountains occur. There is lush grass in the uplands and the hollows are mostly forested, while the slopes towards the lake are scrub-land. Coal is mined at the mouth of the Ruhuhu and various crops are successfully cultivated in the healthy, equitable climate.

Logan, Mount

The second highest peak in North America. Location *Southwest Yukon, near the Alaska border.* Height *19,850 feet.* Map *3, C6.* First climbed *Captain A. H. MacCarthy and party, 1925.*

Like the 3,700-foot mountain of the same name in the Shickshock Mountains of eastern Quebec, Yukon's Mount Logan was named after Sir William Logan, the pioneer geologist and first Director of the Canadian Geological Survey. The greater Mount Logan rises impressively to the north of the main St Elias range. It is of truly Himalayan proportions; its ten-mile summit crest, its northern and southern walls, towering 14,000 feet and more above the vast Logan and Seward glacier-basins, make it one of the most impressive sights of its kind in North America.

Much of the region was explored and surveyed during the operations of the International Boundary Commission, during the first decade of the twentieth century, by American and Canadian surveyors. In 1924 Captain A. H. MacCarthy, a noted Canadian climber, and H. F. Lambert, of the Canadian Boundary Survey, pioneered a way to its lower slopes. In 1925 they set out to climb and conquer the great peak. The party included, beside MacCarthy and Lambert, Lt-Col. W. W. Foster, Lennox Lindsay, Norman Read and Allen Carpe.

The first step was a remarkable preparatory expedition by MacCarthy and a famous "sourdough" guide named Andy Taylor. In the middle of the winter, before the rest of the climbers arrived, they fought their way up the great glaciers to the base of the mountain and established a long series of camps and supply depots. This alone took 70 days in sub-zero temperatures. Then, in late May, the expedition proper began. The climbers served as their own porters, each carrying a load of 70 lbs. week after week. They remained on ice and snow for 44 consecutive days, without once setting foot on rock or earth, lashed by blizzards and windstorms.

Mount Logan, the highest peak in Canada

Logan, as James Ramsey Ullman described it, is not a single, isolated uplift, but almost a range in itself – more than 20 miles in length along the line of its summit ridge. "Starting from the King Glacier, which pours down from the western flank of the mountain," Ullman wrote, "Mac-Carthy and his companions found a way to this ridge, but once there, at a height of 14,500 feet, they were still separated from their goal not merely by a mile of vertical distance but by a seemingly endless succession of intervening peaks and cols. Over this jagged white skyline they proceeded to fight their way. Day followed day while they hacked steps in the ice and floundered in snowdrifts up to their armpits. Almost every morning brought with it a fresh blizzard; at night the temperature frequently fell to as low as 30° F. below zero. But slowly they advanced, following the ridge up and down and then up again, and at last succeeded in pitching a tent at an altitude of 18,500 feet. This tiny shelter. . . is still the highest ever made in North America. . ."

At last, at 8 p.m. on June 23, 1925, they stood on the 19,850–foot summit of Mount Logan. The descent was even more dangerous and arduous. A three-day blizzard riveted them to the mountainside, yet they had to keep going in order to survive. "For endurance and courage," wrote Sir Arnold Lunn "their achievement has rarely been surpassed."

The central peak has only twice been ascended since 1925 and always by the same route. In 1957, however, the east peak, nearly as high as the central peak, was climbed via the very difficult east ridge by five American mountaineers. Recently, several scientific expeditions, under the auspices of the Arctic Institute of North America, have done much important geological and glaciological research.

Mackenzie Mountains

A mountain range, still partly unexplored. Location *Northwest Territories, Canadian Rocky Mountains.* Height *Rising to 9,049 feet.* Map 3, E5-F6.

The Mackenzie Mountains extend about 500 miles southeast to northwest between the British Columbia border and the Peel River valley. The range forms the southern part of the Yukon-Northwest Territories line.

Until the Second World War few white men had penetrated far into these mountains; they remained the preserve of the Yukon Indian and the wild animals he hunts and traps. Travel meant arduous trips by dog-team and snow-shoe in winter; in summer progress by the rivers entailed much exhausting portage. Only a handful of men pushed deep in among the ridges and valleys that fall away from a 5,000-8,000-foot plateau and its summits.

Completion of the Alaska Highway opened up this remote, jagged corner of Canada. Under stress of war, a road and oil pipeline – the Canol pipeline – were laid through the very heart of the range, past the snow-clad summit of Keele Peak (8,500 feet), across untrodden rock and muskeg, alternately frozen and sodden, to Normah Wells on the Mackenzie River.

Later road-builders pushed through 300 miles of mountains – the peaks include Mount Sir James McBrien (9,049 feet), the highest in the range, Mount Hunt, Dome Peak, Mount Sidney Dobson and Mount Ida – from the Alaska Highway to the base-metal deposits of the Mayo district and then northwards to Dawson City on the Klondike. By the late nineteen-fifties, in country where winter temperatures drop to 70° F. below zero, surveyors were plotting an all-weather highway northwards from Dawson through the eastern foothills of the Mackenzie Mountains, across the oil-rich territory to the Indian settlement of Fort McPherson and thence northwards again to the Eskimo-Indian village of Aklavik on the Mackenzie River, a little south of Canada's Arctic coast.

Airlines, too, launched freight and passenger services towards the Mackenzie Mountains; and oil companies sent helicopters to stake claims in Arctic and subarctic territory flanking a once remote mountain barrier which was suddenly no longer entirely remote or a barrier. But though the Mackenzie Mountains game preserve (69,440 square miles) was established in 1938, the vast miles of the range's highland heart have remained largely untouched by man.

McKinley, Mount

The highest peak in North America. Location *Southern central Alaska.* Height *20,270 feet.* Map *3, C5.* First climbed *Archdeacon Hudson Stuck and party, 1913.*

Before it was named after the man who became the twenty-fourth president of the United States, Mount McKinley was known by several other names. The aboriginal Indian tribes of the region called it Denali, the Home of the Sun. Others referred to it as Tralaika or Doleyka; to the Russians it was Bulshaia Gora. The last three names mean the same thing in three different languages – the Great One.

Like the peaks which surround it, with huge glaciers of polar dimensions creeping down their flanks, it is an arctic mountain. It is also a towering giant, for the valley of the Yukon River from which its northern slopes rise is barely 1,500 feet above the sea; the wilderness of forests and glaciers to the south of it is only slightly more elevated. It sweeps up to its full height in a single gigantic, unbroken crescendo of rock and ice.

Apart from its height, it also provides one of the most striking sights in the world. Its snowy crest dominates the northern horizon from Cook Inlet, 200 miles to the south; it appears like a huge white giant, huddled against the sky, from Fairbanks, 150 miles to the north. It appears solitary and huge, dominating over 300,000 square miles of central Alaska.

The first white man to look upon McKinley was George Vancouver, the English navigator, who saw "distant, stupendous snow mountains" in 1794 without approaching them. It was not until the American purchase of Alaska in 1867 that prospectors and trappers began to penetrate the uncharted interior. In 1889 Frank Densmore penetrated the McKinley region, returning with such fabulous tales that for years the Yukon prospectors called the mountain Densmore's Peak. W. A. Dickey, in 1896, reached the outer edge of the great glacier belt. It was he who named the giant McKinley, in honor of the man who was then presidential candidate – and this time the name stuck.

George Eldrige and Robert Muldrow of the United States Geological Survey established the height at 20,270 feet early in the twentieth century. The first actual attempt to climb it was made in 1903 under the leadership of Judge Wickersham, an eminent citizen of Fairbanks. He and his three companions were soon halted by unscalable ice-walls and turned back.

In 1903 and 1906 Dr Frederick Cook – later to win world-wide notoriety for his claim that he was the discoverer of the North Pole – came to Alaska. On the first occasion he did little more than explore the surrounding passes and glaciers, but in 1906 he decided to make a serious attempt in the company of Herschel Parker and Belmore Browne, whose later battles with McKinley were considerable feats of endurance and courage. This time, however, they were stopped by the confused wilderness south of the peak and did not find an approach to the summit, while Cook himself went on alone. He hired a packer named Edward Barrill and disappeared for several weeks. Then he reappeared with the claim that he had climbed McKinley – and showed photographs which he said he had taken on the summit. In his book *To the Top of the Continent* he described his tremendous struggles to reach the top and the magnificent view from it. Although Parker and Browne were highly sceptical, they could not conclusively prove their suspicions of fraud.

The next, perhaps most colorful chapter in the conquest of McKinley began in the spring of 1910, in a saloon at Fairbanks. Three prospectors, Pete Anderson, Billy Taylor and Charley McGonogol, decided, for reasons that have remained a mystery, to make the ascent. They were complete greenhorns as mountaineers and their only capital was $500, provided by McPhee, the saloon-keeper. Their equipment was most primitive, nor did they make any exploratory investigations. Yet – they did it. Or rather, almost did. They chose to approach the mountain by way of the Muldrow Glacier – and their instinct was sound. But even so their route was heartbreakingly difficult. The broad glacier, rising to 11,000 feet, was a jagged, dangerous waste land of ice-cliffs and crevasses. For days they cut and scrambled their way through the ice to the top.

There, where no man had ever stood before, they camped, with the summit still nearly two miles above them. It was amazing enough that they had got so far, but they were still in fine fettle. They waited a few days for fine weather and then struck out for the top. But at 17,000 feet they made their big mistake, for, finding themselves between two peaks – the true summit, to the south, and its twin peak to the north, only 300 feet lower – they climbed the wrong one.

As they dragged themselves up the final slope, McGonogol collapsed with only 500 feet to go. But Anderson and Taylor stood at last on the roof of North America and gazed across the bare waste of Alaska. They shook hands, firmly plant-ed the 14-foot flagstaff which they had hauled all the way up the glacier, along the ice-ridge and up the last peak, and raised the Stars and Stripes. Then they started down, picking up McGonogol on the way. They made the whole climb from the glacier camp to the top and back in a single day.

It was not until the summer of 1913 that Archdeacon Hudson Stuck with his companions, Harry Karstens, Robert Tatum, Walter Harper and two young Indians from the Nenana mission school, named Johnny and Esaias, reached the true summit of Mount McKinley. In the meantime Parker and Browne had made three unsuccessful attempts during which they had come near to losing their lives. Stuck and his companions cut a three-mile staircase in the ice – and on June 23, 1913, they stood on the true summit. They made a rough cross of birch staves which they had carried with them, thrust it into the deep snow and said a solemn, joyful Te Deum. From the peak they could clearly see the flagstaff which, three years earlier, the three lucky prospectors had planted on the lower summit.

Nineteen years later, in the spring of 1932, two separate expeditions tackled McKinley. Erling Strom, a well-known Norwegian-Ameri-

Mount McKinley, in Alaska, the highest peak in North America

can skier, Alfred Lindley of Minneapolis, Harry Liek, superintendent of the McKinley National Park (established in 1917) and Grant Pearson, a park ranger, made up the first. They scaled both the north and south peaks successfully, following the same route as the earlier parties. They found on Karstens Ridge a thermometer left by Stuck – which bore out the Archdeacon's theory that in winter McKinley was the coldest place in the world. The indicator had dropped past the end of the scale, which was 95° below zero, and was stuck in the bulb. The temperature must have sunk to at least 100° below zero – the greatest natural cold ever recorded.

The second expedition, led by Allen Carpe, a most accomplished American mountaineer, had a plane to land supplies at the head of the Muldrow Glacier. He had only one companion, Theodore Koven. Both of them were killed – Koven by a fall into a crevasse, Carpe by some cause never established. Only Koven's body was found by the Strom party on the descent of the mountain.

Since then McKinley has been climbed several times and during the Second World War the United States Army and the American Alpine Club used it to test men and equipment under the severest conditions possible in arctic or mountain warfare. Seven men out of the 17 participants reached the summit on two successive days. In 1961, six Italian climbers led by Riccardo Cassin made the first ascent of McKinley's sheer south face, long known to climbers as the "impossible wall."

Makalu

The fifth highest mountain in the world. Location Nepal-Tibet border, northeast Nepal Himalayas. Height 27,824 feet. Map 11, F5. First climbed Jean Franco and party, 1955.

George Leigh Mallory wrote of the Himalayas: "The great mountains give their flashes of beauty: Makalu is indescribably impressive; but on the whole they are disappointing and infinitely less beautiful than the Alps."

This was the view of the man who was to lose his life during the last of his tenacious and brave attempts on Everest. Makalu, sometimes known as the Armchair Peak because of its cleft formation, remained unconquered and mysterious almost to the day of its first ascent. An isolated pinnacle, 14 miles to the east of Everest, it had been seen and studied at a distance by all Everest climbers, but it was not until 1954 that two expeditions started a serious investigation of the giant's approaches. The first was American, organized by the Sierra Club of California and led by William Siri of the University of California. They tried the south ridge route, but found the mountain not only huge but one of the steepest of the Himalayas – it is, in fact, steeper than Everest. Without a preliminary reconnaissance there was little chance of success, and the Sierra Club climbers turned back at about 23,000 feet.

The second party, led by Sir Edmund Hillary and consisting of New Zealanders, was mainly concerned with exploration and the ascent of some lower, outlying peaks. One of the climbers fell into a crevasse, and Hillary was injured while rescuing his companion. He was found to have cracked three ribs, and made a quick, complete recovery, although for a few days his condition had been reported to be critical. Makalu seems, however, to be unlucky for Sir Edmund: in May, 1961, while leading another expedition, he suffered a mild heart-attack on the mountain, mainly because he had dispensed with oxygen apparatus, and had to be transported back to Katmandu for convalescence.

The third, and successful, expedition to Makalu was French. In the autumn of 1954 a party set out under the leadership of Jean Franco to make a preliminary exploration, and in May 1955 they began the real assault – with unprecedented success. The planning, organization and teamwork of the French were faultless. On May 15 Jean Couzy and Lionel Terray were the first to set foot on the summit. Next day Jean Franco, Guido Magnone and Sirdar Gyalzen repeated the exploit and on May 17 it was the turn of Jean Bouvier, Serge Coupé, Pierre Leroux and André Vialatte. Of the whole expedition only the doctor and the geologists remained in the last camp.

The Franco party had profited in many ways from the experiences of Maurice Herzog and his companions on Annapurna, taking care, above all, to acclimatize themselves, and their triumph, if undramatic, was well deserved.

Mar, Serra do

A great coastal escarpment. Location *Southern and southeast Brazil*. Height *3,000 feet average, rising to 7,365 feet*. Map *6, F7*.

From the Rio Grande do Sul, northeast of the booming city of Pôrto Alegre, to the Paraíba delta in the northern part of Rio de Janeiro province, the Brazilian Highlands sweep unbroken along the shoreline for 800 miles. Though their height is moderate they have for many years raised an impenetrable barrier to the development of the vast Brazilian hinterland. The effect of this barrier still lingers in the immense country in spite of the railways that were constructed to cross the Serra do Mar in the middle of the nineteenth century – an undertaking which required great feats of engineering, especially in the Santos to São Paulo line. It was because of the tendency of all big cities to hug the coast (with the exception of São Paulo) that Brasilia, the new capital, was deliberately established near the geographical center of Brazil, in an attempt to force the population to move inland and open up the still partly uncharted forests and tablelands.

The escarpment crosses the eastern part of the states of Paraná, São Paulo and Santa Catalina. Its various sections are named Serra dos Orgãos (which contains the highest elevation, the 7,365-foot Pedro do Sino), Serra da Estrela, Serra do Cubatão and Serra Paranapiacaba. It divides the coastal strip from the interior plateau, and all major streams drain westward toward the Paraná River from the gentle inland slope. In the front part of the range the average rainfall often reaches 150 inches a year, which means dense, subtropical vegetation. There are only a few gaps in the range, surrounding the valleys of short coastal streams (Ribeira de Iguape, Joinvile lowland, Itajaí Açu) or forming a few deep inlets (Guanabara Bay, Paranaguá Bay); otherwise the escarpment runs close to the coast and even reappears offshore as rocky islands – notably the Ilha Grande, São Sebastião and Santa Catarina.

North of Rio several well-known resorts have been established in the Serra do Mar – Petrópolis, Nova Friburgo and Teresópolis are the most important – to which the more affluent classes can escape from the sweltering summer heat in which even the famous Copacabana Beach becomes too hot to bear. Near Santos, the port of São Paulo, the largest hydro-electric plant of Brazil has been established at Cubatão, making use of the sheer drop from the crest of the escarpment.

Maritime Alps

The westernmost section of the Alps. Location *Franco-Italian border*. Height *Varying from 9,039 feet to 10,817 feet*. Map *8, B10*.

The Maritime Alps extend in an arc of 120 miles from the Ligurian Apennines at Cadibona Pass (east-southeast) to the Cottian Alps at Maddalena Pass (west-northwest). They only just qualify for Alpine status and their easternmost boundary is still debated. They are generally considered to include the Ligurian Alps, and their lower western spurs, which reach out towards the Rhône valley, form the Provence Alps.

East of the Col de Tende (6,145 feet), which carries both road and railway on the most direct route from Nice to Turin, the country rises to scrub-covered summits that place them more truly among the Ligurian Apennines; to the west, as the ridges rise and then turn northwest towards permanent snow, the quality of the country becomes more genuinely Alpine.

From the Col de Tende to the Col de l'Argentière (6,545 feet), the northern boundary of the group, the peaks spread out in pleasant, if undistinguished, array. The highest is Punta Argentera (10,817 feet) with Cima dei Gelas (10,312 feet) and Mont Tinibras (9,944 feet) next in height. Glaciers are small and more reminiscent of the Pyrenees than of the Alps.

The Maritimes, however, can boast one quality that makes them unique and worthy of interest. Only from these summits can one see both the great peaks of the Alps and the blue waters of the Mediterranean.

Matterhorn

A huge rock pyramid, second highest peak of the central Pennine Alps. Location *Swiss-Italian border.* Height *14,701 feet.* Map *8, C8.* First climbed *Edward Whymper and party, 1865.*

Rising between Zermatt on the north and the Val Tournanche on the south, the Matterhorn looks from the Swiss side like an isolated obelisk, though it is really the butt end of a ridge, with the Swiss side not nearly as steep and difficult as the grand terraced walls of the Italian slope. It has been eroded by wind and weather until its four ridges and four faces jut from the surrounding glaciers to a needle-sharp snow ridge, towering over the neighboring peaks. Its dramatic history has made it the subject of radio plays, films, and numerous books. Charles Gos devoted a whole volume to the lore of "Le Cervin," the earlier French name for the great peak. And of course, the great achievement of Edward Whymper, perhaps the most outstanding Victorian mountaineer, was the first ascent of the Matterhorn – a triumph marred by tragedy when,

Gustave Doré's famous engraving of Whymper and his companions at the summit of the Matterhorn

during the descent, four of his companions, Lord Francis Douglas, the Rev. C. Hudson, Mr Hadow and the famous alpine guide Michel Croz, plunged to their deaths.

Most of the early attempts to climb the Matterhorn, as Victorian alpinism developed during the later eighteen-fifties, were made via the Italian ridge. Only the three brothers, Alfred, Charles and Sandbach Parker, and, in a curious winter effort, T. S. Kennedy, tried the Swiss ridge before 1865.

Then the seven-man party, led jointly and disastrously by Hudson and Whymper, found it immeasurably easier than had been expected.

But on the way down tragedy struck. Hadow slipped, knocking Croz over; Hudson was dragged violently from his steps and Douglas after him. The rope broke and the four men were hurled down, falling from precipice to precipice,

The Matterhorn disaster (engraving by Doré)

to the Matterhorn Glacier, almost 4,000 feet below. Douglas's body was never found; the other three were buried in the Zermatt churchyard.

In 1874, Whymper climbed the Matterhorn a second time, but after that he never climbed in Europe again.

Three days after the Whymper ascent Jean-Antoine Carrel with three other Italians made the first ascent from Italy. The Rev. Julius Elliot made the second ascent from Zermatt in 1868 and was followed three days later by Professor John Tyndall, a rival of Whymper in the early attempts, who made the first traverse of the mountain.

In 1871 Lucy Walker became the first woman to climb the Matterhorn – though four years earlier Felicité Carrel, a relative of Jean-Antoine, had got to within 350 feet of the summit. A few weeks later Miss Walker was followed by her determined American rival, Meta Brevoort, who was the first woman to make a traverse of the mountain, ascending from Zermatt and descending to Breuil.

Since then the Matterhorn has become one of the most-climbed mountains in the world. Today it has been scaled by every ridge and every face. The more frequented routes bristle with fixed ropes and ladders, and there are six huts to aid climbers.

The great mountain has been tamed, yet its magic remains. It is a monument and a legend. In the words of James Ramsey Ullman: "As long as men raise their eyes to its heights, they will remember the time when Edward Whymper and his companions set out upon their great adventure – and struggled and won and lost."

Mauna Kea

The highest island mountain in the world. Location *Central Hawaii.* Height *13,825 feet.* Map *2, E10.*

Mauna Kea, a dormant volcano with numerous cinder cones, rises just north of the center of the island of Hawaii. It is not only the highest island mountain in the world but can be counted as the highest individual mountain on earth – over 32,000 feet – if we reckon its height from its base, 18,000 feet below sea level.

"White Mountain," so named from the snow on its summit, blends with Mauna Loa in an intervening plateau. It has a much smaller base than its still active rival, but its slopes are steeper and its crowning cinder cone is the supreme elevation in the Pacific Ocean. It was the pre-historic volcanic activity of Mauna Kea that covered the Kohala Mountains with lava on the land side (these are the remains of the oldest mountains of Hawaii). Mauna Kea is not nearly as old as the Kohala Mountains, but there is no record of its eruption, nor do its lavas appear recent.

The Hawaiians have woven as many legends around Mauna Kea as around Mauna Loa. According to one of them, Mauna Kea was the domain of the goddess Poliahu, the inveterate enemy of Pele, the beautiful goddess of fire who reigns supreme over Mauna Loa. It was out of their rivalry and their recurrent, fearful battles that earthquakes, eruptions and rivers of fire were born, and the present configuration of the islands is all their work, the outcome of their divine conflict.

Meije

A rocky peak with three separate summits. Location *Massif du Pelvoux, Dauphiné Alps, southeast France.* Height *13,081 feet (Grand Pic.)* Map *8, B9.* First climbed *Baron Boileau de Castelnau and Pierre and Joseph Gaspard, 1877.*

Rising as a huge castellated rock wall between the hamlet of La Bérarde in the Veneon Valley and La Grave on the Route Napoleon, the Meije was the last major summit to be conquered by the Victorian pioneer mountaineers. Only when all the peaks of the Valais had fallen in the eighteen-sixties did attention become concentrated on the remaining unclimbed summits of

the Dauphiné. The Meije was a peak involving little snow and ice work but requiring cragmanship of a high order.

From La Grave, on the north, the Meije is seen as a single peak, but from the Etancons Glen which stretches up to its great walls from La Bérarde, its true form can be appreciated. It consists of a rocky ridge, running almost due east and west, which rises into three serrated peaks, separated from each other by sharply incised cols. The western peak is the highest and beyond it, farther west again, lies the great sabre-cut of the Brèche de la Meije. High on the southern face of the peak lies the small and steep Glacier Carre.

The first major attack on the mountain was made in 1870 by W. A. B. Coolidge, the young American climber, with his aunt Meta Brevoort, the pioneer woman mountaineer, for whom the conquest of the Meije was an obsession. They reached the central peak but found access to the higher western peak cut off, as did other mountaineers who followed. Others tried with no success and Coolidge himself tried again in the summer of 1877. A month after his return to England he learned that the brilliant French climber, Boileau de Castelnau, had reached the summit on August 16 with the two Gaspards, father and son, local guides from La Bérarde.

The following year Coolidge set out for the mountain once again. "The Meije had exercised, and indeed still exercises," he wrote later, "the same strange influence over me which the Matterhorn had on its early explorers; and though I knew I could trust my two faithful guides, yet I scarcely dared hope that it would be given to me to attain the much desired summit."

Coolidge succeeded after a slow ascent that was to involve a perilous night bivouac. "It was a moment of my life which I can never forget. . ." he wrote. "The Meije, in my eyes, had been a mountain to be climbed for its own sake, and not for the sake of the view – a fault or merit which I cannot attribute to many other mountains."

The first ascent of the south face of the Meije

was made in 1912 by Angelo Dibona, the brothers Guido and Max Mayer and the guide Luigi Rizzi. It was on this dangerous cliff that Emil Zsigmondy, a noted Austrian climber (by profession a doctor) was killed. "And what have we left but hope?" were the last words he was reported to have spoken before he fell. In the winter of 1925–26 the first ski ascent was made by members of the French Alpine Club, and in 1932 Micheline Morin, Nea Morin and Alice Damesne made a traverse of the Meije with neither guide nor male climber in their party – to prove that women could claim equal skill and courage with men in mountaineering.

Meru, Mount

An extinct, partly shattered volcano. Location *Northern Tanganyika.* Height *14,979 feet.* Map *9, G.7*

Although lower by some 4,500 feet than its volcanic companion, Kilimanjaro, Meru is still a considerable mountain. The greater steepness of its sides makes it from some angles a more striking spectacle than its neighbor, only 44 miles away. Yet some of the earlier maps do not even suggest the existence of a peak other than Kilimanjaro in the region.

Meru's eastern face was apparently blasted away during an eruption. One of the less familiar views of the mountain shows it as a long, asymmetrical curving crest, with a sharply defined pointed peak near the steeper end. Although there are in fact twin craters, the mountain is visible as a single cone from a great distance. At Moshi, as Julian Huxley wrote, "the snow cone of Kibo (as the higher of Kilimanjaro's two craters is called) hangs miraculously over us; fifty miles to the westward is the lovely shape of Meru, almost as high as Mont Blanc, but never snow-covered. . . At sunset, when the Masai steppe beyond is plum-color, and the fine cone of Meru deep violet against the orange sky, the view is unforgettable."

Meru has often been climbed, but can still provide ascents of an alpine standard even on some of the existing routes. It is an excellent rain-collector and its volcanic soil is highly fertile. Its slopes are watered by innumerable streams and Arusha, headquarters of the Northern Province, on its southern base, is the center of a busy farming area. Coffee is the main crop; but since 1948, when pawpaw trees were first planted to provide shade, papain, a substance used in meat-canning, has also proved a highly profitable product and has rapidly brought increased prosperity to the district.

The lower slopes of the mountain are forested and shelter a large animal population, among them elephants and lions. Savanna supervenes above the forest belt; the rocky summit is entirely barren, a small subsidiary cone being visible inside the main crater. The Ngurdoto crater, 24 miles from Arusha, is not strictly part of Meru, but deserves mention for its large population of big game.

Minya Konka

The highest peak of the Tahsüeh Mountains. Location *Sikang province, China.* Height *24,900 feet.* Map *10, F6.* First climbed *Terris Moore, Arthur Emmons, Richard L. Burdsall and Jack Young, 1932.*

Minya Konka (or Minya Gongkar) rises above the ruck of mountains like a white pyramid into the blue Tibetan sky, 30 miles south of the little border town of Kangting, the "gateway to Tibet." But the pack roads lie deep down in the narrow valleys, and the snows are not visible, or even suspected, until one travels southwards or westwards from Kangting and crosses one of the long, parallel, north-south corrugations which form the outer ramparts of the Tibetan plateau.

The climate of the interior of western China is so dry that the snowline is nearly 18,000 feet; so that to the traveler crossing Szechwan from the red basin in the center to the emerald green pastures in the west the country looks brown rather than white. But south of Kangting there are passes 12,000 or 14,000 feet high and on a clear day there is a superb view of the snows. From here Minya Konka is less than ten miles distant.

Missionaries and travelers caught a glimpse of this range before the beginning of the twentieth century, but few of them realized that its peaks vied with some of the Himalayan giants in altitude. It was left for a later generation to put forward the absurd guess that it was higher than Mount Everest. The interest of mountaineers was then aroused and on October 28, 1932, Minya Konka was climbed by a Sino-American team led by Richard L. Burdsall. This was the first American party to climb in Central Asia for more than 20 years. It was a remarkable achievement in its own right, for the ascent was made in October, in violent storms and terrible cold. It whetted the appetite of Americans for Himalayan climbing so that they soon became active contenders for other conquests. It was Burdsall's party which established the true height of the peak by triangulation.

The grass slopes of Minya Konka, just below the glittering glaciers, are a paradise of alpine flowers in summer, including dwarf rhododendrons, yellow poppies, slipper orchids and crimson cushion-primulas, while the view from the summit is a fitting reward for the climber. "At such great heights," Burdsall wrote, "the visible horizon is seen at some considerable distance below the true horizon . . . I fancied I could actually see the curvature of the earth. The panorama of tremendous snow peaks. . . had dwindled to a series of mere white patches against the brown plain."

Misti, El

A dormant volcano with snow-capped cone. Location *Southern Peru.* Height *19,166 feet.* Map *6, C6.*

El Misti is the best known, though not the loftiest, of the massive volcanoes which stud the vast uplands of the Cordillera Occidental in the neighborhood of the Peruvian city of Arequipa. Flanked by the volcanoes Chachani and Pichu Pichu, it dominates the city as Fujiyama dominates Tokyo. The perfect form and great height of El Volcán de Arequipa, as it is sometimes called, make it a landmark for a great distance around and a symbol of southern Peru. It seems to have had great religious significance for the Incas and appears in many old Peruvian legends and poems.

Arequipa itself is at an altitude of 7,500 feet above sea level but because of the extremely clear atmosphere it is very difficult to credit the height of Misti from the town. In fact, it rises almost 12,000 feet above it, and though it appears to be very close, in reality it is more than ten miles to the northeast.

The ascent of the mountain, normally made from the side facing away from Arequipa, may be made without setting foot on the mountain. After an approach in a car, the traveler may mount a mule and be conveyed to the summit; breaking the journey halfway up for the night. The snowline is very high and the main hazard involved in the ascent is the onset of the *sorroche*, the breathlessness and headache induced by altitude in the unacclimatized. The symptoms may be likened to those of severe influenza. The views from the snow-field on top are, however, ample compensation for any discomfort.

In the black, ashy crater of another volcano nearby archeologists have unearthed ruined temples of prehistoric times.

Monashee Mountains

Most westerly of the interior ranges of British Columbia. Location *Canadian Rocky Mountains, British Columbia.* Height *8,000 feet, rising to 10,650 feet.* Map *3, F9.* Explored *Milton and Cheadle, 1863.*

The Monashee range – the word is Celtic, meaning "Mountain of Peace" – extends about 200 miles north from the Washington line between the Columbia River and Arrow Lakes on the east

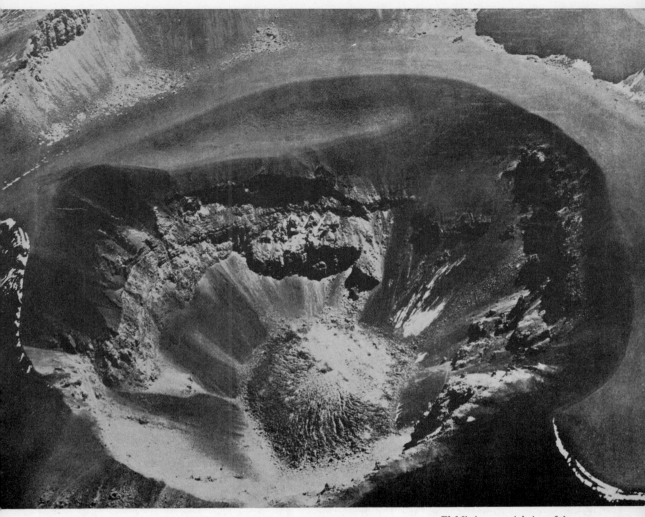

El Misti – an aerial view of the crater

and the upper North Thompson River, Shuswap Lake and Okanagan Lake on the west. At one time these mountains were known as the Gold Range, but this name is now restricted to a narrow strip of territory along the western shore of the Arrow Lakes and the Columbia River,

south of Revelstoke. The area contains gold as well as silver, copper, zinc and lead.

The peaks – which include Hallam Peak (10,560 feet) and Cranberry Mountain (9,470 feet) – form a watershed between the Columbia and North Thompson rivers, extending from the bend of the Canoe River southward across the Canadian Pacific Railway at Eagle Pass as far as Upper Arrow Lake. The greatest uplift is concentrated between the Clemina and Blue River stations of the Canadian National Railway on the North Thompson River. Mount Monashee (10,650 feet), the highest point, was first ascended in 1952 by Hendricks, Hubbart and Wexler. The peaks are not difficult, but the approaches are long and arduous.

When Milton and Cheadle descended the North Thompson valley in 1863, they saw and described a striking snow peak at the northern end of the range which they called Mount Milton. It is visible from the railroad and is now known as Albreda Peak. The triple snow-summits of Mount Begbie, just south of Revelstoke, form the other familiar peak of this range.

Mönch

A famous peak of the Bernese Oberland. Location *Central Switzerland.* Height *13,468 feet.* Map *8, C8.* First climbed *Dr S. Porges and Christian Almer, 1857.*

Forming part of the great north wall of the Bernese Oberland and crossed by two passes (Ober-Mönchjoch, 11,870 feet, and Unter-Mönchjoch, 11,680 feet), the Mönch is more monumental than the Jungfrau to the west and less spectacular in form than the Eiger to the east. It was not an easy mountain to tackle and remained unconquered when the Jungfrau, the Finsteraarhorn and all the peaks of the Wetterhorn had been climbed.

In 1855 a Russian Princess, Helene Kolzow-Massalsky, arrived in Grindelwald and decided to climb the Mönch. She was better known under her pen name of Dora d'Istria and certainly possessed considerable imagination. Four guides carried her up the flank of the mountain in a chair; then, where this was no longer possible, two took her arms, the third pushed from behind and the fourth pulled from the front.

She suffered acutely from mountain sickness during the night spent in a cave, reached the foot of the final snow ridge in a state of collapse and abandoned the ascent at this point. However, in her book about her Swiss tour, she described her arrival on the summit, where she "kissed the Russian flag and raised her heart to God." Three of her guides signed a testimonial affirming her first ascent and praising her for her "heroic endurance." Christian Almer, however, refused to be a party to the deception.

It was not until 1857 that Almer made the first real ascent with Dr S. Porges of Vienna. They followed the east ridge from the Unter-Mönchjoch. It was an extremely difficult climb, and both men were forced to sleep on the mountain both before and after the climb. "The very steep part of rock was worse than any I have encountered during the ascent of the Wetterhorn, the Jungfrau or Monte Rosa," commented Dr Porges, who left a red flag on the summit to mark his success.

The first ascent on skis was made in November, 1901, by Dr Henry Hoek, an Anglo-Dutchman, and the north face of the Mönch was first climbed in 1921 by Hans Lauper and Max Liniger. The Gergli hut of the Swiss Alpine Club now stands within convenient striking distance of the peak and the ascent can be made from here or from the Berghaus on the Jungfraujoch.

Mont-Aux-Sources

A mountain block forming one of the highest areas of the Drakensberg range. Location *Western Natal, South Africa.* Height *10,822 feet.* Map *9, F10.*

The Mont-aux-Sources amphitheater, on the Basutoland-Transvaal border, is the most spectacular section of the Drakensberg wall. Lying at the innermost corner of the range, where it curves to the northeast, the massif includes the Sentinel, the 10,000-foot wall of the amphitheater itself, the Eastern Buttress and the actual peak of Mont-aux-Sources.

The peak is inconspicuous, a small, hill-like protuberance on the level block of lava which forms the upper surface of the mountains at this point. At Beacon Buttress, on the upper plateau near the peak, the borders of Basutoland, Natal, and the Orange Free State meet; on a clear day it is possible to see the Transvaal and Cape Province as well from this point.

The mountain was named by Arbousset and Daumas, two French Protestant missionaries, and the name indicates its chief claim to fame – at least three major rivers have their sources here. The Tugela rises on the summit and cascades spectacularly down the eastern face of the amphitheater. A short distance away is the source of the Elands River, separated from the Tugela by a low, swampy ridge; after a few yards of parallel course, the Elands turns to the north-west, ultimately feeding the Vaal River, the main water-supply of the huge industrial area of the Witwatersrand. Immediately behind the summit rises the Khubedu; it is a tributary of the Orange, South Africa's largest river, into which

the Vaal ultimately flows, but the two streams, rising within a few yards of each other, do not meet until each has flowed nearly 600 miles.

Thoroughly explored before the First World War, the Mont-aux-Sources area is now the site of the Royal Natal National Park, which occupies some 15,000 acres on the northeast side of the range. The opposite side is sparsely populated highland, where the Maluti Mountains begin; they run the whole length of Basutoland and reach 11,000 feet at their highest point, Machache.

Mont Blanc

Highest peak in Europe outside the Caucasus. Location *French Alps.* Height *15,781 feet.* Map *8, B8.* First climbed *Dr Michel-Gabriel Paccard and Jacques Balmat, 1786.*

Until the seventeen-fifties Mont Blanc was commonly known as the "Montagne Maudite" (Accursed Mountain) because of the ill-omens

217

Mont Blanc, the highest peak in western Europe

supposedly surrounding it. The earliest known use of its present name occurs in a letter by St Francois de Sales in 1603.

The first suggestion that it might be possible to climb Mont Blanc was made in 1754 by Jacques Barthélémy Michel du Crest; in 1760, when visiting Chamonix, Horace Bénédict de Saussure, the Swiss natural scientist, offered a prize of two guineas for the discovery of a practical route to the summit. Unsuccessful attempts were made in 1762, 1775, 1783 and 1784 by guides, chamois-hunters and crystal-gatherers from Chamonix. Marc-Theodore Bourrit of Geneva made three assaults (on one of which he was accompanied by Saussure and his son), but all were failures. The first to set foot on the summit were Dr Michel-Gabriel Paccard, the village doctor of Chamonix, and Jacques Balmat, a crystal-gatherer, who acted as his porter. They set out on August 7, 1787, and reached their goal at 7 p.m. on the following day.

Bourrit (who never reached the summit) was extremely jealous of Dr Paccard's success, resenting the fact that he had been beaten by an educated man. He felt that his wounded pride might be healed if the credit for the first ascent could be ascribed to a peasant, and he deliberately launched a campaign of lies and slander to denigrate Dr Paccard's performance and to make Jacques Balmat appear as the real hero. The truth was known in Chamonix and to De Saussure, who was in a position to kill this mendacious propaganda but failed to do so, partly out of jealousy towards Dr Paccard and partly because, for political reasons, he was unwilling to antagonize Bourrit.

The "Balmat legend" therefore persisted and was given worldwide publicity when, in 1832, after Dr Paccard's death, Alexandre Dumas interviewed Jacques Balmat and received from him an account in which his boasts were unrestrained, and which, without verifying any of the evidence, Dumas published. That it was completely untrue has now been proved from a number of contemporary documents including eye-witness accounts, and a critical analysis of the times taken on the different parts of the ascent.

Sixty-one ascents were made between 1786 and 1854. The most famous routes to the summit include three from Chamonix via the Grand Plateau, two from St Gervais via the Aiguille du Goûter and ten from Courmayeur. Most of the ascents were made by Britons, Savoyards and Frenchmen, with Americans, Swiss, Italians, Poles, Swedes, Russians and Germans sharing the honors. The first woman to reach the summit, on July 14, 1808, was Maria Paradis of Chamonix. The first fatal accident occurred on August 20, 1820, during Dr Joseph Hamel's attempt, when three guides were swept into a crevasse by an avalanche and killed. Murray's *Handbook* of 1856 declared tartly: "It is a somewhat remarkable fact that several of those who have made this ascent have been persons of unsound mind."

Professor John Tyndall, the naturalist, made two ascents, in 1857 and 1858. His companions were Thomas Huxley, the great biologist,

Thomas Hirst, and their guide, a Chamonix mountaineer named Simond.

"The summit of the mountain," Tyndall wrote, "is an elongated ridge which has been compared to the back of an ass. It was perfectly manifest that we were dominant over all other mountains; as far as the eye could range Mont Blanc had no competitor... And as our eye ranged over the broad shoulders of the mountain, over ice hills and valleys, plateaus and far-stretching slopes of snow, the conception of its magnitude grew upon us and impressed us more and more..."

Up to 1827 it was always the same route which was followed to the summit. After the disaster of the Hamel party, most climbers avoided the slopes between the Grand Plâteau and the top, following rather the corridor across the Mur de la Côte. In 1855 the Rev. C. Hudson and E. S. Kennedy succeeded in reaching the peak with their party from St Gervais; four years later Hudson managed to scale the Dôme du Gouter; and in 1861 Francis Fox Tuckett and Leslie Stephen climbed the great mountain by the route which Saussure had attempted and abandoned 76 years earlier.

For 50 years Mont Blanc claimed no victims, but in September, 1870, a party of 11 – Randall and Beade of the United States and Corkendale of England, with eight guides and porters – perished after spending two days in a violent snowstorm just beneath the summit. Only five bodies were found above the Mur de la Côte; the other six were never discovered. Four years later the Russian naturalist and traveler, A. D. Fedchenko, lost his life on the Mer de Glace.

In 1872 T. S. Kennedy, accompanied by two guides, Johann Fischer and J. A. Carrel (Whymper's Matterhorn guide) discovered a new route which established a shorter and easier approach from Courmayeur. Fischer later lost his life on the same route, together with the brilliant young mountaineer, J. A. G. Marshall.

A road tunnel through Mont Blanc, to connect France and Italy, and thus considerably shorten the road journey from Paris to Rome, was proposed in 1946, but work was not begun until December, 1958 (on the Italian side) and May, 1959 (on the French side).

There are two observatories on the mountain, one at 14,312 feet on the Bosses du Dromadaire (the northwest ridge) and another just below the summit.

In July, 1960, Mont Blanc was the scene of a remarkable ceremony: members of a religious sect camped high up on the mountain to await the end of the world, which their leader forecast for 2.45 p.m. on July 14. Women began to scream, and a Tyrolean wearing leather shorts began blowing a bugle that represented the trumpet of doom. All this lasted only a minute; then the leader of the Doomsday Cult, Dr Elio Bianca, an Italian pediatrician, announced: "We made a mistake." The *New York Times* reported the fiasco under the headline "WORLD FAILS TO END."

Indeed, Mont Blanc still has new surprises and challenges for the mountaineer and the tourist alike. In March, 1961, two Italians, Walter Bonatti and Giovanni Panei, reached the summit, making the first winter ascent by the so-called "Red Sentinel" route: in August, 1961, three French parachutists made the first successful parachute landing on the mountain – one landed right on the summit.

Mont Blanc, Chain of

The highest Alpine massif, extending about 30 miles. Location *Franco-Italian and Franco-Swiss borders.* Height *Rising to 15,781 feet in Mont Blanc.* Map 8, B8

Bounded by the Col de la Seigne and the Col Ferret and extending from the Little St Bernard Pass to a point overlooking the bend of the Rhône valley at Martigny-Ville, the Chain of Mont Blanc contains not only the highest summit in the Alps but also the famous aiguilles, whose ascent towards the end of the nineteenth century foreshadowed modern rock climbing, and the

Mer de Glace, which was the scene of early glacier exploration and the experiments which helped to establish the principles of glacier movement.

It is a chain rather than a range, since the summits are joined closely together. It drops in only a few places below 11,000 feet; seen from across the Dora Baltea to the south, from Italy, it presents one of the most impressive spectacles in the Alps.

The Grandes Jorasses, the Aiguille Verte and Mont Mallet are three of the 17 peaks of more than 13,000 feet that rise within this group. Other summits are the Mont Blanc du Tacul, Mont Maudit, Aiguille du Géant, Mont Dolent and the Aiguille du Midi. The Dru, the Plan, the Blaitière, the Grépon and the Grands Charmoz are among the most famous of the aiguilles whose conquest was one of the principal events of the "Silver Age" of mountaineering.

From the mid-eighteenth century onwards, exploration of the glaciers of the Mont Blanc chain from Chamonix increased steadily. Their total area on the French side is over 48 square miles. With the spread of mountaineering and the popularity of expeditions, both Chamonix and the village of Courmayeur flourished and expanded.

Numerous glacier traverses of varying difficulty can be made from Chamonix to Courmayeur, the most famous – and the least difficult – being the Col du Géant (11,030 feet), leading through the heart of the Mont Blanc chain, on whose crest Horace Bénédict de Saussure camped for 17 days in 1788.

Of the glaciers, the Mer de Glace, Bossons and Argentière are the best known. There are innumerable hotels and hostels and many of the peaks can be reached by cable railway, but the Chain of Mont Blanc has nevertheless kept much of its beauty and most of its rugged majesty.

Montenegro

A constituent republic of Yugoslavia, largely moun-

tainous. Location *Southern Yugoslavia*. Height *Rising to 5,735 feet*. Map *7, F8*.

The serpentine road from the Bay of Kotor climbs steeply into the heart of Crna Gora, the country of the Black Mountain or Montenegro. It used to be marked with numerous crosses and small wayside shrines in memory of the drivers who had lost their lives on it and the even more numerous people who were killed in the seemingly endless wars waged throughout the centuries by the tall, proud Montenegrins against their various enemies.

Today Montenegro is the smallest and most thinly populated republic within the Yugoslav Federation; its area is 5,343 square miles, and its population under 400,000. Its former capital, Cetinje, little more than an overgrown village, has been declared a "historical monument" and Titograd, the new capital, has been established near Lake Skadar.

Bounded by the Adriatic Sea, Bosnia, Herzegovina, Serbia and Albania, and lying at the southern end of the Dinaric Alps, this mountainous country consists of two main regions. Montenegro proper is barren and karstlike; it culminates in the Lovcen (5,735 feet), a towering basalt peak. The Zeta River separates it from the higher Brda, culminating in the Durmitor, Komovi and the North Albanian Alps; here there are the forests and pastures. There is a narrow strip on the Adriatic, between the Bojana River, which forms the border with Albania, and the Gulf of Kotor. The chief plain of Montenegro is the Zeta lowland.

This was the homeland of the first Serbian kings, the fastness to which the Christian Serbs retired when the Turks overran the Balkans in the fifteenth century. While the whole of the Balkans and most of Hungary fell to the Moslem conqueror, Montenegro was never completely conquered. It was a home for heroes of the resistance movement against the Turks; as it was again, more recently, against the Italians and Germans in the Second World War. An ideal guerilla country, with a long tradition of a harsh code of vendetta and tribal feud, this land of gray, inhospitable mountains has always fought fiercely for independence. Her most famous king, Nikita, was a skilful diplomatist who married off his handsome daughters to kings and grand dukes and was dubbed "the father-in-law of Europe." It was only the First World War that brought his country into Yugoslavia as a province; and even today the Crna Gora has a large amount of cultural and economic autonomy.

Stock raising – mostly sheep and goats – provides the leading source of revenue; the chief crops are corn and wheat in the plains, barley and rye in the mountains and fruit, nuts and vineyards on the coast. There is no manufacturing and very little home industry. The transportation system of Montenegro is still under-developed, with a few motor roads and narrow-gauge railways. There is one important monastery at Moraca, dating from the thirteenth century, near the delightful health resort of Kolasin, with a church of extraordinary beauty and well-preserved Serbo-Byzantine murals.

Monte Piana

An isolated mountain. Location *Eastern Dolomites, Italy*. Height *7,625 feet*. Map *8, G7*.

In general shape, Monte Piana is a cone, the top of which seems to have been sliced off – neatly, but not quite horizontally. As one ascends the mountain, the flat top reveals itself as a limestone pavement, like an unending series of giant molars. But the natural fissures in the porous rock have been enlarged by man – here, as indeed on the neighboring mountainsides, Austrian troops entrenched themselves for almost three years in the First World War.

On Monte Piana the signs of war are more evident than elsewhere, for this was a commanding local position – almost all around the limestone pavement there are cliffs several hundred feet high and nearly vertical. The climbing hostel at the end of the track is full of rusty relics and on the mountain top one can still occasionally find old mess tins, decaying boots, pieces of hand grenade, or links and cases from machine-gun ammunition; in one place a pathetic cross, wreathed in barbed wire, still stands. There are concrete emplacements and a monument to the dead.

Here the Austrians fought the Italians in a bitter local war – in many cases those who had until then lived peaceably together in the area found themselves on opposite sides. At the end of the war the Austrians were pushed back, the mountains were given Italian names and today the Alpini practice mountain tactics nearby.

Monte Rosa

A great, glacier-covered mountain mass with ten summits. Location *Pennine Alps, Italo-Swiss border.* Height *15,203 feet (highest summit).* Map *8, C8.* First climbed *(highest summit) Rev. Charles Hudson and party, 1855.*

Monte Rosa has the best of both worlds. On its northern flanks great glaciers stream down to the mountain pastures above Zermatt, while on the south the line of summit peaks breaks steeply in great precipices to the rich luxuriance of the Italian valleys. In few places is the contrast between northern and southern Europe more dramatically pointed or more beautiful.

The great massif of Monte Rosa, with the Italo-Swiss border running along its crest, rises southeast of Zermatt, at the junction of two lines of high country – the north-south string of peaks to the east of the trench in which Zermatt lies, and the east-west wall of summits which block the prospect to the south of the village. At the angle lies Monte Rosa.

The position of the massif – its name originates in the Aostan patois word *roëse*, meaning a glacier – gives it great prominence from many points in Italy. The five main summits are the Dufour-spitze (15,203 feet), named after the Swiss

General Dufour, head of the great survey which first accurately fixed the position of these points, the Grenzgipfel (15,194 feet), the Nordend (15,132 feet), the Zumsteinspitze (15,004 feet) and the Signalkuppe (14,965 feet).

The exploration of the Monte Rosa massif began in the late eighteenth and early nineteenth centuries. In August, 1778, Jean Joseph Beck of Gressoney, a domestic servant, collected a party and took it up to the Lysjoch (13,625 feet) – an Alpine record until Mont Blanc was climbed. It was in 1801 that Dr Pietro Giordani made a solitary ascent of the peak which was later named after him. The Vincent Pyramid (13,829 feet) was climbed in 1819 by a son of one of the participants in Beck's 1778 expedition. The Signal-kuppe or Punta Gnifetti was first climbed by Giovanni Gnifetti, the parish priest of Alagna, on August 9, 1842. J. Zumstein made five attempts to reach the highest summit of Monte Rosa, once spending a night alone in a crevasse at 14,000 feet. In 1820 he succeeded in climbing the Zumsteinspitze.

Of the two rocky horns of the Dufourspitze, the lower was climbed in 1854 by the three Smyth brothers led by Alrich Lauener; next year came the conquest of the culminating point by a large Anglo-Swiss party. It was a happy coincidence that the conquest of the highest Monte Rosa summit was achieved on the national Swiss fête day.

Three years later Professor John Tyndall made his solitary ascent of the same peak. The first winter ascent was made on January 26, 1884, by the great mountain photographer, Vittorio Sella, with the guides J. J. and Daniel Maquignaz. Geoffrey Winthrop Young, the brilliant British climber, climbed the difficult mountain *after* his right leg had been amputated because of severe injuries received on the Italian front in the First World War. The Grenzgipfel was gained in 1851 by the Schlagintweit brothers. Other notable ascents were that of the Nordend (in 1861), the climb made by Achille Ratti, later Pope Pius XI, in 1889 and the expedition of

Queen Margherita of Italy in 1893 to the Punta Gnifetti. Her retinue included two dogs and was formally welcomed on the summit by a special committee of the Italian Alpine Club.

Monte Viso

Highest peak of the Cottian Alps. Location *North-west Italy*. Height *12,602 feet*. Map *8, C10*. First climbed *William Mathews jr, 1861*.

Standing to the south of the main Alpine watershed and protruding into the Lombard Plain like a gigantic buttress, Monte Viso – the Mons Vesulus of the ancient world and the birthplace of the River Po – for long enjoyed a reputation for inaccessibility almost as formidable as that of the Matterhorn. When William Mathews explored the peak in 1860, he wrote: "Day by day men have watched it crimson-flushed at sunrise, and in the evening seen it standing out with clear-cut profile against the western sky; quarters of cities and streets innumerable have been named after it; but up to within the last two years no attempt has been made to set foot upon its summit... Writers seem to have regarded its precipitous contour rather as an excuse for inaction than as a spur to enterprise."

When seen from Turin, as indeed from closer quarters, the rocky tiers of Monte Viso appear almost perpendicular, and they are in fact so steep that the mountain carries only one minor glacier.

Although such a spectacular sight – "Monte Viso" because it could be seen so easily – the peak is merely the outlier of an extensive system of ridge and counter-ridge which was only poorly surveyed even a century ago. J. D. Forbes had circumambulated the group in 1839 and Edward Whymper had reached the Col de Viso in 1860, on his first mountain tour. But the best maps for the French side of the peak, Mathews found, were still those of the Dauphiné, published between 1749 and 1754. Little was known of the problems which would have to be faced on the slopes of the Viso itself and it says much for Mathews' sense of mountain topography that all went well when, in 1861, he tackled the peak by the southern face. There were loose rocks but no insuperable difficulties and at 9.20 a.m. the party stood on the summit. "The upper sky is one unbroken vault of glorious blue; our standing place is the loftiest summit within a radius of 40 miles, and not one of the innumerable snow-peaks in the north and west is dimmed by the faintest trace of a cloud," wrote Mathews. The following year the indefatigable Francis Fox Tuckett spent a night on the summit, while in 1863 the first Italian ascent was made and in 1879 Lucy Walker became the first woman to reach the top.

Mont Vélan

A peak near the Great St Bernard Pass. Location *Central Pennines, Switzerland.* Height *12,353 feet.* Map *8, C8.* First climbed *J. L. Murith, 1779.*

The ascent of the Vélan, first made more than 180 years ago by a botanically-minded canon of the neighboring Great St Bernard Hospice, presents no real difficulty, yet the peak has retained a surprising popularity. The reason probably lies both in the fine snow protuberance which rises above the rocky upper slopes and in the fine view obtainable from the summit, which embraces the range of Mont Blanc, the Bernese Oberland and the Graian Alps.

Alfred Wills described its magic thus: "When we saw it, the peak just overtopped the clouds; and I think there must have been considerable refraction, for it looked higher than any mountain I ever saw..." William Mathews jr, who ascended it in 1854, wrote: "As we were deploring the dreary monotony of the route, the snowy dome of the Vélan burst suddenly into sight, and shone gloriously in the sunlight at the head of the valley." And he paid this eloquent tribute to the view that opens from its summit: "...I have never seen an Alpine view of such exquisite perfection... Far away above our heads a thin veil of gray mist was stretched over the sky, dimming the sun sufficiently to relieve the eyesight, without destroying the light and shade. As far as the eye could reach in any direction there was not the smallest fleck of vapor to break the beautiful outlines of the Great Alps. We were, of course, far above the long sub-Alpine ridge which divides the Val d'Entremont from the Val Ferret. We could consequently see the whole range of Mont Blanc stretching in unapproached majesty from the Col de la Seigne to the Mont Catogne, with the snowy summit of the mountain itself, the wonderful obelisk of the Géant, and the great glaciers which fall into the Allée Blanche. Southward were the many untrodden summits of the Graian Alps, and a little to the right, in the dim distance, the faraway peaks of the Dauphiné. . ."

All those untrodden peaks have since been conquered, but the view from the summit of Mont Vélan is still as breath-taking as ever.

Mummery, Mount

A twin-peaked mountain. Location *Southeast British Columbia, in the Canadian Rocky Mountains.* Height *10,918 feet.* Map *3, F9.* First climbed *Burr, Cabot, Peabody and Walcott, with the guides G. Feuz and C. Kaufmann, 1906.*

Mount Mummery, named after A. F. Mummery, the outstanding British climber who vanished in the Himalayas in 1895, rises in Hamber National Park, lifting its double snow-peaks above the heavily wooded valley of the Blaeberry River, 65 miles northwest of Banff. The old fur-trade route of the North-West Company, descending from the Continental Divide at Howse Pass, ran past it. David Thompson, the early explorer, passed this way in 1807, but the route was discontinued after 1811 when the more northerly Athabaska Pass was chosen in order to avoid the hostile Piegan Indians.

The mountain stands at the southeast angle of the Freshfield group, which drains through an icefield of 16 square miles on a glacial tongue three miles in length, forming a principal source of the North Saskatchewan River.

The glacier was discovered in 1859 by Dr Hector, of the Palliser expedition. Mummery's old climbing companion, J. N. Collie, first visited the group and named its peaks in 1897; the first ascent was made nine years later. Mount Mummery is not the highest summit in the area but rises in a section still remote, requiring several days of horse-back travel, and offers some of the most magnificent scenery in Canada.

Muztagh Tower

A Himalayan peak. Location *Central Karakoram,* *Kashmir.* Height *23,860 feet.* Map *11, D3.* First climbed *J. M. Hartog, J. Brown, I. McNaught-Davis and T. Patey, 1956.*

The Muztagh Tower lies on the main continental watershed between the basins of the Baltoro and Sarpo Laggo glaciers. Though many of the earlier travelers in the Karakoram – among them Henry Haversham Godwin-Austen and Colonel Francis Younghusband – must have seen the peak, it was first mentioned by Martin Conway, who explored the Baltoro Glacier in 1892, and who described it as "the finest mountain in the district." He added that its extremely precipitous appearance from the upper reaches of the Baltoro Glacier is deceptive.

In spite of this, the peak was long regarded as unclimbable. As late as 1935 it was described by R. L. S. Irving as "Nature's last stronghold. . . probably the most inaccessible of all great peaks." The legend of its inaccessibility was probably due almost entirely to the publication of Vittorio Sella's famous photograph of the Tower, taken on the Duke of Abruzzi's Karakoram expedition of 1909. "It appears, and perhaps is, a true monolith," wrote Filippo de Filippi in the official account of the expedition, "a rocky mass of single formation – without a trace of breaks or divisional planes – no other of any comparable size is known to exist on the globe. . ." Yet a photograph taken from a different angle showed it to be by no means monolithic in form. There are, in fact, other peaks of comparable height which conform more closely to this description and are probably much more formidable.

In 1956 two expeditions set out to attempt to climb the Muztagh Tower a British party, led by J. M. Hartog, and a French one led by Guido Magnone. The British party climbed from the Chararan Glacier and established Camp 3 on a col at the foot of the northwest ridge. On July 5, J. Brown and I. McNaught-Davis established Camp 4 at about 21,500 feet on the ridge and the following day reached the west summit after an extremely difficult climb.

They were followed on July 7 by J. M. Hartog and T. Patey, who crossed the west summit and reached the east summit, a few feet higher. On both occasions they were overtaken by night and forced to bivouac above Camp 4. Hartog's feet were badly frostbitten. On July 12 and 13 the French party reached the east summit from the opposite side. Before this no major peak in the Himalayas or Karakoram had been climbed by more than one route, and only rarely had other summits been reached by all the climbers of respective expeditions. Though it is not among the "giants," the ascent of the Muztagh Tower was probably the most difficult achieved in the Karakoram.

Namcha Barwa

The highest peak of the Assam Himalayas. Location *Eastern Assam Himalayas, China.* Height *25,445 feet.* Map *11, H4.* Explored *Captain H. T. Morshead and others, 1912.*

Namcha Barwa stands isolated in tribal territory, neither under Tibetan nor under Indian administration, and very little is known about its structure or topography. Encircled on all sides except the southwest by the Tsangpo, it has never been reconnoitered at close range and no mountaineer has been on its slopes – nor is any Westerner likely to be permitted to climb it while the Chinese remain entrenched in Tibet.

After its long course in Tibet from west to east, the Tsangpo River is first diverted round the northwest and northern skirts of the mountain and then cuts a gorge at about 9,000 feet through the rocks of its eastern and southern flanks. Here, as often in the Great Himalayas, one finds a defile cut by one of the major rivers in the immediate vicinity of a culminating peak.

The mountain was first known from the journeys of the Survey of India explorers, Nem Singh in 1879 and Kinthup in 1881, but neither fixed its position or height; nor did Captain C. L. Robertson, who saw it in 1900, realize its im-

portance. From the south it is hidden by the high outer forested ranges of the Assam Himalayas and in the nineteenth century no surveyors were allowed in the unadministered territory. During the military expeditions to the areas of the Abors and Mishmi tribes in 1912, Captain C. F. T. Oakes and J. A. Field from the south and Captain H. T. Morshead from the east observed the peak and fixed its position and height.

After the survey of the Mishmi Hills, Morshead and the Political Officer, F. M. Bailey, made an adventurous journey across unknown country to the Tsangpo gorge, which was shown on the older sketch maps, compiled from reports, as being 65 miles farther west than it is. Namcha Barwa has a mantle of ice and permanent snow; Morshead discovered five of its glaciers, the largest of which, the Sanlung, reaches down to within a mile of the Tsangpo at about 9,000 feet. According to Morshead the meaning of the name Namcha Barwa is "Lightning burning in the sky."

After these explorations the mountain was seen by F. Kingdon-Ward during his Tibetan journeys – notably in 1924 when, with Lord Cawdor, he reached the Tsangpo at Tsetang, about 50 miles southeast of Lhasa. From this point they followed the river eastwards to its gorge between Namcha Barwa and the great peak of Gyala Peri. But as far as the Western world is concerned, this giant still remains a mountain of mystery.

Nanda Devi

A twin-peaked mountain massif, the highest in India. Location *Southeast Kumaun Himalayas, northern Uttar Pradesh, India.* Height *25,645 feet.* Map *11, D5.* First climbed *N. E. Odell and H. W. Tilman, 1936.*

Nanda Devi – the Blessed Goddess – has for long centuries been one of the holiest mountains in India. Countless generations of Hindu pilgrims have visited the neighboring jungles to worship at the sources of the sacred Ganges; ever since the beginning of British rule, explorers and mountaineers had gazed longingly at its heights. Yet up to 1934 no human being had even reached its base.

Apart from religious sensibilities, there were good geographical reasons for this. Nanda Devi stands in the heart of a unique natural fortress – a vast ring of mountains 70 miles in circumference with an average height of about 20,000 feet. Nineteen peaks on this ring rise to over 21,000 feet and the only break in it is on the west, where a raging mountain stream, the Rishiganga, hurtles down from the glaciers, piercing both the inner and outer walls of the mountains in a series of fearsome gorges and draining some 240 square miles of ice and snow before joining the Ganges far below.

The position and height of Nanda Devi and of its guardian peaks were fixed more than a century ago by distant observations of the Survey of India, but the lower gorge proved too much of an obstacle for the early surveyors. The Lata Pass, which takes a shepherd's path over the long western ridge of the northern arc, was followed by one surveyor and he sketched a small part of the lower Rishiganga for about six miles, without, however, reaching the upper gorge.

The first real knowledge came from Dr T. G. Longstaff's pioneer explorations in 1905, when he reached the crest of the ring south of Nanda Devi East and for the first time looked down into the inner circle and saw the southern face of the main peak and its glaciers. Later in the same year he corrected the map of the approaches to the southern arc. In 1907, with A. L. Mumm and C. G. Bruce, he forced a passage over the northern arc between Changabang and climbed Trisul from the north. He was deeply impressed and wrote: "I have always believed that Nanda Devi reigned over the most superbly beautiful part of all Himalaya. . . The climbing of the peak would be a sacrilege too horrible to contemplate. . ."

Still, there were plenty of people who did

contemplate it, and when success finally came, Dr Longstaff commented: "Here was humility, not pride, and gratitude for a permitted experience." The attempts after the First World War to find a passage over the mountains to the foot of Nanda Devi were unsuccessful. Then, in 1934, Eric Shipton, who had been with F. S. Smythe to Camp 6 on Everest the year before, solved the problem of entry, with H. W. Tilman and three Sherpa porters. This exploratory journey was perhaps even more remarkable than the final climb itself. For many days the party fought its way along the mile-deep gash in the mountain walls, now high on the faces of the towering cliffs, now deep down beside the bed of the torrent. It was an incredibly demanding and strenuous journey with many detours and dangerous climbs. But at last Shipton and his companions came out into the wooded ravine of the outer basin. But they had done only half the job – or even less. There lay in front of them the second rock wall, thousands of feet high, broken only by the sheer, jagged slot of the gorge, enclosing the "inner sanctuary" in which Nanda Devi stood. It took nine days of reconnaissance and strenuous rock climbing before they penetrated into this sanctuary. It was a lovely, amazing landscape. The encircling mountain walls rose like an immense amphitheater, their flanks covered with fir and spruce. The floor of the valley was a rolling alpine meadow with banks of wild flowers, herds of wild sheep and goats, tiny lakes of cobalt blue and the long, frozen fingers of the many glaciers. The sacred mountain stood in the very center.

For three weeks they continued their explorations – treading where probably no human being had ever walked before them. Then they turned back, barely escaping disaster in the snow-swollen waters of the Rishiganga. At the end of the monsoon they again returned to reconnoiter further, and found a gap in the sheer southern walls by which they descended to the outer valley, proving that the Rishiganga canyon was not the only possible key to the mountain.

The summit of Nanga Parbat

Two years later Tilman and N. E. Odell led an Anglo-American party to the final conquest. The expedition consisted of eight climbers, among them Dr Charles Houston, the young American physician who was later to lead two expeditions to K2.

Again, great difficulty was experienced in forcing the upper gorge since the Rishiganga was in monsoon flood, but by August 2 a base camp had been established near the foot of the coxcomb ridge on which Tilman and Shipton had reached the height of 20,500 feet two years before. After more than three weeks of reconnoitering and stocking four light camps up the ridge, a bivouac was placed at about 24,000 feet; seven of the eight climbers had done all the carrying above Camp 2. Starting at 6 a.m. on August 29 from this bivouac, Odell and Tilman crept up the side of the mountain, up steep snow-slopes, along a gently rising rock ridge, sheathed in ice and snow, and finally up the deep gullies in the face of the summit pyramid. Great snow-drifts engulfed them to the waist, but they went on and finally, at 3 p.m., they stepped from a small rock-rib on to a gentle ridge of snow. As they did so, there was an ominous quiver beneath them and an avalanche carried the drifts below towards the bottom. For a tense, dreadful moment it seemed that the ridge would go too – but it held. A few more steps upwards and they stood together upon the flat, white summit of Nanda Devi. "The air was still," Tilman wrote, "we could bask gratefully in the friendly rays of our late enemy the sun. . . After the first joy in victory came a feeling of sadness that the mountain had succumbed, that the proud head of the goddess was bowed."

Nanga Parbat

A major Himalayan peak. Location *The westernmost massif of the Himalayas.* Height *26,629 feet.* Map *11, C3.* First climbed *Herman Buhl, 1953.*

From the west one can see the whole face of Nanga Parbat, 23,000 feet of rock, ice and snow, rising from the bleak Indus valley to the summit: one of the most awe-inspiring sights even in the Himalayas. The mountain is not only hard to reach but presents formidable difficulties to the climber, with unstable glaciers and ice terraces constantly sloughing off vast avalanches; the terrain is much worse than that of Everest, the approach route longer, and many more inter-mediate camps are needed.

Nanga Parbat was first reconnoitered by the great Victorian climber A. F. Mummery, who set out for the Himalayas in 1895 with the inten-tion of climbing one of the world's highest peaks. With three English companions and some Gur-khas he made rapid reconnaissances and turned back from an assault on the summit only when the Gurkha with him fell ill. He failed to return from a subsequent reconnaissance of another approach.

Not till 1932 was the mountain attacked again, this time by an expedition of Germans and Americans. From then on, it became entirely a German province; a later British proposal to climb it met with indignant protests. The 1934 and 1937 excursions ended in disaster, with a death roll of eleven Germans and fifteen porters, sixteen of them in 1937 when an avalanche over-whelmed a camp at night. The climbers in 1938 had the unnerving experience of finding the bodies of some of their predecessors. Before the Second World War the Germans, under Hitler's regime, became determined to conquer the mountain for the Reich; but when they mounted their 1953 expedition the project had become a sacred trust and a memorial to the dead. The 1953 climbers followed the same route at the same season as before, and every landmark and date was invested with memories – "the whole enterprise. . . moved up the mountain weighed down with thoughts of doom and death." The official account of the expedition is tight-strung with emotion.

The successful ascent of Everest made the Germans feel more than ever committed to con-quer Nanga Parbat. Five weeks later, some two months after establishing their base camp, they did so. The final ascent by Herman Buhl must rank as an amazing feat of endurance and an equally amazing piece of fortune. Leaving his tent alone at 2.30 a.m., without his companion, who was overcome by lethargy, Buhl reached the summit on all fours at 7 p.m., having discarded on the way his rucksack with food and warm clothing, and on the last arête traversed above the almost sheer 14,000-foot southern precipice.

At 7.10 p.m. the sun set, and night caught Buhl after he had come down about 450 feet. He found a large rock and spent the windless night leaning against it, dozing fitfully, and set off downwards again at 4 a.m. the next morning. Not till 5.30 p.m. did he meet his companions. The general atmosphere of the expedition may be judged from the fact that they had not come to meet him, but had spent the time fixing a tablet to a rock in memory of Willi Merkl, who froze to death there in 1934.

So Mummery's project of attempting the summit single-handed was in fact realized more than 50 years later, after seven attempts and 31 deaths. Nanga Parbat is indeed what Kenneth Mason described: "It is the cruellest and most vengeful of mountains and forgives no errors of judgment."

Nan Shan

A system of parallel ranges. Location *Tsinghai-Kansu border, China.* Height *Rising to 20,000 feet.* Map *10, E5-F5.* Explored *Sir Aurel Stein and others, early twentieth century.*

The Nan Shan mountain system divides Kansu from Tsinghai province, merging into the Altyn Tagh of Sinkiang on the west, and overlooking the Tsaidam depression on the south towards the Kunlun range of northern Tibet. The ranges are high and include the Humboldt, Richthofen and Tagung mountains.

The name means "southern mountains" (there is a lesser range, also known as Nan Ling, similarly named in southeast China) and they rise protectively on the left hand of a traveler journeying from inner China towards Central Asia by the famous old Silk Road. The road crosses them at their eastern flank, above Lanchow, the walled city on the deeply cut Yellow River. Guarding the old route on the north runs the Great Wall of China as far as Kiayükway, its western end. But watchtowers and outposts, probably built originally against the Huns, stretch farther west to mark the route by which Chinese imperial power pushed into Sinkiang and Turkestan. The legendary Jade Gate, commemorating the precious cargo of ancient caravans, is situated under the western foothills of the Nan Shan.

Sir Aurel Stein surveyed 24,000 square miles in these almost uninhabited mountains and found abundant grazing grounds up to 13,000 or even 14,000 feet with only wild asses to enjoy them.

Above these the ice-peaks rise to 20,000 feet, with glaciers feeding streams that drain into both Central Asia and the Pacific. The Kanchow River descends the northern slopes through landscapes of alpine beauty to pass into Mongolia as the Etzingol and disappear in the desert.

On the southern slopes of Nan Shan a chain of temples, monasteries and "thousand-Buddha" sites testifies to the Buddhist ascendancy at the time of the Tang dynasty. Here also, at 10,000 feet, is the Koko Nor, China's largest lake.

Nepal

An independent kingdom of about 56,000 square miles. Location *Himalayas, southern central Asia.* Height *Highest point Mount Everest (29,002 feet).* Map *11, E5-F5.*

The State of Nepal, roughly rectangular in shape, is bounded on the west by the Kali River and on the east by the Tamur-Tista watershed. The undemarcated boundary with Tibet roughly follows the high peaks of the Great Himalayas; the southern boundary with India traverses the unhealthy tract of the Terai, south of the foothills, part swamp, part jungle, in which rhinoceroses, elephants, tigers, buffaloes and other wild beasts roam. Geographers recognize three zones of mountains from south to north in the country: the outer foothills or Siwalik Range, geologically the most recent; the Lesser Himalayas of which the Makabharat Lekh, south of Nepal, forms part; and the crystalline core of the Great Himalayas.

The mountains receive the full impact of the southwest monsoon from the Bay of Bengal between mid June and late September. The Himalayas in the east receive over 100 inches of rain in those months; dense tropical vegetation and swollen rivers often impede travel. But though the moisture-laden winds are forced to rise over the Lesser Himalayas, the currents are strong enough to reach the main range, which receives heavy snow at high altitudes.

The Great Himalayas in Nepal are divided into numerous high ridges and peaks, severed from each other by rivers and gorges; these ridges are locally known as *himal*, the Sanskrit word for snow. Nepal is over 460 miles from west to east, and geographers have found it convenient to divide the whole range into three sections, roughly defined by the basins of the three great Ganges tributaries which drain the country – the Karnali or Gogra in the west, the Gandaki in the center and the Kosi in the west. All have powerful tributaries rising in Tibet which cut deep gorges through the Great Himalayas; all collect the drainage of many thousands of square miles within Nepal; but each of them enters the plains of India as a single river. These three rivers begin to rise in March with the melting ice and snow and during the monsoon they carry an immense volume of water, which surges through the outer range and spreads out beyond it in broad flood-beds.

The main range enters Nepal on the north-west, where the Kali cuts through it near Garbyang, and soon reaches a great height in the Byas Rikhi Himal with its two peaks, Api (23,299 feet) and Nampa (22,162 feet). Saipal (23,079 feet) is about 35 miles to the southeast. North of them rises the Humla Karnali; its source is in Tibet, not far from Lake Manasarowar, and it drains a trough between two crest-zones of the Great Himalayas. It joins the Mugu Karnali in a similar trough to the southeast and together they form the main feeder of the Gogra. The eastern part of the Karnali Himalayas drains into the Bheri, which rises north of the Dhaulagiri Himal with its four summits reaching to over 25,000 feet.

Dhaulagiri I marks the eastern end of the Karnali Himalayas. Immediately east of it the Kali Gandaki carves a deep gorge down to 9,000 feet through the range which rises again to its eastern sentinel, Annapurna I, within a few miles. A remarkable feature of the main range in Nepal is that the deepest gorges are flanked by the highest mountains.

The principal peaks of the Gandaki Himalayas are the four Annapurnas, Manaslu (26,768 feet), Himal Chuli (25,801 feet), Ganesh Himal (24,299 feet) and Gosainthan (26,291 feet). The Trisuli Gandaki cuts a gorge between the last two and through it passes the main route from Katmandu to Kyirong and Dzongka in Tibet.

The eastern or Kosi section of the Nepal Himalayas is dominated by the immense Mohalangur Himal, crowned by the massive Everest with its southern satellite Lhotse in the center and flanked by Cho Oyu and Makalu at either end. The Sun Kosi gorge on the west separates it from the Gosainthan; on the east the Arun, having a large basin in Tibet, cuts a tremendous gorge which is quite impassable. The Phung Chu tributary north of the Everest group is 120 miles long and, with smaller tributaries south of it, collects the waters of many glaciers. The easternmost river of Nepal is the Tamur, which drains the western glaciers of Kanchenjunga.

Nepal has three cities in the Nepal Valley – Katmandu, Patan and Bhagdaon – while other main towns are Butwal, Pokhara, Palpa, Doti, Jumla, Nawakot, Gurkha and Biratnagar.

Katmandu, the capital, lies in a low, lush, green valley, spreading along the banks of the Baghmati River. It was founded in about 723 A.D. and originally called after its founder, Manju Pattan. Its present name dates from the building, in 1596, by Raja Lachminna Sing Mal, of a huge wooden hostel for pilgrims (*kath* = wood; *mandu* = house) which still stands in the market place and which, legend says, was constructed from a single enormous tree. It is a great center of pilgrimages; two miles away is the Buddhist temple of Swayambunath, its 600 steps swarming with grimacing monkeys and faced by three huge Dhyani Buddhas; while, a little farther on, in the Hindu temple at Nilkantha, a submerged statue of Vishnu glimmers in the depths of a large pool.

It is a city full of temples and palaces, bazaars, monuments and statues, gaily colored and intricately carved, and crowded with people bustling, jostling and very much alive. For mountaineers it has been of importance as the base, the starting point, of all great expeditions in the Himalayas.

Nepal is predominantly a Hindu country, but there is a considerable admixture of Tibetan blood and Buddhist culture, especially in the north, where there are close contacts between Nepalese and Tibetans. Gautama Buddha's birthplace is at Lumbini Garden, Paderis. Britain's first missions to the country, in 1767 and 1792, were the result of appeals from the Gurkha rulers at Katmandu for help against Tibetan encroachments. Today there are Nepalese communities, such as the Sherpas of the Sola Khumbu district south of Everest, which are Buddhists of almost pure Tibetan stock. They are hardy and natural mountaineers; under expert training they make excellent high-altitude porters and climbers.

At the end of the Nepalese war in 1816, the country was closed to British surveyors and travelers. The position and height of the great peaks were fixed in the early eighteen-fifties from distant survey stations in India, but only in the years 1925–27 were Indian surveyors permitted to map the topography – and then only on a small scale. Nepal was not open to detailed exploration until after India gained her independence in 1947, which meant that no attempts could be made to climb the high peaks before the Second World War and the early expeditions to Everest had to make a long detour to Tibet and attack it from the north. Of the 12 highest mountains in the world, seven are in the Nepal Himalayas.

New Guinea, Mountains of

A range with several sub-ranges. Location *Running almost the entire length of New Guinea.* Height *Rising to 16,404 feet.* Map *12, D2.*

New Guinea is remarkable not only for its shape, which resembles a huge bird facing westwards, but for its surface; for while thousands of square miles consist of low, jungle-covered swamp lands, an equal area is occupied by the most elevated island mountain chain in the world. The Arfak Mountains – one of the lesser ranges, which nevertheless reaches elevations of 10,000 feet – occupy the upper portions of the "head," but from their eastern end to a point which coincides with the base of the "neck" there are no elevations of consequence. Here, however, is the western end of the great backbone of mountains that runs without interruption – under various names – the entire remaining length of the island, a distance of 1,100 miles.

In the western part of this great range, which is called the Nassau Range, there is probably not a single pass less than 13,000 feet high. Mount Carstensz, the highest peak (still unclimbed), reaches 16,404 feet. Mount Idenburg, Mount Wilhelmina and Mount Leonard Darwin in the same range are almost as high and the enormous ridge that lies between Mount Idenburg and Mount Carstensz is capped by many glaciers, which present huge vertical faces of ice topping the most breath-taking precipices to be found anywhere. These gigantic cliffs, which border the ridge on both its northern and southern sides, extend for about 80 miles and present, in their most elevated sections, vertical rock faces that are 10,000 feet high.

In some cases these cliffs are less than 50 miles from the sea – yet they were not discovered until 1911 and their northern faces, much farther from the sea, were not found until 1926. At the other end of the island, in the "tail," lies the Owen Stanley Range.

The mountains of New Guinea generally comprise one of the least-known areas in the world. Very little has been written about them – except, from time to time, sensational stories about vast Stone Age populations in hidden valleys, previously unknown to the outside world. In the Central Highlands of the Australian Trust Territory, which forms the northeast section of the island, live several hundred thousand people who had never seen a white man until 1933. They existed in a state of internecine warfare – hunting game and each other with bows and arrows and long, barbed spears. They ground slabs of brittle, pale green stone into delicate though formidable battle axes and enjoyed a high standard of living in an extremely healthy and fertile land. Their intricate ceremonial included the use of pearl-shells and birds of paradise. They were expert agriculturalists, planting and irrigating great tracts of country in neat checker-board design, and they even decorated their ceremonial grounds with lines of casuarina trees as neat as the drive to a European castle. Although they used pearl-shells extensively, they had no conception of the sea or, indeed, of anything beyond their personal Shangri-La. The gold-lipped pearl-shells and the cowries were traded from village to village along several hundred miles of tortuous trading trails before they arrived, years later, in the Wangi Valley or Mount Hagen. When the first white explorers penetrated into one such area, the local people quickly arranged marriages between their daughters and the white men's native carriers. They reasoned that after the girls returned with the carriers where the shell came from, they would send "cuttings" back to the home tribe. They thought that pearlshell grew on trees.

There still exist limited areas in Australian territory (and very considerable districts of Dutch New Guinea) where the people have never seen a white man. In Australian territory such areas are officially designated "uncontrolled," officially out of bounds to all white men except district officials and a few other experienced people on official or semi-official business. Although missionaries and others have sometimes been killed, district after district has been brought under control with a minimum of friction. Tribal fighting has been outlawed in controlled areas, but this is a habit the mountain people find very difficult to give up.

A health service is established in all controlled areas and mission enterprise, although carefully supervised, is encouraged. The first true settlement in the Highlands, Goroka, has now grown into a thriving little farming township. Before an outsider can purchase land from the natives the district officer must satisfy himself that it is not in use. Today the New Guinea Highlands produce coffee, ground-nuts, passion fruit and vegetables that are sent by air to the coastal areas.

Much of the mountain area, however, still remains largely unexplored. Although the snowfield of Mount Carstensz was reached as early as 1912 by the Wollaston expedition, the most thorough recent examination of any of the higher peaks was that of the 1938–39 Archibald expedition to Mount Wilhelmina (about 15,585 feet). This party of explorers, using a flying boat to take them to Lake Habbema on its slopes, discovered the densely populated Balim Valley. This great valley – and many of its laterals – had been almost completely deforested up to 7,000-8,000 feet on the sides of the surrounding mountains. Whole mountain ridges, as the report of the Archibald expeditions described, had been stripped of their original vegetation and their contours laid bare under a pale coating of grass. On these bald ridges were many village groups of gardens walled with stones. In the main valley the explorers flew over numerous walled or stockaded villages and beautifully patterned gardens laid out on rich alluvial flats. A first estimate of 60,000 people in these – for New Guinea – highly cultivated valleys, was probably too conservative.

The aerial survey found big paths passing east and west through the two upland valleys. One of the largest and most traveled – which the expeditions followed to high altitudes – ascended the range from the inner grass valley and crossed the range in a 12,000-foot pass under the east shoulder of Mount Wilhelmina. Certainly the inhabitants of the Balim Valley system had communications with people living on the southern slopes of the range.

On the rugged main ridge of the Snow Mountains, which comprise the Nassau and Orange ranges, there is considerable low tree growth under bluffs and in other sheltered places up to an elevation of almost 12,000 feet. The higher parts west of Mount Wilhelmina consist mainly of bare grayish-white rock, frequently with a smooth, weathered surface. Several small lakes and shallow ponds occur on both sides of the mountain, about 3,000 feet below the summit. A long, narrow lake lies between two sharp ridges forming a double crest to the range about eight miles to the east of the peak.

The Snow Mountains themselves extend for about 430 miles, containing many peaks above 13,000 feet. Apart from Mount Carstensz the Nassau Range boasts Mount Idenburg (about 15,750 feet), while the highest point of the Orange Range is Mount Wilhelmina. Mount Carstensz itself is known to consist of several peaks, of which Nggapulu (16,404 feet) is the highest.

Nilgiri Hills

A steep, undulating plateau. Location *Southwest Madras, India.* Height *Average 6,500 feet, rising to 8,640 feet.* Map *11, C10-D10.*

The Nilgiris adjoin the southern Deccan Plateau at the point where the Eastern and Western Ghats meet, forming the main, eastern part of the Nilgiri district and separated from the Anaimalai Hills by the Palghat Gap. They form a high plain, intersected by spurs and valleys – the latter often choked with dense woods full of eucalyptus and flowering shrubs. They include several peaks over 8,000 feet and rise to 8,640 feet in Mount Dodabetta.

The higher, rockier northern rim, called the Kunda Mountains, is rich in many types of heavy game, including panthers, the Nilgiri ibex (or muntjak), antelopes, bears and often tigers, which do not breed here but come up from the lowlands below. For the plant-lover there are magnificent rhododendrons, delicate wild straw-

berries, anemones and geraniums. Extensive cinchona, coffee, eucalyptus and tea plantations have been developed; teak, blackwood and bamboo provide valuable timber and there are quarries for building stone and lignite, with gold placers in the mountain streams. The temperature is equable and cool and the rainfall, between 50 and 60 inches a year in the east and up to 100 inches elsewhere, is not too high for comfort.

Early in the century about six aboriginal tribes inhabited this temperate mountain zone, notably the Todas and Kotas. The Todas have especially interested anthropologists because of the mystery of their origins and their strange customs – among them the practice of polyandry. Physically splendid, with long curling hair and sometimes blue eyes, they are classed as "Dravidians"; some ethnologists believe them to be of Aryan descent, others, related to the Polynesians. Some of their words are very similar to Latin; in many barrows and tumuli scattered over the plateau pottery and metal objects (including a gold coin) strongly resembling Roman ones have been found. Now, however, their numbers are shrinking and agriculture has largely replaced the cattle-breeding of the Todas with flower and vegetable gardens and experimental farms of millet, wheat and barley.

Northern Highlands

A mountainous region occupying the northern part of Scotland. Location *Ross and Cromarty and Sutherland counties.* Height *3,000–4,000 feet, average.* Map *7, B4.*

The Northern Highlands contain the most spectacular mountains in Britain, peaks which rise almost from sea level in an isolated grandeur which disguises their comparatively low height. Geological variety, topographical remoteness, a situation so far north that throughout high summer little more than a Scandinavian twilight covers their summits at night – these factors give to this superb landscape an attraction that is unique and relatively unknown. The area covered – sometimes described as "the northwest Highlands" – may be loosely considered as that north of the Great Glen which splits Scotland from Inverness to Fort William. More accurately, and as delimited by the Scottish Mountaineering Club, it lies north of the railway which runs from Dingwall on the Cromarty Firth to Loch Carron. Served by only one railway, which follows the eastern border, and poorly equipped with roads, this great swathe of country is the most sparsely populated of all Britain and contains many large tracts which are virtually uninhabited.

The geological basis of the country is the gray Lewisian gneiss, the oldest rock in Britain, which spreads its lochan-studded face horizontally inland from the western coast. Above this lie the towering architectural bastions of the purple Torridonian sandstone, weathered into the castles and ramparts which stand above the country like massive fortresses. Many of these are in turn capped by the gleaming white quartzite which gives to such peaks as Ben Eighe the illusion of shining summer snow. Eastwards, and forming less exceptional summits, lies a narrow limestone belt and then the country of the Moine schists.

Time and chance have sculptured this rich geological legacy into a series of high narrow ridges, many carrying corries which are unique on the mainland for their fierceness and grandeur. Liathach and Ben Eighe on the north of Glen Torridon – part of the latter forming Britain's first nature reserve – are typical. Northwards across Loch Maree lie Mullal, Coire Mhic Fhearchair, the high ridge of the Teallachs and the great mass of Ben More Coigach standing above the Summer Isles. The shattered ridge of Stac Polly, only 2,009 feet in height yet a uniquely dramatic mountain; the leviathan form of Suilven, riding the flat sea of gneiss; the lonely shoulder of Ben Hope, Britain's most northerly "Munro" (3,000-foot peak); and the five summits of Ben Loyal, thought by some to be the most beautiful mountain in Britain – these are only some of the isolated peaks which give to the Northern Highlands a distinction entirely their own.

Deer forests cover most of the land; there are fine salmon streams – the Helmsdale in the east is renowned throughout the world. Accommodation, even on the coast road which tortuously weaves its path north, east and south, is scanty, and for serious climbing on some of the peaks one must still camp.

North Twin

Third highest mountain of the Canadian Rockies. Location Alberta. Height 12,085 feet. Map 3, F9. First climbed W. S. Ladd, J. M. Thorington and Conrad Kain, 1923.

North Twin rises on the northwest margin of the Columbia Icefield, its western precipice falling nearly 4,000 feet to the Athabaska Valley. In the Canadian Rockies it is overtopped only by Mount Robson and Mount Columbia. The snow spire of the adjacent South Twin reaches 11,675 feet.

Using the lengthy approach from the south which traversed the Columbia Icefield, J. M. Thorington and his companions were true pioneers. "No one who does not follow in our track," he wrote, "will quite understand that journey back across the endless icefield. The exhausting first half-hour in a little blizzard, obscuring the trail 20 feet ahead; clearing, with a crimson, gold and orange sunset banded against lead-blue storm clouds behind the Twins, the unearthly light in the snow banners and mist about Columbia; the soft rosy haze filtering into the distant Selkirks, lifting them up and making them unreal... The field is so huge. In one corner the stars were out; in another, beyond Mount Athabaska, dark clouds hung and lightning flashed... We lit our lantern and went on through the night, pulling into camp at last, with morning light upon the hills as it had been 23 hours before when we departed."

235

Today the normal route is the same as for Mount Columbia, from the icefield chalet, near Sunwapta Pass, or from the Saskatchewan glacier hut.

Olives, Mount of

A hill famous for its Biblical associations. Location *East of the Old City of Jerusalem on the Israeli-Jordan frontier.* Height *2,680 feet.* Map *9, G2.*

The Mount of Olives (or Olivet) forms a north-south ridge some two-and-a-half miles long, rising gently to three summits, separated from Jerusalem by the valley of the Kidron stream. At its foot, outside the city walls, there is the Garden of Gethsemane on the western side, and on the eastern side, along the road to Jericho, lies the village of Bethany.

"Oh, how sweet art thou, fair and lofty summit, whence Christ the Lord beheld the starry spheres!" the monk Sophronius apostrophized Olivet in 610 A.D. "I would pass beneath the roofs and through the greatest gate and at last, going out upon the terrace, would gaze upon the beauty of the holy city as it lay towards the West. How sweet to behold thy loveliness from the Mount of Olives, O thou city of God!"

From the fourth century onwards many churches and convents have been built on the hillside, which was the scene of so many Biblical incidents. King David fled up its slopes from the treacherous Absalom. A thousand years later, in the spring of 30 A.D., in the opposite direction but along the same path, Christ went into the palm-strewn welcoming city for the feast of the Passover.

It was on Olivet's slopes that he found and cursed the barren fig tree; here he wept over Jerusalem, predicted the Second Coming, told the parables of the wise and foolish virgins, of the talents and of the sheep and the goats; here, in the Garden of Gethsemane, he prayed while waiting for his betrayal. And it was on Olivet that, according to St Luke, ". . .he lifted up his

hands, and blessed them. And it came to pass, while he blessed them, he was parted from them, and carried up into heaven."

Olympic Mountains

A mountain mass at the northern end of the Coast Ranges. Location *Olympic Peninsula, northwest Washington.* Height *3,000–7,954 feet.* Map *4, B1.*

Tropical rain forest is a well-known phenomenon – a dense green mantle which covers large areas of the equatorial parts of the globe. Temperate rain forest is something much rarer, found in only a few places: perhaps the most spectacular example of all is the area on the seaward slopes of the Olympic Mountains. Here the rainfall is consistently high, sometimes as much as 140 inches a year, 80 per cent of it crowded into the winter months (as much as 250 feet of snow may fall on the slopes and glaciers above), when 12 inches have been known to fall in 24 hours. This is in strong contrast to the eastern side of the mountains, where the climate is drier than anywhere else on the West Coast except southern California.

The Olympic National Park, in which most of the massif is included, was first established as the Mount Olympus National Monument in 1909. In 1938 it was extended and established as the Olympic National Park with an area of 1,313.8 square miles. It is 50 miles west of Seattle. The highest peaks are Mount Olympus (7,954 feet), Mount Constance (7,777 feet), Mount Anderson (7,321 feet), Mount Tom (7,150 feet), Mount Carrie (7,020 feet) and Boulder Peak (7,000 feet).

Mount Olympus has seven large glaciers. The continuous rainfall, combined with winter temperatures which seldom fall below freezing point, has produced a prodigious tree growth. Here are the largest known specimens of several kinds: Sitka spruce, western hemlock, Alaska cedar (really a cypress), western red cedar (a juniper) and Douglas fir. The biggest trees reach heights of 200-300 feet in a dense, closely packed

canopy, with an undergrowth of seedlings and broad-leaved trees so thick that it sometimes forms an almost impenetrable shrubbery.

Wild life is also abundant. From the inquisitive Oregon jays, which inspect each newcomer for possible profit and announce his arrival with shrieks of delight, or the pretty Columbian black-tailed deer, to the many black bear and the gigantic Roosevelt elk, of which some 6,000 roam the mountains, the visitor is seldom without some interesting creature in sight. In summer one may even see the elk in the lee of the glaciers which crown the higher summits – and of which the seven which radiate from the peak of Mount Olympus are renowned for the pure, brilliant beauty of their blue ice. There are plenty of lake and stream fishing and winter sports facilities in the park, together with hiking and bridle paths and campgrounds.

Olympus

The highest mountain in Greece. Location *Aegean coast, Macedonia-Thessaly border, Greece.* Height *9,570 feet.* Map *7, F9.*

Olympus is a name given to many mountains in Greece and Asia Minor, the most famous of which rises on the Aegean coast, 16 miles south-west of Katerine. More of a lofty ridge than a single peak, it is a mountain of massive appearance, rising in tremendous precipices broken by vast ravines above which the broad summit towers. The lower parts are densely wooded, while the summit is naked rock. The Peneus River, which drains Thessaly, finds its way to the sea through the great gorge of Tempe, close below the southeastern end of Olympus and separating it from Mount Ossa.

Olympus is sometimes known as the higher (or upper) Olympus, *Ano Olymbos* to the Greeks, opposed to the lower Olympus, *Kato Olymbos*, an adjacent range to the south which rises to 5,141 feet in the Metamorphosis and is also separated from Ossa by the Vale of Tempe.

Mount Olympus, the highest peak of the Olympic Mountains, in Washington State

The snow-covered summit, hidden in the clouds, was in Greek religion the home of the Olympian gods. The early poets spoke of the gods as actually living on top of the mountain. Even the fable of the giants scaling heaven must be understood in a literal sense; they did not place Pelion and Ossa upon the top of Olympus to reach the still higher heaven, but they piled Pelion on the top of Ossa and both on the lower slopes of Olympus to scale the summit of Olympus itself.

Homer described the different palaces on the summit of Olympus, where the gods spent the day while the Muses entertained them with lyre and song. A wall of clouds shut them out from the view of men upon earth, the gates of which were kept by the Hours. Later poets transferred the real abode of the gods from the summit of Olympus to the vault of heaven itself.

The position of Olympus, barring the way from Macedonia to Thessaly, gives it great strategic importance, and here, during the Second World War, the British and Commonwealth forces made a brief, desperate stand against the Germans, who came to the aid of their defeated Italian allies and overran the country.

Omei Shan

A mountain sacred to Buddhists. Location *Southwest Szechwan, China*. Height *9,957 feet*. Map *10, F6*.

There were seven holy mountains in China, each sacred to one of the deities of the Buddhist pantheon. Omei Shan ranked third in religious importance, and though the present Chinese regime has severely curtailed religious traditions, pilgrims still wend their way to this, the most important shrine in the west of the immense country, and perhaps the most impressive to the eye. The deity of Omei Shan is Pushien – Samantabhadra in India or Kuntusombo in Tibet. No foothills obscure the view of the mountain from the east; it thrusts upwards starkly from the flat, cultivated plains, with jagged outline and flattened summit. The pilgrim's path consists almost all the way of steep, man-made stone steps, smoothed and hollowed by innumerable feet. The lower part of the mountain with its deep gorges, fantastically shaped rocks and thick pine forests, often wreathed in mists, seems like part of some Chinese landscape painting.

Along the path are strung pagodas and temples, some perched on narrow ledges above the void, housing immense Buddhas on vast thrones or six-tusked elephants. Near the summit there is even the Temple of the Elephant's Bath. Twelve hours or more are needed for the ascent, but the temples used to provide shelter and food for the pilgrims.

The summit is a flat plateau where Pushien resides in a once-famous but now dilapidated Golden Pagoda. As with many of the other temples, there is a terrifying little balcony carved into the rock face above several thousand feet of precipice. To the west, on a clear day, the massive 23,000-foot bulk of Minya Konka shines in the sun, the outstanding feature in a most impressive all-round view.

Two curious phenomena occasionally occur here, both of which are regarded by the pilgrims as special favors. The "Tongues of Flame" is due to immense swarms of fireflies rising from their normal refuges on the ledge of the precipice, as they sometimes do on warm summer nights. "Buddha's Glory" is a Chinese version of the Specter of the Brocken: the shadow of the mountain and figures upon it are seen against a lower layer of mist at sunrise, where they eventually appear to become immense and surrounded by a rainbow halo. Pilgrims have been known to advance towards this vision and fall over the cliff – perhaps deliberately, for they believe that such an act gains them admission to Paradise.

Orizaba, Pico de

An inactive volcano, highest peak in Mexico. Location

Eastern Mexico. Height *18,700 feet.* Map *4, F10.* First climbed *F. Maynard and G. Reynolds, 1848.*

Orizaba (or Citlaltépetl) with its beautifully shaped cone, covered in eternal snow, is the third highest mountain in North America. It rises on the boundary of the Mexican federal states of Veracruz and Puebla, from the southeast margin of the great Mexican plateau.

The timber line is at about 13,500 feet and patches of permanent snow have been found on the southeast side at 14,400 feet. The last recorded eruption of the volcano took place in the period 1545–66, though Alexander von Humboldt, the German naturalist, recorded smoke issuing from its summit early in the nineteenth century. It has been virtually inactive, however, since 1687.

The Pico de Orizaba overlooks the town of Orizaba, which lies at its southeast foot. The town has played an important part in Mexican history: an Indian village existed here long before the coming of the Spaniards and was conquered by the Aztecs in 1457; here Benito Juarez called a gathering of his fellow-Mexicans to organize resistance to European invasion. The French troops sent by Napoleon III made their headquarters here shortly afterwards, and nearby, at an altitude of 4,000 feet, in the pleasant suburb of Jalapilla, was the favorite residence of the ill-fated Emperor Maximilian, who was defeated and executed by the forces of Juarez.

Ortler

An Alpine mountain group. Location *Ötztal Alps, northern Italy.* Height *Rising to 12,792 feet (Ortlerspitze).* Map *8, E8.* First climbed *Joseph Pichler and party, 1804.*

The Ortler (or Ortles) mountain group is the culmination of the Eastern Alps, lying in northern Italy, near the Swiss border, north of the Adamello group and east of the upper Valtellina. The group includes the Ortlerspitze (12,792 feet),

the Gran Zebru (12,661 feet), Monte Cevedale (12,350 feet) and Corno dei Tre Signori (11,020 feet); of its 60 glaciers the largest occupies seven square miles.

The Ortlerspitze itself, a huge, snow-covered rocky dome, is the highest point on the long, scimitar-shaped ridge which encloses the valleys running southeast from Bormio. It is one of the few peaks in the whole range to have been first climbed by royal command.

Early in the nineteenth century Archduke John of Austria, seventh son of the Emperor Leopold II, visited the Tyrol on his journeys as Director-General of Fortifications. Learning that the peak was the highest in the Austrian Empire (today it is entirely within Italy), he ordered its ascent to be made. Dr Gebhard, variously described as a mining manager and a botanist, was commissioned to carry out the climb. He arrived at Sulden, to the north of the group, at the end of August, 1804. Six unsuccessful attempts were made to find a way to the top. Then a local chamois hunter, Joseph Pichler, agreed for a fee to lead Gebhard's men to the summit on September 28, 1804.

"It was impossible for the gallant climbers to remain more than four minutes on the summit," reported Gebhard. "Even in that short period Pichler had his toes frostbitten and one of my men returned with a finger numbed and swollen with cold. . . They were completely caked with snow, and unable to speak, as there was a strong wind which whirled the loose snow about. . ."

The following year Gebhard himself made an ascent, partly for his own satisfaction, partly to discount stories that the peak had not really been climbed, and erected a large cairn on the summit.

Ouachita Mountains

A series of east-west ridges. Location *Eastern Oklahoma and western Arkansas.* Height *500–700 feet, rising to 2,900 feet.* Map *4, G6-H6.* Explored *Hernando de Soto, about 1541.*

The Ouachita Mountains extend about 220 miles west from Little Rock, Arkansas, to Atoka, Oklahoma, lying between the Red and Arkansas rivers. Their highest elevations are Magazine Mountain and Blue Mountain (both 2,850 feet) in Arkansas and Rich Mountain (2,900 feet) in Oklahoma. But what they lack in height, they make up for in their extreme picturesqueness, with pineclad slopes, beautiful lakes, mountain pools and waterfalls. In Oklahoma the ridges include several ranges of rugged, rocky mountains, covered by forests of pine and oak.

Part of the Ouachita National Forest lies in the range, but the most famous and striking part is the Hot Springs National Park, the oldest in the United States. This is a wooded area of 1,019 acres, including within its boundaries Hot Springs, North, West and Sugar Loaf mountains. The famous springs – the only government-owned spa in America – are found along the outcrop of Hot Springs sandstone, in the valley between West and Hot Springs mountains. About 47 of them bubble from the ground with a total daily flow of 1,000,000 gallons.

Hot Springs was probably visited in 1541 by the Spanish explorer Hernando de Soto, who traveled extensively in this region. According to tradition, the healing properties of the springs were known to the Indians long before the advent of the Spaniards. In 1832 the area was set aside as national property and in 1921 it became a National Park.

A popular summer and winter resort, the park has 12 miles of good roads traversing the slopes and crests, with many more miles of forest trails, bridle paths and footpaths.

Owen Stanley Range

The main mountain range of Papua. Location *Southeast New Guinea.* Height *Rising to 13,240 feet.* Map *12, E2.*

The lofty Owen Stanley Range of Papua was named (by Professor T. H. Huxley) after a tragic, somber figure. Captain Owen Stanley, F.R.S. was the skipper of the *Rattlesnake,* the wooden survey ship in which the young Huxley sailed the southern seas from 1846 to 1850. Stanley committed suicide in Sydney Harbour and Huxley, while exploring the jungles of New Guinea, remembered his friend. Today, a century later, the Owen Stanleys, which are jungle-clad and contain Mount Victoria (13,240 feet), the highest peak of Papua, Mount Albert Edward (about 13,000 feet), Mount Scratchley (12,860 feet) and Mount Obree (10,200 feet), are still not fully explored. They are the haunt of birds of paradise and stockade-building bower birds of almost unearthly beauty, and early naturalists, eager to climb them, found there unexpected oak trees and white rhododendrons (indicating former land bridges with Asia) as well as the giant tree-ferns and other vegetation typical of southern rain forests.

Until 1941 few white men other than occasional explorers, district officers and prospectors had crossed the range from Port Moresby to Kododa. Then, after the fall of Singapore, the Japanese swarmed south. The Australian forces were rushed back from the Middle East and advanced to meet them. Neither side could use mechanical transport of any kind – guns and other equipment had to be carried up the precipitous range. Japanese patrols got within 25 miles of Port Moresby, and their advance battalion was not far behind. After an initial Allied victory at Milne Bay, the Japanese were again defeated at Torabaiua ridge. There followed a series of savage clashes between gaunt and hungry men. Both sides suffered terribly from dysentery and malaria, contracted in the lowlands. Finally the Japanese were hemmed against the sea on the northern coastline at Sanaranda and Buna. American troops were flown in to help inflict the *coup de grace*. Apart from saving southern New Guinea and the northern approaches of Australia, the Owen Stanleys victory was of vital importance in showing, for the first time, that the Japanese could be beaten in the jungle,

Tenzing at the summit of Mount Ever

and the tide of Japanese victories was halted for the first time in the war.

Ozark Mountains

A dissected plateau covering over 50,000 square miles. Location Missouri, Arkansas and Oklahoma. Height 1,000–2,500 feet. Map 4, G5.

The Ozark highlands, which cover one third of Missouri, the tenth state in the Union, have been for a long time one of the main wellsprings of American folklore.

In the past, the speech, the philosophy and religion, the general approach to life of the Ozark folk have tended to set them apart from their fellow-Americans. Today many of the hill communities have become much more approachable, and the old ways are dying out. The mild climate and the numerous opportunities for outdoor sports have made the Missouri Ozarks one of the most popular American playgrounds. Four large artificial lakes – Norfolk, Lake of the Ozarks, Taneycomo and Wallapello – have been developed for recreation and fishing, and in the cold, clear streams that snake and twist around rocky cliffs and rugged hills, there is excellent "float fishing" with small-mouthed bass, black perch and rainbow trout the principal catch. Hunters go after quail, duck and geese, white-tailed deer, muskrat, raccoon, opossum and skunk.

The Missouri Ozarks are well-timbered hills with deep valleys and swift streams and they cover over 30,000 square miles. One of their most remarkable features is the number of large and beautiful springs, more than 10,000 in all. The range includes the St Francois Mountains, which rise to 1,772 feet in Taum Sauk Mountain, the highest point in the state. The Bagnell Dam, which has impounded the Lake of the Ozarks, is an important source of hydro-electric power.

In Arkansas the Ozarks have several summits over 2,000 feet in the Boston Mountains – the highest part of the plateau. Here the White River, the North Fork, the Black River and the St Francis, James and Illinois rivers provide excellent fishing, and there are many resort areas. The Black, Gasconade, Osage and White rivers all drain the Ozarks.

In Oklahoma the Ozarks have an average height of 1,100 feet, extending over the north-eastern part of the state.

The mountains are generally rich in timber, mostly valuable hardwoods, while the St Francois Mountains also contain minerals. An outlier of the range extends into southern Illinois.

Pakaraima Mountains

A mountain range forming the drainage divide between the Orinoco and Amazon basins. Location Mainly in southern Venezuela, extending into British Guiana in the east and southwards into Brazil. Height Rising to 9,219 feet. Map 6, D2-E3.

Extending about 500 miles along the Venezuela-Brazil and British Guiana-Brazil borders, the Pakaraima Mountains (or Sierra Pacaraima, in Brazil) have remained undisturbed, apart from erosion and the occasional bursting through of dykes of igneous rocks, ever since they were laid down under the sea in Cretaceous times and subsequently elevated. They have remained horizontally bedded and form perhaps one of the oldest undisturbed land surfaces in the world. Eons of erosion have attacked what was formerly a continuous elevated plateau, gouging into its sides, sometimes deep down to the even more ancient crystalline rocks below, and dividing it into a number of isolated blocks, gigantic flat-topped, vertical-sided mesas which tower above the forests of Guiana and Amazonia and some of which are completely unclimbable, and inaccessible except perhaps by helicopter. The highest of these peaks is Mount Roraima (9,219 feet).

The areas on top of them (like the "Lost World" in Conan Doyle's aptly named novel), thousands of feet above the forest floor, have been so long isolated, like islands in a great ocean, that they have evolved their own unique species of plants, birds, insects and animals. Sometimes neighboring massifs share much the same fauna and flora, showing that, geologically speaking, they have been only comparatively recently eroded apart. On others the flora is almost wholly endemic, as on the recently discovered Sierra Neblina where, of the many kinds of trees growing on the summit, only one is known to exist elsewhere.

The combination of wind and water has worn the upper surface of some of these mountains into an extraordinary sculptured landscape of obelisks, pinnacles and gargoyles. In some cases it has cut vertically into the rock, dividing up whole mountains into series of fragments separated by crevasses which may be thousands of feet deep and only a few feet wide.

These great massifs, presenting a bold face of perpendicular cliffs to the winds, act as magnets for clouds and as collectors of water, which condenses on the rock surfaces, gathers into runnels and then rivers, and pours over the cliffs into the forests below. The summits are sometimes cloudbound for weeks on end, making work on them extremely cold, uncomfortable and depressing. Then come amazingly clear days when the air sparkles, the miles of meadows, grasslands and trees, crowded with blossoms, are bathed in sunlight and great vistas open out over hundreds of miles of the surrounding country.

Here in the Pakaraimas one finds what are almost certainly the world's highest waterfalls. In a flight along the edge of nearly every part of the escarpment one may see half a dozen over 1,000 feet high, ranging from giants 100 yards wide to silvery plumes which dwindle away into a puff of cloud long before they reach the ground below. The highest measured, the Angel Falls, has a total drop of 3,212 feet; there have been reports of others considerably higher, though they may be only seasonal affairs, disappearing in dry weather.

Pamirs

A high mountain region of southern central Asia. Location USSR, China and Afghanistan. Height 11,000-13,000 feet, rising to over 25,000 feet in some peaks. Map 10, B6-C5.

The Pamirs are the true Bam-i-Dunya, the Persian "Roof of the World" – a gigantic roof open to the sky, its parapet formed by mountain ranges, windswept but habitable. Roughly rectangular, they cover about 22,000 square miles, representing a major Asiatic divide, draining westwards by the headstreams of the Amu Darya – Abi-i-Parja, Chund Darya, Ak-su and Murghat – into the inland Aral Sea and eastwards to the Yarkand River and the sand-choked Tarim basin. It is only from the southern parapet that the drainage finds an outlet to the ocean by the Hunza tributaries of the Indus.

The mountains dividing the Pamir valleys have an average height of 17,000 feet with summits 1,000 feet higher, while the bordering parapets greatly exceed these heights. Muztagh Ata and the two Qungurs are the culminating peaks of the eastern wall, and Lenin Peak and Stalin Peak those of the Trans-Alai range in the northwest, where the vast Fedchenko glacier, longest outside sub-polar regions, is also situated.

Alexander von Humboldt, who visited Asiatic Russia in 1829, thought that the Pamirs were a great meridional range from north to south, but most geologists now believe that the fundamental ranges trend from east to west.

Strictly speaking, the Pamirs are not the ranges themselves but the wide open valleys between them, waterlogged when the snow melts but mostly draining from east to west. They differ from each other mainly by their width and altitude and by the amount each has been filled by glacial debris, shattered mountain material and covering alluvial deposits. There are no permanent villages or even buildings except occasional watch-towers, tombs and, on Russian territory, detached forts. In summer the Pamirs

An aerial view of the Pamirs

are grazed by herds of yak, their nomad owners, Kirgiz, Tadzhiks and Sarikolis, still living in their movable *yourts* (large tents).

Eight Pamirs are recognized as separate entities. The Taghdumbash and the Wakhan Pamirs lie in the south; then in succession northwards there are the Little Pamir, Great Pamir, Alichur, Sares and Khargosh Pamirs; the small Rang Kul Pamir is in the northeast. All these feed the Oxus tributaries, except the Taghdumbash, the waters of which cut a gorge east of Tashkurghan to join the Yarkand River, and the Khargosh and the Rang Kul, which have no visible outlet. All embrace lakes of varying sizes, except the Wakhan, the Taghdumbash and the

Sarez. The largest lake is Kara Kul on the Khargosh Pamir; the best known is Zor Kul on the Great Pamir, the main source of the Oxus. All the ranges, except the two southern ones, are in Soviet Tadzhikistan, formerly part of Russian Turkestan. The Taghdumbash is in Chinese territory, the Wakhan in Afghanistan. Their northern boundaries were settled by the Pamir Boundary Commission in 1896.

Historically the Pamirs are of great interest. The ancient silk routes from China to the West crossed them. Buddhist pilgrims and a Chinese army passed this way. The great Venetian traveler Marco Polo was the first European to cross from west to east – *ovis poli*, the magnificent wild sheep unique to this region, was named after him. Lieutenant John Wood of the East India Company's Indian Navy, who accompanied Alexander Burnes on his Kabul mission in 1837, was the first to trace the main course to its source on the Great Pamir in February, 1838. Since then much knowledge has been gained by members of Sir Douglas Forsyth's mission to Yarkand in 1873–74, by individual explorers – such as Sir Aurel Stein – and by various consul-generals stationed at Kashgar. The Russian and Indian surveys met here in 1913. High mountaineering in such a remote region is a more recent development. In 1928 a Russo-German expedition explored the Trans-Alai Range and the Great Fedchenko Glacier, and in recent years there have been several Russian and Chinese expeditions to the Akademiya Nauk and the Peter the First Range.

Paricutin

An active volcano. Location *Michoacán, western central Mexico.* Height *About 8,200 feet.* Map *4, E10.*

The ground had been trembling for nearly a week near the village of Paricutin when, on February 20, 1943, a Tarascan Indian peasant named Dionisio went to plough his cornfield with his son and ox. Suddenly the boy came running to say that he had heard a noise underground – as if the earth had growled. Just behind his furrow Dionisio now observed a spiral of white vapor – then a hissing and spurting as steam forced its way out of the ground. He turned, whipping up the ox, and ran in panic with his son.

By the evening a flaming hole had appeared in the field, black smoke was belching forth and every few seconds a tremor shook the ground, while stones and cinders were spewed out. By nightfall the explosions were thunderous and almost without pause; streams of glowing red rocks were hurled 1,000 feet into the air. By morning a cinder cone 25 feet high had built up

round the vent and for miles around the countryside was blanketed in fine gray ash. Everyone in the village began to collect his belongings, ready to move.

Within a week the crater was a quarter of a mile in circumference and a cone had built up 550 feet high; ten weeks later this height had doubled and "El Monstre," as the peasants called it, was breathing forth a column of fiery vapor three miles high, in gigantic puffs that came every six seconds, throwing aloft fanwise bombardments of rockets by day which looked like flocks of escaping black birds. At night it shot out balls of fire 3,000 feet up and more, like gigantic Roman candles, which fell, rolling and bouncing in cascades down the steep cinder slopes.

Twenty miles away, at Uruapan, a town of some 20,000 inhabitants, traffic came almost to a standstill, so thick was the fall of ash, and only heavy trucks could get near the volcano. People were continually sweeping the dust from the streets, sidewalks, patios and roofs. The street lights were on all day, the lacquer works – one of the city's largest industries – had to cease work, for it was impossible to keep dust out of the layers of drying paint; yet in other respects the new volcano was welcome, for thousands of tourists flocked to see the spectacle. A new hotel was hastily put up to accommodate them.

On June 10 there was a sudden lull; then the mountain, gray by day, glowing by night, split open down one side and a vast tongue of lava, 100 feet high, began moving down the valley. Slowly it advanced, a sea of fantastic, piled-up shapes, flaming at first, then cooling till only the interstices showed the cherry-red molten glow of the interior of the mass. After eight months, when Paricutin had grown to a height of 1,500 feet, a small parasitic cone, Zapicho, "the little fellow," appeared on the slopes, only to seal itself three months later. Then Jaqui, another vent, burst open and a torrent of lava flowed down and over the little town of San Juan de las Colchos, sparing nothing but the church.

Today Paricutin is still alive, if less violent (the last major eruption was in 1952 and it has lost somewhat in height). Around it many square miles are covered with ash, which has killed all vegetation, even the sturdy pines which the Indians formerly tapped for turpentine. The country looks like a barren desert and dust storms whirl among the dead trees – yet already at the edges of the ash and clinker fields it is beginning to bloom again, with the vastly renewed fertility which always follows such a spread of new topsoil dressing.

Parnassus

A massif famous in Greek mythology. Location *Central Greece.* Height *Rising to 8,062 feet.* Map *7, F9.*

Parnassus stands north of the Gulf of Corinth, on the borders of Boeotia, Phocis and Phthiotis. A barren massif, it is usually climbed from Arachova or Delphi – not for its beauty, but because of the magnificent view it offers, including all of central Greece, the Gulf of Corinth and the northern Peloponnesus. The Corycian stalactite grotto, which was the scene of ancient Bacchic festivals, and the sacred Castalian spring are on its slopes.

In classical mythology the name was usually restricted to the highest part of the range, a few miles north of Delphi. The highest summits were called Tithorea and Lycorea and poets described the mountain frequently as double-headed. In pre-Christian times the slopes were well-wooded: laurel, myrtle and olive trees grew at the foot, with conifers higher up; the summit was covered with snow during most of the year. The glens, ravines and numerous caves were celebrated. The whole mountain was dedicated to Apollo and the Muses, the inspiration of poetry and song. The famous Castalian spring issued from between two cliffs which were often called the summits of Parnassus, though they are only small peaks at the base of the mountain.

Dionysus, too, was associated with the mountain and on one of the summits the Thyades celebrated their Bacchic revels. Between Parnassus proper and Mount Cirphis ran the sacred road through the valley of Plistus from Delphi to Daulis and Stiris. On the summit Deucalion, the Noah of Greek legend, landed with his wife Pyrrha in the ark after the floods, and here the two threw the stones behind them which turned into the men and women of a new mankind.

Pelée, Mont

A quiescent volcano. Location *Northern Martinique.* Height *4,429 feet.* Map *5, G10.*

Mont Pelée stands 15 miles northwest of the city of Fort-de-France. Quiescent today, it produced minor eruptions in 1792 and 1851, but these were not sufficiently strong to keep people from building villages and towns and establishing plantations and commercial enterprises at its foot and on its slopes.

On May 7, 1902, visitors flocked to the commercial and trading center of St Pierre, nearly doubling its population. It was the eve of Ascension Day, a public holiday and great religious festival. It was a happy town – except for one Auguste Ciparis, a Negro condemned to die at dawn on the day after Ascension Day and waiting for his execution in the condemned cell, a dungeon in the massive jail. Mont Pelée, except for an occasional plume of smoke above its hollow peak, had been dormant for 50 years. The visitors who climbed to the summit gazed down on a vast boiling lake, 2,000 feet below the lip of the crater, three-quarters of a mile in circumference and practically bottomless – but the awesome sight caused no anxiety. Various warnings had been ignored in the previous weeks: a minor eruption had destroyed a sugar refinery high on the mountainside; and a sudden darkness had fallen on April 25, lasting for over two hours, while a shower of fine whitish ash had fallen, covering the northern end of St Pierre to a depth of nearly half an inch.

At 7.45 a.m. on May 8 the volcano erupted. Fernand Clerc, one of the leading planters of St Pierre, and his family were the only ones who left the town. He and his wife and children watched spellbound as the mountain's entire southern wall burst, emitting a huge black cloud. It seemed as if the other three sides of the volcano had become the mouth of an immense cannon from which a ball of superheated vapor, lava and white-hot masses of molten rock were being fired. This infernal mixture hurtled down with incredible speed over the countryside, searing everything in its path and tumbling buildings to ruins. After the first fearful blast, huge rocks and lumps of lava soared upwards; a huge gray cloud of smoke rolled over the island – a deadly cloud of superheated powdered pumice-stone that smothered everything in its path. It rolled over St Pierre, turning day into night – and then into the sea, which began to boil in a few moments. Many of the smaller craft in the roadstead sank at once under the weight of the powdered lava or were overturned by the wildly seething sea.

After seven hours of spewing destruction, Mont Pelée grew quiet. But then came the rains, turning the volcanic ash into mud. Anyone who had escaped the first ordeal faced the terrors of a moving sea of semi-liquid ash. Of the 28,000 people in St Pierre, apart from the Clerc family, only one man remained alive – Auguste Ciparis, the condemned prisoner, who was found four days later in his cell, still weakly shouting for help. He was freed, as both his accusers and his would-be executioners were dead.

The French authorities burned over 4,000 bodies to prevent an epidemic, but on May 20 a second eruption put an end to all rescue work. This time, however, there were no victims, as all had fled in time.

Pelvoux, Massif du

The principal mountain group of the Dauphiné Alps. Location *Southeast France*. Height *Rising to 13,461 feet in the Ecrins*. Map *8, B9*. First climbed *Victor Puiseaux, 1848*.

The Pelvoux massif, bounded by the Oisans Valley on the north, by the Guisane and upper Durance River valley on the east and the Champsaur on the south and southwest, has a diameter of 25 miles and is almost circular, rising to a glacier-covered crest.

Mont Pelvoux itself, from which the massif takes its name, the Écrins and the Meije are the highest points. Mont Pelvoux is 12,920 feet high. Of noble form, with a semicircular summit ridge rising from a snow-basin which it half encircles, it is both beautiful in itself and offers a magnificent view, yet it demands only moderate efforts from the mountaineer. It was known for far longer than it deserved to be as "a peak trodden only by chamois and angels." This tribute to its inviolability was due partly to its position close to the Écrins, which it faces across the Glacier Noir, and partly to the fact that it is a complex portion of a complex mountain group.

The early mystery surrounding the details of its crinkled ridges was not dispersed by Captain A. A. Durand, who reached the lower summit in 1828, accompanied by two chamois hunters – a summit which now bears his name, Pointe Durand (12,900 feet). It is possible that he also attained the highest peak, but the first undoubted ascent was made by Victor Puiseaux, a young professor at Besançon, who later became a noted astronomer. Only after the ascent by Edward Whymper and R. J. S. Macdonald in 1861 did the detailed topography of the mountain and its quality as a separate peak become known to the mountaineering world. Francis Fox Tuckett and W. A. B. Coolidge were among those who followed.

The view from the Pelvoux is one of the most impressive in the Alps, embracing Monte Rosa, Mont Blanc, Monte Viso and the mountains of the Auvergne, while much of the foreground is filled by the magnificent ridges and peaks of the nearby Ailefroide.

Pennine Alps

A major group of the Alps with three peaks over 15,000 feet and almost 80 over 10,000 feet. Location *Central Alps, Italo-Swiss border.* Height *Rising to 15,781 feet in Mont Blanc.* Map *8, B9-C9.*

The Pennine Alps represent, without doubt, the greatest historical interest and the finest mountaineering possibilities of any chain in Europe. Even if the Chain of Mont Blanc is excluded, the Pennines still include the Weisshorn, the Matterhorn, the Dent Blanche and Monte Rosa, peaks which are almost perfect illustrations of certain mountain forms. Their glaciers, found chiefly on the northern (Swiss) side, though shorter than those of the Bernese Oberland, lack nothing in variety or situation; while Zermatt, at the foot of the Matterhorn and surrounded by a diadem of other great peaks, is one of the oldest centers of Alpine climbing as distinct from Alpine exploration.

The Chain of Mont Blanc was once known as the Western Pennines, which accounts for the names of the other two main divisions in the group. These are the Central Pennines, stretching from the Col Ferret (8,321 feet), leading from Courmayeur to Orsières, to the St Theodule (10,909 feet), leading from Zermatt to Chatillon, and including nearly 40 separate peaks of more than 12,000 feet; and the Eastern Pennines (bounded by the St Theodule and the Simplon passes) including, as well as many other fine summits, the galaxy of peaks forming the Monte Rosa massif.

The main ridge, consistently high, is traversed only by glacier passes and presents a bold wall to the Italian plain. The frontier between Italy and Switzerland follows the main Alpine watershed.

The glory of the Pennines seen from the south has attracted men from the time of Leonardo da Vinci, who climbed an outlier of the Monte Rosa. Since then the Pennines have provided thrills and victories to climbers of almost every nation.

Pennine Chain

A long hill range of upland blocks, separated by transverse valleys. Location *Between the Cheviot Hills and southern Midlands, England.* Height *Rising to 2,930 feet.* Map *7, B5.*

"There, far below, is the knobbly backbone of England, the Pennine Range," wrote J. B. Priestley. "At first, the whole dark length of it, from the Peak to Cross Fell, is visible. Then the Derbyshire hills and the Cumberland fells disappear, for you are descending, somewhere about the middle of the range, where the high moorland thrusts itself between the woolen mills of Yorkshire and the cotton mills of Lancashire. Great winds blow over miles and miles of ling and bog and black rock. . . There is a glitter of water here and there, from the moorland tarns that are now called reservoirs. . . Here are Bodkin Top and High Greave and Black Moor and Four Gates End. . ."

Low enough by Alpine standards, the Pennines are dear to English rock climbers and hikers. They form the hinterland, the often bleak but still beautiful escape from the big industrial cities, spreading across the counties of Cumberland, Northumberland, Lancashire, York, Cheshire, Derby, Stafford and Nottingham – the cradle of the Industrial Revolution and the background scene of so much British history since Roman times. There are three main divisions: the North Pennines are bounded by the Tyne Valley on the north and divided from the Central Pennines by the Tees Valley; the division between the Central and South Pennines, which extend south to the Trent Valley, is marked by the Aire Valley. The moorlands are characteristic features alternating with rough grazing land and more fertile tracts on the lower slopes. There are few lakes but several deep chasms and many caves.

The northern section of the Pennine system is broader and generally higher than the southern. The sharp escarpment overlooking the Eden

247

Valley is the nearest approach to a mountain system anywhere in England. Here is Cross Fell, the highest point (2,930 feet); to the southeast the Pennines rise to 2,780 feet in Milburn Forest and to 2,591 feet in Mickle Fell. For the climber, Helsby, Stanage, Castle Naze, Brassington and Wharncliffe offer the most rewarding exercise, with their great variety of rock outcrops of sandstone, limestone or gritstone, some being, as J. E. Q. Barford put it, "very worthy cliffs."

Pichincha

A dormant volcano of moderate height. Location *Northern central Ecuador.* Height *15,423 feet.* Map *6, B3.* First recorded ascent *Edward Whymper and party, 1880.*

Pichincha stands in the Andes, six miles north-west of Quito, close to the equator. It has been quiescent for 80 years, though it is still emitting gases. It is not high by comparison with the other volcanoes of the Ecuadorian Andes and its rolling grassy slope is so gentle that it tempts the beholder to consider it not as a true mountain at all but merely as a steepening of the local scenery. Unlike Cotopaxi, Pichincha displays a large number of individual craters on its broad summit, though the last eruption occurred as long ago as 1881.

Edward Whymper and his party made the ascent at the end of their Andean expedition. They climbed to the top in a leisurely way, bivouacking halfway up, as was their custom. But it is possible for a fit man to make the ascent in one day, and the views are very fine in clear weather over the Quito bowl and beyond, including Chimborazo, Cotopaxi and the other Andean giants.

When Whymper and his companions reached the top, they came upon a mound of stones which they reckoned could only be a cairn erected by some previous visitor, though there is no record of an earlier ascent.

Pichincha also has its place in history. On its flanks patriot forces under Sucre, with the aid of troops sent by San Martin, fought the Spanish royalist forces on May 24, 1822. It was a decisive battle, ending with the rout of the Spaniards, and next day the patriots entered Quito and liberated the country. The State of Ecuador was established eight years later.

Pikes Peak

An isolated peak in the Front Range of the Rocky Mountains. Location *Central Colorado.* Height *14,110 feet.* Map *4, E4.* First climbed *Major S. H. Long and party, 1819.*

In 1805 Lieutenant Zebulon Montgomery Pike, an army officer born in New Jersey, was commissioned by James Wilkinson, governor of Louisiana Territory, to find the source of the Mississippi. He spent two years exploring the region westward from St Louis to New Mexico, Colorado and Louisiana Territory. In November, 1806, he discovered the peak named after him, and tried to climb it, but took the wrong path and found himself on the summit of Cheyenne Mountain instead. He declared that the mountain was unclimbable – but 13 years later it was conquered without much difficulty by Major Long's party.

There are many other mountains higher than Pikes Peak in Colorado, but as it is isolated from the others and rises on the edge of the Great Plains, it has a fine, commanding appearance and is perhaps the best-known in the state. From the summit, Cameron Cone (10,685 feet), Mount Sachett, Mount Bald (13,974 feet), Mount Rosa (11,427 feet) and Mount Cheyenne (9,407 feet) are well within sight; so are the Sangre de Cristo Mountains, with Blanca Peak, and the Spanish Peaks can also be seen on a clear day.

In 1891 a cog railway was opened which makes a total ascent of 8,100 feet with a maximum gradient of one in four to the level, stony summit, often covered in snow. It was on this summit that Prof. R. A. Millikan conducted his experiments in cosmic radiation in 1923. Summit

Pikes Peak, Colorado

House was built as an observation point and in 1905 a powerful searchlight was erected on the top. But Pikes Peak is also famous for the annual automobile race on Pikes Peak Highway, and for the slogan of the prospectors during the Colorado gold rush: "Pikes Peak or Bust."

Pilatus

An isolated peak at the western end of Lake Lucerne. Location *Central Switzerland.* Height *6,994 feet (highest peak).* Map *8, D7.*

Pilatus, accessible either by cable railway or by the steepest rack railway (steepest grade almost one in two) in the world, with summit hotels and a view that includes both the Black Forest and the Bernese Oberland, is the typical tourist's delight. It has seven summits, of which Tomlishorn (6,994 feet) is the highest, while the Esel (6,965 feet) is the main peak. It is a mountain of finely balanced outline, presenting a perfect background to many views of Lucerne.

The clouds that frequently mask its summit – the name comes from *mons pileatus,* the hooded peak, though until the fifteenth century it was also known as Frakmunt or Frackmünd – form a local barometer, and a Swiss saying claims:

If Pilatus wears his cap, serene will be
 the day.
If his collar he puts on, then mount the
 rugged way.
But if his sword he wields, then keep at
 home, I say.

From the name came the legend that the body of Pontius Pilate, after having been rejected by the Tiber and the Rhône, was sunk in the small lake frequently formed near the summit by melting snows. Throughout the Middle Ages it

249

was believed that a stone thrown into the waters would arouse his spirit. This act, almost inevitably, brought bad weather. Even Conrad Gesner, the medieval climber who made the ascent of the grassy mound of the Gnapfstein, the most westerly of the seven summits, in 1555, had to be accompanied, under a local law, by a respectable citizen who ensured that no stone was thrown. Only in 1858 was the superstition finally killed by the Lucerne State Pastor, who made the ascent, cast numerous stones and called on Pilate to arise. To the relief of the assembled citizens, nothing happened.

The rack-and-pinion railway which today runs to the summit from the lakeside town of Alpnachstad was built in 1889 and until 1937, when the line was electrified, the carriages were drawn by steam-engines. The more modern cable railway is useful in winter, when the line is sometimes blocked by snow.

The ascent of the mountain, with its lower slopes clothed by meadows and forest and its upper, rocky slopes enlivened by many flowers, can be made on foot in a few hours, by good paths, either from Alpnachstad or from Hergiswyl. The summit ridges, among which stand a number of hotels, are traversed by paths often following tunnels in the rock. Here, too, are the camouflaged gun-emplacements from which long-range Swiss artillery commanded many of the northern approaches to the country during the Second World War.

Pitons

Twin mountains consisting of eroded volcanic plugs. Location *Southwest St Lucia, Windward Islands.* Height *Petit Piton, 2,461 feet; Gros Piton, 2,619 feet.* Map *5, G11.*

The two sheer, isolated sugar-loaf peaks rise side by side straight from the sea, almost enclosing a small, semicircular bay. They are the hardened cores of two former volcanoes whose softer outer slopes have been eroded away, and they display perhaps the most spectacular scenery in the West Indies. Their vertical sides are covered with green, yellow and red creepers and mosses; here and there, where ledges afford a foothold, one finds a vertical forest, the roots of the trees above on a level with the crowns of their neighbors just below.

The steeper Petit Piton was first climbed in 1878, according to local tradition. Among many previous attempts which had failed was one made by four English sailors, watched through a telescope by their comrades on the deck of their ship far below. When halfway up one was seen to drop; then a few hundred feet further the second, then the third; the fourth, carrying a Union Jack, was almost at the summit when he, too, stumbled and fell in convulsions. Apparently all had been bitten by the fer-de-lance, one of the deadliest snakes in the world, once common in St Lucia. The Pitons were their favorite breeding ground, where they lived on the lizards and birds which swarmed on the sun-heated rock, but they have now been exterminated by the importation of the Indian mongoose.

Piz Palu

A mountain with three peaks. Location *Bernina group, Central Alps, Switzerland.* Height *12,835 feet.* Map *8, E8.*

Rising in graceful sweeps to the west of the Bernina Pass and clearly visible from Pontresina, Piz Palu is a mountain of no particular difficulty when ascended by the ordinary route. Guidebooks have called attention to the remarkable beauty of its outline and the transparency of its glaciers. Yet it has acquired an enduring reputation or notoriety as a "killer mountain," a reputation which has been nourished by two films and by some of the worst accidents in Alpine mountaineering history.

The summit ridge of Piz Palu is often dangerously corniced and this has been the cause of numerous accidents; one of the most sensational happened in 1879. Mrs Wainwright, a well-known woman climber, and her brother-in-law were conducted to the summit by the famous Pontresina guides Hans and Christian Grass. They trod too near the overhanging cornice and both amateurs and Christian Grass were swept down when the mass of snow and ice broke away beneath them. Hans Grass instinctively jumped to the far side of the ridge, stood firm, and alone held the weight of the other three. His brother then untied himself and climbed back to the ridge and by their combined efforts the two guides succeeded in getting their clients back to safety from their dangling suspension in space.

In January, 1898, another woman climber, the dauntless Mrs Aubrey Le Blond, made the first winter ascent of Piz Palu. The fame of the mountain, which had been growing through the years, was strengthened and widely disseminated by the pre-1939 "White Hell of Piz Palu," a magnificently photographed German film directed by Leni Riefenstahl. On June 29, 1957, one guide and three amateurs, including a newly-married couple, set out to climb the mountain at the same time as an Italian party consisting of 19 amateurs and one guide. Three of the Italian party halted at the foot of the final ridge, but no less than 21 people were on or near the summit when the snow split open, carrying down the Italians and threatening the other party, one of whose members was carried over the brink but held fast by the rope. As the young bride was hauled up (it was she who had fallen), it was found that her rope had become entangled with that of one of the Italian party, and its seven members were then brought back safely to the summit. The remaining ten Italians had fallen or slid some 2,000 feet, and all but one were found dead.

Popocatepetl

A dormant volcano, with snow-capped symmetrical cone and large crater; the second highest peak in Mexico. Location *Central Mexico.* Height *17,887 feet.* Map *4, E10.* First climbed *by some of the soldiers of Cortes, 1595.*

Dominating the horizon from Mexico City are the twin volcanoes of Popocatepetl (17,887 feet) and Ixtacihuatl (17,340 feet), brilliantly snow-capped against the bright blue sky. Their names are Aztec words, meaning "Smoking Mountain" and "Sleeping Woman" respectively. The lower slopes are green with coniferous forest and grasslands, dotted with abundant flowering lupins. Sometimes they seem quite near – the actual distance is 45 miles southeast of the Mexican capital – at others, veiled in clouds and infinitely far away.

It was from the ten-mile ridge between the two volcanoes that Hernando Cortes, on his way to meet the Aztec Emperor Montezuma, first caught sight of the unknown city that he had come to conquer: Tenochtitlan, where Mexico City now stands. He sent some of his soldiers to the great summit.

"Cortes sent thither ten Spaniards," wrote the Friar Lopez de Gomara, "with many Indians, to carry their victuall, and to guide them in the way. The ascending up was very troublesome, and full of craggie rocks. They approached so nigh the top, that they durst not goe unto it, for the ground did tremble and shake, and great quantity of ashes which disturbed the way: but yet, two of them who seemed to be most hardie, and desirous to see strange things, went up to the top, because they would not returne with a sleevelesse answer, and that they might not be accounted cowards, leaving their fellowes behinde them, proceeding forwards. The Indians said, what meane these men? for as yet never mortall man tooke such a journey in hand . . ."

The soldiers later collected sulphur from the crater, which they used in making gunpowder. At various other times sulphur has been mined here – about 150,000,000 tons of it are estimated to exist inside the crater, mostly about 500 feet below the rim – for the mountain is virtually a gigantic natural sulphur manufacturing plant;

Popocatepetl

sulphur is continuously being deposited from the vapor which still rises from the crater, though the last eruption occurred in 1702. The ascent is fairly easy.

The sister volcano, Ixtacihuatl, is extinct. Legend says that the two volcanoes were giant lovers who displeased the gods, whereupon they were turned into mountains; the woman was killed, but the man, Popocatepetl, was given eternal life so that forever he gazes at his beloved. At times in his agony he is convulsed, shaking the earth and uttering fearful groans.

Pumasillo

A peak in the Cordillera Vilcabamba. Location *Cuzco department, southern central Peru.* Height *20,492 feet.* Map *6, C5.* First climbed *Cambridge Andean Expedition, 1957.*

Pumasillo is a most unusual mountain for the Andes. In a part of the world where the high snow mountains are generally isolated, sharply individual spires, Pumasillo, the Puma's Claw, stands out as the culminating point of a large

252

massif, in the manner of Kanchenjunga or other Himalayan peaks. It was discovered by explorers as recently as 1956; its existence was known previously, but it was not until then that its true position – many miles from that given on earlier maps – was determined by George Band of the British Huagaruncho Expedition. Neither he nor the American expedition to the Vilcabamba of that year was able to reach it. The mystery attached to the group persisted mainly because of its inaccessibility; moreover, it cannot be seen from any nearby villages nor from the valley in which the survey traverse of the Cordillera Vilcabamba was made.

All the members of the Cambridge Andean Expedition reached the summit after an ice climb of great difficulty. The initial approach led past Machu Picchu, the "lost city of the Incas," to enter the Cordillera Vilcabamba from the north. A complete lack of maps of the region made the search for the mountain a formidable task and it was only after a month of blind exploration, involving sleeping out tentless at 16,000 feet for several days at a time, that a base camp could eventually be established.

The true summit of Pumasillo is the central point of a gigantic backbone running some eight miles north to south, nowhere falling below 18,000 feet, with subsidiary peaks at either end. From the summit the west ridge falls away; this is the key to the ascent. To the east the whole massif presents a sheer, unbroken wall, which baulked the Americans in 1956.

The ascent was made up the west ridge, 5,000 feet of snow and ice, involving the siting of three mountain camps. On the crux, at 18,700 feet, an overhanging ice section involved the use of artificial techniques; the passage of 150 feet took four hours of climbing to reach a site for Camp 2. The summit ridge was extremely dramatic, with fantastic cornices drooping over sheer abysses to east and west and separated by the merest knife-edges of snow and ice. On reaching a gigantic globe of ice which appeared to be the top, the climbers were faced with a needle summit lying beyond a gap. In order to reach it, they had to lower each other like spiders on a web before Pumasillo was finally conquered.

Pyrenees

One of the principal mountain chains of Europe. Location *Between France and Spain.* Height *Average 3,000-9,000 feet with many peaks above 10,000 feet.* Map 7, *B8.*

"Europe ends at the Pyrenees." Few trite quips seem more true when tested on the spot. Crossing the Alps, the traveler passes from one geographical environment to the next, from one race to another; yet some bond remains. At the watershed of the Pyrenees, which run for almost 270 miles from the Mediterranean to the Atlantic, the wind from across the brown fields of Aragon or Navarre seems the hot breath of Africa itself.

Though lower than the Alps – the highest peak on the Spanish side of the frontier is the 11,168-foot Pico d'Aneto, on the French, the 10,821-foot Vignemale – the Pyrenees are more difficult to cross, dropping in fewer places to readily negotiable passes and providing, in the great width of their approaches on the Spanish side (about 80 miles in the Central Pyrenees) a barrier infinitely more formidable both to men and to ideas. Strictly speaking, the range has two axes, one running inland from either coast; these just fail to meet one another in the Central Pyrenees with the result that the frontier here takes an unexpected north-south turn. With this one exception, the geography of the range is simple. The undulating main ridge is crossed by high and usually roadless "ports"; the lateral ridges, running at right-angles like the fish-bone mountains of childish maps, by cols. A typical feature of the range is the cirque – the most famous is the Cirque de Gavarnie – a huge rock amphitheater, butting up against the main range and providing, in effect, a dead end to a major valley. On the French side, the Pyrenees drop steeply to the plains; on the Spanish, they descend more gradually through a welter of minor ranges and counter-ranges. There are few glaciers and the permanent snowline, about 8,000 feet on the French side, rises to more than 9,000 feet on the south.

The Maladetta massif, in Upper Aragon, just south of the Franco-Spanish frontier and the main watershed, includes some of the highest peaks in the Pyrenees – among them the Pico d'Aneto and the Pico de Maladetta (10,866 feet). This is an area which has long fired the imagination. Shepherds in the Maladetta are said to have set their dogs on some holy person who turned them to stone and thus gave the Accursed Mountain its name. There are many large boulders which may have been the basis of the legend. The massif, some eight miles long, runs southeast and rises between the wild valleys of the Upper Esera and the Malibierne, both noted for their extensive flora. The Pico de Maladetta itself rises south of the glacier of the same name, the largest icefield in the Pyrenees. It was first climbed in 1842. Though the narrow terminal rock ridge is known as the *Pas de Mahomet* – probably in allusion to the tightrope suspended over hell which Moslems must cross to reach paradise – the ascent, now usually made from the Rencluse hut, presents no serious difficulties. The traverse of the Col Maudit, between the Aneto and the Maladetta, first accomplished in 1908, is a more arduous undertaking. The mysterious Trou du Toro lies at the foot of the massif to the north; here the waters of the Aneto glacier disappear underground – to emerge in France, across the Pyrenean watershed, as the young Garonne River.

Scenically, the Pyrenees have their cirques, the Brèche de Roland, Roncesvalles Pass, the Pic du Midi d'Ossau, the Colorado, the Val d'Ordesa and a full quiver of minor but always interesting and comparatively unexploited peaks. It is full of caves, many of them of prehistoric interest, and underground rivers; the highest ice-cave in Europe, the Grotte Casteret, is here.

The population of the Pyrenees is partly of Basque and Bearnese stock; the former still speak an ancient language, unrelated to any other in Europe. The historical links of the great mountain chain are ancient and numerous. Hannibal passed here in 218 B.C., followed by Vandals and Visigoths, and Charles Martel drove back the Mohammedan invaders beyond them after the battles of Poitiers and Tours. The Franco-Spanish frontier has remained unchanged for three centuries, but the mountains have been traversed by innumerable refugees – from Spain to France in the closing stages of the Spanish Civil War and from France to Spain when Hitler overran Europe in 1940.

Queen Maud Range

An Antarctic range with rich coal deposits. Location *Near Beardmore Glacier, Antarctica.* Height *Rising to over 13,000 feet.* Map *1, D3-E3.* Discovered *Roald Amundsen and party, 1911.*

When Roald Amundsen and his party made their sledging journey from the Bay of Whales, Ross Sea, to the South Pole, at a distance of some 400 miles from their base, they crossed the Ross Barrier (Shelf Ice) and came upon the great range running northwest to southeast, which they named for the Queen of Norway. The highest summit, Mount Fridtjof Nansen (13,150 feet), which towers above the Axel Heiberg Glacier, was called after the great Norwegian explorer, scientist and statesman. (There is another Mount Nansen, 800 miles away, in South Victoria Land.) It was not until the first American expedition under Admiral Byrd in 1928–30 that these mountains were again visited, this time by a scientific party led by L. McK. Gould, a geologist. Just previously, in November, 1929, they had been crossed by air over the Liv Glacier by Byrd himself on his flight to and from the South Pole. Although they explored only the northeast flank of the range, and were foiled in their attempt to ascend Mount Nansen, Gould's party conducted an extensive topographical and geological survey to the virtual limit of the range. Beyond this Amundsen's supposed continuation of the range was not substantiated, but immense transecting glaciers were discovered and named the Leverett, Thorne and Amundsen glaciers. Nor could the conjectural "Carmen Land" of Amundsen be found: a great highland, as he claimed, with bordering mountains, striking at right angles to the Queen Maud Range. Geologically it was discovered that these mountains are composed in their lower parts of ancient schists and gneisses and intruded by many granite dykes, which give a bizarre, striped effect. But they are overlaid by the important Beacon Sandstone formation, containing coal seams and dark dolerite sills, first described by the geologists of the earlier British expeditions under Robert Falcon Scott and Sir Ernest Shackleton, working in South Victoria Land. Moreover, the Queen Maud Range is probably an extension, for more than 300 miles to the southeast, of the fault-block mountain structure of South Victoria Land, west of the Ross Sea and Ice Shelf; and its coal areas evidently greatly extend the known occurrences in Antarctica, placing them probably second only to the United States in actual coal reserves.

Qungur Alps

A mountain area within the Pamir region. Location *Southern Sinkiang, China.* Height *8,000–12,000 feet, average, rising to 25,146 feet.* Map *11, C2-D2.* First climbed *Russo–Chinese Expedition, 1955.*

The southern side of the Qungur massif rises from typical Pamir country, open, undulating plateaus with wide, grassy valleys. But on the northwest side, which faces the Tarim basin (a vast, closed depression between the Kunlun, the Pamirs and the Tien Shan), it is flanked by a small but spectacular group of sharp peaks, the Shiwakte group. It is this area to which the name Qungur Alps has been given because of its scenic resemblance to the Swiss Alps. In striking contrast to most of the Pamir region, the valleys of this area are deep, steep-sided and well forested in their middle sections. They form a complex system and some of them are difficult to reach, particularly in the summer when the rivers are flooded by the melting of the glaciers. In spite of this, the rich pastures of the upper valleys are used as summer grazing grounds by the semi-nomadic Kirghiz of the district.

Qungur (25,146 feet) is the highest mountain in the Pamirs. Its dome-shaped mass dominates the great panorama of peaks seen to the southwest from Kashgar. Some of the early travelers in Sinkiang confused it with Muztagh Ata, which lies to the south – largely because Qungur, like most mountains in southern Sinkiang, is known to the local inhabitants as "Muz Tagh," which simply means "ice mountain" in the Turki language. Qungur was first climbed in August, 1955, by the members of a Russo–Chinese expedition. Immediately to the west of Qungur the range is cut by a remarkable defile through which the Gez River flows from the Taghdumbash Pamir to the Tarim basin.

Rainier, Mount

A dormant volcano with the largest single-peak glacier system in the United States. Location *Cascade Range, western central Washington.* Height *14,408 feet.* Map *4, B1.* First climbed *General Hazard Stevens, 1870.*

"King of the range," James Ramsey Ullman called the great peak, "a magnificent snow-dome . . . famous not only as a peak for climbing but as an all-year ski-playground."

One of the highest mountains of the United States, Mount Rainier occupies about one quarter of the wilderness of the National Park established in 1899 and named after it. The total area of the park is 377.4 square miles and it contains 26 great glaciers, five of which – Nisqually, Ingraham, Emmons, Winthrop and Tacoma – originate on the summit of Mount Rainier. Many

Mount Rainier

others of great size are born of snows in rock pockets or cirques; the most notable are Carbon, Cowlitz, Fryingpan, North and South Mowich, Puyallup and Russell glaciers. Many streams are fed by the glaciers, which are themselves slowly retreating.

In striking contrast to the spectacle of the icefields are the gardens of wild flowers surrounding them. These include Spray Park, Van Trump Park, Summerland, Berkeley Park, Klapatche Park, Indian Henry's Hunting Ground and Paradise. Up to 4,500 feet the mountainsides are heavily forested with conifers and there are beautiful alpine meadows, many lakes and abundant wildlife. The region of greatest floral beauty lies at about 5,400 feet. At this elevation a 50-mile belt of flowers encircles the mountain. There are 75 miles of road and 276 miles of trail open to the public, with trail shelters provided at many of the camping sites.

Mount Rainier was discovered in 1792 by Captain George Vancouver, who named it after Rear Admiral John Sprat Rainier of the British Navy. It is also known by the Indian name of Mount Tacoma.

Extinct to all practical purposes, the peak still emits vapor and some 80 years ago an Anglo-American party had an unpleasant experience while spending a night on the flanks of the mountain in a deep cavern formed by the action of the heat and extending under and into the ice. They built a wall of stones, enclosing a space of five feet by six, around a strong jet of heat and steam. "The heat," as E. T. Coleman, the British climber, recorded, "was too great at the orifice to bear for more than an instant; the steam wet them, the smell of sulphur nauseated them; in short, they passed a most miserable night, freezing on one side and in a hot sulphur steam bath on the other."

Today there is certainly no cause to spend such an uncomfortable time on Mount Rainier. Yet the climb over the ridges of crumbling lava and pumice, along inclined and deeply crevassed icefields, is still a difficult one. The Nat-

ional Park authorities insist that all climbers should register with the district park ranger before setting out; they must also give "satisfactory evidence of their physical abilities, knowledge and experience in hazardous climbing, and possession of proper equipment." The ascent is usually made from Paradise Valley or White River.

Rakaposhi

A mountain peak and range in the Lesser Karakoram. Location Northwest Kailas-Karakoram Range, Kashmir. Height 25,550 feet. Map 11, C3. First climbed Captain M. E. B. Banks and Surgeon-Lieutenant T. W. Patey, 1958.

Rakaposhi, one of the best-known Karakoram peaks west of K2, dominates the Hunza Valley from Chalt to Hunza along the main route from Gilgit to the Pamirs. As the traveler emerges from the gorge by Chaichar Parri and approaches Chalt, he is suddenly aware of the extraordinary beauty of its glistening, ice-draped northern precipices, rising above the somber, conglomerate cliffs and terraces of the river and the barren spurs above; as he approaches Aliabad, he constantly turns to gaze. Here the Shina name of Rakaposhi is unknown – on this side it is known as Dumani, "the mother of mist," a most appropriate name for a mountain with so many legends attached to it. A British expeditionary force fought a frontier war on its northern skirts in 1891; sportsmen have scoured its rocky ravines in search of game, ibex and markhor, but to the many travelers who have seen it from the north it has always appeared inaccessible.

Rakaposhi also gives its name to a long range of the Lesser Karakoram from the Hunza gorge eastwards to the head of the Hispar glacier, of which it forms the southern wall. Besides its own dominating massif, there are four other main mountain groups in the range. Three are named after their approach valleys and glaciers – Bagrot, Phuparash and Chogo Lungma – the other is the southern wall of the Hispar, broken only by the difficult glacier pass, Nushik La (17,300 feet). The highest peaks of these five groups were fixed for position and height during the Kashmir triangulation between 1857 and 1860; Colonel Henry Haversham Godwin-Austen of the Survey of India was the first to sketch the Chogo Lungma and to reach the Nushik La. The Bagret valleys and the Hispar Wall were explored and roughly mapped by Martin Conway in 1892. Dr Hunter Workman and his wife made two journeys in 1902 and 1903 to the Chogo Lungma. In recent years all the groups have become better known and maps have been improved.

The Rakaposhi range is affected by monsoon incursions in July and August, but much less so than the Himalayas farther east. There may be long periods, from June to September in a favorable year, when the main peaks have fine weather. Most of the snow comes in the early half of the year, from January to May, and is brought by westerly winds, with depressions passing through Afghanistan, to the south of the Hindu Kush.

During the last 20 years several attempts have been made to climb Rakaposhi. Campbell Secord and Michael Vyvyan reconnoitered it from the Jaglot ravine on the west in 1938. They examined the northwest and southwest ridges and reached an altitude of about 22,500 feet on the former. They thought that the ascent from here was practicable by a strong party. In June, 1947, an attempt was made by a party of four which included Secord and H. W. Tilman. They reached a high altitude on a spur of the southwest ridge short of a snow peak – the Monk's Head – which appeared to offer the best chance of success. A third party of six, led by Dr A. Tissières, reached the Monk's Head in 1954, but was driven back by bad weather.

The first ascent was made by a British-Pakistani Forces expedition in 1958, whose two leaders reached the summit from a final camp at 24,000 feet in five hours, in spite of a blizzard. The top camp was established by the team and six Hunza porters; it was the highest of three at the top of extremely steep 1,500 foot "steps," the snow- and ice-covered faces of which must rank among the steepest ever climbed by laden porters.

Ras Dashan

Nine tower-like peaks. Location *Simen Mountains, Ethiopia.* Height *15,157 feet.* Map *9, G5.*

In the northwest corner of the gigantic table-land covering almost the whole of Ethiopia, about 350 miles west of the southern entrance of the Red Sea, a striking group of mountains rises abruptly from the surrounding 9,000-foot plateau. This is the Simen, the "land of frost," so called because its highest parts are regularly covered with snow in winter, a rare phenomenon in the Ethiopian massif, despite its many peaks over 10,000 feet high. The highest of the Simen Mountains is the ninefold group called Ras Dashan. The group, like the rest of the Simen, is composed of basalt, a volcanic rock, although there are no active volcanoes now in this part of Ethiopia.

Until the Italian occupation of the country – of which the Simen was one of the last regions to be subdued in 1935–36 – no one had set foot on these majestic peaks, since the local tribesmen believed them to be inhabited by hostile spirits. Foreign visitors were infrequent because of the lack of communications with the rest of the country and the general discouragement of outsiders by the Ethiopian authorities. Under Italian occupation, however, a geological survey of the region was undertaken.

The lower slopes of the mountains are used for grazing and growing the hardier cereal crops. The water supply consists of numerous little streams punctuated by waterfalls which descend on the eastern slopes into the Takkaze, a tributary of the Nile. Among the mammals the ibex is found on Ras Dashan and a small species of monkey lives on the lower slopes. A plant characteristic of the region is a giant lobelia, growing as high as 12 feet with blooms several inches long.

Rhodope Mountains

A major mountain system of the Balkan Peninsula. Location *Southern Bulgaria and northeast Greece.* Height *Rising to 9,596 feet.* Map *7, G8.*

Running northwest to southeast from the Struma River to the Maritsa River, the Rhodope Mountains extend about 180 miles between the Thracian plain and the Aegean Sea. In ancient times, the range was sacred to Dionysus, and its beauties inspired many a classical poet.

The range can be divided into three parts: Rhodope proper is separated by the Mesta River from the Pirin Mountains in the west and from the Rila Mountains on the northwest.

The Pirins are divided into three sections: the highest are the northern Pirins, rising to 9,558 feet in Vikhren Peak; the central part of the range culminates in Polezhan Peak (9,351 feet) and the southern Pirin Mountains extend to the Alibotush Mountains on the Greek border, the entire sub-range being within Bulgaria. There are valuable lignite mines near Simitli in Brezhani in the northwest, and copper, manganese and iron deposits, though no longer exploited, are concentrated near Novrokop in the southeast. The valleys of the eastern slopes are areas in which truck-gardening, vegetables and flowers are grown in intensive cultivation. Lumber, woodworking and stock raising occupy the Bansko and Razlog areas.

The Rila Planina, as the Bulgarians call them, form the highest range both in Bulgaria and the Balkan Peninsula, extending about 50 miles from east to west between the Thracian Plain and the Struma River. This range also has different sections: the eastern Rila Mountains are the highest, rising to 9,596 feet in Stalin Peak (formerly Musala); the central Rila Mountains rise to 8,969 feet in the Skakavets; the northwest Rilas have their culmination in the Malovitsa (8,957 feet); and finally the southwest section reaches 8,587 feet in the Aigidik. The Predel Pass separates it from the Pirin Mountains. The subrange has scattered lead, zinc, copper and magnetite deposits, with oil shale near Dimitrovo and lignite and marble quarries in the central part. Around the mineral springs in Sapareve-banya small health resorts have sprung up. There are extensive coniferous forests, and cattle and sheep are raised in the alpine meadows.

The Rhodope proper has its highest section in the west, where Slav Peak (7,576 feet) is the most important summit. The eastern section descends gradually and is drained by the Arda River. The principal passes are the Avramov and Dospat in the west, the Topolov in the northeast and the Makaz on the southeast. The main importance of the Rhodope is in its position as a major continental divide between the Mediterranean climate of the Aegean and the humid inland zone of central Bulgaria. It contains the major forest resources of the country and the best tobacco is grown on the slopes. Some geologists consider that the Rhodope ranges include the southeastern Yugoslav highlands between the Balkan Mountains and the Dinaric Alps, extending along the axis of the Vardar and Morava rivers to the neighborhood of Belgrade.

Rif Mountains

An arc-shaped mountain range. Location *Morocco.* Height *Rising to 8,060 feet.* Map *9, B2.*

It is less than 40 years since the pacification of the Rif Mountains by joint Franco-Spanish forces was completed – and even today the fiercely independent Riffians (the local name of the mountain-dwelling Berber tribes) have their own code of morality, merely paying lip service to their overlords.

The grim, barren mountains have been for centuries the stronghold of pirates and a host of small tribal chiefs. They extend about 180 miles, close to the Mediterranean coast of Africa. Exploration of the Rif did not really begin until Abd-el-Krim was subdued in 1926, having raised a revolt against Spanish rule five years earlier.

Geologically the Rif is a counterpart of the Spanish Cordillera Penibética, from which it is divided by the Strait of Gibraltar. Along the seashore the mountains generally end in lines of cliff, broken at intervals by narrow stretches of sandy beaches, but opening up here and there into beautiful and fertile valleys like that of Albucemas, which gives its name also to a fine, semicircular bay.

The geographical limits of the Rif are from Tangier and Ceuta on the Strait of Gibraltar to the lower Muluya Valley east of Melilla. The highest peak is Tidiguin (8,060 feet) and several of the higher summits in the central Ketama section are covered with snow during part of the year. While there are extensive cedar forests on the slopes, agriculture – still fairly primitive – is limited to the few narrow coastal valleys. Difficult of access, the rich deposits of lead, antimony, graphite and iron (at Beni bu Ifrur) have only been exploited in the last 20 years.

Robson, Mount

Highest peak of the Canadian Rocky Mountains. Location *Eastern British Columbia.* Height *12,972 feet.* Map *3, F9.* First climbed *A. H. MacCarthy, W. W. Foster and the Austrian guide Conrad Kain, 1913.*

In no other area of the Rockies is the landscape dominated so completely by one peak as it is by Mount Robson. The mountain's southwest side rises nearly 10,000 feet above Kinney Lake, above the Canadian National Railway west of Yellowhead Pass. It fills the vast northeast angle of the junction of Robson and Fraser rivers, a spot known from pioneer days as the Grand Forks. It was mentioned as early as 1827, but was known before then by fur traders crossing the main watershed through Yellowhead Pass. The shaly strata gave rise to the Cree Indian name Yuh-hai-has-kun, "the mountain of the spiral road." Today it forms part of the Mount Robson Provincial Park, 65 miles long and 10-20 miles wide, a preserve of striking scenery, high peaks and glaciers. The small Berg Lake resort is at the foot of the peak.

Mount Robson is not only one of the most impressive but also one of the most difficult peaks of the continent. A. P. and L. Q. Coleman, with C. S. Kinney, reached the head of Robson River in 1906 and camped on Robson Pass in 1908 when coming from Moose River. At that time it could only be approached on horseback from Banff or Edmonton. Kinney and Phillips reached the final ice-dome, not far below the summit, in 1909, but it was not until four years later that the peak was finally conquered. Since then Mount Robson has often been reconnoitered but comparatively rarely climbed, as the ascent is made extremely dangerous by frequent avalanches.

Roche Melon

An Alpine peak. Location *Graian Alps, Franco-Italian border.* Height *11,605 feet.* Map *8, C9.* First climbed *Bonifacius Rotarius, 1358.*

The first high Alpine peak to be either attempted or climbed, Roche Melon rises above Susa, covered with a minor glacier on one side, usually free of snow on the other, and crowned by a small chapel built by Bonifacius Rotarius of Asti, who made the first ascent.

The climb was said to have been carried out after the escape of Rotarius from the Moors, when he vowed to build a chapel on the highest summit of the Alps. The Roche Melon had for a long time held this title locally and its claim was supported by Thomas Coryate, who visited the district in 1608 and reported: "Some told me it was 14 miles high; it is covered with a very Microcosm of clowdes. Of this mountain there is no more than a little peece of the top to be seene, which seemeth a farre off to be three or foure little turrets or steeples in the aire."

Once known as "Mons Romulus," the mountain was locally believed to be the hiding place of a great treasure owned by a king of that name. In the eleventh century more than one unsuccessful effort was made to scale the peak by monks from the Benedictine monastery of Novalesa near its foot.

After the first successful ascent, the tradition grew up of an annual pilgrimage to the summit. This is now made on August 5, the festival of Notre Dame de la Neige – Our Lady of the Snows. Charles Emmanuel II of Italy climbed it in 1659, his example being followed by many later sovereigns, including Victor Emmanuel II.

Rocky Mountains - Canada

A major mountain system, forming the Continental Divide. Location *Alberta and British Columbia.* Height *Rising to 12,972 feet.* Map *3, E6-H11.*

In 1789 Peter Pangman, one of the founders of the Northwest Trading Company, ascended the North Saskatchewan River as far as the present site of Rocky Mountain House, the town founded ten years after his journey. Near the mouth of the Clearwater River, three miles beyond the future town site, he blazed a tree from which he was the first to see the Canadian Rocky Mountains. The early travelers in the mountains were fur traders, explorers and geographers. They called them Glittering Mountains because of the countless rock crystals which, so the early pioneers reported, covered their surfaces; when they were not covered with snow they reflected the rays of the sun to an immense distance. The name Rocky Mountains was given to them by later travelers – possibly because of the enormous isolated rocks which are seen here and there.

This great range continues the American Rocky Mountains to the northwest, beyond the point where the forty-ninth parallel divides the United States and Canada. The section running northwest for some 400 miles from the frontier is part of the Northern Rockies; the Canadian part forms an almost continuous backbone of summits, only some 50 miles wide at most and

The Canadian Rockies from the air,
showing Mount Robson

with Mount Robson (12,972 feet) as the culminating point. Mount Robson is actually the lowest part of the region structurally, the bottom of a synclinal fold (a fold dipping towards a common line or point). That is why Mount Robson's almost flat-lying beds of quarzite and limestone seem anomalous in relation to the neighboring mountains, where the strata are often bent up on edge or even tilted back.

There are large icefields and glaciers in an area near the center of the range, east of the Big Bend of the Columbia River, where several of the highest peaks are grouped and the apex of the main watershed, the Columbia Icefield of 100 square miles, forms a tri-oceanic divide and is linked with important snow-fields north and south. But because of their easterly position in relation to the cordilleran ranges, the bulk of the Canadian Rockies receives relatively little rain; therefore glaciers are only of moderate size, while the timber line (which reaches nearly 8,000 feet in the south) is never above 5,000 feet here. It is the configuration of the mountains and the effective climatic barrier they create that are the causes of the renowned Chinook wind with its warming effect that descends upon the low country of the Peace River district and renders its climate far more genial and suitable for farming than other districts at this high northerly latitude.

Between these Northern Rockies and the mountains immediately to the west – the Purcell, Selkirk and Cariboo mountains – which are earlier in origin, lies the great Rocky Mountain Trench, running northwards from Montana more or less continuously for 900 miles; seen from the air it looks like a vast trough, with its floor varying from two to ten miles across.

North of Mount Robson the range changes in character, becoming much lower. Where the Peace River flows eastwards out of the Rocky Mountain Trench, it is at its minimum width of some 25 miles; but beyond, in what is perhaps the least known area of the Rockies, its width increases to 85 miles or more. Here are the al-most inaccessible Lloyd George Mountains, rising to a maximum of about 9,800 feet, which were explored, surveyed and climbed by an American-British-Canadian expedition in 1947. About 100 miles northwest of the Lloyd George group and 480 miles from Mount Robson is Terminus Mountain (6,250 feet), which rises above the Kechika River in the extreme north of British Columbia. It is suitably named, for it is the real northern outpost of the Rockies – even though some authorities suggest that they continue northward in the widespread, almost unexplored complex of ranges in Yukon and Alaska. sometimes called the Arctic Rockies.

The Canadian Rockies are similar in structure to the ranges in the United States, consisting of great faulted blocks in orthoclinal – "writing-desk" – attitude, with a singular absence of any volcanic rocks. It is clear that both the Canadian and American Rockies derive from the same mountain-building epoch, known as the Laramide orogeny. Much of the evidence on these crustal movements comes from deep exploratory drilling in connection with the recent oil-field development in Alberta.

A great deal of the Canadian Rockies is now contained in national parks, for it is a region of great beauty, with many lakes among the peaks. Big game is plentiful and widely distributed. Moose, mule deer, black bear and sheep are often seen. Goats are less common, while caribou are found only in the north. The parks offer an infinite variety of snowy peaks, turquoise lakes among pinewoods surrounded by steep precipices, and waterfalls that descend sheer for hundreds of feet into rock-hewn canyons.

Rocky Mountains - United States

An interlocking chain of ranges forming the easternmost belt of the North American cordillera. Location *From central New Mexico to the Canadian border in Montana.* Height *Ranging from 7,000 feet to 14,000 feet.* Map *4, D1-E6.*

The American Rockies represent a vast natural barrier between the east and west of the continent. They include some 20 or more principal ranges and groups of mountains which form the easternmost part of the vast complex of cordilleran mountains stretching to the Pacific coast. The western ranges are known to be of a different age – mainly earlier than the Mountains.

The structure of all these ranges is composite and complex. With the growth of knowledge geologists have been able to show that, instead of a single rather violent mountain-building movement, there has been a long succession of dynamic events through Mesozoic times leading up to the final movements of the Tertiary era. These movements, or orogenies, to use the technical term, classed as "alpine" in the European succession, are termed "Laramide" in western America, after the Laramie Mountains of eastern Wyoming, where these specific movements were first recognized. The most characteristic structures in the Laramide system are great disturbances compressing the mountain crusts, with folding and faulting, and in places overthrusting eastwards of rock mass upon rock mass. Additional phenomena are great intrusions of igneous rocks known as batholiths, but their actual age and relationship are not always clear.

The southernmost parts of the Rocky Mountain ranges in the United States are the Sangre de Cristo Mountains, running some 220 miles north and south and consisting of several subranges, including the Sierra Blanca, the Culebra Range and the Taos Mountains, which include Wheeler Peak (13,151 feet), the highest in New Mexico. Raton Pass, to the east of the main peaks, is famous not only in the history of the pioneers and their covered-wagon trains, but also in the building of the Santa Fe Railway to the West. To eliminate the former "switchback," the company bored twin tunnels under the crest of the pass. The historic city of Santa Fe, capital of New Mexico, lies on the southwest flank of the mountains, and not far off is the atomic research town of Los Alamos.

A neighboring district of very beautiful scenery is dominated by the heavily forested San Juan Mountains, which run northeast from New Mexico into Colorado. Fundamentally these mountains are a broad, dome-like uplift which later became buried by Tertiary volcanic lavas. Uncompahgre Peak (14,306 feet) is the highest in the range; and Cumbres Pass (10,025 feet), near the New Mexico border, now a state highway, is of historic interest since it was used by Spanish explorers of the sixteenth and seventeenth centuries.

North of these ranges lie the Sawatch Mountains in western central Colorado, extending about 100 miles. Beside Mount Elbert (14,431 feet), the highest point of the American Rockies, they contain the celebrated Mountain of the Holy Cross (13,986 feet); at its top crevices 750 feet long and 50 feet wide, filled with snow, form a huge cross. Part of the group north of St Almo is known as the Collegiate Range, and includes Mount Harvard (14,399 feet), Mount Yale (14,172 feet) and Mount Princeton (14,177 feet). Gold was first found here in 1860 and lead with high silver content in 1877. The earlier fame of the area attracted such celebrities as General Grant, General Sheridan and Oscar Wilde as visitors. But the fall in the price of silver started a long decline after 1893; today important alternative industries are ranching and dairying.

To the north again, but some distance eastwards, lies the Front Range of Colorado, starting at Pikes Peak, ten miles from the town of Colorado Springs and extending some 300 miles. Pikes Peak is remarkable as possessing one of the world's few deposits of cryolite, a rare fluoride of sodium and aluminium used as a flux in the smelting of bauxite for aluminium. In the Cripple Creek district, a few miles southwest of Pikes Peak, there are a number of rich gold and silver mines.

Continuing the Front Range northward is the 100-mile-long Medicine Bow range; the two ranges meet in the Rocky Mountain National Park, occupying 395 square miles, a magnificent mountain area of lofty peaks, glaciers, canyons, waterfalls, lakes and streams. At the northern end, in Wyoming, prominent peaks are Medicine Bow Mountain (12,005 feet) and Elk Mountain (11,162 feet). In Colorado the range runs in part along the Continental Divide and contains many high summits. No less than 65 peaks exceed 10,000 feet, of which Longs Peak (14,255 feet) is the highest.

Although only moderate in size and height, the far-flung eastern mountain arc of the Laramie Mountains is of great significance. Flanked on the east by the great eastern plains of Wyoming, they rise in Laramie Peak to 10,274 feet above the Laramie Basin to the west. Geologically these mountains have been of prime importance for the purposes of dating the mountain-building epoch of the whole system.

The ranges so far described are sometimes grouped together as the Southern Rockies and form both the highest and most homogeneous group. Some 150 miles eastwards from the Laramie Range, across a stretch of high terrain without special features, rises the Wind River Range, trending north-northwest to south-southeast in western Wyoming for some 120 miles from the Sweetwater River to the Wind River. Its highest point is Gannett Peak (13,785 feet), the loftiest in Wyoming. The whole range is one of great beauty, with glaciers, alpine meadows rich in flowers, and forests; it is much visited by mountaineers and tourists.

East again is the lesser Wyoming Range, reaching 11,388 feet in Wyoming Peak. Like the other mountains of southeast Wyoming, it conforms more or less to the ruling Rocky Mountain trend from north to south or from north-west to southeast. But in the Uinta Mountains due south across the inter-state border in northeast Utah, we find a surprising swing in trend to roughly east to west. These mountains, which in Kings Peak and Mount Emmons reach 13,498 feet, and 13,428 feet respectively, are essentially a great flat-crested arc which forms a classical type of folding mountain structure with its two large monoclinical, singly inclined flexures in opposite directions on either flank.

The Uintas are followed by the lesser Wasatch Mountains and the Teton Range – the latter perhaps the finest group in the western United States – with Yellowstone National Park immediately to the north. To the east of the Tetons, forming the eastern boundary of the Yellowstone National Park, is the Absaroka Range, running some 150 miles into northwest Wyoming from the extreme southwest corner of Montana roughly between Yellowstone River and the Bighorn Basin. A northeast spur, known as the Beartooth Range, includes Granite Peak (12,850 feet), the highest point in Montana, while in Wyoming itself there are such notable summits as Francs Peak (13,140 feet), the Washakie Needles (12,496 feet) and Mount Crosby (12,345 feet).

Some distance to the east and virtually separate from the main Rocky Mountain trend are the Bighorn Mountains of northern Wyoming, a massif celebrated among geologists for its structural and glacially sculptural features.

At the northern end of the Absaroka Range the basic direction of the Rockies is markedly westwards once more, with a small parallel group, the Madison Range, the highest peak of which is Sphinx Mountain or Koch Peak (11,293 feet). North of these the mountains become very broken, the main bulk of the Rockies being far to the west, on the eastern edge of what is known as the Idaho Batholith. This is not strictly part of the Rocky Mountain formation, but a huge granite massif, covering more than 16,000 square miles of western Idaho, which forms, with the folded crystalline rocks of the Bitterroot Range on its eastern flank, a great outlying region of disturbance within the "Laramie Belt."

The Bitterroot Mountains, with the Clearwater and Salmon River mountains of the granite batholith formation which are sometimes included, form the southwest part of the Northern Rockies. They extend northwest, petering out near the north end of the Idaho-Montana boundary. Now the main trend of the Rockies is taken up by the Lewis Range, which forms part of the Continental Divide running northwards through Glacier National Park – itself continuous with Waterton Lakes National Park and its mountains in Alberta. Called by the Blackfoot Indians, whose reservation lies on its eastern flank, "The Backbone of the World," this district of great scenic beauty contains some of the most spectacular summits of the Rockies, the highest point being Mount Cleveland (10,448 feet).

Here the forty-ninth parallel makes an arbitrary division of the Rocky Mountains of the United States from those of Canada.

Roncador, Serra do

An unexplored mountain range in the Brazilian jungle. Location *Central Mato Grosso, Brazil.* Height *1,800 feet, average.* Map *6, E6-F6.* Discovered *Portuguese party of explorers, 1743.*

Between the sources of the great north-flowing rivers, Araguaia, Xingu and Tapajos (tributaries of the Amazon) lies one of the least known parts of still largely unexplored Brazil.

In 1743 a small party of six Portuguese with their Negro slaves and Indian guides set out across this great plateau region in search of the legendary gold and silver mines of the interior. They found little mineral wealth, but in the heart of the Mato Grosso they came upon a jagged range of mountains which they named the Serra do Roncador. Beyond these they said they had seen a fertile tableland with the colossal remains of a deserted city, its mighty stones cracked and fallen in some catastrophic earthquake, the hieroglyphics of an unknown language still visible on the ruined walls. Glimpses of strange, fair-skinned men with flowing black hair provided additional evidence of a lost race, before the party started back to the coast to organize a larger expedition. But on the way they disappeared without a trace, and the only record of the discovery which reached civilization was a brief report sent on ahead by an Indian runner.

Filed and forgotten for a long while, this account was rediscovered in the nineteenth century and led to the despatch of a government-sponsored expedition – a total failure because the searchers, deterred by shortage of food and rumors of hostile Indians, soon gave up.

In 1925 a new mystery was added to the riddle of the Snoring Mountains. Colonel P. H. Fawcett, man of action with an overriding streak of mysticism, was convinced of the truth of the old Portuguese tale and set forth into the depths of the Mato Grosso in search of the lost city, this supposed center of a long-vanished civilization. He reached "Dead Horse Camp," north of Cuyaba, the capital of Mato Grosso, then disappeared, together with his son Jack and one other white man. Enquiries made by the Brazilian government in 1927 showed that they had probably perished. But doubts remained and there were various reports of a mysterious white captive of the Indians. Commander George Dyott led a large search party over Fawcett' route in 1928. He turned back, suspicious of an ambush, before he could track down the source of the rumors. In 1933 another expedition tracked Indian reports of Fawcett's progress and finally emerged on a "camp" of tall grass. According to most maps, the rocky summits of the Serra do Roncador should have been visible from this spot – but the horizon was empty. The mountains, guideposts to the lost city for which Fawcett had searched and probably lost his life, did not even exist.

Today the Serra do Roncador is marked on the maps at 14° S latitude and is described as separating the headwaters of the Xingu River from the left tributaries of the Araguaia. Perhaps this is the range which figured in the 1743 report – more likely, it is a newer discovery to which the old name has been given. After the Second World War Brian Fawcett, the Colonel's younger son, flew over this region in a light plane, searching for his father's lost city, and photographed weird monolithic edifices like the ruins of some vanished civilization. But they were not ruins, merely rock outcrops of fantastic shape, the product of ages of weathering in this ancient landscape.

Roncesvalles Pass

A rocky defile. Location *Navarre province, northern Spain.* Height *3,468 feet.* Map *7, B8.*

The legendary scene of the death of Orlando (Roland), "praefect of the Breton march," has been a favorite place of pilgrimage for more than ten centuries. It was on the return of his uncle, Charlemagne, from Spain that the hero of the *Song of Roland*, in command of the rearguard, fell into a Moorish ambuscade and perished with the flower of Frankish chivalry.

The fact that Roncesvalles lies on the main pilgrimage route to Santiago de Compostela probably served to propagate the story throughout the nations of Europe. The *Chanson de Roland* was ascribed to the Norman troubadour Théroulde or Turoldus and was supposed to have been sung by the minstrel Taillefer at the battle of Hastings.

In the little village of Roncesvalles, three miles south of the pass, the shade of Roland is still alive, for it is to him that the village owes its fame. In the monastery and collegiate church of the Augustines there are a number of relics associated with the hero.

Roraima, Mount

A giant table mountain, highest point of Guiana Highlands. Location *Pakaraima Mountains, on the border of Brazil, British Guiana and Venezuela.* Height *9,219 feet.* Map *6, D3.* First climbed *Sir Everard im Thurn and W. Perkins, 1884.*

An immense mountain with a total surface of 26 square miles (of which six are divided between British Guiana and Brazil, while the rest lie in Venezuela), Mount Roraima rises as a perpen-

dicular wall of red rock 1,500 feet in height from the forest-clad slopes below the summit. It was discovered by Robert Schomburgk in 1838, but was considered completely inaccessible until Sir Everard im Thurn and W. Perkins found a ledge by which the top could be reached. The summit itself is a tableland with an area of some 12 square miles; here Sir Arthur Conan Doyle placed his "Lost World."

It is a series of conglomerates, red and white sandstone and red shale, resting upon a foundation of gneiss which has formed both Roraima and Mount Kukenaam, which is of similar structure though 700 feet lower. Michael Swan wrote of a "vast pink ribbon of sandstone," marking the gateway between the two mountains. "I was never to see that gateway," he continued, "without heavy cloud pouring from it like expressed smoke; it was like some volcanic Avernus. The closer we came to the walls the more insistent became the analogy of a fortress; turrets and, at points, bastion towers appeared." Roraima presents the highest mural face in the world, standing 5,000 feet above the surrounding tableland. A long, steep ledge, covered with forest for half its length, leads to the summit.

"The summit came with extraordinary suddenness," Swan's record of his ascent in 1956 continued. "Not knowing how much further it would be, I put my foot up to a boulder and pulled myself over to find I could climb no higher. The roof of Roraima lay about us. During those first astonished moments of arrival it seemed to me that the monsters of the Lost World had been turned into black, frigid monoliths: swirled in constantly moving mist and rising from an irregular surface of rock were gigantic forms carved by the elements from the sandstone and blackened by chemical action to resemble basalt; pinnacles with rudimentary limbs, ragged-edged pyramids and 20-foot hourglass shapes, with waists so fragile that it seemed as if the heavy wind must bring the upper dolmen thundering to the ground. Nature, it seemed, had placed and carved these stones as the scene for a primitive rite; a Stonehenge disorganized, stones turned to the shapes of a mad fantasy."

Ruapehu

A dormant volcano, highest mountain in North Island. Location Central North Island, New Zealand. Height 9,175 feet. Map 12, J8.

Ruapehu, a bulky volcanic mountain, occupies a prominent position in the Tongariro National Park (the first to be established in New Zealand). It is the culminating point of the volcanic belt of the island, which includes Ngauruhoe (7,515 feet) and Tongariro (6,458 feet).

With its great snow-covered summit, Ruapehu is an imposing sight from the lower surrounding country, particularly at sunrise or sunset when there may be beautiful alpenglow effects. Apart from the higher perpetual snow-fields, a number of small glaciers occupy hollows in the mountain flanks and descend to about 7,000 feet. In recent years they have been shrinking considerably. Unlike its frequently active neighbor, Ngauruhoe, Ruapehu is a semi-dormant volcano, which in historic times first erupted in 1886. There are no Maori records or legends of earlier activity. Various gas and steam jets can be found on the flanks of the mountain and may be in the stage of waning activity called "solfatara" – a name

The eruption of Mount Ruapehu in 1945

applied to any volcanic opening which is in a dormant or decadent stage and from which gases (especially sulphur dioxide) and volatile substances escape. But in the remarkable summit crater with its lake of warm water, about 600 yards across and surrounded by ice-cliffs, there is evidence of earlier, moderately violent eruptions. As recently as 1945 a mass of molten lava rose in the volcanic "neck" to form an island in the lake and then to occupy the entire floor of the crater, having blown out the water as steam, besides throwing out ash over the mountain flanks.

On Christmas Eve, 1953, Ruapehu was responsible for a national disaster. The restored water of the crater lake broke out to cause a flood that carried away the railway bridge over the Whangaehu River at Tangiwai, 25 miles distant. The Wellington-Auckland express was just approaching and plunged into the raging torrent, killing 151 people in all. There was no evidence of actual volcanic agency to cause this outbreak, but rather it appeared that the ice-dam at one point in the rim of the crater lake had given way and sent the waters rushing down the mountainside to cause havoc far below.

Rushmore, Mount

A National Memorial of giant sculptures. Location *Black Hills, western South Dakota.* Height *6,200 feet.* Map *4, E3.*

Mount Rushmore National Memorial, 1,220 acres in area, was established in 1929 to provide a setting for one man's lifelong dream. John Gutzon de la Mothe Borglum, born in Idaho, in 1871, was a sculptor who studied in San Francisco and the Julien Academy of Paris, though his inspiration and his aims were entirely American. His first encounter with monumental sculpture was the design and partial execution of the Stone Mountain (Georgia) memorial to the Con-

The sculptured heads of Mount Rushmore National Memorial

federacy – a gigantic bas-relief a quarter of a mile long. But he quarreled with the sponsors of the project and withdrew. It was in 1927 that he began his work for the Mount Rushmore National Memorial, at which he toiled until his death, in 1941, at the age of 70. It was completed in November, 1941, by his son, Lincoln.

The Mount Rushmore sculpture is the largest ever attempted. The heads of Washington, Jefferson, Lincoln and Theodore Roosevelt rise from the gigantic outcropping of granite at the top of the mountain. Each face is between 60 and 70 feet high, carved with a perfection of detail and expression that represents a considerable achievement.

Washington, according to Borglum's concept, symbolizes the founding of the Union, Jefferson the adoption of the Constitution and the Louisiana Purchase, Lincoln the preservation of the Union and Roosevelt the expansion of the United States and the building of the Panama Canal. It is estimated that the Memorial could exist for 100,000 years without any appreciable change.

Ruwenzori

A mountain group of six snow-capped masses. Location *Congo-Uganda border.* Height *Rising to 16,795 feet.* Map *9, F6.* First climbed *Duke of Abruzzi's expedition, 1906* (*Mount Stanley, Mount Margherita and Mount Alexandra*).

Ruwenzori, the great mountain group between Lake Edward and Lake Albert, has been generally identified with the fabulous "Mountains of the Moon" which the ancients supposed to be the source of the Nile. Homer, Herodotus and Strabo all put forward different theories, based obviously on rumor – though Egyptian envoys, including Greeks, may have reached Ethiopia and the source of the Blue Nile in Lake Tana before 500 B.C. But it was Ptolemy (90–168 A.D.) who was first known to have used the name, having obtained his information from the description of the travels of a sailor named Diogenes by Marinus of Tyre. Whether Diogenes actually saw the mountains and lakes is doubtful; but Ptolemy's map recorded an enormous range, hundreds of miles long, running east and west below the equator.

The Arabs, who penetrated deeply into East Africa during the dark ages and later, spoke of the Nile as rising in the Mountains of Cumr – probably a variation of "Kamar," the Moon – but they gave no exact description. When in the nineteenth century the sources of the White Nile in Lake Victoria, Lake Albert and Lake Edward and in various small rivers draining into them were at last discovered, a controversy started about the identity of the true "Mountains of the Moon." Today it is generally accepted that Ruwenzori, whose melting snows do in fact feed some of the furthermost Nile sources, has the best claim to the name.

The first white man to see Ruwenzori was Henry Stanley in 1888. For most of the year the summits, down to 9,000 feet or lower, are clothed in mist, so that it is possible to pass close by without being aware of their existence. Emin Pasha lived for ten years on Lake Albert and never once saw the range – a fact which, as John Buchan says, may be partly explained by his bad eyesight. And if it happened that somebody – such as General Charles Gordon's emissary, Gessi – actually saw them, this was recorded as a strange apparition of "snow mountains in the sky." The snowline is at 14,500 feet, but even within historical times it seems to have extended much lower and in the great Ice Age it came down to 4,600 feet.

Ruwenzori, as Patrick M. Synge and others explained, cannot be considered as a single mountain. About 75 miles long and 40 miles wide, the six main snow-topped masses are separated by gorges several thousand feet deep. Unlike the other great mountains of Equatorial Africa, Ruwenzori is not a volcanic mass, but consists of very ancient rocks, squeezed up at some past time of geological activity like a section from an orange. Many of these contain mica schists and sparkle like great slabs of silver in the sun, adding greatly to the beauty of the scene.

Stanley, in 1888, had a sudden vision of the range from the southwest shore of Lake Albert. "While looking to the southeast," he wrote in a famous passage, ". . . my eyes were directed by a boy to a mountain said to be covered with salt, and I saw a peculiar-shaped cloud of a most beautiful silver color, which assumed the proportions and appearance of a vast mountain covered with snow. Following its form downward, I became struck with the deep blue-black color of its base. . . then, as the sight descended to the gap between the eastern and western plateaus, I became for the first time conscious that what I gazed upon was not the image or semblance of a vast mountain, but the solid substance of a real one, with its summit covered with snow. . . It now dawned upon me that this must be Ruwenzori. . ."

It was 18 years later, in April, 1906, that the Duke of Abruzzi led an expedition to solve definitely the riddle of the mountains. He took four famous alpine guides and a staff of eminent scientists with him as well as Vittorio Sella, the greatest of living mountain photographers. A hundred and fifty native porters were used to carry stores: the expedition's aim was to climb every summit and map accurately every mountain, valley and glacier.

In this, though held up by bad weather and sidetracked by faulty information, the Duke and his companions were entirely successful. The first peak they ascended was Mount Alexandra (16,750 feet). A short descent and a difficult passage of snow cornices took them to the summit of Mount Margherita (16,795 feet), the highest point of the range.

Since then a Belgian expedition in 1932 has thoroughly explored the massif with its extensive glaciers, glacial lakes and dense equatorial forests. All the highest peaks have been climbed – but so infrequently that a new ascent is still a notable event and the less ambitious traveler can climb many minor peaks that are still virgin and traverse country so fantastic and beautiful that it will always remain with him as a cherished memory.

St Elias Mountains

An important section of the Coast Ranges of Alaska. Location *Southwest Yukon and southeast Alaska.* Height *Rising to 19,850 feet in Mount Logan.* Map *3, C6-D6.*

Running for over 200 miles northwest to southeast, the St Elias Mountains are set between the Wrangell Mountains on the northwest and the Waxell Ridge, Chugach Mountains and Kenai Mountains on the west. Here one finds Mount Logan, the second highest mountain of North America, and such important peaks as Mount St Elias (18,008 feet) Mount Lucania (17,250 feet), Mount King (17,130 feet), Mount Steele (16,439 feet), Mount Bona (16,420 feet), Mount Wood (15,880 feet), Mount Vancouver (15,696 feet) and Mount Hubbard (14,950 feet).

In the seas of ice that stream from the summits and saddles of Mount Logan glaciers predominate; they sprawl in a chaos of crevasses towards British Columbia and into Alaska, filling the valleys between the peaks. Even more impressive is the flow of ice from Mount St Elias. It forms the largest single icefield in Alaska, the Malaspina, some 1,500 square miles in area, which extends 50 miles along the seaward base of the mountain and spills into the Gulf of Alaska. Indeed, this glacier, with the Guyat, Hubbard, Bering and other glaciers of the St Elias Range, belongs to a single icefield that stretches 235 miles between Cape St Elias and the Alsef River, and forms the largest icefield outside polar regions.

It was Vitus Bering who first saw and named the magnificent peak of St Elias in 1740. The first determined attempt to climb it was made by H. W. Topham and his companions, in 1889. Their approach from the coast was long and difficult over the stone-covered frozen waves of the vast, flattish Malaspina Glacier. From the Libbey Glacier under the long east snow ridge they had a good view of the southeast face; it was covered with hanging glaciers and looked quite unassailable. They retraced their steps for several miles and camped on Coal Glacier – so called because of the coal on its surface – and made an attempt from the Tyndall Glacier farther west. They had a hard time with very loose shale and then a long spell of step cutting on a slope where the ice lay under varying depths of a granular stuff that "could hardly be called snow" and so reached the rim of something like a crater. They crossed nearly half the rim and stopped at a height of over 11,000 feet. Just east of them was the highest point of the rim, preventing them from seeing into a gap in the south arête of the great peak, which rose close to them to the north. The southwest face to the left of this arête was in view and it appeared unclimbable. Topham concluded that Mount St Elias was likely to be conquered from the north, where the slopes tended to be less precipitous.

It was this route which the conqueror of Mount St Elias, the Duke of Abruzzi, followed in 1897 with his admirably organized party. They approached the peak by the Seward Glacier and the Newton Glacier, running behind the lost eastern arête; the final camp was on a col at nearly 12,000 feet on a ridge connecting St Elias with Mount Newton to the northeast of it. It was a remarkable climb, accomplished when mountaineering was still in its infancy, and involved some 40 days on glaciers and snow-fields. St Elias was not climbed again until 1946, when an American expedition, with air support provided by the United States Army Air Force's Tenth Rescue Squadron, reached the summit by way of the southwest ridge.

Many Alaskans regard the St Elias Mountains with something of the reverence with which the Indians regarded (and some still regard) the highest peak of the vast state: Mount McKinley, or *Denali*.

St Gotthard

A famous pass and the surrounding mountain group. Location *Lepontine Alps, southern central Switzerland.* Height *6,929 (feet pass); 10,483 feet (highest peak of mountain group).* Map *8, D8.*

Famous for the 28 great zig-zags by which the road descends the southern slopes and for the campaign fought around it by the Russian General Suvorov in 1799, the St Gotthard Pass is second only in importance to the high knot of country which it traverses.

Here, where the Swiss cantons of Uri, Grisons, the Ticino and the Valais meet to form the Lepontine Alps, rise the Rhine, the Rhône, the Ticino and the Reuss rivers. This nodal area of the Alpine system sends down waters to the North Sea, the Mediterranean and the Adriatic. Although rising mainly to less than 10,000 feet – the highest peak is Pizzo Rotondo (10,483 feet) – the area is of great strategic importance, a fact underlined by history and by the presence of the Swiss garrison at Andermatt. The St Gotthard road, offering fine views, leads through the mountains.

The principal pass of the Central Alps, leading from Altdorf on Lake Lucerne to Bellinzona on Lake Maggiore, the St Gotthard has been in use, in spite of the narrowness and difficulty of both the Reuss and the Ticino valleys, at least since the days of Charlemagne, who made the route practicable for pack animals. It was first crossed on wheels by an Englishman in 1775.

The track was widened to form a proper carriage road only in 1820, and 52 years after this work began on what was to be, when opened ten years later, the longest tunnel in the Alps. Financed by the Swiss, German and French governments, just over nine miles long, it made possible the Lucerne-Bellinzona railway and was designed by a M. Favre, who died of apoplexy in the tunnel shortly before its completion. Exceeded in length only by the 12½ miles of the Simplon, the St Gotthard took eight years to bore and presented more difficult problems than the Mont Cenis, the only other transalpine railway then in existence. A further 53 tunnels, with a total length of nearly 26 miles, 43 bridges, five viaducts and avalanche galleries to protect the track also form part of the line, which enters the main tunnel at Göschenen on the north and emerges above Airolo on the south.

On the ascent to Göschenen, the most notable stretch lies through the Schöllenen Gorge, spanned by the Devil's Bridge. When the latest bridge – there have been many – was opened, the Swiss remembered the legend according to which the Devil had agreed to the construction of the first bridge only on condition that he could claim the soul of the first living being to cross it. As on an earlier occasion, a he-goat was solemnly sent across the bridge before the opening ceremony.

Sajama

A volcanic peak, highest in the Western Cordillera of the Bolivian Andes. Location *Oruro department, western Bolivia.* Height *21,390 feet.* Map *6, C6.* First climbed *Prem and Ghiglione, 1939.*

The volcanic zone of the Cordillera Occidental of the Andes, which begins in the *altiplano* area of southern Peru, continues south through Bolivia, beyond Lake Titicaca. Like El Misti near Arequipa, these Bolivian mountains reach a considerable height, bearing witness to a great period of extrusive igneous activity in the past. Near the Bolivia-Chile border, close to the western edge of the widest stretch of the Andes, is Sajama.

The height of this mountain, reputedly the highest peak in Bolivia, has been variously es-

The famous zigzag road through the St Gotthard Pass

timated at 21,390 and 21,425 feet. However, no independent estimates of its altitude are known to agree, as with so many of remote Andean summits.

Like the majority of high mountains of volcanic origin, Sajama offers an ascent of no great difficulty but very considerable hardship and demands on endurance. Its summit region is snow-capped and indeed the peak is referred to by Martin Conway as "White Sajama." The great mountaineer and explorer had designs on its virgin summit, but delays and difficulties in arranging transport to the remote peak prevented his ascent. It was not until 1939 that the highest point was reached after a long attack. The climb was repeated in 1953 by Hans Ertl and his party after their expedition to Illimani and the neighborhood.

Salcantay

Sajama

One of the best-known peaks in the Peruvian Andes. Location Southern central Peru. Height 20,551 feet. Map 6, C5. First climbed Bernard Pierre, Madame Claude Kogan and party, 1952.

Salcantay is the monarch of the great Cordillera Vilcabamba, a range of the eastern Andes lying between the rivers Apurimac and Urubamba, to the north of Cuzco. After Huascarán it is the most outstanding snow peak in Peru. It may be seen from many places of habitation and regularly in fine weather from the air route between Cuzco and Lima, for planes fly very close to its massive walls of rock and tumbling fluted ice. Lying at the eastern end of the Vilcabamba, it is among the more accessible mountains of the range.

After many attempts, Salcantay was finally conquered in 1952 by the Franco-American expedition led by Bernard Pierre. Pierre, with Claude Kogan and four experienced American mountaineers, reached the summit after a long and arduous ascent, involving two camps and the overcoming of extremely steep snow slopes

in adverse weather at the end of the season. They started their attempt on the summit from a low level; in addition they found deep snow on the broad upper ridge which slowed their progress considerably. It was not until late in the afternoon that, in pairs, they were able to attain the delicate snow spire in which Salcantay culminates, before turning back to Camp 2. They were caught by the onset of darkness, and spent a frigid night sheltering in a crevasse, but no ill effects resulted. In 1954, however, two men were killed – one of them the redoubtable Fritz Kasparek, who was among the original conquerors of the north wall of the Eiger. Salcantay was climbed again in 1956 by the Dutch geologists Egeler and De Booy, with the French guide Lionel Terray.

Sangre de Cristo Mountains

The southernmost section of the Rocky Mountains. Location *Colorado and New Mexico.* Height *Rising to 14,363 feet.* Map *4, E5*.

The range named after the Blood of Christ runs for 220 miles south-southeast and south, between the Great Plains on the east and the San Luis Valley and the upper Rio Grande on the west. Starting at Salida in southern central Colorado and ending in Santa Fe county, in the northern part of New Mexico, it contains many beautiful peaks and large areas of national forests.

Part of the mountains, spreading over three southern counties in Colorado, is known as the Sierra Blanca. This is the highest part of the Sangre de Cristo, with Old Baldy rising to 14,125 feet and Blanca Peak to 14,363 feet. The latter stands isolated, about eight miles from the Great Sand Dunes National Monument, which occupies about 46,000 acres in the San Luis Valley, at the western slope of the Sangre de Cristo range. There are several other important peaks of the main mountain chain in Colorado – Horn Peak (13,400 feet), Trinchera Peak (13,540 feet), Purgatory Peak (13,719 feet), Kit Carson Peak (14,100 feet), Humboldt Peak (14,044 feet) and the Crestone peaks (14,291 feet, with Crestone Needle 14,191 feet).

The highest summit in New Mexico is Wheeler Peak (13,151 feet) though it has been accorded this paramount position only after a recent survey; until then the three Truchas peaks, all over 13,000 feet, were thought to be higher, but the topmost of them is 40 feet lower than Wheeler. Another part of the Sangre de Cristo, between the La Veta Pass in Colorado and the New Mexico line, is sometimes called the Culebra Range with Culebra Peak (14,069 feet) its highest point.

Apart from the many parks and forest areas, the Sangre de Cristo Mountains also contain valuable mineral resources; coal is mined near Trinidad (Colorado) and there are gold, silver, lead, zinc and coal mines near Santa Fe (New Mexico). The peaks and valleys of the range are considered to be the most beautiful of the Southern Rockies.

San Marino

The smallest and oldest republic in the world. Location *Apennines, near Adriatic coast.* Height *Highest point Mount Titano, 2,438 feet.* Map *8, G11*.

San Marino, a miniature state, lies southwest of Rimini, not far from Urbino, on the eastern edges of the Apennines. It has an area of 23 square miles and a population of 14,000; the whole country consists largely of a mountain, Mount Titano, crowned by an ancient castle. The capital, San Marino, which has a population of under 2,000, is connected with Rimini, 11 miles away, by road and rail.

The tiny country grows corn, grapes and fruit and raises cattle and pigs but its main sources of revenue are tourists and the issue of postage stamps. It is also diligent in bestowing honorary citizenship on distinguished strangers – among whom Abraham Lincoln must have been the most outstanding. He accepted this honor in 1861, and his bust was unveiled in the capital in 1937.

San Marino was founded by a Dalmatian stone-cutter, a Christian fleeing from religious persecution, who later became St Marinus, in the fourth century – his tomb is in the fourteenth-century cathedral. With only a few interruptions, it has remained independent ever since, avoiding most of the wars that ravaged Italy in the Middle Ages and skilfully countering the successive attempts made on its freedom by the Dukes of Urbino, Sigismondo Malatesta, the tyrant of Rimini, and Cesare Borgia. It was neutral in both World Wars (though bombed by the Allies in the second) and still enjoys its liberty and separateness, though economically dependent on Italy. It is governed by two Regents, elected half-yearly from a council of 60. Between 1946 and

1957 the ruling majority were Communist – in spite of which it continued to sell titles of nobility, ranging from a barony costing about $10,800 to a dukedom priced at $81,000. In 1957 a bloodless revolution ended the Communist rule.

Saramati

Highest peak of the Naga Hills. Location *Patkai Range, Burma-India border.* Height *12,553 feet.* Map *11, H5.*

Saramati provides a rich hunting ground for the naturalist – or would do so, for it is still one of the practically unknown mountains of Assam. From the point of view of any outsider wishing to penetrate the area this beautiful mountain with a symmetrical cone is most unfortunately situated. In the first place, it stands on the frontier itself, so that permission to enter the region must be sought from two governments instead of one. Then the peak is surrounded by the territory of the "unadministered" Naga tribes. Government has the loosest possible control over their activities and whenever India tries to assert its authority there is instant and violent trouble. Whether or not they are still active head hunters is uncertain. Within the last 30 years they have certainly been so and in view of the constant friction it is likely that old tribal practices have been revived – not so much as a demonstration of hostility towards the Indian or Burmese governments as a symbol of Naga unity and solidarity.

The country round Saramati is steep and thickly forested. The approach to the peak is from Kohima (the most advanced point of the Japanese invasion during the Second World War) in the west or from Tamanthi on the Upper Chindwin, whence a southerly or easterly spur is reached. The name rarely appears in travel books, though the mountain is a beautiful and distinct landmark, but is mentioned in survey reports as being covered with snow in winter which may last until the end of April. Up to the last thousand feet or so, Saramati is covered with forest. Above that, air photographs show dwarf scrub and alpine turf – the scrub probably being dwarf rhododendrons in considerable variety.

Naturalists have long been interested in climbing Saramati – far more so than mountaineers. Being isolated and surrounded by lower mountains, it is like an island in the midst of an ocean and may be the last refuge of certain animals and plants no longer found elsewhere. The mountain was once climbed by a Burmese forester. Two botanists attached to a government punitive expedition spent three brief days on Saramati in the nineteen-twenties, during which they managed to climb to 9,000 or 10,000 feet. In any case they could not have reached the summit by their chosen route – a deep impassable cleft in the ridge they were following barred the way. They were deeply impressed by the plants they managed to collect and determined to return for a more thorough investigation; a plan which, unfortunately, they were never able to carry out. Saramati is still virgin ground.

Sawatch Mountains

A range of the Rocky Mountains. Location *Central Colorado.* Height *Rising to 14,431 feet in Mount Elbert.* Map *4, D4-E4.*

Stretching south for about 100 miles from the Eagle River to Saguache, bounded on the east by the Arkansas River and on the west by the Elk Mountains, the massive, immense granite slab of the Sawatch Mountains has some of the finest peaks of the American Rockies. There is Ouray (13,955 feet) at the southern tip of the range, the striking Mount of the Holy Cross (13,986 feet), Grizzly Mount (14,020 feet), Shavano Peak (14,179 feet), Mount Antero (14,245 feet), La Plata Peak (14,342 feet), Mount Massive (14,418 feet, the second highest of the Rockies), and the highest of all, Mount Elbert (14,431 feet). The Collegiate Range, just north of St Elmo, is part of the Sawatch Mountains and contains the appropriately named peaks of

Mount Yale, Mount Princeton and Mount Harvard. The main passes include Hagerman (11,495 feet, between Lake and Pitkin counties), Monarch (11,312 feet), west of Salida, carrying a highway, and Marshall (10,846 feet) serving the railroad. Ten miles west of Leadville the range is pierced by the Busk-Ivanhoe tunnel, which was originally built for rail traffic but is now also a motorway.

Sayan Mountains

A mountain system in two main sections. Location *Siberia-Mongolia border.* Height *Rising to 11,453 feet.* Map *10, E4.*

The Sayan Mountains are divided into an eastern and a western branch; the former lies partly in Mongolia, the latter entirely in the USSR. The Eastern Sayans extend southeast from the Yenisei River in the Russian SFSR along the right watershed of the Mana River to within 100 miles of the southwestern end of Lake Baikal, forming the boundary between the Russian SFSR and Mongolia in their eastern section. The Western Sayans run northeast from the Altai Mountains to the central section of the Eastern Sayan Mountains, forming the border between Krasnoyarsk Territory and the Tuva Autonomous District. The Yenisei River has carved a gorge through them and they are also crossed by the Kyzyl-Minusinsk highway.

The highest peak of the Eastern Sayans is Munku Sardyk (11,453 feet), which has several small glaciers. The Irkutsk-Jibhalanta highway passes through them.

The Sayans are the eastern continuation of the Sailughem or Altai range; orographically they form the northern border ridge of the north-west Mongolian plateau. The principal passes are Muztagh (7,480 feet), Mongol (6,500 feet), Tenghyz (7,480 feet) and Obo-sarym (6,100 feet). They slope up gently from the Mongolian plateau but are much steeper on the Siberian side, though here the range is fringed with a broad belt of subsidiary ranges of an alpine character. The native name of the mountains is Ergik-targak-taiga.

Gold, graphite, coal, silver and lead are mined in the higher reaches and from the northern slopes lumber is floated down to the Trans-Siberian Railroad. The highlands are thickly covered with forests of cedar, pitch-pine, larch, elder and birch, with huge tracts of rhododendrons, and there are Scotch firs in the lower, drier part of the valleys. The summits and slopes are boulder-strewn and thickly carpeted with lichens and mosses, but the flora is poor as a rule and there are comparatively few varieties of flowers.

The Sayans are one of the regions which have been closed to outsiders for many years and little is known of their more recent development and mineral exploitation.

Schreckhorn

A peak with several minor summits. Location *Bernese Oberland, southern central Switzerland.* Height *13,390 feet (Gross Schreckhorn).* Map *8, D7.* First climbed *Leslie Stephen and Christian Michel, 1861.*

Few European peaks appear more closely surrounded by ice than the Schreckhorn, the highest point on the long rock ridge which separates the Upper and Lower Grindelwald glaciers. To Leslie Stephen, who made the first ascent, it suggested a landscape from Greenland.

Green Alpine pastures are, in fact, singularly lacking from the views gained from the half-mile summit ridge of this fine peak with its rough crags. It is essentially a rock peak, and only on its northern flank are there snow slopes of any considerable size. The summit ridge runs from the Gross Lauteraarhorn (13,272 feet) in the south (first climbed by Edouard Desor in 1848) through the Schreckhorn and then, over a succession of minor summits, to the Klein Schreckhorn (11,474 feet) first climbed by Eustace Anderson, Christian Almer and Peter Bohren in

1857, when making an unsuccessful attempt on the main peak.

The ridge itself is narrow and crumbling. It was here that the Rev. Julius Elliott – leader of the second party to climb the Matterhorn from Zermatt – was killed in 1869 making a rash, unroped jump. The first winter ascent was made by W. A. B. Coolidge and Christian Almer in 1879; the formidable west face was not climbed until 1935, when it was conquered by Dr Oscar Hug.

The summit of the Schreckhorn offers a rich reward in a panoramic view. Leslie Stephen wrote of it ". . . on that perfect day on the top of the Schreckhorn, where not a wreath of vapor was to be seen under the whole vast canopy of the sky, a delicious lazy sense of calm repose was the appropriate frame of mind. One felt as if some immortal being, with no particular duties upon his hands, might be calmly sitting upon those rocks and watching the little shadowy wrinkles of the plain, that were really mountain ranges, rise and fall through slow geological epochs. . ."

Shasta, Mount

A dormant volcano, symmetrical in form. Location *Cascade Range, northern California.* Height *14,162 feet.* Map *4, A2.* Discovered *P. S. Ogden, 1827.* First climbed *E. D. Pearce, 1854.*

Discovered in 1827 by P. S. Ogden and first climbed 27 years later, Shasta has been dormant for centuries, with only a few steam vents and boiling water jets on its eastern flank, close to its ultimate 400-foot pinnacle, to remind the climber that it is still potentially active. It is an easy mountain to climb and rewards those making the ascent with a most extensive and striking panorama, across the snow plateau (there are five glaciers above 10,000 feet) from the crumbling crater wall to the subsidiary 12,433-foot cone of the Shastine and the arid lava plain below.

The town of Mount Shasta, at the foot of the mountain, is the headquarters of the Shasta National Forest; the Recreation Area within the forest includes Mount Shasta itself, Medicine Lake, Shasta Lake, the headwaters of the Sacramento, Shasta and McCloud rivers and their many tributary streams and lakes. The winter sports areas are on the slopes of Mount Shasta and Snowmen's Hill, while the largest fish hatchery in the world is also at the foot of the mountain.

The Shasta Indians believed that their mountain, which takes its name from them, stood at the dawn of Creation, the sole point of land sticking up out of the primordial ocean. For millions of years, since Eocene times, periodic upsurges of viscous lava have forced through the cone and flowed over the surrounding country, sometimes hardening in crusts over the still molten lava below and rucking up like a carpet as the mass moved on. Slowly the mountain built up, till it towered 10,000 feet above the surrounding country, a great cone 80 cubic miles in volume – coated, by the last eruption a few centuries ago, with an ankle-deep surface of pumice and ash. This and the porous lava below absorb the snow and glacier melt-waters of today which issue from the mountain base as gigantic springs, each pouring forth hundreds of cubic feet of water per second, mostly into the Pit River, largest tributary of the Sacramento. Shasta's foot, especially around the old Indian graveyards, was said to be haunted by ghosts whose flickering will-o'-the-wisp light brought ill-luck or death to whoever saw it. The wizards who controlled these ghosts were themselves guarded by five mysterious and dreaded apparitions who sometimes took the form of men or, invisible, hurled avalanches and boulders down the slopes.

The Shasta Indians are of a tribe which migrated years ago from the far north, but few of them nowadays dig out the floors of their huts below ground level or use primitive snow-shoes in the tradition of long ago.

277

Sierra Madre

The chief mountain system of Mexico, consisting of several ranges. Location *Mainly in Mexico with a sub-range in Guatemala.* Height *Rising to 18,700 feet in the Pico de Orizaba*, Map *4, C7-F11*.

This immense chain of mountains, extending 1,500 miles from the United States-Mexico border towards the isthmus of Tehuantepec, has played a decisive part in Mexican history, climate, agriculture, economics and communications, and continues to do so.

The three main divisions of the Sierra are the Sierra Madre Oriental, the Sierra Madre Occidental and the Sierra Madre del Sur. They frame the great central plateau which is itself part of the system. Block ranges and *bolsons* (depressions) form barriers and breaches in it. There is a sub-range which runs past the isthmus – the Sierra Madre de Guatemala – and joins with the main cordillera of Central America, which in turn is connected with the Andean ridges close to the borders of Panama and Colombia. In the northeast the Rio Grande separates the Sierra Madre Oriental from the Southern Rockies of Texas.

South of Mexico City the high plateau is rimmed by the striking east-west axis of the great volcanoes. The Cordillera de Anáhuac, as this section is sometimes called, contains the highest peak of the entire range, the Pico de Orizaba. Here stand Popocatepetl, Ixtacihuatl and the youngest volcano in the New World, Paricutin. More than three-quarters of Mexican soil is covered by the great complex of ranges, forming a rough triangle with its base on the United States border and extending between the Pacific and Gulf of Mexico coasts, descending to tropical lowlands. The variety of the Sierra Madre is considerable – from hot valleys and cooler highlands to broken ridges and impassable *barrancas* with sheer peaks rising above them. Here, too, is one of the richest treasure-houses of minerals in the world – silver and gold, copper and iron, tungsten and manganese, lead and arsenic, much of which is still not fully exploited, the true "Treasure of the Sierra Madre." The division of the vegetation of the *tierra caliente*, *tierra templada* and *tierra fria* varieties (hot, temperate and cold) is also determined by the mountain system. The main drainage is by the Santiago-Lerma, Las Balsas and Pánuco rivers.

Of the three main ranges, the Sierra Madre Oriental starts in the bleak hills of Coahuila and Nuevo León, just south of the Rio Grande, and continues with a width of about 200 miles parallel with the coastal strip of the Mexican Gulf, merging with the volcanic belt in the south. The Occidental section, parallel with the Gulf of California and the Pacific, is both wider and more striking; the escarpment is steeper and more rugged, the ascent from the coast more difficult. Its greatest width is 300 miles and the average elevation 7,000 feet. Many snow-capped peaks – the Cerro del Pimal, the Nevado de Colima (14,240 feet) and the Volcán de Colima (12,631 feet) are the most notable – and several subranges belong to this range. It also contains Lake Chapala, the largest of the lakes of Mexico. Finally, the Sierra Madre del Sur, a complex mass of uplifted summits, touches the Pacific coast but is too tumbled and irregular to form a clearly defined range. It slopes gradually to the Isthmus of Tehuantepec, to be continued by the Sierra Madre de Guatemala.

Sierra Morena

A highly eroded range dividing the valleys of the Guadiana and Guadalquivir rivers. Location *Southern Spain.* Height *Rising to 4,340 feet.* Map *7, A9-B9*.

The Sierra Morena, or Cordillera Mariánica, flanks the great plateau that rises along the northern boundary of Andalusia. Known in ancient times as *Montes Mariani*, the system also includes several minor Spanish ranges as well as the mountains of southern Portugal. The much eroded, partly wooded mountains have an average height of about 2,500 feet, and are more than 40 miles wide. Eastwards the range ends at the steppe region of Albacete and in the west it extends to the valley of the lower Guadiana, having a total length of about 375 miles. Its main pass is the famous Despenaperros, which is crossed by the Malaga-Madrid railroad.

The range is not continuous; there are frequent interruptions, especially in the western part, and the eastern and middle portions are composed of numerous ridges, irregular and complex. Many of them have distinctive names. The easternmost and highest is called the Sierra de Alcaraz, while some of the ridges in the extreme west are known collectively as the Sierras de Aracena.

Because of its great breadth, the Sierra Morena has for a long time been an important barrier between Andalusia and northern Spain and has often played a decisive part in the economic and military history, and even the social development of Spain. A large part of the country's mineral wealth lies here: copper, iron, pyrites, manganese, tin, tungsten, coal and nickel are all mined at various points. The copper mines of Tharsis and Rio Tinto are especially famous; but there are others at La Carolina, Santa Elena, Linares, Espiel, Pueblonuovo, Bélmez and Nerva. On the slopes livestock are raised and grapes, cereals, olives and fruit grown.

Sierra Nevada - Spain

The main chain of the Cordillera Penibética, extending about 60 miles. Location *Granada and Almeria provinces, southern Spain.* Height *Rising to 11,411 feet.* Map 7, *A9-B9.*

This fine mountain range of Andalusia, running parallel to the Mediterranean, within 25-30 miles of the coast, has several peaks which rise to over 10,000 feet, well above the level of perpetual snow and contrasting strikingly with the black schist. The range is part of the watershed between the Mediterranean and the Atlantic; on the north it towers above the city of Granada

and on the south it provides an impressive sight, particularly in winter, from on board ship in the Mediterranean.

The highest peak, Cerro de Mulhacén (11,411 feet), exceeds anything in the Pyrenees and is the loftiest point in continental Spain. Other snowy peaks are Veleta (11,128 feet) and Alcazaba (11,043 feet). One of the highest valleys contains a small glacier, the Corral de Veleta, the southernmost in Europe, but for the most part the deep *barrancas*, or transverse valleys, show only relics of former glaciation in the well-formed cirques at their heads. The range is structurally related to the Alpine system, being similarly constituted of *nappes* (rock-sheets) which have been thrust from the south towards the north, but it also has a connection with the Rif mountains of Morocco. Rich in minerals (copper, iron, lead, mercury and zinc), there are also fruit and olive orchards, sugar cane fields and vineyards, on the southern slopes.

To climb up the Sierra is a fascinating experience. All manner of tropical flowers flourish at its foot and above the cultivated fields and orchards there is a band of evergreen and deciduous oaks. Finally, one reaches the alpine zone, where the fine specialized botanical treasures of the range can be found among the black and gray schist and scree.

Sierra Nevada - United States

A great mountain range dividing the Central Valley from the Great Basin. Location *Eastern California.* Height *Several summits over 14,000 feet.* Map *4, B4.*

From Death Valley, 280 feet below sea level, surrounded by blistering salt flats, with a terrible dry, desiccating wind draining the moisture from the human skin and temperatures up to 120° F. in the shade, one can gaze at the long, lofty wall of the Sierra Nevada, a mere 80 miles away. Extending for more than 400 miles southeast from a gap south of Lassen Peak at the southern end of the Cascade Range to Tehachapi Pass, southeast of Bakersfield, this great range includes Mount Whitney (14,495 feet), the highest point in the United States outside Alaska.

On a geographical scale the unity of cause and effect is clearly demonstrated, for the dreadful aridity of the Californian deserts is produced by those seemingly near mountains, which extract every drop of moisture from the foggy sea winds blowing in off the Pacific. Here the skies are perpetually blue – there they are veiled with mists as the clouds, creeping up the westward slopes, unload among tall dark forests of sequoia, incense-cedar, pine, fir and aspen.

The single colossal block that structurally forms the Sierra Nevada has been covered by volcanic flows, especially in the northern part, and there is considerable faulting along the eastern margin. Extensive glaciation is evident at higher altitudes.

Three great national parks – Yosemite, Kings Canyon and Sequoia – straddle the heart of the range, containing within them the finest scenery, wildlife, forests and geological features. The landscape is of great variety and beauty. From deep glacier-worn valleys rise immense bald domes of granite, 4,000 feet or more sheer, with long spumy waterfalls coursing down their sides, then leaping in free, spectacular beauty. Behind are the high uplands of forest and meadow and over all tower the mountains of the Sierra's spine. The steep, bare eastern front rises sharply, the product of faulting and tilting, over the Great Basin; the western slope is longer and more gradual, losing itself in the grass-covered foothills that rim the Central Valley. The High Sierras, forming the highest portion, are south of Lake Tahoe, partly in Nevada, between the main chain and the Carson Range. Mount Williamson (14,384 feet), North Palisade (14,254 feet), Mount Russell (14,190 feet), Split Mountain (14,025 feet), Mount Langley (14,042 feet), Mount Tyndall (14,025 feet), Mount Muir (14,025 feet) and Mount Barnard (14,003 feet) are worthy companions of Mount Whitney, and there are many other peaks over 13,000 feet.

In a narrow strip between 4,000 and 8,000 feet on the western slopes lie what to many constitute the Sierra Nevada's most wonderful natural feature – the groves of giant sequoia trees. Fossil remains show that these were once as widely distributed as pines are today. Now they are found wild only here, over a stretch of 250 miles. Rising to nearly 300 feet, with a trunk diameter exceeding 30 feet, several thousand of these trees still survive. The larger trees are almost the oldest of all living things, over 3,500 years old in many cases. They were probably saved over this span of time by their extraordinary, beautiful bark, sometimes as much as three feet thick, fire-resistant and so full of tannin as to be almost insect- and fungus-proof. They are also of an extraordinary vigor in growth, healing rapidly after injury by fire, lightning or man. One tree in General Grant's Grove, sawn almost completely through some 50 years ago, still stands, growing as strongly as ever, and its cut has almost entirely healed.

The three great national parks within the Sierra Nevada include the striking gorges of the Kern, Kings, Merced and Tuolumne rivers, the spectacular Yosemite Falls and others, granite monoliths – like the Half Dome – and many glacial lakes and meadows of great beauty. The Sierra Nevada's heavy snowfall gives rise to eight fair-sized rivers which, in turn, supply irrigation water to the Central Valley and are used in various hydro-electric plants. In the western part there is the Mother Lode, which has been mined for gold ever since 1848 and is the center of a rich gold-bearing belt. Ten major passes cross the Sierra Nevada from north to south at altitudes varying from Beckwourth (5,250 feet, also carrying the railroad) to Kearsarge (11,823 feet).

Sikhote-Alin Range

Parallel ranges along the Sea of Japan. Location *Maritime and Khabarovsk territories, Russian SFSR.* Height *Rising to 5,200 feet.* Map *10, H3-4.*

The Sikhote-Alin Range is really a complex of several mountain systems, though usually represented as a single range. Running from Vladivostok north to the Lower Amur River, the mountains rise to 5,150 feet in the Golaya Gora, while the average elevation of the few passes is about 2,500 feet. There is a large depression occupied by Lake Kidzi which some geographers consider an outflow of the Amur to the sea.

In spite of some exploitation of their timber, the Sikhote-Alin mountains are still covered with almost impenetrable forests. The flora and fauna of the region (especially in the Usuri district) show a striking cross-section of warm and subarctic species. Wild vines, larches, cedar pines and firs form a background for the bear and the sable – and there are even some Siberian tigers. The rivers teem with fish, the Amur and Usuri being especially noted for their salmon.

But above all, the Sikhote-Alin Range is known as the "Treasure Mountains." The mines produce iron ore, manganese, tin, zinc, lead, mercury, silver and gold. Platinum, marble, molybdenum and graphite are also mined here and considerable industrial settlements have been established or are in the planning stage. There are sawmilling centers at Lesozavodsk, Iman and Bikin along the Usuri, and several game preserves.

Sikkim

A small state east of Nepal. Location *Eastern Himalayas.* Height *Highest point Kanchenjunga (28,146 feet).* Map *11, F5.*

Sikkim, about 70 miles from north to south and 40 miles from west to east – its area is 2,745 square miles, a little larger than that of Delaware – is an independent mountain state between Nepal, Tibet, Bhutan and India. Under a 1950 treaty India has assumed responsibility for the state's administration, but a large measure of autonomy is retained by Sikkim. With the exception of Kashmir, it is the loveliest country on the Indian borderland. The forested slopes and ridges, the magnificent vistas of ice-clad peaks framed by dense tropical vegetation and the changing pattern of sunshine and shadow, of mist and cloud, of falling water after rain, make it an artist's paradise.

Geographically, Sikkim is the basin of the Tista River, which rises north of the Great Himalayas where the open valleys of the Lhonak Chu and Lachen Chu have a Tibetan aspect. Here the passes leading into Tibet proper – the Choten Hyima La, the Natu La and the Naku La – though high, are quite easy. But as the Lhonak Chu collects the glacier drainage of the great Kanchenjunga ridges on the western boundary of Sikkim and is joined by the Lachen and Lachung rivers, the volume of water in the narrow valley becomes immense. Added to this is a heavy rainfall, since Sikkim receives the full force of the monsoon which sweeps northwards through Bengal and plays havoc with the Sikkim mountains. It has demolished the outer Siwalik Range east of the Kosi River and eaten into the mountains so that the original alignment of folds is lost. Only the great massif of Kanchenjunga with its supporting ridges and buttress peaks, many of them above 23,000 feet, bars the way to the destructive, moisture-laden monsoon.

Sikkim has three distinct zones: tropical (up to 5,000 feet), temperate (5,000–13,000 feet) and alpine (over 13,000 feet, with a perpetual snowline at 16,000 feet). Botanically it is one of the richest areas in India, if not in the world; there are roughly 4,000 species of flowering plants, including nearly 700 kinds of orchids, and around these flutter several thousand species of butterflies and moths. Ferns, rare fungi and immense thickets of rhododendron add to the variety. The first western traveler of note to describe the beauties of the small country was Joseph Hooker, the famous naturalist, who visited Sikkim in 1848–49 and wrote of his travels in his *Himalayan Journals.* But though the mountains are within a week's journey from Calcutta, it was only in the course of a minor campaign in 1861 that their geography became known. The regular survey was started in 1878 by Captain H. J. Harman and continued by Captain H. C. B. Tanner, both of the Survey of India. They were assisted by trained "pundit explorers," among them Rinzin Namgyal, who made the first circuit of Kanchenjunga. Political officers, attached to the Maharaja as advisers, such as Major L. A. Waddell and Claude White, added greatly to the outside world's knowledge, as did Douglas Freshfield's reconnaissance of Kanchenjunga in 1899.

The most active mountaineer in the early years of the present century was Dr A. M. Kellas of Glasgow, who visited Sikkim six times between 1907 and 1921. His most successful year was 1910, when he climbed Langpo (22,500 feet) for the second time, Pauhunri (23,180 feet) and Chomino (22,430 feet). Between the two wars many other expeditions climbed in the Sikkim mountains and most of the great peaks on the divide between Sikkim and Nepal were conquered. These include the Tent Peak (24,089 feet), climbed by a Swiss-German party in 1939; Jongjong Peak (24,344 feet), by an international party in 1930; and Kabru (24,002 feet), by C. R. Cooke in 1935. In 1936 Paul Bauer led a small party consisting of Adolf Göttner, G. Hepp and a number of Darjeeling porters which made the first ascent of the lovely ice-peak Siniolchu (22,600 feet), which is considered by many to be the most beautiful mountain in the world.

Sikkim has over 40 great Buddhist monasteries, of which Pemiongchi, Rumtek, Sangachelling, Tashiding and Tulung are the most famous. The original inhabitants of the country were Lepchas, ruled by rajas of Tibetan origin. There were two Gurkha invasions in the eighteenth century. In 1835 the British annexed the site of what later became Darjeeling; in 1849 some other territory was ceded to Britain. Today the population is mainly Nepalese and the various tribes include Limbus, Gurungs, Kamis and Newars with some Tibetan and Lepcha elements, all speaking Tibeto-Burman dialects. In 1947 Sikkim became independent, but three years later handed over its administration to India. Since 1947 travel within the country has been greatly restricted for outsiders.

Silvretta

A mountain group of several summits. Location *Rhaetian Alps, Swiss-Austrian border*. Height *Rising to 11,200 feet*. Map *8, E7*.

To the east of the Fluela Pass, near Klosters, the line of snowy mountains which bounds the Engadine on the north rises to 11,200 feet in the Piz Linard, the highest peak in the group known as the Silvretta. To the north, the mountains throw out a long rocky spur which sinks to the Schlappinerjoch and then rises again to a succession of summits culminating in the 9,736-foot Scesaplana. The spur, sloping gradually down on its northern side towards the Arlberg and more steeply to the south towards the Rhine and the Prestigau valleys, forms the adjoining Rhätikon Alps, whose watershed today marks the Swiss-Austrian frontier.

An ideal introduction to the Alps themselves, these summits provide a district more for the walker than for the mountaineer and are well served by paths, inns and huts.

Simplon Pass

An important trans-Alpine route. Location *Southern Switzerland*. Height *6,589 feet*. Map *8, C8*.

The Simplon is one of the few great international trans-Alpine routes whose history was of only local importance until comparatively modern times. Bounded on the northeast by Monte Leone – under which runs the 12⅓-mile Simplon Tunnel – and on the southwest by the Fletschhorn and Lagginhorn, the pass has always been exposed to avalanches. The Swiss used it frequently during the fifteenth century on their raids into Italy, but at some danger. It was not until 1800, when Napoleon, recovering from the victory of Marengo and counting the cost of his passage of the St Bernard, decided to construct a road (it took about six years to build), that this strategically important route came into popular use. The road, which connects Brig with Domodossola, leads through a 735-foot tunnel, the Gallery of Gondo, between the pass and the Italian frontier, then continues along the Ravine of Gondo, one of the wildest and most striking in the Alps. The Simplon Pass itself marks the divide between the Pennine and Lepontine Alps.

When the road was finished, barracks were built on the summit of the pass; subsequently these became the New Hospice, and the old one, dating back at least to the thirteenth century, was converted to other uses.

The Simplon Tunnel, opened in 1906, after work on it had begun in 1898, runs some miles to the east of the Simplon Road. It is the lowest of the trans-Alpine tunnels, rising to only 2,313 feet, but it is the longest main-line tunnel in the world.

The Simplon Pass

Sinai, Mount

A mountain massif. Location *Sinai Peninsula, Egypt.*
Height *7,497 or 8,651 feet, according to identification.*
Map *9, F2.*

The sandy plateau of El Tih lies in the central
area of the Sinai Peninsula. In the south it rises
to a barren massif of granite, porphyry and
greenstone rocks. The highest peak is Gebel
Katherina (8,651 feet). Just northeast of it stand
Gebel Musa ("Mount of Moses" in Arabic,
7,497 feet), Gebel Serbal and Gebel Umm
Shomer, all of which have had supporters as the
original Mount Sinai – though the first two
seem to have the strongest claim to this distinction.

The massif has a roughly triangular shape between the two arms of the Red Sea, facing towards the two gulfs with strips of red sandstone.
The whole forms a huge plateau, intersected by
wadis.

The Bible speaks of "the glory of the Lord"
that abode upon Mount Sinai with a cloud
covering it for six days. ". . .And the sight of the
glory of the Lord was like devouring fire in the
eyes of the children of Israel. . . and Moses was
in the mount. . . with the Lord forty days and
forty nights. . . he did neither eat bread nor
drink water. And he wrote upon the tables the
words of the covenant, the Ten Commandments."

About 250 A.D. Dionysius of Alexandria described the church and strong refuge tower which
the persecuted Egyptian Christians had built in
the Sinai mountains as a defence against the
Saracens. Later the 6,000 holy anchorites living
in the region appealed for aid to the Byzantine
Emperor, Justinian, and at his orders a great
sacred fortress was built; the marble tablet over
its door still bears the name of the Emperor and
his consort, Theodora, with the date 521 A.D.

The new foundation was named after St Catherine of Alexandria and soon became a great
center of pilgrimage. Among those who came to
worship in the 30 chapels of the convent is said
to have been the young Mohammed – by virtue
of which a charter of protection was later
granted to the convent by the sultans of Constantinople.

Through the centuries a unique collection of
ikons and ancient manuscripts has been accumulated here, the most famous (though it now
reposes in the British Museum) being the Codex
Sinaiticus, of which 43 leaves were discovered in
1844 by Konstantin von Tischendorf, the German scholar, in the wastepaper basket in the
library, where they had been discarded by the
tidying monks. Tischendorf returned in 1859,
financed this time by the Russian government,
and acquired the remainder of the manuscript
for the Czar. The British Museum purchased it
from the Soviet government in 1933 for
£100,000. The codex was until recently the earliest known version of much of the Old Testament, the complete New Testament and other
non-canonical books.

Today only some 30 monks remain to give
food to the weary traveler but the lovely walled
garden with its olives, vines and almond trees
is still carefully tended, while in the nearby
"House of Bones" are tumbled heaps of skulls
and ribs, the remains of the long line of their
predecessors.

The area around the mountains is now a
frontier province of Egypt. But the description of
Dr Durbin, who ascended the peaks over a century ago, still applies: "No one who has not seen
them can conceive the ruggedness of these vast
piles of granite rock, rent into chasms, rounded
into smooth summits, or splintered into countless
peaks, all in the wildest confusion. . . When we
did arrive at the summit (Gebel Serbal) and cast
our eyes over the wide plain. . . one glance was
enough. . . Here and here only could the won-
drous displays of Sinai have been visible to the
assembled host of Israel, as that here the Lord
spoke with Moses, that here was the mount that
trembled and smoked in the presence of its
manifested Creator!"

Siniolchu

A twin-peaked mountain, difficult of access. Location *Sikkim Himalayas.* Height *22,600 feet.* Map *11,F5.* First climbed *Karl Wien and A. Göttner, 1936.*

"Peerless Siniolchu," as Kenneth Mason, a former Superintendent of the Survey of India, called it, rises east of the Zemu Gap, not far from the Simvu massif. To many who have seen it, this twin-peaked giant with sharp, knife-edged ridges and incredibly steep flanks, is the most beautiful mountain in the world. The sides are usually covered with ice and snow and furrowed with the ice-flutings so typical of the Himalayas. The crest of the cornice-crowned summit stands up like a thorn.

For some time there was considerable confusion between Simvu and Siniolchu, and W. W. Graham, who visited Sikkim in 1883 and claimed to have climbed Kabru, mixed up the two hopelessly.

It was only in 1936 that a determined assault was mounted on Siniolchu, when Paul Bauer took a small party to Sikkim. He was accompanied by Karl Wien, A. Göttner, G. Hepp and the Darjeeling porters Hishey Bhutia, Tewang, Nima Tsering II, Mingma Tsering, Mingma Bhutia and Purbu Bhutia, all of whom had taken part in the French expedition to Gasherbrum. A base camp was established about the middle of August. Their first task was to explore the head of the Zumtu glacier, southeast of Siniolchu. During early September they made two unsuccessful attempts to climb the eastern Twin and Tent Peak. They had to give up the ascent principally on account of dangerous avalanches.

After being imprisoned by bad weather in their base camp on the Zemu Glacier, the four climbers, accompanied by Nima Tsering and Mingma Tsering, set out on September 19 to climb Siniolchu by its northwest ridge. An advance camp was set up two days later at the foot of Little Siniolchu at about 18,700 feet, and on the following day the porters remained behind while Bauer and his companions reached the ridge between Siniolchu and Little Siniolchu at 20,340 feet. They spent the night on the ridge under extremely uncomfortable conditions sitting in their tent-bags with their feet in their rucksacks and with every available piece of clothing or equipment wrapped around their bodies. On September 23, at about 21,230 feet, Bauer decided to halt with Hepp and provide support while the other two unladen men made for the summit. Wien and Göttner reached the top soon after 2 p.m. and returned to their companions. A second night was spent on the ridge and the party regained the base camp without any ill effects two days later.

There was a tragic sequel to this fine achievement when Wien, Göttner, Hepp, Nima Tsering II and Mingma Tsering were all killed by an avalanche on Nanga Parbat nine months after their ascent of Siniolchu.

Sinkiang

The largest province of China. Location *Northwest China.* Height *Varying from the heights of the Dzungarian Ala-Tau (rising to 16,650 feet) to the Tarim Basin and the Taklamakan Desert, below sea level.* Map *10, D5.*

Sinkiang (also spelled Hsin-chiang, and meaning "New Territory") lies in the heart of Central Asia and is surrounded by formidable natural obstacles. An area of some 700,000 square miles, with a population of about 4,000,000, it was until recently one of the most inaccessible parts of the inhabited world. Access from China proper involved a journey of thousands of miles across the Gobi Desert and two or three decades ago it could be reached only by foot or animal transport. The journey to Kashgar from India took two months. Now, however, air transport and the opening of motor roads across the desert from Kansu have brought it within easy reach of China – though not of the West.

The province is divided by the Tien Shan range into two sections, which differ from each other in almost every respect: Southern Sinkiang, sometimes called Kashgaria, and Northern Sinkiang.

Southern Sinkiang consists of the Tarim Basin, a vast, oval plain completely surrounded by lofty mountain ranges: the Kunlun on the south and southeast, and the Pamirs on the southwest and west, merging into the Tien Shan which, stretching in an arc nearly 1,000 miles long, forms the northern rim.

Here is the Dzungarian tableland, set between the Tien Shan and the Altai, a high country that is more ridge than rim, for Dzungaria, to the southeast of the Dzungarian Ala-Tau, is mountainous but lower than the surrounding country.

Running up through this area extends a long gulf-like trench containing the great lakes of Ebi-Nor and Ayar and rising slowly to a broad depression at the eastern end of the Dzungarian Ala-Tau itself. This is the Dzungarian Gate, an entrance to the northern plains through which countless thousands of nomads have passed on their way to a less bleak existence. The anthropologist, J. E. Welker, has suggested that Neanderthal man was the first invader of the west through the Gate, to be followed in historic times by Attila, Genghiz Khan and lesser chieftains. It was through the Dzungarian Gate that more than 3,000 families made their mass exodus on their way from Dzungaria to Russia at the end of the eighteenth century – the ancestors of those who still live on the Volga more than 150 years later. The lowest point on a route rather than a pass in the accepted sense of the word, the Dzungarian Gate provides a direct link between the Ebi Nor in Sinkiang and the Ala-Kul in the Kazakh SSR.

The rivers draining from the mountains around the Tarim Basin, though many of them are fed by some of the largest snow-fields outside polar regions, can do no more than irrigate a narrow fringe of country, an elliptical belt of oases nearly 2,000 miles long, before they are swallowed up by the arid interior of the Basin, the Taklamakan Desert.

These glacier-fed rivers are the life blood of southern Sinkiang. Though precipitation in the high mountains is heavy, rainfall in the plains is negligible (in Kashgar, for example, the average is about two-and-a-half inches a year and the average for the whole province is less than ten inches), and agriculture is entirely dependent on irrigation. The archeological researches of Sir Aurel Stein have shown that in ancient times large cities existed far out in what is now complete desert. This seems to prove that the extent of the oases was once many times greater than it is today and there is evidence of the continued encroachments of the desert. The people of the oases were mostly Turki, an agricultural community closely akin in name and language to the Ottoman Turks. Despite the great migrations that have swept through Central Asia, the Turki seem to have been there for at least 2,000 years. The valleys of the mountain perimeter, on the other hand, are sparsely inhabited by nomad tribes, such as the Kirghis and Tajibs, who live mostly in dome-shaped tents (*akoi*) and subsist on the produce of their herds.

Northern Sinkiang, or Dzungaria, consists largely of steppeland which is very sparsely populated except for towns such as Urumchi (Tihwa), the capital of Sinkiang, Ili and Hani, arranged along the southern side of the area. Here the population is much more mixed than in Southern Sinkiang, chiefly Turki, Han, Chinese, Tungan and Mongol. Among the nomad tribes of Dzungaria the Kazakhs predominate.

Sinkiang became a Chinese province in 1885, but for many years her ties with China were extremely weak and economically she had far stronger links with the USSR. In 1944 the Turkis revolted and set up an autonomous East Turkestan Republic. This lasted only six years, as the victory of the Chinese Communists led to the reassertion of the central authority, and the Uigur population began to dominate the provincial government.

Slieve League

A mountain rising above the Atlantic. Location *County Donegal, Ireland.* Height *1,972 feet.* Map *7, B5.*

Slieve League, in the extreme west of County Donegal, stands in a lonely district, far from roads or railways and with few villages or inhabitants. It is a mountain well known through William Allingham's popular poem *Up the airy mountain, down the rushy glen,* in which the old king of the fairy troop of Green Jacket, Red Cap and White Owl's Feather makes his stately journeys on a bridge of white mist "from Slieve League to Rosses," the area of lakes in northern Donegal.

Slieve League is most decidedly an airy mountain. It is not high, but is rooted in the Atlantic and springs direct out of the sea by a splendid precipice, proving that feet alone are not the measure of a mountain.

On either side, Donegal bulges into the Atlantic to form the northern flank of a double bay which stretches across to Sligo and County Mayo. In this direction the summit gives a panorama of blue ocean and distant blue summits. Consisting of quartzite and gneiss, Slieve League rises to a narrow, smooth tilted edge known as the One Man's Pass, which is by no means wide enough for two. On one side the mountain drops to the sea. On the other, though not quite so far, it slopes to a little lough, full of trout and water lobelia. Bare and rather savage glens offer a multiple vista on the inland side and are filled with shadows as the sun drops towards the Atlantic.

Slieve League dominates a district of moors and high mountainous cliffs – eastwards to Kilcar and Killybega and into Tirconaill Bay and the country around the bulge to the north, past Malinbeg and Glencolumbkille (where St Columba has a holy well) and then to Glen Lough and under the neighboring mountain of Slieveatooer, which is also precipitous and rooted in the ocean.

Alpine plants such as dryas, saxifrages, holly ferns, rose-roots and others are found on Slieve League, in spite of its low height. They mostly congregate in lofty shelter on the landward side of the One Man's Pass.

Snowdon

The highest mountain in Wales, comprising five peaks separated by passes. Location *Caernarvonshire, North Wales.* Height *3,560 feet.* Map *7, B5.*

Lying between Anglesey and the northern end of Cardigan Bay, the Snowdon group, the most rugged area in Wales, has for much of the last 2,000 years played a dominating role in the Principality's history, literature and legend.

The glory of a mountain resides in many things. With Snowdon, the unique appeal lies in the ridges, radiating like starfish from the main peak of Wyddfa, and the deep glaciated cwms (valley heads), studded with lonely llyns (lakes), which lie between them. In summer all the ridges can be followed with ease, although the round of the Snowdon Horseshoe, the finest walk of its kind south of the Scottish Border, demands care on the narrow ridge of Crib Coch and during the traverse of the rocky pinnacles between the summit of Crib Coch itself and that of Crib y Ddisgyl.

In twin-headed Lliwedd, the Snowdon massif can claim one of the most dramatic rock peaks of Britain and in Clogwyn d'ur Arddu, one of the most formidable rock faces.

There are five tracks to the summit, of which the Pig Track from the top of Llanberis Pass is the finest, if roughest. The Watkin Path runs from beyond Beddgelert, while others leave Beddgelert itself. Llanberis is the most frequently used but by far the dullest.

Hardly dramatic in outline – although the Snowdon ridges viewed across the Mymbyr Lakes at Capel Curig present one of the world's finest mountain profiles – Snowdon itself has attracted surprising devotion. David Hewitt, a Beddgelert artist, climbed the mountain 580 times, while

Snowdon, seen across the waters of Llyn Llydaw, with the remains of old copper mines on the shore

C. E. Mathews, who in 1871 founded the "Welsh Rabbits," a club whose aim was to explore Snowdon in winter, made more than 100 ascents. Yet loyalty to Snowdon is perhaps best represented by P. S. Minor, an enthusiastic mountaineer who had climbed the peak 87 times at the age of 56. He then spent three weeks at Rhyd Ddu, the village to the south of Snowdon, and made another 19 ascents – once on each of eight days, twice on each of four days and once three times in a single day.

For those who are less energetic there is a railway running to the summit from Llanberis. A large part of the Snowdon area is owned by the British National Trust.

Soufrières, The

Four volcanic peaks, sharing the same name, but situated on different islands. Location *West Indies.*

Height I (Guadeloupe): 4,869 feet; II (Montserrat): 2,999 feet; III (St Lucia): 4,000 feet; IV (St Vincent): 4,048 feet. Map 5, F10-G11.

Soufrière literally means "sulphur-mine," but the geologists of France have adopted the word, instead of the more generally accepted term "solfatara," to mean a volcanic vent emitting vapors which are mainly sulphurous; the original Solfatara is the famous one near Pozzuoli, west of Naples, in the Phlegraean Fields. This particular old crater has not been in active eruption since 1198 A.D. but is continuously exhaling heated vapors, chiefly hydrogen sulphide, sulphur dioxide and steam. The term solfatara has been extended to all dormant or semi-quiescent volcanoes of this type, and a volcano which has ceased to emit lava or ashes but still produces heated vapors is said to be in the solfataric stage.

There are four Soufrières in the West Indies. The first, also called La Grande Soufrière, is the highest peak of Guadeloupe and of the Lesser Antilles. It is situated in the southern part of Basse-Terre island (one of the two islands that make up Guadeloupe) four miles northeast of Basse-Terre. It is 4,869 feet high and was active in 1797, while in 1843 its violent eruptions destroyed several cities, but today only a few thermal springs and volcanic vents provide signs of activity.

The second Soufrière is a volcanic hill (2,999 feet) on Montserrat, one of the Leeward Islands. It is still active, though no violent eruptions have taken place in the last 40 years.

The third Soufrière (4,000 feet) is on St Lucia in the Windward Islands, rising over the town of Soufrière which stands at the head of the beautiful bay of the same name. The St Lucia Soufrière, not far from the spectacular Pitons, is a great, jagged, semi-quiescent volcano that forms the background to the whole striking scene. The crater, a mile in diameter and 300 feet deep, is filled with boiling sulphurous springs and mud holes among gray rocks and blighted vegetation. Nearby a series of stone troughs in an enclosure

A view in the Pennine Alps, showing the Obergabelho

in the forest are all that remains of the medicinal spa established by decree of Louis XVI for the use of the royal troops in the Windward Islands when St Lucia was French.

Finally, the fourth Soufrière is that of St Vincent, 13 miles north-northeast of Kingstown. It erupted violently in 1812 and 90 years later it devastated the more fertile portion of the island, a more or less level tract to its north called Carib County. There had been signs of activity for some time, and on May 7, 1902, just a day before the terrible outburst of Mont Pelée on Martinique, the St Vincent Soufrière sent a stream of lava and red-hot stones down its slopes which, together with the subsequent earthquakes and further eruptions, killed over 2,000 people and totally destroyed many sugar and arrowroot plantations. Since then the volcano has been quiet, but by no means extinct.

South Pass

Former important unit in the Oregon Trail. Location *Western central Wyoming.* Height *7,550 feet.* Map *4, D3.*

Today South Pass forms a broad, level valley in the Wind River Range of the Rocky Mountains. The little village of South Pass City, now a ghost town, lies above it at 7,805 feet. It has a population of about 50 – quite a shrinkage from that of 90 years ago, when over 4,000 people crowded into its houses and it served as the center of a large gold-mining district.

Twenty years after Meriwether Lewis and William Clark had followed the Missouri River northwestwards and reached the Rocky Mountains in what is now Montana, fur trappers who followed along the route of the two pioneers discovered South Pass, easiest of all the Rocky Mountain crossings. Leading into the Wyoming Basin, South Pass was used after 1824 by most of the early settlers and travelers and was of inestimable value in the opening up of the West. Even though it was later replaced by a rather more southerly route now followed by the Union Pacific Railroad, it remained in use for many years for crossing the Continental Divide and has many historical associations for the conquerors of the vast territories west of the Rockies.

Stalin Peak

The highest point of the USSR. Location *Border of Gorno-Badakhshan Autonomous Oblast and Garm Oblast, Tadzhik SSR.* Height *24,590 feet.* Map *10, C5.* First climbed *Russian Tadzhikistan-Pamirs Expedition, 1933.*

Stalin Peak is situated at the junction of the Akademiya Nauk Range and Peter the First Range of the Pamir-Alai mountain system, between Izvestia and Pravda peaks, looking across the Molotov Glacier to the German Communist Party, Communist Academy and OGPU peaks (the latter being named after the Russian secret police).

Until the nineteen-thirties the complicated geography of this high knot of mountain country lying on the southern fringe of the Soviet Union was only imperfectly understood. Then a series of Russian expeditions began to explore and map the region, largely in order to discover its mineral deposits. Nearly 300 scientists carried out preliminary work in 1932. The following year a unit of the Tadzhikistan-Pamirs Expedition was given the task of ascending Stalin Peak in order to install meteorological instruments and build an automatic radio station. This station, the highest in the world, was established on a neighboring glacier.

Before this series of expeditions, it was thought that the highest peak in the Soviet Union was Lenin Peak (formerly called Mount Kaufmann, 23,382 feet) in the Trans-Alai Range.

The mountain was climbed only after considerable difficulty and the use of eight separate camps. During the last 20 years many Russian expeditions have gone to the Pamirs, most of them linked with scientific development, but some organized as purely mountaineering expeditions through the All-Union Alpine Section of the Ministry of Physical Culture and Sport.

Stanovoi Range

A mountain divide, forming the watershed between the Lena and Amur basins. Location *Southeast Siberian Russian SFSR.* Height *Rising to 8,143 feet.* Map *10, G3.*

As far back as the seventeenth century, the Stanovoi (or Stanovoy) Range, running about 450 miles from the Olekma River to the Mayar River (an affluent of the Uda River) has played a part in Russian history. It was on August 27, 1689, that China signed her first treaty with any Western power – the Treaty of Nerchinsk – establishing the frontier between eastern Siberia and Mongolia. The treaty, which ensured peace between the two countries for a century and a half, set the boundary partly across the wild Stanovoi Range, running down to the Sea of Okhotsk.

The highest point of the Stanovois is Skalisty (Rocky) Mountain, which rises to 8,143 feet. The name of the range has been also applied to its continuation, the Yablonoi or Yablonovy Range, which extends from the upper Ingoda River past Chita to the Olekma River; if the two ranges are considered as one, their total length is well over 1,000 miles. Just like the Stanovoi proper, the Yablonoi forms an important watershed between the Arctic and the Pacific oceans. This section has an average altitude of 4,000-5,000 feet, rising to 5,280 feet in the Bolshoi Sarakanan, north-northeast of Chita.

Stromboli

An active volcano. Location *Lipari Islands, off the coast of Sicily.* Height *3,038 feet.* Map *7, E9.*

Stromboli is one of the few volcanoes still active in Europe, though its serious eruptions are rare; the last was in 1921. However, its record of volcanic activity is practically unbroken since earliest antiquity. It occupies most of the small island of Stromboli, the northernmost of the Lipari group, which has an area of 4.7 square miles and a population of about 1,200.

Stromboli has always been a striking sight. Henry Swinburne in 1790 admired "the fiery operations of the island of Stromboli, that lay due west of us. . . It is a very blunt cone, and throws up fire from a huge orifice on its side. The convulsions of this incessant projection of flames and other substances have riven its summit almost in two, and destroyed so much of the soil that used to be cultivated, that the inhabitants can no longer procure subsistance. . . The explosions intermit, and the inhabitants very dextrously seize the quiet moment to pass along the strand; if they mistimed it, they would be buried under a shower of red-hot stones. . ."

Sugar Loaf Mountain

A spectacular granite peak within the city limits of Rio de Janeiro. Location *Rio de Janeiro, Brazil.* Height *1,296 feet.* Map *6, G7.*

There are several Sugar Loaf mountains – in Monmouth (England), County Cork (Ireland), Sierra Leone, Maine and Maryland. But beyond doubt the most famous and most striking is the Pao de Açúcar which stands sentinel at the entrance to Guanabara Bay, one of the series of bays which sweep along the waterfront of Rio de Janeiro.

A two-stage aerial railroad leads to the top, and from the halfway stop at Urca Hill there is a superb view of the city and its beaches, among them the scimitar-like arc of sand known as Copacabana, with its skyscraper hotels and apartment houses. Across the heights one can also see Corcovado, the "Hunchback," the peak crowned by the huge statue of Christ the Redeemer.

Sulaiman Range

A mountain mass along the Baluchistan-Punjab border. Location *West Pakistan.* Height *Rising to 11,000 feet.* Map *11, B5.*

The Sulaiman (or Suliman) Range extends about 280 miles north along the border country of Baluchistan and the Punjab, stretching into the southern North-West Frontier Province, its general width about 40 miles. The prehistoric home of the Pathan highlander, it has always housed wild and independent tribes, such as the Bozdars, a Baluch tribe of Arab extraction who lived in constant, turbulent feuds with their neighbors and had to be subdued by a British expedition in 1857.

The actual Sulaiman system of mountains starts south of the Gumal River, which cuts through the forest-covered northern end of the mass. It still represents a most formidable barrier between the plains of the Indus and Afghanistan, finally merging into the hills of Baluchistan. The climate is clear and bracing, without great extremes of temperature, and the vegetation of these long ridges of rough but picturesque highlands is often alpine.

The chief mass of the Sulaimans is known as Takht-i-Suliman ("Solomon's Throne"). The twin peaks rise to 11,290 feet and 11,085 feet respectively, 55 miles west-southwest of the town of Dera Ismail Khan. The gray, flat-looking rampart rises from the lower line of mountains north and south of it, slightly saddlebacked in the middle but thrusting up a clearly defined peak at its northern end. The legend of the mountain relates that Solomon visited India in order to marry Balkis (the Mohammedan name of the Queen of Sheba) and as they returned through the air, on a throne carried by genii, the bride implored her lord and master to let her look back for a few moments on her beloved land. Solomon thereupon commanded the genii to scoop out a hollow for the throne on the summit of the mountain. The hollow is a cavity some 30 feet square, cut out of the solid rock at the southern end of the mountain to which both Moslems and Hindus make annual pilgrimages. The shrine itself is about two miles south of the highest peak.

The Sulaiman massif was first surveyed by the Takht-i-Suliman Survey Expedition of 1883. They explored the connecting tableland between the two parallel ridges which is about 9,000 feet high. The two ridges run roughly north and south; one of the twin peaks is at the southern end of the eastern ridge (this is the Takht proper with the shrine nearby), while the western ridge culminates in the higher peak also known as Kaisargarh. The plateau and the interior slopes are covered with chilgosa (edible pine) forests. There are olive trees in the center of the massif and the hill resort, Fort Munro, is in the southern section.

Sunset Crater

A brilliantly colored volcanic cinder cone. Location *Northern central Arizona.* Height *1,000 feet.* Map *4, C5.*

Sunset Crater and the National Monument established in 1930 and named after it are situated 14 miles northeast of Flagstaff and are one of the most spectacular features of Arizona. The dry climate has preserved the lava flows, spatter cones, squeeze-ups, cinder cones and fields and dunes around the crater so perfectly that they look as if they have barely had time to cool. The billowing, foaming waves of a lava flow have solidified while still in motion, their crests still curling over, and have remained perfect and uneroded ever since. They halted only a few feet from the edge of the surrounding pine forests, which they seem about to overwhelm.

The crater, 400 feet deep and a quarter of a mile in diameter, is difficult to reach because of the loose cinders covering the slopes; but once reached, the rim offers magnificent views over the Painted Desert and the San Francisco Peaks. Some four hundred volcanoes have been found in this region, of which Sunset Crater is the most recent. The date of its eruption has been determined at 1064–65 A.D. from the growth rings on trees buried beneath its lava and ashes, which once covered 800 square miles. Its eruptions were followed by the only prehistoric land rush known in the Americas, for the dust and cinders acted as a mulch on the dry soil, increasing its water-holding capacity and fertility. Between 1100 and 1200 A.D. about 8,000 Indians swarmed into this previously sparsely inhabited region. Then a number of years of severe, localized drought turned the area into a dust-bowl. Wind carried away the cinders or piled them into dunes and the people, the ancestors of the present-day Hopi Indians, migrated towards the high mesas further east in the Painted Desert where they still live.

Sunset Crater National Monument is in the Coconino National Forest and has an area of 3,040 acres. The name of Sunset Crater has its origin in the peculiar reddish glow of the decomposed and waterstained sulphuric rock of the summit, which gives the mountain the appearance of always being bathed in the rays of the setting sun. Dark at the base, it takes on a rosy hue farther up and shades to yellow at the crater.

Table Mountain

A flat-topped mountain which overlooks Cape Town. Location Southwest Cape Province, South Africa. Height 3,549 feet. Map 9, E11.

The great Portuguese navigator, Bartholomew Dias, rounding the Cape of Good Hope in 1487, was probably the first European to see the looming bulk of Table Mountain, with its cloud lifting like a flag over the summit, and Table Bay lying sunlit at its feet. The early Portuguese navigators soon made the mountain famous throughout Europe, and Camoens, in his epic *The Lusiad*, suggested that it might take the

Table Mountain

place of the Colossus of Rhodes as the seventh wonder of the world.

On one side the mountain overhangs False Bay in precipitous sandstone cliffs and on the other it overlooks Table Bay, rising like some giant castle to dominate the old city of Cape Town and its sprawling modern suburbs. Scarred by ravines, the great gray face of the mountain is one of the most impressive natural sights in the world. On the western side lies the long, broken skyline with its humped peaks known as the Twelve Apostles, and on the east it dominates the Cape Flats. The Gorge, a deep, romantic ravine, is one of the harshest scars in the mountain face, and by it lies the shortest route to the summit. Lion's Head (2,100 feet) and Devil's Peak (3,300 feet) are the western and eastern outriders of the main bulk, while to the south Hout's Bay Nek connects the mountain with the last stragglers of the range as they run down to the Cape of Good Hope.

On the eastern slopes, by the Flats, lie the Cape Town suburbs of Newlands, Rondebosch and Wynberg. From here the ascent of the mountain via Hout's Bay Nek is comparatively easy. On a fair day the summit of the Table is truly beautiful, for this is no barren plateau but a vast, rich plain broken by miniature valleys and small hills. It is secret country, remote from the bustle of the great docks at its foot and the noise and roar of Cape Town's streets and industry. The vegetation is rich and tropical. Orchids abound, among them one of the loveliest of all, *Disa grandiflora*, with large flowers in scarlet and yellow. The contrast between the awe-inspiring approaches of the mountain – its craggy bluffs and inhospitable sides – and the luxuriance of the tableland has led more than one South African to maintain that this is the seventh holy mountain described by Ignatius which "had delightful pasture and was wholly fruitful. . ."

Table Mountain has its own special cloud, known locally as "The Tablecloth." This usually forms when the wind is in the southeast and it covers the whole summit in a gray-white blanket.

It forms very quickly, so that it is possible within a quarter of an hour to find a world of sunny uplands and tropical vegetation transformed into a damp fog with visibility of only a few feet. The cloud is to a great extent responsible for the lushness of the vegetation and flora. The rainfall on the summit is extremely heavy, over 70 inches a year on the average, while in Cape Town it is only 25 inches.

Many varieties of coniferous trees grow on the slopes, as well as the beautiful silver-tree with its strange leaves covered in fine, silky hairs. During the spring the valleys, gorges and ravines are starred with innumerable wild flowers. It is little wonder that the Dutch East India Company, which established a settlement near Table Bay in 1652, quickly realized the value of the region, not only as an anchorage but also as a storehouse and vegetable garden for their whole fleet.

On the western shore of the mountain the cold water of the Benguela Current moves in against the peninsula, but on the east lie the warm waters of False Bay, a resort and one of the best bathing beaches in South Africa. Here, in the suburb of Muisenberg, within sight of the mountain he loved, Cecil Rhodes passed his last days.

Tasman, Mount

The second highest peak of New Zealand. Location *Western central South Island, New Zealand, in the Southern Alps.* Height *11,475 feet.* Map *12, H8.* First climbed *E. A. Fitzgerald, Matthias Zurbriggen and Jack Clark, 1895.*

Mount Tasman is considered one of the finest, if not the finest, snowy summit of the whole range of the Southern Alps. Clothed in ice from crest to base, with little rock protruding, it sends down great cascading glaciers to the surrounding valleys; the Fox Glacier, on the western side, reaches to within 700 feet of sea level. Its situation on the Main Divide, a little over two miles north of Mount Cook, gives it a position of rivalry with that supreme peak.

Named in honor of the first European discoverer (in 1642) of New Zealand, Abel Tasman, its altitude – like that of Mount Cook – was established by survey from the sea. It has a southern satellite summit of 10,757 feet, the Silberhorn, named after the well-known satellite peak of the Jungfrau in Switzerland. Tasman was first climbed by E. A. Fitzgerald with

The Tasman Glacier

Matthias Zurbriggen, the Swiss guide, and Jack Clark, the New Zealand guide, by the southwest ridge and over the Silberhorn, in a 16-hour day from a camp on the Hochstetter Ridge. It was not an easy climb; Zurbriggen complained that "he had never known such toilsome snow or ice in Switzerland, or any ascent like this one for almost 6,000 feet on an ice arête." In 1913 Freda du Faur, a famous Australian climber, made the ascent with P. and A. Graham. She was greatly impressed by the north ridge of Mount Tasman. "I felt cold shivers running down my spine," she wrote, "as I viewed the last 1,000 feet of our proposed climb from close quarters. From the Tasman Glacier the ridge seems to rise out of the Silberhorn in a gentle, softly inviting slope. From our newly gained summit it rears a knife-like edge for 1,000 feet at the most appalling angle I had ever beheld or imagined."

H. E. L. Porter, who climbed in the Southern Alps in the nineteen-twenties, made it clear that Mount Tasman was a prize well worth winning. "From every direction," he wrote, "it stands out in unique majesty, draped in a bridal robe of shimmering white, through which the rocky framework peeps out here and there to reassure one that the vision is not merely a creation of fantasy."

There are several more recent routes to the summit, from the east and the west, and during the 1953–54 season a record number of 11 parties reached the top.

Flowing at the eastern foot of Mount Tasman is the great Tasman Glacier, some 18 miles in length, New Zealand's longest ice-stream, and one of the largest glaciers in the temperate zone outside the Himalayas. For several miles in its lowest reaches it is covered by a great stony blanket of moraine, and there is much evidence of considerable shrinkage in the last 60 years. In winter this is a popular ski-ing center while, using as a base the Malte Brun hut (5,700 feet), about 11 miles up the southeast side of the Tasman Glacier, the New Zealand Antarctic party under

Sir Edmund Hillary underwent a training scheme here for men and sledge-dogs before they left for the Ross Sea Dependency in 1956.

Taurus Mountains

A great mountain chain running parallel to the Mediterranean coast. Location *Southern Turkey.* Height *Rising to over 12,000 feet.* Map 7, *H9.*

Seen from the Mediterranean, the Taurus Mountains appear like a great rampart barring entry to Turkey, their formidable crest-line of barren peaks rising above steep and rocky slopes. This crest-line follows the swinging line of the coast and from a distance no way can be seen through it. The mountains do not appear easy to cross even at closer acquaintance; indeed, they become more bold and impressive. Shoulders of bare, white limestone are common, with darker ribs near the jagged edges and summits. The highest – Ala Dag (12,251 feet) and Erciyas Dag (12,848 feet) in the outlying offshoot of the Amanos Mountains are the culminating peaks – range in height from 10,000 feet to over 12,000 feet. Some of the slopes up to a height of 7,000 feet have scattered trees of pine, cedar, oak, oriental beech and juniper, and among the trees various species of deer find a home. In the western part of the Taurus there are a number of open plateau regions, with several large lakes. Small settlements are found here but the mountain region as a whole is very thinly populated. Nomadic tribes (Yuruks) use the mountain pasture grounds, descending to the plains in winter, when they often become timber-cutters as well as herdsmen, using camels for transport. The whole range is snow-covered in winter and there are permanent snow patches on some of the higher slopes. When the snow melts in spring, the rivers swell and cascade in great torrents to the Mediterranean.

The routes across the Taurus today still follow the same passageways used by the early Christian evangelists, the armies, caravans, the travelers of the past. Of these routes the most famous is the one known as the Cilician Gates, between Cappadocia and Cilicia, a precipitous cleft in the highest part of the Taurus which has for centuries been the main channel of communication across the mountains, and which has seen the passage of the armies of Alexander the Great, and of the Romans, Byzantines, Crusaders, Saracens and Turks. At its narrowest point, 3,800 feet above sea level, the pass is less than 50 feet wide and tremendous cliffs overhang the road, sensationally cut on a lip of rock above a thundering torrent. Equally sensational is the nearby railway – the only one crossing the Taurus – which twists and turns through a series of tunnels. Of the other routes across the mountains, that connecting Konya (the ancient Iconium) with Antalya was followed by St Paul and that from Karaman to Silifke (the ancient Seleucia) by the Crusader army under the Emperor Frederick Barbarossa in the late twelfth century. Both these routes are difficult and at the present day the main channel of approach to the Anatolian plateau across the western Taurus is the road from Antalya to Burdur and Afyonkarahisar. Near Burdur the lake of the same name provides a welcome change of landscape in the long journey over rough mountains from the coast.

Across the Seyhan River and extending northeast is an extension of the Taurus proper called the Anti-Taurus. The Amanos Mountains run along the eastern shore of the Gulf of Iskinderum. The mineral riches of the Taurus, only partly exploited, include silver, copper, lignite, zinc and arsenic.

Teton Range

A branch of the Rocky Mountains. Location *Northwest Wyoming and southeast Idaho.* Height *Rising to over 13,000 feet.* Map *4, D3.* Discovered *John Colter, 1807–09.*

The isolated and beautiful peaks of the Teton

Range, perhaps the finest group in the western United States, were formed at the same time as the Rocky Mountains themselves, by the fracture of a great block of the earth's shell which was tilted back and thrust up 10,000 feet above the adjacent country. Later, Pleistocene glaciers inched down the steep face to channel canyons thousands of feet deep. Their melting ice filled the 400-foot-deep Lake Jackson in Jackson Hole – a perfect mirror for these great mountains of the Continental Divide, so long a barrier to the Far West.

The Teton peaks lie immediately to the south of the Yellowstone National Park, but are strongly contrasted in character. The early French travelers, coming from the west, named the three most prominent points the "Trois Tétons," the "Three Breasts;" these were the Grand, Middle and South Tetons, their height being 13,766, 12,798 and 12,505 feet respectively.

The range is one of the most impressive examples of "fault-block." The extraordinary and continuous steepness of the eastern flank, the absence of any foothills, and the upward sweep of precipices to the amazingly jagged summit crest, within which small glaciers nestle, distinguish this eastern view as one of the most spectacular on the continent. At its foot lies a chain of lakes, of which Jenny Lake is perhaps the most beautiful; these are fringed or interspersed by meadows and forests, while many high tarns are found in the inner recesses of the peaks. Although the eastern aspect of the group has no doubt been mainly responsible for its celebrity, the view from the west, across Teton Basin (Idaho), is scarcely less splendid, though in great contrast, since foothills and forested plateaus intervene. This range, over 40 miles long, forms for all practical purposes an insuperable barrier, except for the Teton Pass (8,429 feet) at its southern end. It has inevitably become the mecca of mountaineers and climbers, with many routes of the utmost difficulty. In 1929 it became the Grand Teton National Park, enlarged in 1950 to an area of 465 square miles, and since then it has formed the winter feeding ground of the largest herd of American elk.

Tibesti Massif

The highest mountain group of the Sahara. Location *Mainly in northwest Chad.* Height *Rising to 11,204 feet.* Map *9, D4-E4.* First explored *Gustav Nachtigal, 1869–71.*

This immense mountain massif – occupying 38,600 square miles – extends southeast to northwest, largely in northwest Chad Territory, for over 300 miles and has a width of 175 miles. Its highest point is the Emi Koussi volcano (11,204 feet).

It was in 1869 that Gustav Nachtigal, German ambassador to the Sultan of Omar, paid a formal call in Murzuk, an oasis in southwest Libya, upon Alexandra Tinne, the Dutch woman explorer. This extraordinary woman, whose conduct and reputation assured her habitual treatment as a royal princess, remarked casually that she was intending to explore Tibesti – the "mountain land of hunger," "the kingdom of Satan" or the "dwelling-place of Djinns," as it was variously called.

Tibesti was 400 miles away to the southeast, across trackless desert. It had never been visited by a white man, scarcely ever seen by outsiders and was in the territory of the ferocious Tebu, the "Men of the Rock," a nomadic Berber tribe of fanatical Moslems who loved nothing better than to kill an unbeliever if he strayed into their remote fastnesses.

Nachtigal, who had come to North Africa as a consumptive doomed to an early death, had been court physician to the Bey of Tunis. His illness was largely cured and by 1869 he was Bismarck's envoy, a key figure in winning wide Moslem support for German expansion in the Middle East. Now he was fired by the dream of reaching Tibesti first. He immediately started to collect a party and set out, ill-prepared, almost at once.

It was a terrible journey, but he and his men eventually reached the approaches to the massif and could make out the huge walls of black volcanic rock, worn into fantastic shapes by the erosive force of timeless storms, the gaunt and ghostly turrets of "Shaitan's Castle," towering silent, grave-like, where no plant grew or bird nested, and where even the bark of the desert fox was unknown.

The expedition dragged on. Mohammed, Nachtigal's servant, was the first to sight the Tarso peaks, with Tusidde standing 10,430 feet high at their head. With mixed feelings of fear and joy he announced that Tibesti was within reach. His fears were justified, for Nachtigal decided to explore the Tarso Range, despite the obvious hardships of prolonging the expedition and the danger that most of his men would refuse to accompany him.

With only a skeleton party he set off over the loose, jagged rocks towards the main ridge. Unsheltered, roasting at midday, frozen at night (the temperature at 8,000 feet ranged from 120° at midday to 20° before dawn, while in wet years snow and ice cover the mountain summits), they struggled on. On the far side of Tusidde they found a gaping crater three miles wide and 2,400 feet deep, filled with blinding white, soft, loose masses of pure sodium. Today this remarkable natural phenomenon is a tourist attraction; then it, and all the other marvels that might lie beyond the next ridge, did not prevent Nachtigal's men from deserting. Helpless now, the explorer made his way with the rest of the party to the town of Bardai – his real goal, the central Tibesti peak of Emi Koussi, unattained.

Today, because of slightly improved rainfall, the few oases of Tibesti provide the Tebu with dates, vegetables, barley, hard wheat, millet, corn, watermelons, tobacco and some pasturage for their camels, donkeys, sheep and goats. But when Nachtigal entered Bardai with the tattered, exhausted remnants of his party, it had been a very bad year and the desperate people of the town regarded the expedition's meager rations as bounty from Allah. Attacked and robbed of nearly everything, Nachtigal was able to save at least his notes and maps – the maps which half a century later guided Commandant Jean Tilho on the second expedition to Tibesti.

It was left to later explorers to determine the nature of the great dry water-courses cut deeply in the faces of the massif, underlining the theory that in earlier geological times the Sahara climate had been much more humid and its vegetation plentiful. But by the time of the outbreak of the First World War, Tilho, after five years of endeavor, had thoroughly explored and mapped some 40,000 square miles of desert around and including the mountains.

Tibet

The highest country in the world. Location *Central Asia, between India and China.* Height *Average 13,000–16,000 feet.* Map *11, E4-G4.* First Western expedition *Colonel Francis Younghusband and party, 1904.*

A high tableland of about 500,000 square miles, Tibet is the highest country in the world and the source of many of Asia's great rivers – the Indus, the Brahmaputra, the Salween and others. Known for centuries as "The Forbidden Land," it has been open to Westerners for less than 50 years and it is now once again practically closed to outsiders since the Communist annexation. Until this happened, Tibet had been for centuries a theocracy, ruled by its own "God-King," the Dalai Lama, who was always chosen in childhood and then brought up by a carefully selected cabinet of teachers and advisers until old enough to rule. The present Dalai Lama is an exile in India.

Religion has always dominated Tibetan life – and the Tibetan landscape. Everywhere there were wayside shrines and statues, fluttering prayer flags on every roof, prayer wheels, cairns marking holy sites and the trance-inducing inscription "Om Mane Padme Hum." From the great monasteries perched on cliffs fantastic dances and strange ceremonials marked special days in the year, while every second person seemed a monk. There was small room for individual ambition, as the social castes were clearly defined and the deepest satisfactions were believed to be spiritual. The real industry of the country was religion, with cattle-raising and agriculture (largely confined to the deep river valleys and flood plains between 10,000 and 15,000 feet) a long way after. The most general occupation was prayer, at every level, from the profound meditation of the hermit to the prayer-wheel twirl given by a yak-herd.

The bleakness of the country – a high, wind-swept plateau bounded and crossed by the highest mountains – has offered little temptation to invaders. The Himalayas in the south and the Kunlun mountains in the north stood sentinel. The Tibetans have always been fiercely independent, but today, with the Dalai Lama in exile, the world's only theocracy is in process of transformation into a modernized Marxist state.

Tien Shan

A great mountain system of Central Asia. Location *China and the USSR, partly separating Russian and Chinese Turkestan.* Height *Rising to over 24,000 feet.* Map *10, C5-D5.*

Stretching in an arc nearly 1,500 miles long, the main range of the Tien Shan (a Chinese name meaning "Celestial Mountains") forms the northern rim of the Tarim Basin, which is probably the site of an ancient inland sea. Though in length the range is comparable to the Himalayas, its highest peaks are all concentrated in a comparatively small knot in the center around Khan Tengri (22,949 feet). For several hundred miles to the east of this central group, the range carries peaks of some 19,000 feet and is well glaciated. Westward the general elevation decreases more rapidly and it merges into the Pamirs as a rela-

Soviet scientists in the Tien Shan

tively minor massif. The highest peaks are composed of granitic rocks, though there are large areas of limestone and other sedimentary formations. In some parts there is evidence of geologically recent volcanic activity. From a point about 200 miles east of Khan Tengri a subsidiary range runs in a northeasterly direction enclosing the very fertile basin of Kuldja. This range is little known to Western travelers, though it seems to be similar in form to the main chain; it is partly glaciated and contains peaks of about 19,000 feet.

A conspicuous feature of the Tien Shan is the labyrinth of deep gorges which dissect the massif on both sides of the main chain. For this reason, travel across the mountains is very hard and virtually the only caravan route over the range from the oasis towns of southern Sinkiang to the important trading city of Ili (Kuldja) is by way of the Muzart Pass (11,400 feet), which includes the passage of a difficult glacier, 14 miles long.

When one travels along the edge of the Taklamakan Desert under the arid southern foothills of the Tien Shan, it is difficult to realize that rainfall on the main range, only a few miles away, is exceptionally heavy. In addition to creating luxuriant vegetation, the heavy precipitation is also the cause of the very large glaciers on the higher part of the range. In the Khan Tengri group, for example, there are two, each about 45 miles long, more than twice the length of any Himalayan glacier and comparable with the largest in Asia. The Tien Shan is also remarkable for the abundance and variety of its fauna. The wild animals include *ovis poli*, ibex, snow leopard, fox, ermine and a wild horse known locally as *khulan*.

The central Tien Shan was explored in 1903 by an expedition led by Professor G. Merzbacher. During these last two decades a great deal of work has been done by Soviet scientists and mountaineers in the Russian (northwestern) section of the range. Very little of the rest of the Tien Shan has been explored in detail. Khan Tengri was climbed in 1936 by a Swiss, Lorenz

Saladin, with the Russians, L. Guttmann, M. Dadiomov and E. and M. Abolakov. Ill-equipped, they approached the mountain from the west and established a base camp, consisting of only one tent, at the head of the Innultchek Glacier. Beyond this point they took no tent and passed the nights in holes dug in the snow. They made four of these bivouacs, the first at 18,600 feet, where they were confined for two days by a storm, and the highest at 22,800 feet, from which they reached the summit on September 5. On the way down they ran into a terrible blizzard. One of the Russians fell 600 feet, and in rescuing him Saladin was so badly frostbitten that he died soon after the party reached the glacier. In 1943 Soviet explorers discovered a peak higher than Khan Tengri, lying ten miles south of that mountain, which was named Pobeda (Victory) Peak, its height being calculated at 24,406 feet. It was later climbed by Soviet mountaineers.

Transylvanian Alps

Southern section of the Carpathians. Location *Central and southwest Rumania.* Height *Rising to over 8,000 feet.* Map 7, *F8-G7.*

For centuries the enchanted and enchanting land of Transylvania has been uneasily balanced between east and west: the last outpost of Europe, a bulwark against Turk and Tartar and at the same time a bridgehead of the east where Asia and the West found a meeting ground. A miniature melting pot (compared to the vastness of the New World), it has been the home of Hungarian, Saxon and Wallachian, with Armenians, Turks and half-a-dozen other minorities mingling, fighting for supremacy and the preservation of their national cultures. It has been an independent principality, supplying some of the greatest kings of Poland and many leaders of Hungary; it has been under Habsburg rule, part of Hungary within the Dual Monarchy and now, with a brief interruption, a province of Rumania since 1919.

It is a country in which almost every hill, every river and every village has three names – German, Rumanian and Hungarian. In its hidden valleys and on the massive mountains customs and legends have survived long after they have disappeared from the plains. Folklore and folk art have flourished in spite of wars and often gruelling poverty. When Bela Bartok and Zoltan Kodaly, the great Hungarian composers, searched for the sources of the true folk music of southeast Europe they wandered through the Transylvanian mountains with their primitive recording apparatus. These mountains have produced great writers, artists, musicians and scientists. Heavily wooded, with some primeval forests (in spite of centuries of exploitation), with sudden tarns, medicinal springs and secret caves, the Transylvanian Alps have a typical Alpine topography though no permanent snow cover.

The Transylvanian Alps extend about 170 miles, with a width varying from 25 to 40 miles, from the upper valley of the Prahova River on the east to the Danube at the Iron Gates in the west, separating Rumania (Wallachia) proper from the Transylvania. The highest peaks are the Negoi (8,361 feet) and the Moldoveanu (8,344 feet), both of them in the Fagaras (Fogaras) Mountains.

There are six main sections in the range. The Fagaras Mountains run for about 35 miles between the Turnu-Rosu Pass and the upper Dambovita River; the Bucegi Mountains, a horseshoe-shaped group, rise to 8,236 feet in Omu Peak, with bare, precipitous slopes (they are a favorite area for ski-ing and alpinism, with beautiful caverns); the Vulcan Mountains, famous for the ewe-cheese made by the shepherds, extend about 25 miles between Oltena and Transylvania along the right bank of the upper Jiu river and rise to 6,133 feet, with very extensive forests; the Retezat (Retyezat), perhaps the most beautiful and picturesque, have many glaciated lakes and rise to 8,236 feet; the Godeanu lie southwest of the Retezat, about 25 miles west-southwest of Lupeni; and finally the Tarcu, in the Banat, rise to 7,402 feet, with huge primeval forests, valuable magnetite deposits and excellent ski-ing facilities, especially at Muntele Mic (5,290 feet).

In almost every section of the range there are cirques, lakes and moraines, relics of former glaciation. Coal and iron ore are mined in the Banat and the mountain pastures are extensively used. The range is cleft by the narrow, picturesque gorges of the Olt and Jiu rivers and the passes of Bran, Turnu Rosu, Surduc and Porta Orientalis.

Trisul

A mountain on the southern edge of the Central Himalayas. Location *Garhwal district, northwest Uttar Pradesh, India.* Height *23,360 feet.* Map *11, D5.* First climbed *Dr T. G. Longstaff and guides, 1907.*

In the Garhwali section of the Himalayan chain, only some 50 miles across and still relatively unknown, between the Trisul group and the Tibetan border, there are over 100 peaks above 20,000 feet. The most majestic, apart from Nanda Devi, is Trisul, at the southern edge. Streams cut their way westwards out of this fastness to join the sacred headwaters of the Ganges. The stream from the southwest foot of Trisul is the Nandakgiri. In Hindu lore, Trisul is the trident of Shiva, in a region where peaks and streams, caves, cliffs and glaciers, are all associated with some event or figure, good or evil, of legend and religion. The association goes back even further than the coming of the Aryans and of Brahmanism, and a pre-Hindu tradition survives among the local community of Doms. Though many of the hill-people seem far from orthodox, reverence for the mysterious grandeur of the mountains is shared by all, not least by isolated Europeans who have come, seen the skyline of Trisul, Nanda Kot and Nanda Devi, and stayed. The early explorers and climbers, like Traill in 1830 and Graham in 1883, had trouble in getting their porters to approach the haunted heights.

It was not until 1907 that Dr T. G. Longstaff, the veteran climber, tackled the peak. He found the approach from the Nandakgiri unpromising and took a chance on the invisible northeast face, leading his party round into the central sanctuary of the Nanda Devi group by the Rishi Gorge. He had to send his coolies back when they were not much beyond the highest pastures (12,000 feet) and took four Gurkhas to the last halt from which he and his companions reached the summit, climbing 6,000 feet in a single day.

"Spread below were all the middle hills we had marched through:" wrote Longstaff, "then the foothills: then the plains with rivers winding. To the west all was clear; the whole scarp of the western Himalayas so vast that I expected to see the earth rotating before my eyes. The western foothills gave the impression of those little waves that on a calm day are born as the sea shallows and lap gently on the shelving shore of some great bay. I was very lucky. I had not the very least feeling of exultation or achievement: the reward was far greater."

The second ascent of Trisul was made in 1933 by P. R. Oliver, and in 1951 two more ascents were made – the first organized by Gurdial Singh, a staff officer of the Indian Military Academy at Dehra Dun, and including R. D. Greenwood, also a professor at the Academy, N. D. Jayal, Surendra Lal and three Sherpas. Of these, Gurdial Singh, Greenwood and Sherpa Dawa Thondup reached the summit. The second ascent was made by the French doctor, R. Walter of Pondicherry, who, with one Sherpa, Nima Tenzing, climbed the peak independently the following day.

Tsinling Mountains

Eastern outlier of the Kunlun. Location *Southern Shensi province, China.* Height *Rising to over 12,000 feet.* Map *10, F5-G5.*

Composed of granitic ridges in the north and folded sedimentary rocks in the south, the Tsinling Mountains extend between the Wei and Han rivers, stretching within Kansu to the borders of Anhwei. The northern slopes, over-looking the Wei River, are steep and precipitous, especially near Sianfu. The southern slopes are more gradual.

The Tsinling and its associated ranges are of great geographical importance. They separate the northern loess lands from the southern forest soils, the dust-blown, semi-arid north from the green, humid south. They have been equally effective as a barrier to commerce and a bastion against invaders. They checked the Mongol hordes and in the nineteenth century separated the areas of Moslem and Taiping rebellion.

The Tsinling Shan is the name given by some geographers and Chinese historians to the entire Kunlun system which, with its various outliers and subsidiary groups, extends eastwards from Tibet almost to the Pacific. The Tsinling Mountains proper are placed within this immense system between the snow-capped, alpine range of the Min Shan and the Tapa Shan farther south.

In the west, where the Tsinling Mountains join the Min Shan, they rise to 12,000 feet in the Taipai Shan, while south of Sian the peaks are about 2,000 feet lower. The heart of the range is a wild, inaccessible area with rounded summits and deep, impassable gorges. The series of ridges generally run southeast; their valleys are often steep canyons whose walls rise abruptly to heights of 1,000 feet and more.

The climatic importance of the range lies in the fact that in winter it tends to keep the Siberian air from the southern provinces where the maritime climatic influences still prevail. In summer the Tsinling Mountains act as a barrier to some of the tropical winds. But the dry plains of the north heat up faster than the forest-covered sections of the south, so that they may become warmer in spite of their higher latitude.

Tungurahua

A quiescent volcano. Location *Central Ecuador.* Height *16,512 feet.* Map *6, B4.*

The volcanoes of Ecuador, while generally considered to be extinct, or dormant to the point of extinction, have a tendency to awake suddenly at intervals into fearful eruption. Perhaps the most noteworthy of these treacherous fire-throwers is Tungurahua, which had been quiescent from 1773 to 1886 when it devastated Baños, the prosperous town at its foot.

There had been a considerable fallout of volcanic dust earlier at Guayaquil and Edward Whymper related that he was agreeably impressed to meet a native of that city who had had the presence of mind to collect some of the sediment. In his zeal Whymper bought the specimen and duly transported it to England for analysis.

The most intriguing point of interest attached to Tungurahua lies in the amazing story related by Alexander von Humboldt about the volcanic fish, a tale whose extravagance fascinated Whymper and for which he could find no explanation. It was alleged that when Tungurahua erupted, a rain of fish was wont to descend upon the plains – and these were presumed to have occupied a crater lake. To try credulity yet further, the fish arrived not boiled or smashed by their fall but miraculously alive. Apart from this, Whymper showed little interest in Tungurahua and time has not increased the enthusiasm of later mountaineers. Its summit just penetrates the snowline and, apart from forming a section of the mountain scenery which gives such beauty to inland Ecuador, it remains individually slighted.

Tupungato

A peak of the Andes. Location *Argentina-Chile border.* Height *21,490 feet.* Map *6, C8.* First climbed *Stuart Vines and Matthias Zurbriggen, 1897.*

After E. A. Fitzgerald and his party had conquered Aconcagua, they turned their attention to the south, where Tupungato, an unclimbed giant on the border of Chile, presented almost as great a challenge.

Fitzgerald himself was not well enough to make the climb and a series of assaults was made by Stuart Vines with the guides Matthias Zurbriggen, Nicola Lanti and Joseph Pollinger. The fine season was already far advanced and time and again Vines was forced to retire by bad weather. These difficulties apart, the expedition suffered severely from *sorroche*, as high altitude sickness is termed in the Andes. At last, on April 12, Vines, Zurbriggen and Pollinger left a bivouac at 17,000 feet. It was 6.30 a.m.

"At 20,500 feet," Vines reported, "Joseph Pollinger, who had only suffered a little in the legs up to this point, threw himself down, complaining of pains in the stomach. I divided his load with Zurbriggen and, leaving what we could best spare behind, we continued the ascent. Pollinger turned to descend by the easy slope of the ridge to the high bivouac. A dome which seemed to be the highest point was close to, when another summit some distance beyond was sighted. It was too much for Zurbriggen. He sat down exclaiming 'It can't be done! I'm finished! I'm not going any further!' He declared his legs would work no more and that the top was another hour away."

Vines continued and reached the actual summit in a little more than an hour. Zurbriggen – who had done such sterling work on Aconcagua – soon recovered and finished the climb.

Ural Mountains

A great mountain system forming the boundary between Europe and Asia. Location USSR. Height 6,000 feet, average. Map 10, B2-3. First explored Russian fur hunters, twelfth century.

This great range, running north and south for about 1,300 miles, forms the traditional boundary between the vast eastern European plain and western Siberia. It is remarkable for its continuous straightness. Other comparable folded mountain systems are usually curved in some degree (for instance, the Alps and the Carpa-

thians) but only the northern continuation of the Urals, the Pai-Khoi Mountains, extending into Novaya Zemlya, are at all arched. Geological examination, however, has shown that the Urals have much in common with other great folded ranges. Their origin lay in the initial deposition in a huge trough (geosyncline) of a vast column of sedimentary materials. These, during Carbo-

Thick forest covers most of the northern Urals

niferous and early Permian times, were transformed by compression (as in the jaws of a vice) into the great ridge we now see. There is also evidence to show that this so-called "Hercynian movement" was contemporaneous with that of such other ancient mountain systems as the Harz (whence the term Hercynian) of Europe and the Altai and Tien Shan of Asia.

The highest peak is Naroda (6,184 feet) in the Northern Urals, where there are several small glaciers. The Trans-Siberian Railway crosses the mountains in a low pass (1,345 feet) west of Sverdlovsk, in the Central Urals. The Southern Urals consist of several parallel ranges with a combined width of about 100 miles. The whole range forms a major watershed between the Volga and Pechora basins as well as the Ob-Irtysh Basin, giving rise to the Usa, Pechora, Vishera, Belaya and Ural rivers on the gradual western slopes, while the Sosva, Tura, Iset, Miass and Tobol have their sources on the steep eastern sides. The Urals form a considerable climatic barrier between the more moderate western region, with its Atlantic atmospheric influences, and the more severely continental area of Siberia. Thick forests cover much of the range, with conifers predominating in the north and on the eastern (Siberian) slopes and deciduous trees on the western (European) flank. Eight hundred years ago the fur hunters of Novgorod had penetrated into the Northern Urals and beyond, and one of the earliest industrial activities appears to have been the salt-trading carried on by the great merchant family of Stroganov in the sixteenth century.

Accompanying the pressure which created the Urals was a considerable amount of igneous intrusion and this gave rise to a large number of important mineral deposits for which the range has been justly famous. Indeed, it is one of the most highly exploited regions in the USSR for mineral resources. For about 100 years after the discovery of platinum in the northern Urals in the early nineteenth century Russia was the leading and almost the only source of the precious metal. It was won from gravels on both sides of the range and worked under similar conditions to placer gold. Base metals also have been mined in large quantities, including copper, nickel, manganese, chromium and iron, as well as bauxite, precious stones, asbestos, potash, coal and petroleum. In the time of Peter the Great, charcoal metallurgy flourished. Though developments elsewhere then eclipsed the Ural mines, the range is now – mainly as a result of the Second World War – a leading industrial region, especially in the production of asbestos, potash, bauxite, emery and gemstones; among the last the Takovaya emeralds are famous.

Ushba

A twin-headed peak. Location *Greater Caucasus, USSR.* Height *15,410 feet.* Map *7, J7.* First climbed *John Garforth Cockin and Ulrich Almer, 1888 (northeast peak); Helbling, Schulze, Reichert, Schuster and Weber, 1903 (southwest peak).*

The popular name of this huge twin-headed peak, rising in rocky precipices from its drapery of snow-fields and glaciers, was fixed from the moment John Garforth Cockin described it. "Next to the Matterhorn, Ushba is the most imposing mountain I have seen," he wrote. "There is a strong suggestion of likeness between the south peak and the Matterhorn and, though the latter is more symmetrical, Ushba is much the greater. It is nearly 1,000 feet higher. . . and whilst the Matterhorn is not much over 9,000 feet above Zermatt, Ushba towers 11,000 feet above Betsho. Its mass is double that of the Matterhorn. The upper rocks of the south peak to be climbed must be nearly 6,000 feet, against little more than 4,000 feet on the Matterhorn." And so, to mountaineers and travelers alike, "the Matterhorn of the Caucasus" it became.

In 1868 C. C. Tucker and his companions found themselves face to face with "the astounding pyramid of Usch Ba." To the first visitors to the Caucasus it presented formidable climbing

problems. In 1886 Clinton Dent and his party again had a distant view of it, but Dent was incapacitated by illness. It was only tackled seriously by Cockin in 1888 when, together with H. W. Holder, H. Woolley and the guides Ulrich Almer and Christian Roth, he made a number of important ascents in the range.

Two peaks of almost equal height – the southern is some 12 feet higher than the northern – rise 600 feet from a snow saddle between them. It was this saddle Cockin and Almer (son of "old" Christian Almer, the great Grindelwald guide) reached late in September 1888. Conditions were poor, the route up the southern peak looked impracticable and when Cockin and Almer finally reached the northern peak, they were enveloped in mist. On the descent, there were several mishaps. A heavy stone fell on the rope between them, but luckily caused no damage. Then Cockin lost one of his boots and completed the descent with his foot wrapped in leggings. And after their return it became evident that they had, in fact, climbed only the lower of the two Ushba peaks.

It was not until 15 years later that a strong German party succeeded in climbing the southern summit, and in the same year, 1903, three Germans made the ascent of both peaks. In 1937 the Oxford University Mountaineering Club organized an expedition to the Caucasus, which had been closed ground for any but Russians after the First World War. J. R. Jenkins, Charles Taylor, L. Hodgkin and T. Beaumont planned and carried out safely a new ascent of the south peak of Ushba.

Uspallata Pass

A pass crossing the Andes between Puente del Inca and Las Cuevas (Argentina) and Portillo (Chile). Location Argentina-Chile border. Height 12,650 feet. Map 6, C8.

For more than four centuries the high and desolate Uspallata Pass has been the chief passage over the southern section of the Andean Cordillera. In colonial times the Spaniards drove their pack mules by this precipitous track – the famous Camino de los Andes. In 1817 one of the columns of General San Martin's liberating army, marching westwards from Mendoza (Argentina), climbed the pass and descended into Chile to defeat the Spaniards in the battle of Chacabuco. The liberation from Spain threw South America open to British and American enterprise and scores of merchants, engineers and adventurers (sometimes accompanied by their wives and children) followed the ancient route on mule-back, fortifying themselves with onions and garlic, which were supposed to counteract the effects of high altitude. In winter the path through the snow was so narrow that the traveler had to put his feet on his mule's ears.

When he reached the highest point in the Cordillera in 1825, Captain Francis Head (a future Governor of Upper Canada) looked down towards the Pacific Ocean. "What a magnificent view!" he exclaimed to one of the Cornish miners who were accompanying him on his mission to the Chilean copper mines. "What thing could be more beautiful?" His companion pondered for a while, then smiled and replied: "Them things, sir, that do wear caps and aprons."

When the snow has gone, the heights are covered with dry, loose stones and dust. Travelers have seen the dried bodies of mules that have lain there for countless years in the rarefied air, as light as cork. An old Andean muleteer told the tale of how he was once surprised to see a man seated on the ground as if enjoying the scenery. He approached quietly and tapped him on the shoulder – whereupon the stranger rolled to the ground. The man had been dead over 40 years, for a paper in his pocket showed that he was a Spanish soldier and had probably fled after the defeat in Chile.

Today the Transandine railway between Argentina and Chile passes beneath the Uspallata Pass, piercing the mountains at an altitude of 10,408 feet, by a two-mile tunnel which was

alf Dome peak in Yosemite National Park

305

opened in 1910; the line connects Valparaiso with Mendoza. Above the pass stands a spectacular statue of Christ, lifting a cross to the sky and extending a hand in blessing over the now peaceful Argentina-Chile frontier. *Christo Redentor* was dedicated on March 13, 1904, to commemorate a series of peace and boundary treaties between the two countries. Even the normal aeroplane route from Mendoza to Santiago di Chile crosses the Andes at this point. In clear weather passengers in the aircraft have a splendid view of the statue of Christ down below and of the dazzling, sunlit peak of Aconcagua rising above it.

Ventoux, Mont

A ridge overlooking the Rhône Valley. Location *Provence Alps, southeast France.* Height *6,273 feet.* Map *8, A10.*

Mont Ventoux, the *Mons Ventosus* or Windy Mountain, is a western outlier of the Alps, a bald hump of limestone high enough to catch and hold the few clouds of a Provençal afternoon. It rises isolated and severe above the country bordering the Rhône, above the farms, vineyards and fields of artichokes and melons, all protected by long, parallel cane-breaks from the winds which sweep past the mountain. The fields end and a fringe of wood darkens the base of the mountain, which then rises to a cloud crest in a suavity of slopes, here and there planted with trees but increasingly naked and reflected towards the sky, a blue mountain which collects on its slopes a mixture of vermilion and purple while the clouds, which also change color with the evening, hold lightly in long lines to the summit.

Petrarch climbed the Mons Ventosus one day at the end of April, 1336, during the time of his retreat at Vaucluse, not far away. An inquisitive poet, he had longed for years to reach a summit seen from all the countryside and known to him since his boyhood days at Carpentras. At last, with his brother, he made the ascent from

Malaucène, 12 miles to the north. His description of the ascent and the prospect is one of the earliest records of mountain-climbing for its own sake.

A shepherd in one of the lower dells tried to dissuade the brothers, saying that he had climbed the mountain 50 years before and had endured nothing but misery – and had never heard of anyone else climbing it before or since. After exertions which caused him to reflect on the pilgrimage of life, Petrarch at last rested on Le Petit Fils, the highest point. "I was so affected by the unaccustomed spirit of the air and by the free prospect, that I stood as one stupefied. I looked down; clouds were beneath my feet. I began to understand Athos and Olympus, since I found that what I heard and read of them was true of a mountain of far less celebrity." He looked at the "great rugged Alps" and though he could not see the Pyrenees "by reason of the impotence of mortal sight," he could see the Rhône and the Mediterranean off Marseilles.

He took out his copy of the *Confessions of St Augustine,* opened it at random and read: "There are men who go to admire the high places of mountains, the great waves of the sea, the wide currents of rivers, the circuit of the ocean, and the orbits of the stars – and who neglect themselves. . ." – and walked down in silence, angry with himself for admiring earthly things and neglecting the greatness of the soul.

Vesuvius

The only active volcano on the European mainland. Location *Bay of Naples, southern Italy.* Height *3,891 feet.* Map *7, E9.*

"The ashes now began to fall upon us," wrote Pliny the younger in his famous letter to Cornelius Tacitus, "though in no great quantity. I looked back; a dense dark mist seemed to be following us, spreading itself over the country like a cloud. 'Let us turn out of the highroad,' I said, 'while we can still see, for fear that, should we fall in the road, we should be pressed to death in the dark, by the crowds that are following us.' We had scarcely sat down when night came upon us, not such as we have when the sky is cloudy, or when there is no moon, but that of a room when it is shut up, and all the lights put out. You might hear the shrieks of women, the screams of children, and the shouts of men; some calling for their children, others for their parents, others for their husbands, and seeking to recognize each other by the voices that replied; one lamenting his own fate, another that of his family; some wishing to die, from the very fear of dying; some lifting their hands to the gods; but the greater part convinced that there were no gods at all, and that the final endless night of which we have heard had come upon the world. . . It now grew rather lighter, which we imagined to be rather the forerunner of an approaching burst of flames (as in truth it was) than the return of day: however, the fire fell at a distance from us; then again we were immersed in thick darkness, and a heavy shower of ashes rained upon us, which we were obliged every now and then to stand up to shake off, otherwise we should have been crushed and buried in the heap. . ."

This is perhaps the most graphic description there is of the havoc that Vesuvius worked in 79 A.D., when it destroyed Pompeii, Herculaneum and Stabiae – the flourishing Roman towns which were dug up more than 17 centuries later and provide today the most complete galleries of Roman life.

Vesuvius, the Mountain of the Fire-God, rises gently at first from the Campanian plain, increasing its steepness to almost 35° in the upper reaches, above the cone. On the east and north sides it descends to the plain from Monte Somma (3,714 feet), a semicircular ridge half-encircling the cone. Long centuries of lava flows have deeply scarred and furrowed its sides. The Atrio del Cavallo, a valley with sheer walls, about three miles long and one third of a mile wide, stretches between the cone and Monte Somma. On the western slope stands the earthquake observatory, at 1,995 feet; a road and an electric railway connect it with Resina. The railway continues to the foot of the cone, and a funicular takes visitors to the verge of the crater, which is 2,300 feet across. A panoramic railroad runs around the base, which is 45 miles in circumference.

For 3,000 years the people of Campania have learned to live on and under the volcano. The lower slopes are extremely fertile. Here the grapes of the famous Lachryma Christi wine are grown, and oranges, lemons, vegetables and walnuts bear rich harvest. Though Vesuvius has never been quiet for long periods, the eruptions have never driven away the hardworking, thrifty countryfolk. In 1631 five large communities – Boscotrecase, Torre Annunziata, Torre del Greco, Resina and Portici – were wiped out. There were violent eruptions in 1779, 1794, 1822, 1872, 1906 and 1929. In the late eighteenth century Henry Swinburne admired the striking spectacle. "An immense river of blazing lava ran down the side, supplied by streams of red-hot matter vomited at intervals out of the summit of the mountain," he wrote. "The whole atmosphere was illumined and a long train of light, reflected from it across the gulf upon the tremulous surface of the waves, was as beautiful, if not more so, than the real fiery torrent. . ."

In 1944 another eruption destroyed San Sebastiano al Vesuvio, but for the last decade or so there has been only minor activity. However, Vesuvius is far from dormant and still provides the same impressive spectacle as it did in Pliny's day.

Victoria, Mount

The highest point of the Chin Hills. Location *Burma. Height 10,018 feet. Map 11, H7.*

The Chin Hills consist of a number of parallel ranges of moderate height, running from north to south for 250 miles and forming the western wall of Burma. Situated in the southern section is Mount Victoria. Though the highest mountain in tropical Burma, it is neither conspicuous nor impressive from a distance, and from the east the sky-line of the southern Chin Hills looks quite level for many miles. It has always been a somewhat remote and neglected region, whereas the Shan plateau on the opposite side of the Irrawaddy Valley is far better known and much more accessible by road, rail and plane.

Few white men have visited Mount Victoria, yet today it is easily reached by plane from Rangoon, which takes passengers to the foot of the Chin Hills. All who have been there in the spring to escape from the burning heat of the plains testify to the delights of the cool air, laden with the fragrance of the pine forests which clothe the middle slopes, and to the brilliance of the blood-red rhododendrons which are so abundant above 6,000 feet. In spite of being in the tropics, the summit is partly covered with familiar deciduous trees, such as maple, cherry and birch, and with temperate and even alpine plants, such as saxifrage, vils, monkshood and anemone. But perhaps the most unexpected plant is a brilliant blue gentian found all over the summit and closely allied to one which grows on the Tibetan grasslands. There are hard frosts here in winter, but no snow ever falls, as the climate in that season is very dry.

The country round Mount Victoria is sparsely populated by Chins, a Tibeto-Burman tribe of primitive culture and unknown origin, though it is believed that they came from the north. Their small, rather poor villages and clearings are found up to 6,000 feet. Farther west, towards Arakan and Bengal, and especially in the northern Chin Hills, much larger villages are found.

In March or April the visitor to Mount Victoria, which is situated near the edge of the dry zone of central Burma, might easily get the impression that it never rains here, so dried up is everything and so hard the soil, even though the forest above 5,000 feet is still green. In the foothills all the streams are dried up and the teak forests naked. In August, however, the same visitor might get the impression that it is always raining and will never stop. In both seasons visibility is reduced to a minimum – in spring by the fine dust blown off the plains and the smoke of innumerable forest fires where new clearings are being prepared and in summer by the dense mists which roll over the highlands during the southwest monsoon.

In the clear air of the winter months, however, one can plainly see the Irrawaddy, like a silver snake, 70 miles distant, and the extinct volcanic cone of Mount Popa, which is even farther away. After dark the lights of Kyauk, the big oil town on the Irrawaddy, illuminate the sky.

Many wild animals live in the great forests which clothe Mount Victoria and the Chin Hills generally, including bears, carnivores, deer and large herds of bison. Naturalists who have visited this region include ornithologists and botanists, but though much is known about the wild life and vegetation, there is still place for further exploration. The south face and the west ridge of Mount Victoria in particular have been almost entirely neglected.

Virunga Mountains

A volcanic range with dormant and active volcanoes. Location *Eastern central Africa.* Height *Rising to over 14,000 feet.* Map 9, F6-7.

Africa's Great Rift Valley can be clearly traced by the lakes that stud its length. Between Lake Edward and Lake Kivu in the western branch of the Rift stand the volcanic Virunga mountains (also called Mfumbiro); formed at a cross-fracture of the valley in Pleistocene times, they block the northern outlets of Lake Tanganyika and deprive the Nile of a considerable water supply.

They are elusive – difficult to reach and difficult to see together at any one time. The African Lake District is widely known for its sudden storms and, as the steep slopes of the Virunga group provide an ideal stimulus for the condensation of damp air, a swiftly changing background of cloud is a common feature of their appearance.

With their subsidiary cones, the eight volcanoes fall into three groups. Nyamlagira (about 10,000 feet) and Nyiragongo (about 11,400 feet) stand to the north of Lake Kivu in the Albert National Park; Vishoke (12,370 feet), Mikeno (about 14,600 feet) and Karisimbi (14,780 feet) form a triangular group northeast of the lake in a less accessible part of the same park; still farther to the northeast, Sabinio, Mgahinga and Muhavura lie in a roughly east-west line on the border of Uganda and Ruanda-Urundi. Only Nyiragongo and Nyamlagira are still active. The latter is the least impressive of the group and least attractive to the climber, for in spite of its height its base is so broad that it presents a squat appearance and climbing it is little more than an uphill walk. It has been quiescent since 1938, when the pool of lava in the crater overflowed, the cone collapsed and a new crater (Shambena) was born, to the accompaniment of violent explosions and earth tremors. A stream of lava poured from the cone towards Lake Kivu, reaching it in December, some ten months after the eruption had begun and shortly before it ceased altogether.

Nyiragongo is still in a state of latent activity. Its last eruption in 1948 was on a more impressive scale than the Nyamlagira outburst; the last of three lava flows reached Lake Kivu about three weeks after its start. The night sky glows above the pool of liquid lava that still lies at the bottom of the central crater.

Vishoke in the central group is the least accessible of all. Overgrown with dense vegetation all the way to the crater lake at its summit, it affords a tiring though not a difficult climb. Karisimbi is the highest peak of the range, with four sharply divided belts of vegetation from the dense forest at its base to the barren volcanic cone, from which the whole range is visible on the infrequent clear days. A forested saddle links this mountain to Mikeno, the hardest climb of all.

Rain or cloud are almost invariably present and above the forest and savanna belts there is a considerable area of treacherous, moss-covered rock where dangerous traverses are sometimes necessary. The crater has disappeared from the heavily eroded summit.

Muhavura is the highest (about 13,550 feet) of the three mountains bordering on Uganda. Its faces are deeply gullied by erosion, but the summit crater remains, with a small lake. It is also linked by a saddle to its neighbor Mgahinga (11,400 feet), where the only sign of former volcanic activity is a small pool at the western end of the crest. Dense vegetation persists nearly to the summit.

The northern flank of Sabinio (about 12,000 feet) is heavily eroded, but its most conspicuous feature is the group of five jagged rock pinnacles making up its summit ridge. Of these the second from the eastern end is the highest. Sabinio has the usual belts of vegetation except that the topmost alpine flora are lacking, and near its base it has the thickest growth of bamboo in the entire range. Seventeen square miles of Sabinio's northern face were proclaimed a gorilla sanctuary in 1930.

Of the many people who have climbed in the Virunga group – among them King Albert of Belgium – the most remarkable was probably Earl Denman, who later attempted to climb Everest alone. Accompanied only by African guides and wearing no shoes, he was the first white man to climb all eight of the peaks. "I had not expected to see Mikeno again," he wrote, "but at a bend in the road it could be seen with its cathedral peak silhouetted against a reddened sky. I felt the mountain to be so close to me that I wanted to put out my hands and stroke its sheer sides."

Vosges

A mountain range separating the Alsatian plain from the southern Lorraine plateau. Location *Eastern France.* Height *1,000-4,000 feet average.* Map *8, C5-6.*

An island of mountainous country, rising from the plains of France which stretch away from its western fringes, the Vosges are bounded on the south by the Belfort Gap and on the east by the deep trough of the Rhine Valley. Geographically they continue northwards until cut by the swing of the Rhine as it curves west through Mainz on its way to the sea; the name, however, is now generally applied only to the portion of the group on the French side of the political frontier. And here politics count, for to the east lies Alsace, to the west, Lorraine.

Stretching for 120 miles south-southwest and north-northeast, the Vosges are basically sandstone in the north, but as the hills gain height in the south, this gives way to granite. Here the high rounded summits, rising above the pine forests, are known as *ballons*. The highest is the Ballon de Guebwiller (4,672 feet). Throughout the whole length of the range there is a considerable difference between the gradual western slope, cold and wet, from which rise the Moselle, the Meurthe and the Sarre, and the more favored, steeper, eastern slopes.

In character the Vosges have much in common with the Black Forest, which they face across the trench of the Rhine. The lower slopes are studded with small lakes, which themselves are surrounded by a wealth of trees – the fine forests in whose clearings cattle graze and which yield only on the upper slopes to the rolling, open country reminiscent of the South Downs of England. From many of these summits there are magnificent views both eastwards into Germany and south into Switzerland.

Wasatch Range

A range of the Rocky Mountains. Location *Idaho and Utah.* Height *Rising to 12,008 feet.* Map *4, D3.*

The Wasatch Range lies west of the Uintas, striking across the trend of the latter range, but having a quite different, complex formation. It extends for about 250 miles south from the bend of the Bear River in southeast Idaho, stretching past the Great Salt Lake and Salt Lake City to the mouth of the San Pitch River in central Utah. It has a topography which differs considerably from that of the flanking ranges. The highest point is Mount Timpanogos, which rises to 12,008 feet, ten miles north of the city of Provo. On the northwest slope of this impressive peak the Timpanogos Cave National Monument, covering 250 acres, was established in 1922. It consists of a series of caves with beautiful pink and white formations, of which the most famous is the Great Heart of Timpanogos, a large stalactite shaped like the human heart.

The range includes parts of the Wasatch and Uinta national forests, and is drained by the Ogden, Provo and Weber rivers. At its southern end lies the high tableland of the Wasatch Plateau, which rises to 10,986 feet in Musinia Peak and to 12,300 feet in South Tent. A number of elaborate irrigation tunnels pass through it, conducting water from the headstream of the San Rafael River to the Sanpete Valley. Within the range there are many delightful rustic places in natural settings – Provo, Ogden, Weber, Little Cottonwood and Big Cottonwood canyons all provide beautiful scenery and pleasant camping.

It was at the foot of the Wasatch mountains that the Mormons, after their epic trek through the Rocky Mountains, settled and created their state in the late eighteen-forties. They developed irrigation and created an oasis in the barren Wasatch Plateau.

Washington, Mount

The highest peak in the northeastern United States. Location *Presidential Range, White Mountains, New Hampshire.* Height *6,288 feet.* Map *5, B2.* First climbed *Darbey Field, 1642.*

Mount Washington, center of a popular summer and winter resort area, rises east of the Crawford Notch. Its formation is chiefly granite, and the Tuckerman Ravine, a glacial cirque on the southeast slope, is proof of its early scouring by local glaciers. Its snowcap melts during July and August and re-forms during winter. The eastern side has many deep gorges and there are also several on the northern face, while the western slope is especially steep. Its summit is rocky, and has scanty vegetation compared to the lower slopes, which are covered by a coniferous forest, and the base, where there are many large trees. At 3,820 feet there is a belt of gnarled, stunted trees which disappear at higher levels.

An auto highway has replaced the former carriage road, which was built in 1861 and which, in turn, replaced the earlier bridle path of 1840. In 1869 a rack-and-pinion railway to the summit was opened. There is a federal meteorological station on the top and a large hotel, and above the tree line there are vivid alpine gardens.

Mount Washington was first ascended by a white man in 1642, and in 1784 it was named after the first president by Manasseh Cutler.

Weisshorn

A symmetrical pyramidal peak. Location *Pennine Alps, southern Switzerland.* Height *14,792 feet.* Map *8, C8.* First climbed *John Tyndall and Johann-Joseph Bennen, 1861.*

The Weisshorn, which rises between Zinal and Randa, is notable for its remarkable form. "Perhaps the most beautifully sharp and symmetrical of the pyramidal peaks of the Alps," is how John Ball described it.

Leslie Stephen made an attempt to ascend the Weisshorn in 1859, and C. E. Mathews and Melchior Anderegg made another in 1860. But it was Professor John Tyndall who conquered the peak, with the guide Johann-Joseph Bennen, and it was Bennen who solved the problem of what Tyndall called, in his classic account, the "snow catenary." Here the snow ridge they were ascending narrowed, for some 60 feet, to a mere thin wall of rock; upon this was a wall of snow, dwindling to a knife-edge. Tyndall, an experien-

ced mountaineer, failed to see how the place could be passed. "Bennen's practical sagacity was, however, greater than mine," he wrote. "He tried the snow by squeezing it with his foot, and to my astonishment commenced to cross. Even after the pressure of his feet, the space he had to stand on did not exceed a hairbreadth. I followed him, exactly as a boy walking on a horizontal pole, with toes turned outwards. Right and left the precipices were appalling; but the sense of power on such occasions is exceedingly sweet." Later, when the summit had at last been gained, Bennen was upset because they had brought no flag, so he knocked off the head of his axe, used the handle as a flagstaff and tied a red handkerchief to it.

In 1862 Leslie Stephen made the second ascent, and G. A. Passingham was the first to climb the very formidable west face. During the past century the Weisshorn has become one of the favorite Pennine targets for climbers.

The Weisshorn

Western Australian Mountains

Long, broken ranges of low mountains. Location *Western Australia.* Height *1,200–3,000 feet.* Map *12, A5.*

The low, scattered ranges in the vast area of Western Australia are divided into several groups – the Darling Range (up to 1,500 feet), just inland from the state capital, Perth; the Hammersley Range, 600 miles farther north, containing Mount Bruce (4,024 feet), highest point in the state; the King Leopold Range, nearly 1,000 miles farther northeast; and various other ranges in between, including the Throssell, Ophthalmia, Barlee, Robinson, Rawlinson and Sterling ranges.

The mountains vary from high, red sandhills framing salt lakes to fine, bold massifs with rugged-looking peaks, bluffs and pinnacles – but they are mostly barren sandstone, from which numerous rocky creeks have torn their way through the sand. The large lakes are usually dry and the largest rivers (such as the Swan) mostly intermittent. There are still about 21,000 aborigines living – or struggling to live – in these barren deserts.

More than half of Western Australia is composed of gold fields, largely in the central area. The smallest but most profitable is the East Coolgardie. It was partly across the Western Australian Mountains that the 1,000-mile rabbit-proof fence was built to try and keep out the small but persistent pests which menaced the sheep-raising industry.

Wetterhorn

A triple peak rising above Grindelwald. Location *Bernese Oberland, southern central Switzerland.* Height *12,153 feet (highest peak).* Map *8, D7.* First climbed *S. T. Spear, 1845 (highest peak).*

Few peaks are better known to the non-mountaineer than the Hasli Jungfrau, usually called the Wetterhorn, whose grand rock precipices, carrying snow and ice slopes, rise to the east of Grindelwald and fill the background of so many postcard views of the village. Few peaks have caused so much amiable argument as to when, how and by whom the first ascent was made, and the Wetterhorn is surely the only peak to have been climbed annually for more than 50 years by the same guide, who always carried a fir tree – or climbed by the same man on his golden wedding anniversary together with his 71-year-old wife.

The confusion surrounding the first ascent is partly due to the fact that the mountain mass has three summits – the Hasli Jungfrau (12,149 feet), which is most easily seen from Grindelwald, the 12,153-foot Mittelhorn, a mile to the east, and the 12,110-foot Rosenhorn, yet another mile away. The dramatic description which Alfred Wills gave of his ascent of 1854 overshadowed all the ascents made a decade earlier. It is now established that S. T. Spear, an Englishman, climbed the highest summit in 1845, a year after the Rosenhorn had been conquered by Desor, the geologist, and the Hasli Jungfrau climbed by his three guides. Alfred Wills arrived in Grindelwald in 1854 and was persuaded that the peak had still to be climbed for the first time. How his party was met on the mountain by two local guides who tried to outflank them; how the parties joined forces; and how one of the local men, Christian Almer, planted his fir tree beside the iron flag taken up by Wills, has become part of Alpine history.

Thirty years after this ascent, Almer made the climb with Wynnard Hopper and his youngest son, Peter Almer, who carried the customary fir tree – with "a grave, earnest air about him," as Hopper wrote later. Twelve years later, on June 22, 1896, Almer and his wife Margherita, their eldest daughter, two sons, a local doctor, porters and the local photographer climbed the Wetterhorn. Cold prevented a long or convivial stay on the summit but the weather was good and their numerous friends in Grindelwald were able to watch the party being photographed on the summit.

Today the Wetterhorn has been ascended by numerous routes. The Gleckstein Cave, in which early parties slept, has been replaced by the comfortable stone Gleckstein hut, and all three peaks can be climbed in a single expedition.

White Mountains

A mountain mass occupying about 1,000 square miles. Location New Hampshire. Height Rising to over 6,000 feet. Map 5, C2.

There are three White Mountain ranges in the United States. That of eastern Arizona lies in the Fort Apache Indian Reservation and boasts Greens Peak (10,115 feet) and Baldy Peak (11,590 feet). The second is shared by California and Nevada and rises to 14,242 feet in White Mountain and to 13,145 feet in·Boundary Peak, the highest point in Nevada.

But of the three the New Hampshire range is both the most extensive and the best known. Part of the great Appalachian system, it spreads over most of the northern part of the state, from the Connecticut River to western Maine. Because of its nearness to the big New England cities and to New York itself, and because of its strikingly varied scenery and many rivers, it has become in the last few years a favorite playground of the eastern United States, in both summer and winter.

The highest point of the group is in the Presidential Range, which lies north of the Saco River, within the White Mountain National Forest: Mount Washington rises to 6,288 feet, with Mount Madison (5,363 feet), Mount Adams (5,798 feet), Mount Jefferson (5,715 feet), Mount Clay (5,532 feet), Mount Monroe (5,385 feet), Mount Franklin (5,004 feet), Mount Pierce (also called Clinton, 4,310 feet), Mount Jackson (4,052 feet) and Mount Webster (3,910 feet) all honoring American presidents and statesmen. The beautiful Small Star Lake, 4,900 feet up, is

between Mount Adams and Mount Madison, and the two Lakes of the Clouds, 100 feet higher, are spread on the slope of Mount Washington.

The Crawford Notch – the local name for a scenic pass – separates the Franconia Mountains from the Presidential Range. Their principal peaks are North Twin Mountain (4,769 feet), South Twin Mountain (4,926 feet), Mount Garfield (4,488 feet), Mount Lafayette (5,249 feet, the highest of the range), Mount Lincoln (5,108 feet), Mount Liberty (4,460 feet) and Flume Mountain (4,327 feet). There are several other ranges in the sprawling group: the Carter-

The Old Man of the Mountain, a notable rock formation in the White Mountains

Moriah Range, south of the Androscoggin, east of the Presidential Range, with the Carter Dome (4,843 feet), the highest point, and Imp Mountain (displaying the celebrated rock profile of the Imp Face), and the Sandwich Range, with Mount Passaconaway (4,060 feet) as its culmination. The Old Man of the Mountain, another striking rock profile, is on Profile (Cannon) Mountain in the Franconia group. The most striking and beautiful "notches" are the Crawford, Dixville, Franconia, Kinsman and Pinham notches.

The long-vanished glaciers have carved deep ravines and glacial cirques into the granite of the White Mountains. Much of the area is within the White Mountain National Forest and there are about a dozen popular resorts, ranging from Conway to Randolph and Dixville Notch and Woodstock.

Whitney, Mount

Highest peak in the United States outside Alaska. Location *Sierra Nevada, eastern California.* Height *14,495 feet.* Map *4, B4.* First climbed *John Lucas, A. H. Johnson and Charles Begole, 1875.*

Mount Whitney, which was, until Alaska achieved statehood, the highest peak of the United States, rises on the eastern border of the Sequoia National Park on the line of Inyo and Tulare counties. With steep slopes in the east, it rears abruptly for about 11,000 feet from the Owens Valley.

It was in 1864 that Josiah D. Whitney, the eminent geologist, and his party discovered the great mountain. Whitney had been state geologist for California from 1860 to 1874 and the mountain, climbed for the first time 11 years after its height was established, was named after him.

Today a scenic highway connects the highest point of California with the lowest in America – Death Valley – so that the visitor can, in a single day, experience the two extremes of climate and altitude.

Wrangell Mountains

A range of volcanic origin with large glaciers. Location *Southeast Alaska.* Height *Rising to over 16,000 feet.* Map *3, D6.*

The Wrangell Mountains run for some 150 miles southeast from the Cooper River to the St Elias Mountains near Mount Logan. The larger valleys were first traversed, but never thoroughly explored, by the Russian hunters when the vast territory was part of the Tsarist Empire. The range was named after the eminent Russian explorer, Baron F. von Wrangell. The name was first attached to Mount Wrangell itself, since this, at 14,005 feet, was long considered the highest mountain in the range. But eventually, when the United States acquired the territory in 1867 and a survey of the region was carried out, other summits proved to be considerably higher, with Mount Sanford (16,208 feet) the loftiest. Among the many high peaks in the group are Mount Blackburn (16,140 feet) and University Peak (15,100 feet). In fact, the limits of the range are somewhat arbitrary and it is arguable that Mount Lucania (17,150 feet) in the extreme southwest should be included.

The greater number of these peaks have been climbed in recent years. Among the immense glaciers descending from them the most famous is the Barnard Glacier, more than 30 miles in length. It is a wide glacier, fed in the first place by two main branches, and as it proceeds from its 10,000-foot head-snows on either side of Mount Natazhat (13,440 feet) to its terminus at 2,000 feet in the Chitina Valley, many tributaries join it at right angles, particularly on the eastern side. These united yet individual ice-streams, some 13 in number, preserve their identity in a remarkably regular fashion, each marked by its own lateral moraines. As these join the main glacier or run along it, they appear as a spectacular series of parallel bands, gray against white, looking like a gigantic highway running between the steep, bare mountains – a highway doomed

The Barnard Glacier, in the Wrangell Mountains

never to be used. The Barnard and the other glaciers of the range are comparable with many glaciers of the Himalayas and the Karakoram.

During the first decades of the century the Wrangell Mountains achieved fame because of their rich copper deposits. The Kennecott Range above McCarthy yielded 10,000 to 20,000 tons of copper annually for many years, especially from the rich Bonanza and Jumbo mines, situated at an elevation of 6,000 feet above the Kennecott Glacier.

Mount Wrangell itself was notable until recently as the only active volcano in the range, and the highest erupting center in North America. To the Copper River Indians it was known as Kah-Una-Lita (the Smoke Mountain), since its volcanic activity had been mainly restricted to the discharge of vapor and light ash, which at times spread a film of dust over hundreds of square miles of the Copper River Valley. In 1909, at the time of their first ascent of Mount Wrangell by the glaciers of the south face, R. Dunn and W. T. Soule found a great, steam-filled crater in the broad summit and many fumaroles emitting gases. In contrast, when a cosmic ray laboratory was established in 1953 by scientists from New York University and the University of Alaska at about 13,700 feet, the crater had become dormant and filled with snow. Outcropping rocks, however, were still warm nearby. The existing summit plateau provided an excellent landing field for the ski-fitted air-craft of Dr Terris Moore, President of the University of Alaska, who, with great enterprise and skill, undertook a number of flights to transport personnel and supplies to the top of the mountain.

Yellowstone National Park

The oldest and largest national park in the United States. Location *Mainly in northwest Wyoming.* Height *Average 7,000–8,000 feet.* Map *4, D2.*

When it was discovered in the winter of 1807–08 by John Colter, a member of the Lewis and Clark expedition, the first reports of Yellowstone's wonders were dismissed as fiction. Established in 1872, and situated in the northwest corner of Wyoming (with small strips in Montana and Idaho) it is today one of the most popular vacation centers in America, visited every year by over 500,000 tourists. Wild life flourishes, completely protected; there are bison on the eastern ranges, goats on the crags, deer, elk, antelope and bear (both black and grizzly) in the more moderate situations of pasture or forest, and a multitude of birds and flowers. There are mountains over 11,000 feet – ranges rising 2,000–4,000 feet above the tableland, with the Absaroka Range forming the eastern boundary. Part of the Gallatin Range lies in the extreme northwest of the 3,458-square-mile territory, the Washburn Range is in the north and the Red Mountains in the south. There are glaciers and gorges – the headwaters of the Madison, Gallatin, Yellowstone and Snake rivers drain the park and the trough of the Grand Canyon of the Yellowstone alone is 20 miles long, 1,200 feet deep and 2,000 feet wide. There are waterfalls (the Upper and Lower falls have drops of 109 and 308 feet respectively), and lakes (the Yellowstone Lake is 139 square miles, 7,731 feet above sea level, with a maximum depth of 300 feet, while Heart Lake, Lewis Lake and Shoshone Lake are smaller, but equally beautiful). There is a marvelous variety of high plateaus, barren crags, grasslands and forests, including a fossil forest.

The most popular attraction is "Old Faithful" – one of the 3,000 geysers and hot springs of the park – which discharges a column of 12,000 gallons of nearly boiling water 170 feet into the air every hour or so, taking about four minutes to do it. Giant, another geyser not far away, shoots to 200 feet – but at intervals of two-and-a-half days to three months, while Daisy (75 feet) is notably irregular. There are 120 named geysers, with varying performances.

Growls, grunts, splutters, hisses and mutterings come from all sides in this thermal region, which the local Sioux, Algonquin and Shoshone Indian tribes used to approach in awe, believing it to be a haunt of powerful spirits. The landscape is certainly fantastic enough, moulded out of flowing water by the deposition of calcium carbonate or silica into steps, mounds, terraces and basins, weirdly striated and colored in strange browns, greens, oranges, blues, yellows and pinks by growths of algae – a landscape which seems not to belong to this world at all. Most extraordinary are the 200 acres of the Mammoth Hot Springs, in the north of the park, where over 70 springs, closely clustered, have transformed an entire hillside.

The main road through Yellowstone is the Grand Loop Highway, about 140 miles long, and there are ample facilities for boating and camping.

Yerupajá

A peak of the Andes. Location *Cordillera Occidental, Peru.* Height *21,758 feet.* Map *6, B5.* First climbed *Dave Harrah and G. Maxwell, 1950.*

The local name of Yerupajá, "El Carnicero" (The Butcher), has a sinister ring and the mountain has lived up to its title. Yerupajá Grande, to distinguish it from Chico, a nearby and lower peak, resembles an axe resting blade up. It surges from the tangled glaciers in two terrifyingly steep faces, united in a summit ridge of knife-like sharpness. It was long recognized as a challenge to mountaineers, and for many years it was the highest unclimbed peak in the Americas. In 1936 a German party attempted the ascent; it was a tribute to the mountain's difficulty that they were unable to get within 2,000 feet of the summit.

It was not until 1950 that Yerupajá was next tackled, this time by the Harvard Andean Expedition. Aided by good weather, they made steady progress up extremely steep ice slopes, set up their high camps and at last approached the razor crest. Despite the favorable weather, they were conscious of the cold and had trouble keeping their feet from freezing. In addition to the cold, they experienced the dreaded *sorroche,* or altitude sickness. On July 31, only Harrah and Maxwell were fit to attempt the summit.

They made their way gingerly along the heavily corniced summit ridge, with sheer drops on either side, while the ever-present danger of their foothold collapsing nagged at their minds. They were tempted to stop just short of the top on safer ground, but decided to go on. They made the true summit and The Butcher was vanquished. It was a great triumph, but they paid for it dearly. On the descent they were retracing their careful steps when, without warning, Harrah fell clean through the cornice, tumbling helplessly down the precipitous face towards the glaciers thousands of feet below. By the greatest good luck Maxwell was able to hold him on the rope and he climbed back, making a fantastic effort. After this harrowing experience their descent was a nightmare. They were caught by darkness and had to spend 12 hours in freezing cold, already weakened by the strain of a long climb and the accident. They survived, but suffered severe frostbite. Harrah lost all his toes and Maxwell several of his.

El Carnicero had become, if anything, more fearful now that it had been climbed.

Yosemite National Park

A spectacular region of canyons, peaks, cliffs and water falls. Location *Eastern central California.* Height *7,000–8,000 feet, average.* Map *4, B4.*

Few places in the world offer such a series of beautiful waterfalls as Yosemite: the Upper Yosemite Fall plunges 1,430 feet, the Lower another 320 feet – equal to 11 Niagaras – with a long glissade, 675 feet high, in between; Ribbon Fall (1,612 feet) is one of the highest single cataracts in the world; Silver Strand Fall (1,170 feet), Bridalveil Fall (620 feet), Nevada Fall (594 feet), Illilouette Fall (370 feet) and Vernal Fall (317 feet) are almost as spectacular. They are at their finest in May and June, charged with the melting snow waters of early summer, but in August and later they diminish and some may even dry up completely. The falls form a ring, descending from the great precipices that encircle the flat, lush, green meadowlands and woods of the broad Yosemite Valley, from an upland region of vast granite peaks and domes which slopes from the glaciers and snows of the Sierra Nevada to the east.

These uplands strike a wonderful contrast to the luxuriance of the level valley floor with its rich clay soils. They consist of miles of undulating country, of silver-gray granite, deeply cut here and there by rivers (and by glaciers in the Ice Age), clothed with dense coniferous forest, where the soil is deep and varied by innumerable lakes, tarns and streams. In the higher country there are wonderful stretches of sub-alpine meadows – such as the Tuolumne, at 8,600 feet, ten miles long and two miles wide – vivid green and dotted with innumerable flowers.

It is the variety of Yosemite – the combination of the intimacy of meadow and stream with the extraordinary grandeur of the peak-enclosed valley – that gives it its great appeal and has made it one of the most famous resorts in the United States. Here lies the Yosemite Valley, seven miles long and half a mile deep, a U-shaped canyon through which the Merced River has carved its steep way. The peaks that rise above the valley – all of them more than 3,000 feet above its floor – are Liberty Cap (7,072 feet), Taft Point (7,503 feet), El Capitan (7,564 feet), with precipitous northern cliffs, Profile Cliff (7,508 feet), North Dome (7,531 feet), Basket Dome (8,602 feet), Eagle Peak, (7,773 feet), Sentinel Dome (8,117 feet), Half Dome (8,852 feet), an immense split monolith with a vertical face of 2,000 feet, Clouds Rest Peak (9,929 feet), Cathedral Rocks and, close by, the Cathedral Spires. The Grand Canyon of the Tuolumne River is a mile deep in places and includes Hetch Hetchy Valley with Hetch Hetchy Dome (6,200 feet) rising above it. The tallest peaks are on or near the eastern boundary of the park, with Mount Dana (13,055 feet) and Mount Lyell (13,095 feet) the highest. The three great groves of sequoia trees – Merced, Tuolumne and Mariposa – are in the western and southern sections of the park respectively.

Yosemite is a sort of miniature Switzerland, full of hikers, campers, fishermen and naturalists in summer and skiers in winter. As in Switzerland, it is possible, if one is so inclined, to live in luxury in the midst of wild and unspoilt scenery.

Zagros

A major mountain system of Iran. Location *Southwest Iran.* Height *Rising to 14,000–15,000 feet.* Map *9, H1-2.*

The Zagros forms the western barrier to the heart of Iran, a natural fortress of high parallel ranges separated by deep, canyon-like valleys. Some of the gorges cut across the grain of the country and here the precipitous valley sides are several thousand feet high. The sheer steepness of these great clefts in the mountains – known as *tangs* – can be seen from the Trans-Iranian railway, which in its route through the Zagros follows the Diz valley. The line twists, tunnels, crosses and re-crosses, with bridges and viaducts set high above the roaring waters of the river. Southeast of this railway, in the Karun Basin, are the highest parts of the whole chain, Zardeh Kuh reaching nearly 15,000 feet. The ranges are often shaped like great whale-back ridges, sometimes narrow at their summits, sometimes rounded. A thin forest of oak and other deciduous trees covers the lower slopes. Heavy snow falls in winter and stays on the higher summits until late spring. In the center of the range extraordinary salt domes, up to 5,000 feet in height, are common.

Within the zone of rugged peaks and canyons are a number of cultivated upland plains which contrast sharply with the gauntness of the moun-

Jagged peaks in the Zagros Mountains

tains. Some of them are extensive, especially those round the towns of Kermanshah, Khurramabad and Shiraz, and it is through these that the traditional caravan routes passed. Before reaching the Iraq plain and the Persian Gulf these routes have to cross the Zagros foothills which, though relatively low compared with the main chain, are steep-sided, severely eroded and have the same northwest to southeast trend. The rich oil-bearing beds of southwest Iran are in the foothills near Dizful.

The highest and most impressive part of the

great Zagros chain is formed by the Bakhtiari Range. Its western border is usually taken as the valley of the Diz River and it extends about 150 miles southeast to include the tangled head-streams of the Karun and its tributaries. The rivers flow in rocky chasms and gorges many hundreds of feet deep, above which the mountains rise to heights of over 12,000 feet, with several summits over 14,000 feet. Although mountains and gorges predominate, gentler, more open country is occasionally found, these intermontane plains forming oases of summer grazing in the wild and inhospitable landscape.

The Zagros mountains are especially interesting to the student of ancient history. Here are found the remains of past monarchies – the palaces of Darius the Great and Xerxes at Persepolis and of Cyrus the Great at Pasargadac (both near Shiraz). At Behistun, near Kermanshah, there is a series of rock-carved inscriptions in the cuneiform script dating from the time of Darius (522–486 B.C.), first deciphered by Sir Henry Rawlinson in 1847. Behistun lies along one of the classic routes across the mountains known in ancient times as the Zagrian Gates and now followed by the main road from Baghdad to Teheran.

If the Zagros mountains have nurtured past civilizations, they have also provided secure retreats for numerous independent tribes and clans – the Kurds on the northwest borders, the Lurs west of the Diz, and the Bakhtiaris and Qashqais east of this river. Of these the Bakhtiaris are a group of tribes who have long made the region named after them their home. Their customs and method of tribal government were described as early as the fourteenth century by Ibn Battuta, the Arab geographer and traveler, who visited their strongholds in about 1330. There are two main tribal divisions, the Haft Lang and the Chehar Lang, each with a number of sections or clans. The tribal chieftains still hold an important position in the Bakhtiari social structure but their power and influence have been curtailed in recent years – especially as the hostility of some of them to the central government of Iran led to repressive measures, including the destruction of many of their forts.

The Bakhtiaris, like the other tribes, are mainly nomads but there are a number of permanent settlements owned by the ruling tribal families. Many of the tribes spend summer in the high pasturelands and move to the plains with the approach of winter. Physically the Bakhtiaris and the other tribes of the Zagros are strong and hardy, as befits a race reared in the mountains.

Gazetteer

Gazetteer

Abajo Mountains   SE Utah, in La Sal National Forest. Highest point is Abajo Peak (11,357 ft), 7 m. wsw of Monticello.

Abor Hills   Hill ranges in NE Assam, India, NW of Sadiya; rise to *c.* 15,000 ft.

Abruzzi, Mount   Peak (10,700 ft) in the Rocky Mountains, SE British Columbia, near the Alberta border, 55 m. SSE of Banff.

Absaroka Range   Range of the Rocky Mountains in s Montana and NW Wyoming. Highest point is Francs Peak (13,140 ft), *c.* 40 m. ssw of Cody, Wyoming.

Abuna Josef   Peak (*c.* 13,120 ft) in Shoa province, central Ethiopia, on the NW escarpment of the Great Rift Valley.

Acatenango   Inactive volcano (12,992 ft) in s central Guatemala, 10 m. wsw of Antigua. One of its 3 craters exudes gases.

Acay, Nevado del   Andean mountain (20,800 ft) in w central Salta province, Argentina, 20 m. SE of San Antonio de los Cobres.

Achacollo, Serranía de   w outlier of the Cordillera de Azanaques, in the Cordillera Oriental of the Andes, w Bolivia. Extends 15 m. N-s, rising to 14,500 ft.

Aconquija, Nevado del   Pampean mountain range on the Catamarca-Tucumán province border, Argentina. Extends *c.* 50 m. NNE-ssw, rising to 18,000 ft. Also called Nevado del Anconquija.

Adai-Khokh (Aday-Khokh)   Peak (15,239 ft) in main range of central Greater Caucasus, 27 m. sw of Alagir.

Adamant Mountain   (10,980 ft), SE British Columbia, in the Selkirk Mountains, 50 m. NNE of Revelstoke.

Adamello   Mountain group in the s part of the Rhaetian Alps, N Italy. Highest peaks are Monte Adamello (11,660 ft) and Monte Care Alto (11,358 ft). Contains over 50 glaciers.

Adula   Mountain group in the Lepontine Alps, SE Switzerland. Highest peaks are the Rheinwaldhorn (11,173 ft) and the Güferhorn (11,103 ft).

Aghil-Karakoram Range   N lateral range of the Karakoram mountain system, in NE Kashmir. Extends *c.* 200 m. from the China border to the headwaters of the Kara Kash River. Consists of a series of ranges connected by high tablelands. Average height 20,350 ft.

Agua   Inactive volcano (12,310 ft) in s central Guatemala, 8 m. s of Antigua.

Aguada, La   Andean volcano (*c.* 19,000 ft) in N Catamarca province, Argentina, 7 m. s of Antofalla volcano.

Agua Negra Pass   (*c.* 15,650 ft) in the Andes, on the Argentina-Chile border, on the road between Rodeo (Argentina) and Coquimbo (Chile).

Aguas Blancas, Cerro   Andean volcano (18,960 ft) on the Argentina-Chile border, 33 m. NNW of Cerro Colorados.

Aguas Calientes, Sierra de   Sub-Andean mountain range on the Catamarca-Salta province border, NW Argentina. Extends *c.* 70 m.N-s and rises to over 17,500 ft in Cerro Gordo.

Aguilar, Sierra de   Sub-Andean mountain range in N central Jujuy province, Argentina. Extends 25 m. N-s, rising to *c.* 16,000 ft.

Aguita Pass   (16,700 ft) in the Andes, on the Argentina-Chile border.

Agung, Mount (Mount Agoeng)   Highest volcanic peak (10,308 ft) in Bali, Indonesia, 30 m. ESE of Singaraja. Also called Peak of Bali.

Aiguille de Chambeyron   Peak (11,155 ft) of the Cottian Alps, SE France, near the Italian border. Glaciers.

Aiguille du Géant   Peak (13,170 ft) of the Mont Blanc massif, on the French-Italian border, 6 m. SE of Chamonix.

Ajusco, Cerro   Extinct volcano (*c.* 12,900 ft) in central Mexico, 19 m. ssw of Mexico City. Last eruption believed to have been *c.* 5,000 B.C. The peak is in the Sierra de Ajusco.

Akademiya Nauk Range   Highest branch in the central Pamir-Alai mountain system, on border of the Gorno-Badakhshan Autonomous Oblast and Garm Oblast, Tadzhik S S R.

Ak Dag   1. Peak (10,125 ft) in Antalya province, sw Turkey, in the Bey Mountains.
2. Peak (10,021 ft) in Antalya province, sw Turkey, in the Elmali Mountains.

Ala Dag   1. Range in s Turkey, easternmost and highest of the Taurus Mountains proper; extends 45 m. ssw-NNE, rising to 12,251 ft in Kaldi Dag, N of Adana.
2. Range of E Turkey, extending sw from Mount Ararat to Lake Van, rising to 11,545 ft.

Ala Dagh   One of the Turkmen-Khurasan ranges, in NE Iran. Rises to 10,000 ft in the Shah Jehan.

Alai Range (Alay Range)   One of the w ranges of the Tien Shan mountain system; extends 200 m. from upper reaches of Kara Darya on China border w to Sokh River headwaters; rises to *c.* 16,500 ft.

Alaji (Alagi)   Peak (11,279 ft) in Tigre province of N Ethiopia, at w edge of Great Rift Valley.

Alakshan (Alashan) Mountains   Range in SE Ningsia

province of China, extending parallel to Yellow River; rise to over 10,000 ft 40 m. NW of Yinchwan. Also called Holan Mountains.

Ala-Tau Generic name for several ranges of the Tien Shan system.

Albert Peak Peak (10,008 ft) in SE British Columbia, in the Selkirk Mountains, 15 m. E of Revelstoke.

Alexandra, Mount Second highest summit (16,750 ft) of the Ruwenzori, E central Africa, on the Congo-Uganda border.

Aling Kangri (Alung Gangri) Mountain range of NW Trans-Himalayas, W Tibet. Extends *c.* 480 m. WNW-ESE. Highest point Aling Kangri peak (24,000 ft), 80 m. NNE of Gartok.

Allahuekber Dag Peak (10,246 ft) in NE Turkey, 22 m. W of Kars.

Allalinhorn Peak (13,224 ft) in the Pennine Alps, s Switzerland.

Allalin Pass (11,703 ft), SW of peak of Allalinhorn.

Almagrerea, Sierra de Range in Almeria province, s Spain.

Alphubel Peak (13,809 ft) in the Mischabelhörner of the Valaisian Alps, s Switzerland.

Alphubeljoch Pass (12,418 ft) SE of peak of Alphubel.

Altar, Cerro Andean massif in central Ecuador, 15 m. E of Riobamba. Extinct volcano, with 2 snow-capped peaks, resembling an altar; highest cone rises to 17,300 ft. Also called Capac-Urcu.

Altels Peak (11,918 ft) in the Bernese Alps, s Switzerland.

Altin Dag Peak (10,836 ft) in SE Turkey, in the Hakari Mountains, 15 m. SE of Beytussebap.

Altiplano High intermontane plateau (*c.* 12,000 ft) between the Cordillera Occidental and the Cordillera Oriental of the Andes, situated largely in W Bolivia and extending N into SE Peru and s into extreme NW Argentina.

Alverstone, Mount (14,500 ft) in SW Yukon, on the Alaska border, in the St Elias Mountains.

Alwand (Alvand, ancient Orontes) Mountain (11,640 ft) in W central Iran, rising just s of Hamadan.

Amargosa Range Barren range in E California and s Nevada, forming E wall of Death Valley; extends *c.* 110 m. SSE from Grapevine peak (8,705 ft) to Amargosa River.

Ambato, Sierra de Sub-Andean range in SE Catamarca province, Argentina, extending *c.* 100 m. SSW from area of Andalgalá to the Río Colorado; rises to *c.* 11,000 ft.

Amerrique, Cordillera (Cordillera Amerrisque) Section of main continental divide in s central Nicaragua.

Amery, Mount (10,940 ft) in SW Alberta, near British Columbia border. Part of the Rocky Mountains, it is in the area of Banff National Park.

Ampato, Nudo de Andean massif (20,670 ft) in s Peru, in Cordillera Occidental, 40 m. NW of Arequipa.

Anaconda Range SW Montana, portion of the Continental Divide in the Rocky Mountains. Highest point Mt Evans (10,635 ft).

Andrew Jackson, Mount Peak (13,750 ft) in s part of Palmer Peninsula, Antarctica.

Aneto, Pico de Highest peak (11,168 ft) of the Pyrenees (central range) in the Maladetta group, NE Spain.

Animas, Cerro Andean peak (13,917 ft) in SW Colombia, in Cordillera Central, 40 m. NE of Pasto.

Ankenbälli Peak (11,838 ft) in Bernese Alps, s central Switzerland, 5 m. E of Grindelwald.

Ankogel Peak (10,705 ft) of the Hohe Tauern, s Austria, NW of Spittal.

Ansilta, Cordillera de Andean range in SW San Juan province, Argentina, 30 m. W of Tamberias: extends *c.* 35 m. N-S; rises to *c.* 19,000 ft.

Anta Dhura (Unta Dhura) Pass (*c.* 17,590 ft) in E Kumaun Himalayas, on Tibet-India border, 10 m. NNE of Milam, India. Also called Kyunam La.

Antelao Second highest peak (10,705 ft) in the Dolomites, N Italy; has small glaciers.

Antelope Range Range in central Nevada, *c.* 35 m. SW of Eureka. Highest point Sharp Peak (10,100 ft).

Antero, Mount (14,245 ft) in Sawatch Mountains, central Colorado, 15 m. NW of Salida.

Anti-Atlas Range of the Atlas Mountains, North Africa, SW of the High Atlas, to which it is linked by Djebel Siroua (10,840 ft).

Antofalla Volcano (21,100 ft), 50 m. NW of Antofagasta, Argentina.

Antuco, Cerro Andean volcano (19,000 ft) in W Salta province, Argentina, 25 m. WSW of San Antonio de los Cobres.

Api Mountain (23,399 ft) in main range of W Nepal Himalayas, NW Nepal.

Apolobamba, Nudo de Andean massif in Cordillera Oriental, on the Peru-Bolivia border, 45 m. SW of Huancané; rises to 18,924 ft in the Palomaní.

Aquarius Plateau High tableland in Wayne and Powell counties, s central Utah; most of it lies in Dixie National Forest. Rises to 11,253 ft in Blue Bell Knoll.

Aracar, Cerro Andean peak (19,950 ft) in W Salta province, Argentina, near the Chile border.

Aragats, Mount Extinct volcano (13,435 ft) in NW Armenian S S R, in the Lesser Caucasus, 30 m. NW of Erivan. Has astrophysical research center at *c.* 5,000 ft. Also called Mt Alagez.

Arapahoe Peak (Arapaho Peak) Peak (13,506 ft) in N Colorado, in Front Range, *c.* 20 m. W of Boulder; has glacier on E face.

Argapura, Mount Peak (10,131 ft) in E Java, Indonesia, just W of Bondowoso. Also spelled Argopuro, Argapoera.

Argentera, Punta (Rocca dell' Argentera) NW Italy; highest peak (10,817 ft) in Maritime Alps.

Argentière, Aiguille d' Peak (12,818 ft) 5 m. ESE of Argentière village, on Franco-Swiss border.

Argentine Mountain (10,000 ft) SE British Columbia, in

the Selkirk Mountains, on the w edge of Hamber Provincial Park.

Argentine Pass (13,132 ft) in central Colorado, in Front Range, between Clear Creek and Summit counties.

Arjuno, Mount (Mount Ardjuno, Mount Ardjoeno) Volcanic peak (9,968 ft) E Java, Indonesia; 40 m. ssw of Surabaya. Also spelled Arjuna.

Arkhon Peak (13,957 ft) in N front range of the central Greater Caucasus, 21 m. ssw of Alagir.

Arnas Dag Peak (11,645 ft) in E Turkey, in Van Mountains, 9 m. sw of Satak.

Artos Dag Peak (11,400 ft) in E Turkey, in Van Mountains, 3 m. SE of Gevas.

Asagi Dag Peak (10,730 ft) in E Turkey, 10 m. SSE of Kagizman.

Aso-san Group of 5 volcanic cones in Kumamoto prefecture, central Kyushu, Japan. Highest cone Taka-dake (c. 5,225 ft). All inactive except Naka-dake (4,340 ft). Crater floor (15 m. N-s, 10 m. E-w) is largest in the world.

Assam Himalayas E subdivision of the Himalayas, s central Asia, in the great bend of Brahmaputra River; from upper Tista River in Sikkim they extend 450 m. E through Bhutan and N Assam, along the Tibet border to the Brahmaputra near Namcha Barwa, the highest peak (24,445 ft).

Asungate, Cordillera de NW spur of Cordillera de Carabaya, in Cordillera Occidental of the Andes, SE Peru. 100 m. in length, extending from the area of Macusani NW to the Cordillera de Vilcanota; rises to 20,187 ft in the peak of Asungate.

Atacama, Puna de High Andean tableland (above 10,000 ft) on Argentina-Chile border, traversed by the Eastern Cordillera.

Atacazo, Cerro Extinct Andean volcano (14,623 ft) in Pichincha province, N central Ecuador, 12 m. sw of Quito.

Atajo, Sierra Sub-Andean range in E central Catamarca province, Argentina, 15 m. N of Andalgala. It is a sw spur of the Nevado del Aconquija; extends c. 25 m. E-w, rising to 12,000 ft. Also called Sierra Capillitas.

At-Bashi Range Range of the Tien Shan mountain system in Tyan-Shan oblast, Kirghiz S S R. Extends from Chatyr-Kul (lake) c. 100 m. NE to headwaters of At-Bashi River; rises to 15,000 ft.

Athabaska, Mount (11,452 ft) in sw Alberta, near the British Columbia border, in the Rocky Mountains, between Jasper and Banff national parks. On the edge of the Columbia Icefield and surrounded by Athabaska and Saskatchewan glaciers.

Atitlán Inactive volcano (11,565 ft) in Sololá department, sw central Guatemala, on the s shore of Lake Atitlán, 5 m. ssw of San Lucas. Was active 1524–1843.

Aucanquilcha, Cerro Andean peak (20,275 ft) in Antofagasta province, N Chile, near the Bolivia border.

Augusta, Mount (14,070 ft) on Yukon-Alaska border, in St Elias Mountains, 190 m. w of Whitehorse, on s edge of Seward Glacier.

Ayachi, Djebel Peak (12,300 ft) of the High Atlas, in central Morocco, 18 m. sw of Midelt. Seasonally snow-covered.

Ayapunga, Cerro Andean peak (15,416 ft) in s central Ecuador, 23 m. ESE of Alausí.

Aylmer, Mount (10,375 ft) in sw Alberta, near the British Columbia border, in the Rocky Mountains, in Banff National Park, 12 m. NE of Banff.

Azanaques, Cordillera de Range in the Eastern Cordillera of the Andes, w Bolivia; extends c. 90 m. s from point 30 m. ENE of Oruro to Mt Azanaque, c. 15 m. SE of Challapata. Rises to 17,060 ft at Morococala peak.

Azufre, Cerro del Andean peak (17,965 ft) on the Atacama-Antofagasta province border, N Chile.

Azufre, Paso del Pass (14,720 ft) in the Andes, on the Argentina-Chile border, on the road between Antofagasta and Taltal.

Azufre Norte, Paso del Andean pass (11,955 ft) on the Argentina-Chile border, 32 m. s of Cerro Llullaillaco. Also called Paso de la Chapetona.

Azufre Sud, Paso del Andean pass (12,018 ft) just s of Paso del Azufre Norte.

Azufre Volcano Andean volcano (18,635 ft) on Argentina-Chile border, 32 m. s of Cerro Llullaillaco. Also called Lastarria Volcano.

Baba-Dag Peak (c. 11,930 ft) in the SE Greater Caucasus, Azerbaijan S S R, 32 m. NW of Shemakha.

Badda, Mount Peak (13,560 ft) in s central Ethiopia, in Arusi province, at E edge of the Great Rift Valley, 23 m. ENE of Asselle.

Badrinath Peak (23,190 ft), 13 m. w of Badrinath (village) in the central Kumaun Himalayas.

Bagirpasa Dagi Peak (10,768 ft) in E central Turkey, in the Mercan Mountains, 12 m. E of Pulumur.

Baisun-Tau (Baysun-Tau) Range in SE Uzbek S S R, forming sw continuation of the Gissar Range, along the border of the Kashka-Darya and Surkhan-Darya oblasts; rises to 10,500 ft.

Baitak Bogdo (Baitik Bogdo, Baydag Bogdo) Mountain range on the China-Mongolia border, rising to 10,456 ft. Also called Peita Shan.

Baker, Mount (10,750 ft) in N Washington, in the Cascade Range, 30 m. E of Bellingham. Included in Mt Baker National Park.

Bakhtiari Mountains Wild mountain group in sw Iran, inhabited by nomadic Bakhtiari tribes.

Balbi, Mount Peak (10,170 ft) in the Emperor Range, N Bougainville, Solomon Islands; highest mountain of the Solomon Islands and an active volcano.

Bald Mountain Peak (13,964 ft) in Rocky Mountains, N central Colorado.

Baldy Peak 1. Peak (11,590 ft), E Arizona, in the White Mountains, 20 m. SE of McNary.

2. Peak (12,491 ft) in E Sangre de Cristo Mountains, N New Mexico, 18 m. NW of Cimarron.

3. Peak (12,623 ft) in sw Sangre de Cristo Mountains, N central New Mexico, 15 m. NE of Santa Fe.

Balfour, Mount   Peak (10,741 ft) in sw Alberta, near the British Columbia border, 50 m. NW of Banff. Part of the Rocky Mountains, and included in Banff National Park.

Balinhard, Mount   Peak (10,270 ft) in w Alberta. Part of the Rocky Mountains and included in Jasper National Park.

Ball, Mount   Peak (10,865 ft) in sw Alberta, near the British Columbia border. Part of the Rocky Mountains and included in Banff National Park.

Bam La   Pass (14,500 ft) in E Tibet, near the Yangtze, 50 m. ssw of Paan, and on the main road to Chamdo, on historic border between Tibet and China.

Bañados, Cerro de los   Andean peak (17,520 ft) on the Argentina-Chile border, 45 m. WNW of Rodeo, Argentina.

Banded Peak   Peak (12,760 ft) in San Juan Mountains, sw Colorado, near New Mexico border, 24 m. SE of Pagosa Springs.

Bara Lacha La   Mountain pass (16,000 ft) in the Punjab Himalayas, in Kangra district, NE Punjab, India. On caravan route to SE Kashmir.

Barbalo, Mount   Peak (10,807 ft) in main range of E Greater Caucasus, Georgian S S R.

Barisan Mountains   Volcanic range in Sumatra, Indonesia, extending c. 1,000 m. through almost the whole length of the island, parallel with w coast. Highest peak is Mt Kerinchi (12,467 ft).

Baroghil Pass   (12,460 ft) in E Hindu Kush, on the Afghanistan-Pakistan border. Also spelled Broghil.

Bartles, Mount   Peak (10,047 ft) in the West Tavaputs Plateau, E Utah, 23 m. ENE of Price.

Baset Dag   Peak (12,300 ft) in E Turkey, 24 m. SE of Van.

Bavarian Alps   Northeasternmost division of the Central Alps along the Austro-German border; extends c. 70 m. WSW-ENE. Highest peak Zugspitze (9,721 ft).

Bayan Kara Mountains   w spur of the Kunlun system, s central Tsinghai province, China, rising to over 15,000 ft.

Bear, Mount   Peak (14,850 ft) in s Alaska, in the St Elias Mountains, 130 m. NNW of Yakutat.

Beartooth Range   NE spur of the Absaroka Range, between Stillwater River and Clark Fork of Yellowstone River. Part in s Montana, part in NW Wyoming, its highest peak is Granite Peak (12,850 ft). The range includes parts of Custer and Shoshone national forests.

Bedel Pass   (14,016 ft) in Kokshaal-Tau section of Tien-Shan system on U S S R-China border.

Belen, Cerro de   Andean peak (17,135 ft) in N Chile, 60 m. E of Arica.

Belford, Mount   Peak (14,052 ft) in the Rocky Mountains, Chaffee county, central Colorado.

Belknap, Mount   Peak (12,139 ft) in the Tushar Mountains, sw central Utah.

Bellevue Mountain   Peak (12,350 ft) in the Rocky Mountains, Gunnison county, w central Colorado.

Belukha   Highest summit (15,157 ft) of the Altai Mountains, in the Katun Alps, s Siberia; rises in 2 peaks and gives rise to 16 glaciers.

Ben Lomond   Mountain (3,192 ft) in NW Stirling, Scotland, overlooking Loch Lomond.

Ben Macdhui   Second highest peak in Scotland (4,296 ft), in Cairngorm Mountains, sw Aberdeen, Scotland. Also spelled Ben Muich-Dhui.

Benna Beola   Mountain range, extending 10 m. E-W, in the Connemara district, NW County Galway, Ireland. Highest peak is Benbaum (2,395 ft). Also spelled Bennebeola and Bunnabeola; sometimes called the Twelve Bens or the Twelve Pins.

Bergamasque Alps   Lombardy, N Italy. s outliers of the Rhaetian Alps, extending from the Valtellina s to the Po plain at Bergamo. Highest peak Pizzo di Coca (10,013 ft).

Bertha, Mount   Peak (10,182 ft) in SE Alaska, in Fairweather Range. Part of Glacier Bay National Monument.

Berthoud Pass   (11,314 ft) in Front Range, N central Colorado, c. 40 m. w of Denver.

Bertrand, Cerro   Peak (10,730 ft) in the Patagonian Andes, on the Argentina-Chile border; westernmost point of Argentina.

Bess, Mount   Peak (10,550 ft) on the Alberta-British Columbia border, in the Rocky Mountains, at the NW edge of Jasper National Park, 65 m. WNW of Jasper.

Bey Dag   Highest peak (10,020 ft) of the Tahtali Mountains, s central Turkey.

Bey Mountains   Range in sw Turkey, extending 35 m. SSW-NNE. Rise to 10,125 ft in Ak Dag.

Biafo Glacier   Great glacier in the Karakoram, between the main range (E) and the Kailas-Karakoram Range (w). Height of snout 10,360 ft.

Bierstadt, Mount   Peak (14,048 ft) in N central Colorado, in the Front Range, 9 m. s of Georgetown.

Bieshorn   Peak (13,652 ft) in Pennine Alps, s Switzerland.

Bietschorn   Peak (12,918 ft) in the Bernese Alps, s Switzerland.

Binalud Range   One of the Turkmen-Khurasan ranges in NE Iran, rising to 10,000 ft 40 m. w of Meshed. Range is continued NW by the Ala Dagh. Persian name is Kuh-i-Binalud.

Bingol Dag   Peak (11,975 ft) in E central Turkey, 14 m. wsw of Hinis.

Birdwood, Mount   Peak (10,160 ft) on Alberta-British Columbia border, in the Rocky Mountains, near s edge of Banff National Park.

Birghorn   Peak (10,650 ft) in the Bernese Alps, s central Switzerland.

Birhan   Highest peak (13,625 ft) in the Choke Mountains, NW Ethiopia.

Bismarck Mountains Range in NE New Guinea. Highest peaks Mount Wilhelm (14,107 ft) and Mount Herbert (13,123 ft).

Bison Peak (12,427 ft) in Tarryall Mountains, central Colorado.

Bitterroot Range Part of the Rocky Mountains, extending s along the Idaho-Montana line, from the Clark Fork to Monida. Highest point is Garfield Mountain (10,961 ft). Also in the range are Trapper Peak (10,175 ft), and Ajax Mountain (10,900 ft).

Blackburn, Mount Peak (16,140 ft) in the Wrangell Mountains, s Alaska, 100 m. ENE of Valdez.

Blackhead Peak (12,500 ft) in the San Juan Mountains, Archeluta county, sw Colorado.

Black Mountain 1. Peak (10,760 ft) in the Rocky Mountains, Jackson county, N Colorado. Also known as Basaltic Peak.
2. Peak (11,656 ft) in the Rocky Mountains, Park county, central Colorado.

Black Mountain Range s spur of the w Assam Himalayas, central Bhutan. Highest point is Black Mountain (16,130 ft).

Black Range sw New Mexico, extending N-s through parts of Grant and Sierra counties. Lies largely within Gila National Forest. Highest point Reeds Peak (10,011 ft).

Blanca, Cordillera E section of the Cordillera Occidental of the Andes, in Ancash department, w central Peru. Extends 110 m. SSE from area of Sihuas to area of Chiquián and rises to 22,305 ft in Huascarán.

Blanca Peak Highest point (14,363 ft) in the Sierra Blanca of the Sangre de Cristo Mountains, sw of Old Baldy.

Blue Bell Knoll Highest peak (11,253 ft) in Aquarius Plateau, s central Utah.

Blümlisalp (Frau) Mountain in the Bernese Alps, s central Switzerland, sw of Jungfrau. Its highest peak is the Blümlisalphorn (12,032 ft); other peaks include Weisse Frau (11,992 ft), Morgenhorn (11,864 ft), Oeschinenhorn (11,448 ft), Rothorn (10,828 ft), Wilde Frau (10,705 ft) and Blümlisalpenstock (10,560 ft).

Bogart, Mount (10,315 ft), sw Alberta, near British Columbia border, near SE edge of Banff National Park.

Bogos Range N spur of the E Greater Caucasus in w Dagestan; extends 35 m. and rises to 13,570 ft.

Bolkar Mountains s Turkey, part of the Taurus Mountains, extending c. 70 m. WSW-ENE. Highest peak is Medetsiz Dag (11,762 ft).

Bona, Mount (16,420 ft) in s Alaska, in the St Elias Mountains, 150 m. ENE of Cordova.

Bonnet Mountain (10,615 ft) in sw Alberta, near the British Columbia border. Part of the Rocky Mountains and included in Banff National Park.

Bonney, Mount (10,194 ft) in SE British Columbia, in the Selkirk Mountains. Included in Glacier National Park.

Borokhoro Range Branch of the Tien Shan, NW Sinkiang province, China. Forms right-bank divide of upper Ili River. Rises to 10,000 ft.

Bou Iblane, Djebel Peak (10,466 ft) of the Middle Atlas, N central Morocco.

Bou Naceur, Djebel Highest peak (10,794 ft) of the Middle Atlas, N central Morocco.

Boundary Peak 1. Mountain (12,800 ft) in the Sangre de Cristo Mountains, Costillo county, s Colorado.
2. Mountain (13,145 ft) in sw Nevada, in N White Mountains, near California border. Highest point in Nevada.

Brahui Range, Central Range in N central Baluchistan, w Pakistan, extending from the s bend of the Mula River in a N direction to just N of Quetta and thence SE, enclosing N end of the Kachhi plain, to central Sibi district. It is c. 240 m. long and 60 m. wide. Generally above 6,000 ft, rises to c. 11,740 ft in peak E of Quetta; Khalifat Mountain (11,434 ft) and Takatu Mountain (11,340 ft) are in the N section.

Bravard Andean peak (18,865 ft) in w Mendoza province, Argentina, near Chile border. Tupungatito peak (18,500 ft), just NW, is sometimes called Bravard.

Brazeau, Mount (11,386 ft) in w Alberta, in the Rocky Mountains, and included in Jasper National Park. Near British Columbia border.

Brea, Cordón de la Andean range in w La Rioja province, Argentina, near the Chile border. Extends c. 40 m. NNE-SSW and rises to over 14,000 ft.

Brecon Beacons (Brecknock Beacons) Range in central Brecknock, Wales, at E end of Black Mountain. Extends 2 m. E-w and includes peaks of Corn Du (2,863 ft) and Pen-y Fan (2,906 ft).

Breithorn 1. Peak (12,419 ft) in the Bernese Alps, s central Switzerland, 6 m. s of Mürren.
2. Peak (Lötschentaler Breithorn) (12,428 ft) in Bernese Alps, s central Switzerland, 9 m. s of Visp.
3. Peak (13,684 ft) in the Pennine Alps, on the Swiss-Italian border s of Zermatt, between the Matterhorn and Monte Rosa.

Brewer, Mount Peak (13,577 ft) of the Sierra Nevada, E California, in Kings Canyon National Park.

Brian Head Peak (11,315 ft) on w rim of Markagunt Plateau, sw Utah, 13 m. E of Cedar City.

Bridger Peak (11,007 ft) in the Sierra Madre, s Wyoming.

Bristenstock Peak (10,091 ft) in the Glarus Alps, central Switzerland, 8 m. WNW of Disentis.

Broad Peak Peak (26,400 ft) in the main range of the Karakoram mountain system, N Kashmir.

Brocken Highest peak (3,747 ft) of the Harz Mountains, central Germany.

Brooks, Mount (11,910 ft) in s central Alaska, in the Alaska Range and included in Mount McKinley National Park.

Bross, Mount (14,169 ft) in central Colorado, in the Park Range, 12 m. NE of Leadville.

Bruin Peak (10,285 ft) in West Tavaputs Plateau, E Utah.

Bryce, Mount (11,507 ft) in SE British Columbia, near the Alberta border. Part of the Rocky Mountains, and included in Hamber Provincial Park.

Buey, Páramo del Andean massif (13,780 ft) in SW Colombia; part of Cordillera Central.

Buffalo Peaks (13,541 ft) in Rocky Mountains, on Chaffee and Park border, central Colorado.

Bum La Pass (14,210 ft) in central Assam Himalayas, on undefined India-Tibet border, 12 m. NNE of Towang (India).

Burji La Pass (16,830 ft) in Deosai Mountains, W central Kashmir, 9 m. SW of Skardu.

Burzil Pass (13,775 ft) in main range of W Punjab Himalayas, W Kashmir, on main Srinagar-Gilgit road.

Büttlassen Peak (10,483 ft) in Bernese Alps, S central Switzerland.

Buz Dag Peak in S central Turkey, 25 m. SSW of Malatya. Height is given as either 9,191 ft or 11,850 ft.

Cachi, Sierra Nevado de Andean range in W Salta province, Argentina; extends *c.* 25 m. N-S and rises to over 21,000 ft.

Cajón, Sierra del (Sierra de Quilmes) Sub-Andean range on Catamarca-Tucumán-Salta province border, Argentina. 50 m. in extent, the range rises to over 16,000 ft.

Cakirgol Dag Peak (10,049 ft) in NE Turkey, in the Trebizond Mountains, 31 m. S of Trebizond.

Calalaste, Sierra de Sub-Andean range of the Puna de Atacama, in Catamarca and Salta provinces, Argentina. Extends *c.* 120 m. between Cerro Negro Muerto (S) and Salar Pocitos (N). Rises to 17,850 ft at the Cerro Calalaste, 25 m. NW of Antofagasta.

Calchaquíes, Cumbres Mountain range in NW Tucumán province, Argentina, extending 40 m. N to Salta province border; rises to *c.* 10,000 ft.

Callaqui Volcano (Callaquén Volcano) Andean peak (10,135 ft) in Bío-Bío province, S central Chile, near Argentina border, 60 m. SE of Los Angeles.

Cameron, Mount Peak (14,233 ft) in Park Range, central Colorado.

Cameron Cone Peak (10,705 ft) in the Rocky Mountains, El Paso county, central Colorado.

Cameron Pass Highway pass (10,285 ft) in S tip of Medicine Bow Mountains, N Colorado.

Campanario, Cerro de Andean peak (13,190 ft) on Argentina-Chile border, 55 m. SW of Malargüe (Argentina). At N foot is a pass (*c.* 10,000 ft).

Campo Tencia Peak (10,090 ft) in the Lepontine Alps, S Switzerland.

Canby Mountain Peak (13,466 ft) in the San Juan Mountains, San Juan county, SW Colorado.

Capitan Mountains S central New Mexico, NE spur of the Sacramento Mountains, in Lincoln county. Highest point is 10,205 ft; also in the range is Capitan peak (10,083 ft). Lies within part of Lincoln National Forest.

Carabaya, Cordillera de SE section of the Cordillera Oriental of the Andes, in Cuzco and Puno departments, SE Peru. A continuation of the Nudo de Apolobamba, it extends *c.* 190 m. NW, rising to 19,193 ft at Nudo de Quenamari.

Carbon, Mount (14,259 ft) in W central Colorado, highest point in the Elk Mountains, 12 m. NNE of Crested Butte. Also known as Castle Peak.

Carihuairazo, Cerro Extinct Andean volcano, Tungurahua province, central Ecuador, just NE of the Chimborazo. Has 4 peaks, the highest rising to 16,496 ft.

Carnes Mountain (10,000 ft) in the Selkirk Mountains, SE British Columbia, E of Glacier Park.

Carstensz, Mount Highest peak (*c.* 16,400 ft) of New Guinea. Situated in the Nassau Range, W central New Guinea, it is the highest island peak in the world.

Castle Peak 1. (10,514 ft) in S Alaska, in the Wrangell Mountains, 100 m. ENE of Valdez.
2. Peak (11,820 ft) in the Sawtooth Mountains, S central Idaho.

Catacombs Mountain (10,800 ft) in W Alberta, near the British Columbia border. Part of the Rocky Mountains, it is included in Jasper National Park.

Cathedral Peak Mountain (10,933 ft) of the Sierra Nevada, in E California, in Yosemite National Park.

Catherine, Mount Peak (10,082 ft) in Pavant Mountains, central Utah.

Cathkin Peak (Cathkin's Peak) (10,438 ft) in the Drakensberg, W Natal, South Africa, on Basutoland border.

Celaque, Sierra de Section of the main Andean divide in W Honduras. Rises to 10,000 ft, and forms divide between Mocal River (E) and Alash River (W).

Celo Dag Peak (10,660 ft) in SE Turkey, in Hakari Mountains.

Ceniza, Pico Peak (17,989 ft) in Aragua state, N Venezuela, in coastal range; the highest elevation of the state.

Cerro Vista Peak (11,947 ft), N New Mexico, in the Sangre de Cristo Mountains.

Cevedale, Monte Glacier-topped peak (12,350 ft) in center of Ortles group, N Italy.

Chaba Peak (10,540 ft) on the Alberta-British Columbia border. Part of the Rocky Mountains, and in the Columbia Icefield.

Chacaltaya Peak (15,224 ft) in the Cordillera de la Paz, W Bolivia, 15 m. NNE of La Paz.

Chachacomani Peak (20,528 ft) in the Cordillera de la Paz, W Bolivia, 22 m. SE of Sorata.

Chachani, Nevado de Volcanic massif (19,960 ft), Arequipa department, S Peru. Has meteorological station.

Chalcedony Buttes Peak (10,400 ft) in Rocky Mountains, Park county, central Colorado.

Champagne Castle Mountain (11,075 ft) in the Drakensberg, w Natal, on the Basutoland border.

Chang Chenmo Range SE extension of the Kailas-Karakoram Range, E Kashmir and w Tibet; extends c. 120 m. W-E and rises to 22,120 ft in N.

Changoreal, Sierra Sub-Andean range in E central Catamarca province, Argentina, 40 m. NNE of Belén. Extends 30 m. SSW-NNE and rises to c. 15,000 ft.

Chang Tang Vast arid plateau with numerous salt lakes, covering most of N Tibet; c. 700 m. long (E-W), c. 300 m. wide; average altitude is 16,000 ft.

Chañí Sub-Andean range on Salta-Jujuy province border, Argentina; rises to c. 20,000 ft.

Chapman, Mount (10,150 ft) in SE British Columbia, in the Selkirk Mountains, 65 m. N of Revelstoke.

Charemai, Mount (Mount Tjareme) Peak (10,098 ft) in w Java, Indonesia, 16 m. sw of Cheribon. Also called Peak of Cheribon.

Chatkal Range Branch of NW Tien Shan mountain system, in NW Kirghiz S S R and along Kazakh-Uzbek border. Extends 125 m. sw from the Talas Ala-Tau to plain near Tashkent; rises to 13,385 ft.

Chaur Peak (11,966 ft) in NW Kumaun Himalayas, in s Himachal Pradesh, India, 23 m. SE of Simla.

Chephren, Mount (10,715 ft) sw Alberta, near the British Columbia border, in the Rocky Mountains and included in Banff National Park.

Cherangani Hills Section of w rim of Great Rift Valley, in w Kenya, E of Kitale; rise to over 11,000 ft.

Cherski Range (Cherskiy Range) Arc-shaped mountain system of NE Siberian Russia, extending from Indigirka-Yana river divide SE to Kolyma River. 625 m. long and 90–125 m. wide; highest peak is Chen Peak (10,215 ft) in s section.

Cheviot Hills Range extending 35 m. NE-sw on Scotland-England border. Highest point is The Cheviot (2,676 ft), 6 m. sw of Wooler, in England.

Chichas, Cordillera de Section of the Eastern Cordillera of the Andes, sw Bolivia; extends c. 100 m. SSE from SE of Rio Mulato to Portugalete. Rises to 18,422 ft at Mt Chorolque.

Chichoy Pass s central Guatemala, in central highlands, on branch of Inter-American Highway. Alt. c. 10,000 ft. Offers panoramic view of volcanoes Agua and Fuego.

Chicoma Peak Highest point (11,950 ft) in Valle Grande Mountains, N New Mexico, 34 m. NW of Santa Fe.

Chilai La Pass (c. 12,000 ft) in w Assam Himalayas, w Bhutan, on main Ha-Paro road. Chilai La peak (13,475 ft) is 1 m. NW.

Chilca, Cordillera de Snow-capped Andean range, Arequipa department, s Peru, 75 m. N of Arequipa. Forms a semicircle about 40 m. long, reaching to Cuzco department border. Rises to c. 20,000 ft.

Chiles, Nevado de Andean peak (15,577 ft) on Ecuador-Columbia border. Extinct volcano.

Chillán, Nevados de Andean range in Nuble province, s central Chile. Extends c. 20 m. SE to the Argentina border and rises to 10,370 ft. Among its peaks are active volcanoes and at its w foot are the famed sulphur baths Baños de Chillán.

Chin Hills Mountain ranges of Upper Burma, on Assam border, between Manipur Hills (N) and the Arakan Yoma (s); rise to 10,018 ft in Mount Victoria. Consist of series of parallel ranges broken by deep gorges.

Chiriquí Inactive volcano and highest peak (11,410 ft) of Panama, near Costa Rica border, just s of continental divide. Also called Barú.

Choke Mountains NW Ethiopia, in Gojjam province, in a great bend of the Blue Nile. Chief peaks Birhan (13,625 ft) and Tala (c. 13,450 ft).

Chorolque, Mount Ir Cordillera de Chichas, sw Bolivia; rises to 18,422 ft.

Chown, Mount (10,930 ft) in w Alberta, near the British Columbia border. Part of Rocky Mountains, and included in Jasper National Park.

Chugach Mountains Part of the Coast Ranges of s Alaska. Extend 300 m. E-w in crescent between Turnagain Arm and Cape Yakataga; they are a w continuation of the St Elias Mountains. Highest peak is Mount Marcus Baker (13,250 ft).

Chuquiananta, Nevado Andean peak (18,005 ft) in N Chile, near Bolivia border.

Churchill Peak (10,500 ft) in N British Columbia, in the Rocky Mountains.

Chuya Alps One of highest ranges of Altai Mountains, in sw Siberian Russia; rises to 13,000 ft at peaks Irbistu, Iiktu and Dzhan-Iiktu.

Cilo Dag Peak (13,675 ft) in SE Turkey, in Hakari Mountains, 16 m. ESE of Hakari. Sometimes called Resko Dag.

Cima di Cantone Peak (11,010 ft) in the Alps, SE Switzerland.

Cime de l'Est Second highest peak (10,433 ft) of the Dent du Midi. Sometimes called Dent Noire.

Cinnamon Mountain (13,300 ft) in sw Colorado, peak of the San Juan Mountains.

Cinnamon Pass (12,300 ft) near Cinnamon Mountain, 11 m. NE of Silverton.

Circleville Mountain (11,276 ft) 7 m. WNW of Circleville, Jackson county, NE Kansas, in the Tushar Mountains.

Citará, Farallones de (Farallones de Chocó) Andean range on Chocó-Antioquia department border, w Colombia border, in Cordillera Occidental; 28 m. long N-s, rising to 13,290 ft.

Cithaeron Mountain on Attica-Boeotia border, E central Greece; rises to 4,623 ft. Sacred to Dionysus.

Civetta Mountain (10,558 ft) in the Dolomites, N Italy.

Clan Alpine Mountains w central Nevada, in Churchill county, E of Humboldt Sink. Highest peak is Mount Grant (11,247 ft).

Claridenstock Peak (10,728 ft) in the Glarus Alps, central Switzerland.

Claudio Gay, Cordillera w parallel spur of the Andes in Atacama province, N Chile. Extends 45 m. N-S near Argentina border and rises to over 18,000 ft.

Cline, Mount (11,027 ft) in sw Alberta, in the Rocky Mountains, near the edge of Banff National Park.

Cloud Peak Highest point (13,165 ft) in the Bighorn Mountains, in N Wyoming, 30 m. SSW of Sheridan. Has large glacier.

Coast Mountains Range extending c. 1,000 m. in w British Columbia and s Alaska, reaching from the Yukon border to the Fraser River. Parallel to the Pacific coast. Highest peak is Mount Waddington (13,260 ft); other high peaks are Mount Tiedemann (12,000 ft), Monarch Mountain (11,714 ft), Mount Munday (11,000 ft), Mount Queen Bess (10,700 ft), Mount Goodhope (10,670 ft), Razorback (10,667 ft), Mount Ratz (10,290 ft), Mount Grenville (10,200 ft) and Mount Gilbert (10,200 ft).

Coca, Pizzo di Highest peak (10,013 ft) in Bergamasque Alps, Lombardy, N Italy. Has small glaciers.

Cochabamba, Cordillera de E branch of the Eastern Cordillera of the Andes, in Cochabamba department, central Bolivia. Extends c. 160 m. in an arc. Rises to 17,060 ft in Tunari peak.

Cochetopa Pass (10,032 ft) in Continental Divide, sw central Colorado.

Cochinoca, Sierra de Sub-Andean mountain range in NW Jujuy province, Argentina; extends c. 45 m. NW-SE and rises to c. 14,000 ft.

Coipasa Peak (16,080 ft), rises on island in Lake Coipasa, w of Coipasa salt flat, in Oruro department, w Bolivia.

Colangüil, Cordón de Andean range in w San Juan province, Argentina, NW of Rodeo. Extends c. 40 m. NNE-SSW and rises to 17,160 ft in Cerro Colangüil.

Coleman, Mount (10,262 ft) in sw Alberta, in Rocky Mountains, near the NE edge of Banff National Park.

Colima, Nevado de Inactive volcano (14,240 ft) in Jalisco, w Mexico, near the Colima border. Just s is the Volcán de Colima, a smoking volcanic peak (estimated at 12,631 or 12,750 ft).

Cololo Peak (19,406 ft) in Cordillera de la Paz, w Bolivia.

Colorados, Cerro Andean volcano (19,846 ft) on Argentina-Chile border. Sometimes called Cerro Ceros Colorados.

Columna, La Andean peak (16,411 ft) in Mérida state, w Venezuela, highest peak of the Sierra Nevada de Mérida. Bolívar is the name commonly given to the highest of La Columna's twin peaks.

Combin de Corbassière Peak (12,200 ft) in the Pennine Alps, sw Switzerland.

Come Caballos, Cerro Andean peak (16,995 ft) on the Argentina-Chile border.

Concha, La Andean peak (16,148 ft) in Mérida state, w Venezuela, N of La Columna peak.

Conconta, Cordón de Andean range in w San Juan province, Argentina, w of Rodeo. Rises to 17,437 ft.

Cóndor, Cordillera del E Andean range on Peru-Ecuador border, 60 m. SE of Cuenca; extends c. 160 m., rising to 10,640 ft in the Cerro Tres Cruces.

Condoriri Peak (21,998 ft) in the Cordillera de la Paz, Bolivia.

Conejos Peak (13,180 ft) in the San Juan Mountains, s Colorado.

Constantine, Mount (10,290 ft), sw Yukon, near Alaska border, in St Elias Mountains.

Cook, Mount (13,760 ft) on Yukon-Alaska border, in St Elias Mountains.

Cooper Mountain (10,100 ft) in SE British Columbia, in the Selkirk Mountains, 50 m. N of Nelson.

Coppercrown Mountain (10,218 ft) in SE British Columbia, in the Selkirk Mountains, 70 m. NE of Nelson.

Corazón, Cerro Andean volcano (15,718 ft) in Pinchincha province, N central Ecuador; snow-capped twin peak, with crater lake containing sulphurous water.

Corona, La Andean peak in Mérida state, w Venezuela, in Sierra Nevada de Mérida, N of La Columna peak. Consists of 2 peaks, Humboldt (16,214 ft), a name sometimes given to the entire massif, and Bompland (16,040 ft).

Coropuna, Nudo Snow-capped Andean massif, Arequipa department, s Peru, in Cordillera Occidental. Has several peaks, of which the highest rises to 21,696 ft.

Corral Peak (11,333 ft) in Rocky Mountains, Grand county, N Colorado.

Coruh Mountains NE Turkey, extending 110 m. NE from Bayburt, and rising to 11,033 ft in Deve Dag.

Costilla Peak (12,634 ft) in N New Mexico, in Sangre de Cristo Mountains, near Colorado border.

Cotacachi, Cerro Extinct Andean volcano (16,292 ft) in Imbabura province, N Ecuador. Has several craters and crater lakes.

Craig, Mount (13,250 ft) in sw Yukon, near Alaska border, in St Elias Mountains.

Crazy Mountains Range of the Rocky Mountains, in s central Montana; extends c. 30 m. s towards Yellowstone River. Highest point is Crazy Peak (11,214 ft).

Crested Butte Peak (12,172 ft) of the Rocky Mountains, just NE of Crested Butte town, w central Colorado.

Cristallo, Monte Glacier-topped mountain (10,551 ft) in the Dolomites, N Italy, 4 m. NE of Cortina d'Ampezzo.

Crocker Mountains N Borneo, near w coast. Extend c. 40 m. from Marudu Bay, and rise to 13,455 ft in Mount Kinabalu, the highest peak of the island.

Croda Rossa Peak (10,298 ft) in the Dolomites, N Italy, 7 m. N of Cortina d'Ampezzo.

Cub Mountain Peak (10,623 ft) in Front Range, Jefferson county, N central Colorado.

Cuchumatanes Mountains Huehuetenango and Quiché departments, w Guatemala; extend c. 100 m. NW-SE and rise to c. 10,000 ft.

Culebra Peak (14,069 ft), s Colorado, in Culebra Range of Sangre de Cristo Mountains.

Cumbal, Nevado de Extinct Andean volcano (15,630 ft) in Nariño department, sw Colombia, near Ecuador border.

Curutú, Cerro Peak (17,700 ft) in the Andes, on Argentina-Chile border, 50 m. NW of Susques.

Dahr el Qadib (Dahr eq Qadib or Zahr al-Qadib) Mountain (*c.* 10,000 ft) in the Lebanon range, N Lebanon, 40 m. NE of Beirut. At its foot are remains of the Cedars of Lebanon.

Dais Mountain (10,612 ft), sw Alberta, near British Columbia border. Part of the Rocky Mountains, and included in Jasper National Park.

Daly, Mount Peak (13,193 ft) in Rocky Mountains, Pitkin county, w central Colorado.

Damas, Paso de las Andean pass (10,000 ft) on Argentina-Chile border, on road between San Rafael (Argentina) and San Fernando (Chile).

Dampier, Mount Peak (11,287 ft) in Tasman National Park, Southern Alps, w central South Island, New Zealand.

Dana, Mount Peak (13,055 ft) of the Sierra Nevada, E California, on E boundary of Yosemite National Park.

Darkot Pass (15,380 ft) in range of E Hindu Kush, on border between Kashmir and North-West Frontier Province (Pakistan). Lies on route between Gilgit and Chitral.

Darvaza Range Branch of Pamir-Alai mountain system, extending from Stalin Peak *c.* 110 m. between Obi-Khingou and Panj rivers; rises to *c.* 18,000 ft and includes many glaciers.

Dawson, Mount (11,123 ft) in Selkirk Mountains, SE British Columbia, in Glacier National Park.

Deborah, Mount Peak (12,540 ft) in the Alaska Range, E Alaska, 90 m. SSE of Fairbanks.

Deep Creek Mountains Extend from w Utah to E Nevada, sw of the Great Salt Lake Desert. Highest point is Haystack Peak (12,101 ft).

De La Beche, Mount (10,058 ft) in Southern Alps, w central South Island, New Zealand.

Delano Peak Highest point (12,173 ft) of the Tushar Mountains, sw central Utah, 32 m. ssw of Richfield.

Del Norte Peak (12,378 ft) in San Juan Mountains, sw Colorado, 13 m. wsw of Del Norte.

Democrat, Mount Peak (14,142 ft) in Park Range, central Colorado.

Dempo Mount Active volcanic peak (10,634 ft) in Barisan Mountains, sw Sumatra, Indonesia.

Dents de Veisivi 2 peaks in the Alps, s Switzerland, 9 m. NW of the Matterhorn: Grande Dent de Veisivi (11,214 ft) and Petite Dent de Veisivi (10,445 ft).

Deosai Mountains N lateral range of Punjab Himalayas, w central Kashmir; extends *c.* 120 m. SE from Indus River bend N of Bunji to Suru River. Several peaks rise to over 18,000 ft.

Descabezada Grande, Cerro Andean peak (12,565 ft) in Talca province, central Chile, near Argentina border, 50 m. ESE of Talca. Cerro Descabezado Chico (10,660 ft) is just NE.

Deseret Peak (11,031 ft) in Stansbury Mountains, NW Utah, 19 m. wsw of Tooele.

Deve Dag Peak (11,033 ft) in Coruh Mountains, NE Turkey.

Diablerets Mountain in Bernese Alps, sw Switzerland; its highest peak is Le Diableret (10,650 ft), also known as Le Dôme.

Diamond Mountains Central Nevada, NE of Eureka. Highest point is Diamond Peak (10,626 ft), 9 m. NE of Eureka.

Dikte, Mount Highest peak (7,048 ft) of Crete. Famous in Greek mythology. Also spelled Mount Dhikti.

Dinar, Kuh-i- Mountain (*c.* 14,000 ft) in Zagros ranges, s Iran, 100 m. NW of Shiraz.

Diphu Pass Northernmost crossing (14,280 ft) on Burma-India border, at Tibet line, 55 m. NE of Putao.

Disgrazia, Monte Peak (12,067 ft) in Rhaetian Alps, N Italy, near Swiss border, near Bernina Alps. Has several glaciers.

Dodici, Cima Peak (10,151 ft) in the Alps, on Bolzano-Belluno province border, 12 m. NE of Cortina d'Ampezzo.

Doldenhorn Peak (11,966 ft) in Bernese Alps, s central Switzerland.

Dolent, Mont Alpine peak (12,342 ft) of Mont Blanc massif, 8 m. E of Chamonix. From it descends Argentière glacier.

Dom Highest peak (14,923 ft) of the Mischabelhörner and third highest of the Alps, s Switzerland, 7 m. NNE of Zermatt.

Domeyko, Cordillera de w spur of the Andes, in N Chile. Extends *c.* 230 m. NNE-ssw and rises to over 16,000 ft.

Domjoch Pass (14,056 ft) s of Dom (peak), s Switzerland.

Domuyo, Cerro Andean volcano (*c.* 15,500 ft), NW Neuquén national territory, Argentina. Several geysers on slopes.

Doña Ana, Cerro Andean peak (18,670 ft) on Coquimbo-Atacama province border, N central Chile.

Doña Rosa, Cordillera de Andean range in Coquimbo province, N central Chile; extends *c.* 20 m. wsw from Argentina border and rises to over 15,000 ft.

Donga La Pass (12,500 ft) in central Assam Himalayas, E Bhutan, 37 m. E of Byakar. Sometimes called Drongkhya La.

Dongkya Range s spur of w Assam Himalayas along Sikkim-Tibet border; extends *c.* 40 m. N-s. Highest point Pauhunri or Pawohumri peak (23,385 ft), 18 m. NNE of Lachung.

Dorah Pass Mountain pass (*c.* 14,900 ft) in the Hindu Kush, on Afghanistan-Pakistan frontier, 35 m. NW of Chitral. Closed winter and spring.

Dos Conos Volcano (19,350 ft) in Catamarca province, NW Argentina, in the Puna de Atacama.

Dos Hermanas, Cerro Andean volcano (18,175 ft) on Argentina-Chile border, 55 m. sw of Cerro Incahuasi.

Doubletop Peak (11,715 ft) in w Wyoming, 26 m. ESE of Jackson; highest point in Gros Ventre Range.

Dreiherrnspitze Peak (11,499 ft) on Austro-Italian border at w end of the Hohe Tauern.

Dreiländerspitze Peak (c. 10,500 ft) in Silvretta Group of Rhaetian Alps, on Swiss-Austrian border; on Austrian border it forms Tyrol-Vorarlberg boundary.

Drum, Mount (12,002 ft) in Wrangell Mountains, E Alaska, 85 m. NE of Valdez.

Dufourspitze Highest peak (15,203 ft) of Monte Rosa group and of Pennine Alps, on Italo-Swiss border, 28 m. ssw of Brig. Also second highest Alpine peak.

Durika Peak (12,726 ft) in the Cordillera de Talamanca, SE Costa Rica, 13 m. NNE of Buenos Aires.

Dykh-Tau Peak (17,054 ft) in front range of central Greater Caucasus, on Russian-Georgian border.

Dyulty-Dag (Dyul'ty-Dag) N outlier of the E Greater Caucasus, in Dagestan Autonomous SSR and Russian SFSR, rising to c. 13,500 ft in Taklik peak, 20 m. wsw of Kuli.

Dzhanga Peak (16,568 ft) in main range of central Greater Caucasus, on Russian-Georgian border.

Dzhumgol-Tau Range in N Tyan-Shan oblast, Kirghiz SSR, to the N of Dzhumgol River. Rises to c. 13,000 ft.

Dzungarian Ala-Tau Northernmost branch of Tien Shan mountain system, on USSR-China border, separated from main Tien Shan range by Ili River. Extends from Dzungarian Gates 250 m. sw to Ili river bend and rises to 16,550 ft.

Eagle Peak Mountain (11,825 ft) in Mono county, E California, in the Sierra Nevada.

East Humboldt Range NE Nevada, in Elko county, E of Elko. Rises to 11,276 ft; lies within Humboldt National Forest.

Edith Cavell, Mount (11,033 ft) in w Alberta, near British Columbia border, in Rocky Mountains, in Jasper National Park, 15 m. s of Jasper.

Egan Range (6,000–10,000 ft) in White Pine county, E Nevada, just w of Ely. Extends c. 100 m. s from Cherry Creek Mountains.

Elbert, Mount Peak (14,431 ft) in the Sawatch Mountains, central Colorado. Highest peak in the U.S. Rocky Mountains.

El Diente Peak (14,200 ft) in the Rocky Mountains, Dolores county, sw Colorado.

Electric Peak Highest point (11,155 ft) in Gallatin Range, sw Montana, in NW part of Yellowstone National Park.

Elie de Beaumont Mountain (10,200 ft) in the Southern Alps, w central South Island, New Zealand.

Elk Mountain Outlying peak (11,162 ft) in NNW tip of Medicine Bow Mountains, s Wyoming.

Elk Mountains Range of Rocky Mountains in Pitkin and Gunnison counties, w central Colorado, just w of Sawatch Mountains. Chief peaks are Sopris Peak (12,823 ft), Pyramid Peak (14,000 ft), Snowmass Peak (14,077 ft), Capitol Peak (14,126 ft) and Mt Carbon (14,259 ft), the highest point of the range. sw extension, called West Elk Mountains, rises to 12,714 ft in Mt Gunnison.

Ellen, Mount Highest peak (11,485 ft) in Henry Mountains, s Utah, c. 50 m. NE of Escalante.

Elmali Mountains sw Turkey, extending 55 m. ssw from Lake Sogut and rising to 10,021 ft.

Emi Koussi Extinct volcano (11,204 ft) in Tibesti Massif. Crater is 12 m. wide and c. 4,000 ft deep.

Engineer Mountain Peak (13,190 ft) in San Juan Mountains, sw Colorado.

Enkwolo, Mount Peak (c. 14,240 ft) in Ethiopia, E of Lake Shala, at E edge of Great Rift Valley.

Eolus, Mount (14,079 ft) in San Juan Mountains, sw Colorado, 12 m. sse of Silverton.

Erasmus, Mount (10,700 ft) in sw Alberta, near British Columbia border. Part of the Rocky Mountains and included in Banff National Park.

Erciyas Dagi Peak (12,848 ft) in central Turkey, in an offshoot of the Taurus Mountains, 12 m. s of Kayseri.

Erebus, Mount (10,234 ft) in w Alberta, near British Columbia border. Part of the Rocky Mountains, and included in Jasper National Park.

Erimanthos (Erymanthos) Mountain massif in NW Peloponnesus, Greece, on border of Achaea and Elis, rising to 7,294 ft; haunt of the boar killed by Hercules.

Erzincan Mountains E central Turkey; extend 60 m. wsw-ene just N of and parallel to the Euphrates River. Rise to 11,604 ft in Kesis Dag.

Evans, Mount 1. (10,460 ft) in w Alberta, near British Columbia border. Part of the Rocky Mountains, and included in Jasper National Park.

2. Peak (14,260 ft) in Front Range, N central Colorado, 35 m. wsw of Denver. High Altitude Laboratory at summit.

Eveque, L' Peak (12,203 ft) in the Alps, s Switzerland, 12 m. wsw of Zermatt.

Excelsior Mountain Peak (12,440 ft) of the Sierra Nevada, E California, 8 m. w of Mono Lake.

Fairweather, Mount Highest peak (15,300 ft) of the Fairweather Range, on border between SE Alaska and British Columbia, 17 m. NE of Cape Fairweather.

Fairweather Range s mountain group of St Elias Mountains, SE Alaska, paralleling Gulf of Alaska for c. 35 m. Highest peak Mt Fairweather (15,300 ft).

Famatina, Sierra de Sub-Andean mountain range in N central La Rioja province, Argentina, NW of Famatina; extends 45 m. N-s from Catamarca province border and rises to 20,500 ft in the Cumbre de la Mejicana.

Farnham, Mount   (11,342 ft) in Selkirk Mountains, SE British Columbia, 65 m. SW of Banff.

Fedchenko Glacier   One of the longest mountain glaciers of the world, in Pamir-Alai mountain system; flows c. 50 m. N. Site of meteorological observation post (alt. 14,800 ft).

Fergana Range   Branch of the Tien Shan mountain system; extends from China border c. 125 m. NW to Naryan River, rising to 15,860 ft.

Fiambalá, Sierra de   Sub-Andean range in Catamarca province, Argentina, SE of Fiambalá; extends c. 60 m. NNE-SSW, rising to c. 13,000 ft.

Fierro-urcu   Andean peak (12,428 ft) in El Oro province, S Ecuador, 14 m. E of Zaruna.

Fiescherhörner   2 groups of Alpine peaks, S central Switzerland: 1. Grindelwalder Fiescherhörner, culminating in the Gross Fiescherhorn (13,294 ft), 5 m. S of Grindelwald.
2. Walliser Fiescherhörner, culminating in the Gross Wannehorn (12,825 ft), 9 m. S of Grindelwald.

Findlay, Mount   (10,780 ft), SE British Columbia, in Selkirk Mountains, 55 m. NE of Nelson.

Finisterre Range   NE New Guinea, SE of Astrolabe Bay, extending into Huon Peninsula. Highest peaks Mt Sarawaket (13,454 ft), Mt Gladstone (11,400 ft) and Mt Disraeli (11,000 ft).

Fisher Peak   (10,015 ft), SW Alberta, near British Columbia border, in Rocky Mountains, 35 m. SE of Banff.

Fitz Roy, Cerro   Patagonian peak (11,073 ft) in the Andes, on Argentina-Chile border, 10 m. NW of Lake Viedma. Also called Chaltel.

Fletschhorn   Peak (13,121 ft) in Lepontine Alps, S Switzerland, 9 m. S of Brig.

Flint Creek Range   In Rocky Mountains of W Montana; extends c. 25 m. S from just S of the Clark Fork towards Anaconda, rising to 10,400 ft.

Fluchthorn   Peak (11,165 ft) in Silvretta Group of Rhaetian Alps, on Swiss-Austrian border, 7 m. NNW of Schuls.

Fluchtkogel   Peak (11,526 ft) in Ötztal Alps of Tyrol, W Austria, SW of the Wildspitze.

Foraker, Mount   (17,280 ft), S central Alaska, in Alaska Range. Included in Mt McKinley National Park.

Forbes, Mount   (11,902 ft), SW Alberta, near British Columbia border, in Rocky Mountains. Included in Banff National Park.

Forel, Mount   (11,023 ft), SE Greenland, near coast and at edge of inland icecap. Glacier de France extends 40 m. SE to the sea.

Foster Peak   (10,511 ft), SE British Columbia, in Rocky Mountains, on W edge of Kootenay National Park.

Four Forest Cantons, Alps of the   N division of the Central Alps, central Switzerland, bounded by the Reuss (E), the Aar (W) and Furka Pass (S). Main peaks are the Dammastock (11,922 ft), Sustenhorn (11,507 ft) and Titlis (10,639 ft).

Fraile, Cerro (Cerro El Fraile)   Andean volcano (19,620 ft) on Argentina-Chile border, 5 m. W of Cerro Incahuasi.

Frailes, Cordillera de los   Section of Eastern Cordillera of the Andes, W Bolivia; extends c. 50 m. S from S of Mt Azanaque to SE of Rio Mulato; rises to c. 17,000 ft. Name sometimes also applied to Cordillera de Azanaques (N). Continued S by Cordillera de Chichas.

Freel Peak   (10,900 ft), E California, in the Sierra Nevada, just SE of Lake Tahoe and on El Dorado-Alpine county border.

Fremont Pass   (11,318 ft) in Park Range, central Colorado, 10 m. NE of Leadville. Crossed by highway.

Fremont Peak   Peak (13,730 ft) in Wind River Range, W central Wyoming, c. 50 m. NW of Lander.

Freshfield, Mount   (10,945 ft) on Alberta-British Columbia border, in Rocky Mountains, on W edge of Banff National Park.

Fridtjof Nansen, Mount   Peak (13,156 ft) at head of Ross Shelf Ice, Antarctica.

Frontino, Páramo   Andean massif (13,385 ft), Antioquia department, NW central Colombia, in Cordillera Central.

Front Range   In Rocky Mountains, extending c. 300 m. SE and S from Casper in E central Wyoming to Fremont county, S central Colorado. Range lies largely within National Forest area.

Fründenhorn   Peak (11,063 ft) in Bernese Alps, S central Switzerland, 4 m. ESE of Kandersteg.

Fryatt, Mount   (11,026 ft), W Alberta, near British Columbia border. Part of Rocky Mountains, and included in Jasper National Park.

Fuego   Active volcano (12,582 ft; alt. of crater 11,854 ft) in S central Guatemala, 12 m. SW of Antigua.

Galán, Cerro   Peak (15,400 ft) in the Andes, W Jujuy province, Argentina, 25 m. SW of Rinconada.

Galena Mountain   Peak (13,300 ft) in San Juan Mountains, San Juan county, SW Colorado.

Galenstock   Peak (11,749 ft) in the Alps, S central Switzerland, S of the Rhonestock and NE of the Rhone Glacier. The Galengrat (a mountain ridge) and the Galensattel (a mountain saddle) are nearby.

Galeras Volcano   Active Andean volcano (13,996 ft) in Nariño department, SW Colombia, near Ecuador border. Sometimes called Pasto Volcano.

Gallatin Range   Range in Rocky Mountains of NW Wyoming and SW Montana. Rises S of Boseman in Montana and extends c. 45 m. S between Gallatin and Yellowstone rivers into NW corner of Yellowstone National Park, Wyoming. Main peaks are Mt Holmes (10,300 ft), Mt Blackmore (10,196 ft) and Electric Peak (11,155 ft), highest point in range.

Gangotri Peak   (21,700 ft), 9 m. SSW of Gangotri, noted

Hindu mountain shrine, Tehri district, N Uttar Pradesh, India, in w Kumaun Himalayas.

Gannett Peak (13,785 ft) in Wind River Range, w central Wyoming; highest point in state.

Gardiner, Mount (12,903 ft) in the Sierra Nevada, E California, 15 m. w of Independence.

Gatico, Cordillera de w spur of the Andes, N Chile, 70 m. E of Iquique; extends *c.* 70 m. NNW-SSE and rises to over 16,000 ft.

Géant, Col du Pass (11,056 ft) in Mont Blanc massif, on French-Italian border, 4 m. ENE of Mont Blanc.

Geddes, Mount (11,000 ft) in Coast Mountains, SW British Columbia, 180 m. NW of Vancouver.

Gelememi Dag Peak (10,560 ft) in Hakari Mountains, SE Turkey, 15 m. WSW of Beytussebap.

Gerdine, Mount (12,600 ft) in Alaska Range, S Alaska, 90 m. WNW of Anchorage.

Gerizim, Mount Peak (2,890 ft) of Palestine, after 1948 in w Jordan, in Samarian Hills. Summit was scene of traditional Samaritan Passover rites. Arabic name Jebel et Tur or Jebel et Tor.

Ghost Mountain (10,512 ft), SE British Columbia, near the Alberta border. Part of the Rocky Mountains, and included in Hamber Provincial Park; on the edge of the Chaba Icefield.

Giant's Castle Peak (10,868 ft) in the Drakensberg, w Natal, South Africa, on the Basutoland border.

Gilbert, Mount (10,200 ft), SW British Columbia, in the Coast Mountains, 120 m. NNW of Vancouver.

Giresun Mountains NE Turkey; extend 60 m. E from a point 10 m. NE of Mesudiye, rising to 10,154 ft in Kiliclar Dag.

Gissar Range Branch of the Tien Shan mountain system in w Tadzhik SSR. Extends just s of and parallel to the Zeravshan Range; rises to *c.* 20,000 ft.

Glacier Mountain (12,438 ft) in Rocky Mountains, Summit county, central Colorado.

Glacier Peak (10,436 ft) in Cascade Range, NW Washington, *c.* 50 m. ENE of Everett.

Glarus Alps N division of the Central Alps, mainly situated in Glarus canton, E central Switzerland. Highest peak is Tödi (11,886 ft).

Gletscherhorn Peak (13,064 ft) in the Bernese Alps, s central Switzerland, 13 m. SSE of Interlaken.

Goode, Mount (10,600 ft) in Chugach Mountains, s Alaska, 65 m. E of Anchorage.

Goodhope, Mount (10,670 ft) in Coast Mountains, SW British Columbia, 140 m. NNW of Vancouver.

Goodsir, Mount (11,686 ft), SE British Columbia, in the Rocky Mountains and on the s edge of Yoho National Park.

Gordo, Cerro Andean peak (17,500 ft) on Salta-Catamarca province border, NW Argentina, in central Sierra de Aguas Calientes.

Gore Range Part of Park Range in N central Colorado; extends SSE from Kremmling to Breckenridge, between Eagle and Blue rivers. Chief peaks Red Peak (13,183 ft), Blue River Peak (13,000 ft) and Mt Powell (13,398 ft).

Gornergrat Sharp, rocky ridge (10,283 ft), part of the Rifflehorn, in the Pennine Alps, s Switzerland. Noted for its view of the Monte Rosa-Breithorn-Matterhorn group of mountains.

Goroken Peak (10,748 ft) in the highlands of central Ethiopia, 45 m. ENE of Nakamti.

Gothic Mountain Peak (12,646 ft) in the Rocky Mountains, Gunnison county, w central Colorado.

Goûter, Dôme du Peak (14,121 ft) of the Mont Blanc massif, just w of Mont Blanc.

Grafton, Mount (10,983 ft) in outlying section of Egan and Shell Creek ranges, E Nevada, 40 m. SSE of Ely.

Graham, Mount Highest peak (10,713 ft) in Pinaleno Mountains, SE Arizona, 13 m. SW of Safford.

Grampian Mountains Range extending SW-NE across Scotland, dividing the Lowlands from the Highlands; rises to 4,406 ft in Ben Nevis. The Cairngorm Mountains form part of the range.

Grand Cornier Peak (13,008 ft) in Pennine Alps, s Switzerland, 7 m. WNW of Zermatt.

Grande-Casse Peak (12,668 ft) of the Massif de la Vanoise (Savoy Alps), Savoie department, SE France; has glaciers.

Grand-Motte Peak (12,018 ft) of the Massif de la Vanoise (Savoy Alps), Savoie department, SE France; glacier on N slope.

Grande-Sassière Peak (12,333 ft) of the Graian Alps, on the French-Italian border, 3 m. NE of Tignes; has glaciers.

Grandes-Rousses Range of the Dauphiné Alps, Isère and Savoie departments, SE France; rises to 11,394 ft.

Grand Laget Peak (10,282 ft) in the Pennine Alps, SW Switzerland, 11 m. SE of Martigny-Ville.

Grand Mesa Flat-topped mountain (10,000 ft) in Delta and Mesa counties, w Colorado. Lies within part of the Grand Mesa National Forest; *c.* 50 square m. in area.

Grand Mountain (10,842 ft) in Selkirk Mountains, SE British Columbia; lies within Glacier National Park.

Granite Peak Highest peak (12,850 ft) in Montana; in Beartooth Range, s Montana, near Yellowstone National Park.

Gran Paradiso Highest peak (13,323 ft) of the Graian Alps, NW Italy, 16 m. SSE of Aosta.

Grant, Mount 1. Peak (11,247 ft) in Churchill county, w central Nevada; highest peak in Clan Alpine Mountains. 2. Peak (11,303 ft) in Mineral county, w Nevada; highest peak in the Wassuk Range.

Grant Range Nevada, in NE corner of Nye county, s of White Pine Mountains. Highest peaks are Troy Peak (11,263 ft) and Timber Mountain (10,280 ft).

Gran Zebrù Glacier-topped peak (12,661 ft) in the Ortles mountain group, N Italy.

Grauhorn Peak (10,695 ft) in the Rhaetian Alps, SE central Switzerland, 10 m. NNE of Biasca.

Gravelly Range   In Rocky Mountains of sw Montana; rises E of Ruby River, near Idaho border, and extends *c.* 40 m. N to Virginia City. Lies mostly within Beaverhead National Forest. Highest peak is Black Butte (10,546 ft).

Grays Peak   (14,274 ft) in Front Range, N central Colorado, between Clear Creek and Summit counties, 45 m. w of Denver.

Greenhorn Mountain   Peak (12,334 ft) in Wet Mountains, s Colorado, 22 m. NW of Walsenburg.

Greens Peak   (10,115 ft) in White Mountains, E Arizona, 16 m. ENE of McNary.

Grenville, Mount   (10,200 ft) in the Coast Mountains, sw British Columbia, 120 m. NNW of Vancouver.

Griffeth Mountain   Peak (11,500 ft) in the Front Range, Clear Creek county, N central Colorado.

Grizzly Peak   (13,738 ft) in San Juan Mountains, sw Colorado, between Dolores and San Juan counties.

Grosshorn   Peak (12,353 ft) in the Bernese Alps, s central Switzerland, 5 m. s of Mürren.

Grossvenediger   Second highest peak (12,008 ft) of the Hohe Tauern, s Austria, on the Salzburg-East Tyrol border, 16 m. w of the Grossglockner.

Gros Ventre Range   Part of the Rocky Mountains of NW Wyoming, just E of Snake River and Jackson Hole. Highest peak in range is Doubletop Peak (11,715 ft); others are Triangle Peak (11,525 ft) and Darwin Peak (11,645 ft).

Grünhorn (Gross Grünhorn)   Peak (13,277 ft) in Bernese Alps, s central Switzerland, 7 m. s of Grindelwald. Klein Grünhorn (12,849 ft) is N.

Gspaltenhorn   Peak (11,287 ft) in Bernese Alps, s central Switzerland, 5 m. sw of Mürren.

Güferhorn   Peak (11,103 ft) in the Alps, SE Switzerland, in the Adula group.

Gughe, Mount   Peak (*c.* 13,780 ft) in s Ethiopia, in the mountains forming the edge of the Great Rift Valley, w of lakes Abaya and Chamo.

Gugu Mountains   Forested highland region in E central Ethiopia, on the border between Arusi and Harar provinces, at the edge of the Great Rift Valley, sw of the Chercher Mountains; rise to 11,886 ft in Mt Gugu, 95 m. SE of Addis Ababa.

Gumusane Mountains (Gumush-Hane Mountains) NE Turkey. They extend 25 m. w from Gumusane, N of Kelkit River, and rise to 10,319 ft.

Guna   Peak (13,881 ft) in the highlands of Begemdir province, NW Ethiopia, 20 m. SE of Debra Tabor.

Gunnbjorn, Mount   Highest known peak (12,139 ft) of Greenland, in the SE part of the island, near Blosseville Coast. Has large glaciers extending to Denmark Strait.

Gunnison, Mount   (12,714 ft) in West Elk Mountains, w Colorado, 12 m. ESE of Paonia.

Guramba, Mount   (11,045 ft) in the highlands SE of Lake Awusa, s Ethiopia, 160 m. s of Addis Ababa.

Gurla Mandhata   Peak (25,355 ft) in the Himalayas, sw Tibet, near Nepal border, 105 m. SSE of Gartok.

Guyot, Mount   Peak (13,370 ft) in the Rocky Mountains, central Colorado, between Park and Summit counties.

Hagen Range   E central New Guinea. Height about 13,000 ft.

Hakari Mountains   SE Turkey, covering an area of 100 m. by 50 m. between Iranian frontier (E), Iraq frontier (s) and Buhtan River (N); rise to 13,675 ft in Cilo Dag.

Ha La   Pass (13,975 ft) in w Assam Himalayas, Bhutan, 10 m. WNW of Ha.

Haleakala   Mountain (10,032 ft) in E Maui, Hawaii; part of Hawaii National Park. It has the largest inactive crater in the world: 2,000 ft deep, 7.5 m. long and 2.4 m. wide. Rare silver sword plants grow here.

Hallam Peak   (10,560 ft), SE British Columbia, near Hamber Provincial Park, 55 m. sw of Jasper.

Hamill Peak   (10,640 ft) in Selkirk Mountains, SE British Columbia, 60 m. NE of Nelson.

Hamta Pass   (*c.* 14,050 ft) in the SE Pir Panjal Range of the Punjab Himalayas, NE India, 60 m. E of Dharmsala. Also spelled Hamtah.

Hancock, Mount   Peak (10,000 ft) in the Rocky Mountains, NW Wyoming, in s Yellowstone National Park, 10 m. s of Yellowstone Lake.

Handies Peak   (14,013 ft) in San Juan Mountains, sw Colorado, 11 m. NE of Silverton.

Haramukh   Peak (*c.* 16,000 ft) of the w Punjab Himalayas, w central Kashmir, 22 m. N of Srinagar.

Harvard, Mount   (14,399 ft) in the Collegiate Range of the Sawatch Mountains, central Colorado, 23 m. s of Leadville. It is the third highest peak in the Rocky Mountains of the U.S.A.

Hasan Dag   Peak (10,672 ft) in central Turkey, 29 m. WNW of Nigde. Sometimes called Buyukhasan.

Hawkins Peak   (10,060 ft) in the Sierra Nevada, Alpine county, E California, *c.* 15 m. s of Lake Tahoe.

Hawk Peak   (10,600 ft) in the Pinaleno Mountains, SE Arizona, near Mt Graham.

Hayes, Mount   (13,740 ft) in Alaska Range, E Alaska, 90 m. SSE of Fairbanks.

Haystack Peak   Highest point (12,101 ft) in the Deep Creek Mountains, w Utah, near the Nevada border.

Hazar Masjid Range (Hezar Masjed Range)   One of the Turkmen-Khurasan ranges, in NE Iran; a SE continuation of the Kopet Dagh; rises to 10,000 ft N of Meshed.

Heard Island   Sub-Antarctic volcanic islet in s Indian Ocean, *c.* 300 m. SE of the Kerguelen Islands, rising to *c.* 11,000 ft in Big Pen Peak. Largely covered by snow and glaciers.

Hector, Mount   (11,135 ft), sw Alberta, near British Columbia border. Part of the Rocky Mountains and included in Banff National Park.

Henry Mountains Garfield county, s Utah, w of Dirty Devil River. Chief peaks Mt Hillers (10,650 ft), Mt Pennell (11,320 ft) and Mt Ellen (11,485 ft).

Hesperus Peak (13,225 ft) in La Plata Mountains, sw Colorado, 16 m. NW of Durango.

Hess, Mount (12,030 ft) in the Alaska Range, E Alaska, 80 m. s of Fairbanks.

Highland Peak (10,955 ft) in the Sierra Nevada, Alpine county, E California, c. 30 m. SSE of Lake Tahoe.

Hilgard, Mount Peak (11,527 ft) in Fish Lake Plateau, s central Utah, 30 m. ESE of Richfield.

Hochalmspitze Peak (11,007 ft) of the Hohe Tauern, s Austria, SE of the Ankogel.

Hochfeiler Highest peak (11,555 ft) of the Zillertal Alps, on the Austro-Italian border, 12 m. E of Brenner Pass.

Hohe Tauern Range of the Eastern Alps, in s Austria; extends from Katschberg Pass c. 70 m. w to Zillertal Alps at Italian border. Rises to 12,460 ft in the Grossglockner.

Holy Cross, Mount of the Peak (13,986 ft) in the Sawatch Mountains, w central Colorado, 18 m. NW of Leadville. Snow-filled crevices c. 50 ft wide form a huge cross near the summit.

Hombre Muerto, Sierra del Sub-Andean range, 40 m. long and rising to 16,500 ft; 80 m. SE of the Salar de Hombre Muerto (salt desert) in Puna de Atacama, N Catamarca province, Argentina.

Hood, Mount Highest point (11,245 ft) in Oregon, in Cascade Range, N Oregon. Snow-capped volcanic cone with large glaciers.

Hoosier Pass (11,541 ft), central Colorado, in the Rocky Mountains, between Park and Summit counties. Crossed by highway.

Horseshoe Mountain Peak (13,902 ft) in the Rocky Mountains, between Park and Lake counties, central Colorado.

Hotaka, Mount Peak (10,527 ft) in central Honshu, Japan, on Gifu-Nagano prefecture border, 20 m. WNW of Matsumoto; highest peak in Chubu-sangaku National Park.

Hpungan Pass (10,000 ft) on Burma-India border, 30 m. WNW of Putao.

Huagaruancha, Cerro Andean peak (18,858 ft), Pasco department, central Peru, in the Cordillera Oriental.

Huaitiquina Pass (14,025 ft) in the Andes, on the Argentina-Chile border.

Huanzo, Cordillera de Section of the Cordillera Occidental of the Andes, s Peru, on Ayacucho-Apurímac department border. Extends c. 100 m. w from Cotahuasi to Puquio and rises to c. 20,000 ft.

Huayna Potosí Peak (20,328 ft) in the Cordillera de la Paz, w Bolivia, 17 m. NNW of La Paz.

Hubbard, Mount (14,950 ft) in the St Elias Mountains, on the Yukon-Alaska border, 140 m. w of Whitehorse.

Hühnerstock Peak (10,864 ft) in the Bernese Alps, s central Switzerland, 10 m. s of Meiringen.

Huila, Nevado del Snow-capped Andean volcanic peak (18,865 ft), s central Colombia. Highest peak in the Cordillera Central and second highest in Colombia. 50 m. SE of Cali.

Humboldt Glacier NW Greenland. Largest known glacier; discharges into Kane Basin along a 60-m. front.

Humboldt Mountains Range of the Nan Shan system, N Tsinghai province, China, rising to c. 20,000 ft.

Humboldt Peak (14,044 ft) in Sangre de Cristo Mountains, Custer county, s Colorado.

Humphreys, Mount (13,972 ft) in the Sierra Nevada, E California, on the Fresno-Inyo county border, 17 m. wsw of Bishop.

Humphreys Peak (12,655 ft), N Arizona, 10 m. N of Flagstaff, on the rim of an eroded volcano; highest point in the state.

Hunter, Mount (14,960 ft) in Alaska Range, s central Alaska, in Mt McKinley National Park, 130 m. NNW of Anchorage.

Hunts Peak (12,446 ft) in N tip of Sangre de Cristo Mountains, s central Colorado, between Fremont and Saguache counties.

Huxley, Mount (12,560 ft) in the St Elias Mountains, SE Alaska, 20 m. N of Icy Bay.

Hymettus Mountain range in Attica nome, E central Greece. Extends 10 m. s from just E of Athens to the coast of the Saronic Gulf. Known for its honey. Rises to 3,367 ft.

Hyndman, Mount (Hyndman Peak) Highest peak (12,078 ft) of Pioneer Mountains, central Idaho, 11 m. ENE of Sun Valley.

Ichinskaya Sopka Extinct volcano (11,834 ft) in the central range of the Kamchatka Peninsula, Russian S F S R, 185 m. NNW of Petropavlovsk.

Iconoclast Mountain (10,630 ft) in Selkirk Mountains, SE British Columbia, on the E edge of Hamber Provincial Park.

Ida, Mount 1. (10,472 ft) in the Rocky Mountains, E British Columbia, 100 m. E of Prince George.
2. Highest peak (8,058 ft) of Crete, near its center, 23 m. sw of Candia. A grotto on its slope is commonly identified with the cave where Zeus was raised, according to a Cretan myth.

Ifigguig, Djebel Peak (11,663 ft) at the sw end of the High Atlas, sw Morocco, 20 m. N of Taroudant.

Ikhe Bogdo (Yihe Bogdo) Highest peak (over 13,000 ft) of the Gobi section of the Altai Mountains, in E Mongolian People's Republic, 250 m. SE of Uliassutai.

Ilaló, Cerro Andean peak (10,433 ft) in Pichincha province, N central Ecuador, 7 m. E of Quito.

Iliamna Volcano Active volcano (10,085 ft) in s Alaska, w of Cook Inlet, 150 m. sw of Anchorage.

Iliniza, Cerro Andean peak (17,405 ft) in Cotopaxi province, central Ecuador, 18 m. w of Cotopaxi volcano.

Illampu W Bolivia; highest mountain in the Eastern Cordillera of the Andes, in the N part of the range, *c.* 5 m. SE of Sorata. Consists of 2 peaks, Illampu (21,275 ft) and Ancohuma (21,490 ft). Sometimes called Mt Sorata.

Imatong Mountains Uganda-Sudan border, SE of Juba; rise to 10,456 ft in Mt Kinyeti.

Imbabura, Cerro Extinct Andean volcano (15,026 ft), Imbabura province, N Ecuador, 7 m. SW of Ibarra.

Inca, Paso del Pass (15,520 ft) in the Andes, on Argentina-Chile border, on the road between San Juan (Argentina) and Tránsito (Chile).

Incahuasi, Cerro Andean volcano (21,720 ft) on Argentina-Chile border, 90 m. SW of Antofagasta.

Inyo Mountains E California. Extend 70 m. SSE from S end of White Mountains to a point just SE of Owens Lake; rise to 11,127 ft in Waucoba Mountain, 18 m. SE of Big Pine.

Irazú Highest volcano (11,260 ft) in the Cordillera Central, central Costa Rica, 8 m. NE of Cartago.

Isluga Volcano Andean peak (18,145 ft) in N Chile, near the Bolivia border.

Ispiriz Dag Peak (11,604 ft) in E Turkey, 40 m. SE of Van.

Istoro Nal Mountain (24,271 ft) in the Hindu Kush, Chitral state, N North-West Frontier province, w Pakistan.

Italian Mountain Peak (13,350 ft) in the Rocky Mountains, Gunnison county, w central Colorado.

Ixtacihuatl (Ixtaccihuatl, or Iztaccihuatl) Dormant volcano (17,342 ft) in central Mexico, on Puebla-Mexico state border, N of the Popocatepetl, 35 m. SE of Mexico city. A twin volcano, snow-capped and of irregular shape; popularly known as the Sleeping Woman.

Jacque Peak (13,205 ft) in the Rocky Mountains, Summit county, NW central Colorado. Also known as Eagle River Peak.

Jagüel, Sierra de Sub-Andean mountain range in NW La Rioja province, Argentina, N of Vinchina; extends *c.* 30 m. SSW from Catamarca province; rises to *c.*10,000 ft.

James Peak (13,260 ft) in Front Range, N central Colorado, *c.* 35 m. WNW of Denver.

Jayuri, Cerro Andean peak (18,543 ft), Apurimac department, S central Peru, 6 m. NNW of Abancay.

Jeannette, Mount (11,700 ft) in the St Elias Mountains, SW Yukon, near the Alaska border, 200 m. W of Whitehorse.

Jefferson, Mount Peak (10,495 ft) in Cascade Range, NW central Oregon, 65 m. ESE of Salem.

Jelep La Pass (14,390 ft) in the SW Assam Himalayas, on the Tibet-India border, 16 m. ENE of Gangtok; main India-Tibet trade route.

Joffre, Mount (11,316 ft) in the Rocky Mountains, SE British Columbia, on the Alberta border.

Jones Pass (12,453 ft) in Front Range, N central Colorado, between Grand and Clear Creek counties.

Jumbo Mountain (11,217 ft) in the Selkirk Mountains, SE British Columbia, 70 m. NNE of Nelson.

Juncal, Cerro Andean peak (19,880 ft) on the Argentina-Chile border, N of Nevado del Plomo massif.

Jurisdicciones, Cerro Las Andean peak (12,631 ft) in the Cordillera Oriental, N Colombia, 45 m. W of Cúcuta.

Kabru Peak (24,002 ft) in Singalila Range, on Nepal-Sikkim (India) border, 40 m. NNW of Darjeeling.

Kackar Dag Highest peak (12,917 ft) of the Rize Mountains, NE Turkey, 38 m. ESE of Rize.

Kahusi Range Group of extinct volcanoes in E Congo, extending *c.* 60 m. parallel to the W shore of Lake Kivu; rises to 10,738 ft.

Kailas-Karakoram Range S lateral range of the Karakoram mountain system, N Kashmir. Extends *c.* 200 m. SE from Hunza River bend to main bend of Shyok River, parallel to main range. Highest peak is Masherbrum (25,660 ft) and the average altitude is *c.* 18,000-19,700 ft.

Kailas Range Mountain range of the SW Trans-Himalayas, SW Tibet. Extends *c.* 360 m. ESE from the upper Indus River. Average width *c.* 20 m.; highest peaks Kailas (22,028 ft) and Lombo Kangra (23,165 ft).

Kaiser Peak (10,300 ft) in the Sierra Nevada, E central California, 50 m. NE of Fresno.

Kaldi Dag Highest peak (12,251 ft) of the Ala Dag, S Turkey, 30 m. SE of Nigde.

Kandil Dag Peak (12,841 ft) in E Turkey, 16 m. SE of Karakose.

Kangto Peak (23,260 ft) in the main range of the central Assam Himalayas, on Tibet-Assam border.

Kaolikung Mountains SE outlier of the Tibetan highlands, on the China-Burma border. Extend over 200 m. N-S and rise to 13,000 ft.

Karabakh Range Branch of the Lesser Caucasus, in SW Azerbaijan SSR; extends *c.* 70 m. SE from Armenian SSR to Aras River and rises to 11,000 ft.

Kara Dag Peak (11,910 ft) in SE Turkey, 7 m. N of Hakari.

Karakoram Pass (18,290 ft), Aghil-Karakoram Range, NE Kashmir, 95 m. N of Leh. Important pass on the main Kashmir-China trade route.

Karanfil Dag Peak (10,154 ft) in the Ala Dag, S Turkey, 32 m. E of Ulukisla.

Karasu Mountains E central Turkey. Extend 70 m. E from Tercan, between Euphrates and Tuzla rivers; rise to 10,335 ft in Saksak Dag.

Karategin Range NE Stalinabad oblast, Tadzhik SSR. Extends 60 m. SW from the E end of the Gissar Range to the area of Faizabad; rises to *c.* 12,000 ft.

Karcal Dag Peak (10,990 ft) in NE Turkey, 18 m. NNE of Artvin.

Karisimbi, Mount Extinct volcano and highest peak (*c.* 14,780 ft) of the Virunga Range, E central Africa, on the Congo-Ruanda-Urundi border, 18 m. NE of Goma.

Karo La Pass (*c.* 15,000 ft) in the E Himalayas, S Tibet, on main India-Lhasa trade route. In 1904, scene of battle between Tibetans and Younghusband's expedition.

Kates Needle Peak (10,002 ft) on Alaska-British Columbia border, in the Coast Range, 40 m. NE of Petersburg.

Katun Alps Highest range of the Altai Mountains, SW Siberian Russia, in bend formed by upper Katun River. 85 m. long, 35 m. wide; rise to 15,155 ft at Belukha peak. Include 15 glaciers.

Kearsarge Pass (11,823 ft) in the Sierra Nevada, E California, c. 10 m. w of Independence.

Kedarnath Peak (22,770 ft) in the central Kumaun Himalayas, N Uttar Pradesh, India.

Kemer Dag Peak (10,660 ft) in the Trebizond Mountains, NE Turkey, 38 m. SSE of Trebizond.

Kendall Mountain Peak (13,000 ft) in the San Juan Mountains, SW Colorado, just E of Silverton.

Kendall Peak (13,451 ft) in the San Juan Mountains, SW Colorado, 3 m. ESE of Silverton.

Kendrick Peak (10,418 ft) in Coconino county, N central Arizona, 18 m. NW of Flagstaff. Rises from a high plateau.

Kenosha Hills Park county, central Colorado, in Front Range. Rise to 12,350 ft in Kenosha Cones. Kenosha Pass (10,001 ft) crosses the hills in the NW tip.

Kesis Dag Peak (11,604 ft) in Erzincan Mountains, E central Turkey, 15 m. ENE of Erzincan.

Khalifat Mountain N spur and one of the highest points (11,434 ft) of the Central Brahui Range, in Sibi district, NE central Baluchistan, w Pakistan.

Khanghai Mountains (Hangay Mountains) Major mountain massif in w central Mongolian People's Republic, extending c. 500 m. WNW-ESE parallel to the Mongolian Altai; rises to 13,225 ft in the Otkhon Tengri, 35 m. ESE of Uliassutai.

Khan Tengri Peak (22,949 ft) in the central Tien Shan mountain system, on the China-USSR border, 100 m. E of Issyk-Kul (lake).

Kharkhira Outlying massif (13,504 ft) of the Mongolian Altai, in w Mongolian People's Republic, 35 m. SW of Ulankom.

Khawak Pass (11,640 ft) in the Hindu Kush, NE Afghanistan, at the head of the Panjshir valley.

Kiliclar Dag Peak (10,154 ft) in NE Turkey, 21 m. ENE of Mesudiye.

Kilik Pass (15,600 ft) in N extension of the Karakoram on the Kashmir-China border, 21 m. NNW of Misgar (Kashmir), on important trade route from Gilgit to Kashgar.

King, Mount 1. (17,130 ft) in St Elias Mountains, SW Yukon, near Alaska border, 190 m. w of Whitehorse.
2. Peak (12,909 ft) of the Sierra Nevada, E California, in Kings Canyon National Park, 14 m. w of Independence. Sometimes called Mt Clarence King.

King Edward, Mount (11,400 ft) in the Rocky Mountains, on the Alberta-British Columbia border, on the S edge of Jasper National Park.

King George, Mount (11,226 ft), SE British Columbia, near the Alberta border, 40 m. s of Banff.

Kings Peak Highest point (13,498 ft) in Utah, in Uinta Mountains, 80 m. E of Salt Lake City.

Kion-Khokh Highest peak (11,230 ft) in N front range of the central Greater Caucasus, Russian SSR, 35 m. WSW of Dzaudzhikau.

Kirghiz Range w branch of the Tien Shan mountain system, USSR. Extends 225 m. w from Boom Gorge on Chu River to area of Dzhambul; rises to 14,800 ft.

Kirklar Dag Peak (11,348 ft) in Rize Mountains, NE Turkey, 35 m. s of Rize.

Kirkpatrick, Mount Highest peak (14,603 ft) of Queen Alexandra Range, Antarctica, between Beardmore Glacier and the head of Ross Shelf Ice.

Kit Carson Peak (14,100 ft) in Sangre de Cristo Mountains, Saguache county, s Colorado.

Kitchener, Mount (11,500 ft) in the Rocky Mountains, SW Alberta, near the British Columbia border, on s edge of Jasper National Park.

Klyuchevskaya Sopka Highest active volcano (15,912 ft) of the Eurasian continent, in the E mountain range of Kamchatka Peninsula, Russian SSR, 220 m. NNE of Petropavlovsk. Perfect conic shape, with crater 650 ft in diameter. Frequent eruptions.

Kodor Range s spur of the w Greater Caucasus, in NW Georgian SSR. Extends. c. 50 m. SW to the Black Sea and rises to 10,856 ft.

Koh-i-Baba w outlier of the Hindu Kush, in central Afghanistan. Extends 125 m. E-W and rises to 16,872 ft in the Shah Fuladi, 17 m. SW of Bamian.

Kokse Dag Peak (10,830 ft) in E Turkey, 12 m. WNW of Aleskirt.

Kokshaal-Tau Branch of the Tien Shan mountain system on the China-USSR border. Extends 300 m. SW from Pobeda to the area of Chatyr-Kul (lake); rises to 17,380 ft.

Kolekole Peak (10,000 ft) in s Maui, Territory of Hawaii.

Kopet Dagh One of the Turkmen-Khurasan ranges, SW Turkmen SSR and Khurasan, NE Iran. Extends c. 200 m. NW-SE along USSR-Iran border; rises to c. 10,000 ft.

Kordevan Dag Peak (10,000 ft) in NE Turkey, 23 m. ESE of Artvin.

Kose Dag Peak (9,190 ft; sometimes given as 11,735 ft) in N central Turkey, 13 m. NE of Zara.

Koshtan-Tau Peak (16,880 ft) in the N front range of the central Greater Caucasus, in Kabardian Autonomous SSR, 35 m. SW of Nalchik.

Kratke Range NE New Guinea; rises to c. 10,000 ft.

Kronotskaya Sopka Active volcano (11,909 ft) on E Kamchatka Peninsula, Khabarovsk Territory, Russian SSR; terminates (s) on Kronotski Gulf.

Krönte Peak (10,203 ft) in the Alps of the Four Forest

Cantons, central Switzerland, 7 m. ESE of Engelberg.

Kuh-i-Rang Mountain (14,000 ft) in Zagros ranges, SW Iran, 100 m. W of Isafan.

Kula Kangri Peak (24,780 ft) in the main range of the W Assam Himalayas, on the Bhutan-Tibet border. Kangri peak (24,740 ft) is 16 m. SSW, also on border.

Kumaun Himalayas W central subdivision of the Himalayas, s central Asia, extending from the upper course of the Sutlej River in SW Tibet and Himachal Pradesh in India to Kali (Sarda) River on the India-Nepal border. Length c. 200 m.

Kumon Range Kachin State; Upper Burma. Extends between Hukawng Valley (W) and the Mali headstream of the Irrawaddy. Rises to 11,190 ft 20 m. WNW of Sumprabum.

Kungei Ala-Tau Branch of the Tien Shan mountain system in Kirghiz SSR. Extends 180 m. E from Boom Gorge on Chu River to the area of Kegen; rises to 16,300 ft.

Ladakh Range Trans-Shyok lateral range of the Karakoram mountain system, E Kashmir. Extends c. 230 m. SE from Shyok River mouth to Tibet; rises to crest line of c. 20,000 ft.

Lamington, Mount Volcano in the Owen Stanley Range of SE New Guinea. Erupted violently in January, 1951, killing many thousands.

Langley, Mount (14,042 ft) in the Sierra Nevada, E California, on the E border of Sequoia National Park.

Lanín Volcano Andean peak (c. 12,300 ft) on the Argentina-Chile border, s of Mamuil-Malal Pass.

La Paz, Cordillera de Highest range in the Eastern Cordillera of the Andes, W Bolivia. Extends 170 m. SE from Nudo de Apolobamba on the Peru border to La Paz River. Rises to 21,490 ft in the Ancohuma.

La Perouse, Mount (10,750 ft) in the Fairweather Range, SE Alaska, near the Gulf of Alaska, in Glacier Bay National Monument.

La Plata Mountains Spur of the San Juan Mountains, in SW Colorado and NW New Mexico, extending N-S between La Plata and Animas rivers. Highest points are Helmet Peak (11,976 ft) and Hesperus Peak (13,225 ft).

La Plata Peak (14,342 ft) in the Sawatch Mountains, central Colorado, 18 m. SW of Leadville.

Laquinhorn Peak (13,036 ft) in the Pennine Alps, s Switzerland, 11 m. s of Brig.

Laramie Mountains N extension of the Front Range, Colorado, in the Rocky Mountains; they reach into SE Wyoming as far as Casper and N Platte River. Highest point is Laramie Peak (10,274 ft), 65 m. N of Laramie.

Lares Pass (14,711 ft) to the N of Lares (town), Cuzco department, s central Peru.

La Sal Mountains Range in La Sal National Forest, San Juan and Grand counties, E Utah. Chief peaks are Mt Tomasaki (12,271 ft), Mt Waas (12,586 ft) and Mt Peale (13,089 ft).

Lástimas, Cerro Andean peak (10,000 ft), Linares province, s central Chile, 25 m. SE of Linares.

Latir Peak (12,723 ft) in the Sangre de Cristo Mountains, N New Mexico, near the Colorado border, 9 m. NE of Questa.

Laussedat, Mount (10,035 ft) in the Rocky Mountains, SE British Columbia, near the Alberta border, 65 m. WNW of Banff.

Lauteraarhorn (Gross Lauteraarhorn) Peak (13,272 ft) in the Bernese Alps, s central Switzerland, 5 m. SE of Grindelwald.

Lawu, Mount (10,712 ft) in central Java, Indonesia, 25 m. E of Surakarta. Also spelled Mt Lawoe.

Leavitt Peak (11,575 ft) in the Sierra Nevada, E California, 32 m. NW of Mono Lake.

Lechkhumi Range s spur of the central Greater Caucasus, in NW Georgian SSR, forming watershed between Tskhenis-Tskali and upper Rion rivers. Rises to 11,844 ft.

Lefrov, Mount (11,230 ft) in the Rocky Mountains, on the Alberta-British Columbia border, on W edge of Banff National Park, 35 m. WNW of Banff.

Leidy, Mount Peak (10,317 ft) in the Rocky Mountains, NW Wyoming, 40 m. NE of Jackson.

Lejía, Cerro Peak (17,585 ft) in the Puna de Atacama, Antofagasta province, N Chile.

Lemhi Range NW-SE mountain chain between Salmon city and Snake River Plain, E Idaho, in Salmon National Forest. Highest point is Portland Mountain (10,821 ft).

Leon, Pico El Andean peak (15,561 ft) in Sierra Nevada de Mérida, Mérida state, W Venezuela, 11 m. SSE of Mérida.

Leone, Monte Highest peak (11,683 ft) of the Lepontine Alps, on Italo-Swiss border.

Leones, Cerro (Cerro Alto de los Leones) Andean peak (19,455 ft) in Aconcagua province, central Chile.

Léon Muerto, Sierra Sub-Andean mountain range in Catamarca and Salta provinces, Argentina, E of Antofagasta; extends c. 20 m. E-W and rises to c. 17,500 ft.

Levanna, Monte Peak (12,070 ft) in the Graian Alps, on the French-Italian border, SW of the Gran Paradiso.

Lewis Range E front range of the Rocky Mountains in NW Montana. Extends c. 160 m. SSE from near Waterton Lake on the Alberta border, through Glacier National Park, to Blackfoot River. Forms part of the Continental Divide. Chief peaks are Mt Cleveland (10,448 ft), Mt Stimson (10,165 ft), Kintla Peak (10,110 ft), Mt Jackson (10,033 ft) and Mt Siyeh (10,014 ft).

Licancábur Volcano Andean peak (19,455 ft) in Antofagasta province, N Chile, near Bolivia border.

Lincoln, Mount Highest peak (14,284 ft) in Park Range, central Colorado, 12 m. NE of Leadville.

Lingshi La Pass (16,118 ft) in the main range of the W Assam Himalayas, NW Bhutan, c. 2 m. NNW of Lingshi (village).

Lípez, Cordillera de Range in the Andes, forming the

southernmost part of the Eastern Cordillera, sw Bolivia. Extends *c.* 160 m. sw from Portugalete to Mt Zapaleri on Bolivia-Chile-Argentina border; rises to 19,225 ft.

Lipu La Pass (17,000 ft) in se Zaskar Range of the Kumaun Himalayas, sw Tibet.

Lister, Mount (13,350 ft) in Royal Society Range, Antarctica, w of McMurdo Sound, along w shore of Ross Sea.

Little Bear Mountain (14,040 ft) in the Rocky Mountains, Costilla county, s Colorado.

Litzner (Gross Litzner) Peak (10,208 ft) in the Silvretta Group of the Rhaetian Alps, on the Swiss-Austrian border, 7 m. e of Klosters.

Liupan Mountains se Kansu province, China. Separate Wan-King River basin from the rest of Kansu; rise to *c.* 10,000 ft 10 m. nne of Lungteh.

Llaima Volcano Andean peak (10,040 ft) in Cautín province, s central Chile, 45 m. ene of Temuco; active volcano.

Llanganates, Cordillera de los e Andean massif, central Ecuador, e of Ambato; includes several volcanic peaks, the highest of which is Cerro Hermoso (15,216 ft).

Llaretas, Cordón de las Andean range in w central Mendoza province, Argentina; rises to over 16,000 ft.

Lloyd George, Mount (10,000 ft) in the Rocky Mountains, n central British Columbia.

Llullaillaco, Cerro One of the highest peaks (22,015 ft) of the Andes. Extinct snow-capped volcano on the Argentina-Chile border, 140 m. wsw of San Antonio de los Cobres.

Loggia, La Peak (10,095 ft) in the Lepontine Alps, s Switzerland, 9 m. nne of Biasca.

Lohner (Gross Lohner) Peak (10,013 ft) in the Bernese Alps, sw central Switzerland, 3 m. se of Adelboden.

Lombo Kangra Highest peak (23,165 ft) in the Kailas Range, s Tibet, 40 m. nw of Saka.

Lone Cone Peak (12,761 ft) in the San Juan Mountains, sw Colorado, between San Miguel and Dolores counties.

Longaví, Nevado Andean peak (10,600 ft) in Linares province, s central Chile, 35 m. se of Linares.

Longs Peak (14,255 ft) in the Front Range of the Rocky Mountains, n Colorado, 10 m. ssw of Estes Park town. Highest point in Rocky Mountain National Park.

Los Coconucos Volcanic massif in the Cordillera Central, sw Colombia, 20 m. se of Popayán. Has 2 major peaks, rising to 14,908 ft.

Loser, Mount (11,092 ft) in n Barisan Mountains, n Sumatra, Indonesia, near the w coast, 110 m. w of Medan.

Lost Park Mountain Peak (11,800 ft) in the Front Range, Park county, central Colorado.

Lost River Range Custer and Butte counties, e Idaho, between Big Lost and Little Lost rivers, in part of Challis National Forest. Chief peaks: Borah Peak (12,655 ft), Dorion Peak (12,016 ft), Leatherman Peak (12,230 ft), Invisible Peak (11,343 ft) and Dickey Peak (11,140 ft).

Loudon, Mount (10,550 ft) in the Rocky Mountains, sw Alberta, near the British Columbia border, near Banff National Park, 65 m. nw of Banff.

Loveland Pass (11,992 ft) in the Front Range, n central Colorado, *c.* 55 m. w of Denver.

Lucania, Mount (17,150 ft) in St Elias Mountains, sw Yukon, near the Alaska border, 190 m. w of Whitehorse.

Lyell, Mount 1. (11,495 ft) in the Rocky Mountains, on the Alberta-British Columbia border, on the w edge of Banff National Park, 75 m. se of Jasper.
2. Peak (13,095 ft) in the Sierra Nevada, e California, on the e boundary of Yosemite National Park. Has large glacier.

Lyskamm w summit (14,888 ft) of the Monte Rosa group, on the Swiss-Italian frontier. On the e side is the Alpine crossing of Lysjoch or Lys Pass (13,934 ft).

McArthur, Mount Peak (14,400 ft) in the St Elias Mountains, sw Yukon, near the Alaska border, 180 m. w of Whitehorse.

Macdonnell Ranges Two parallel ranges in s Northern Territory, Australia; highest peak is Mt Zeil (4,955 ft).

Madison Range In the Rocky Mountains of sw Montana. Rises sw of Bozeman and extends *c.* 40 m. s between Gallatin and Madison rivers to Hebgen Lake. Highest points are Lone Mountain (11,194 ft) and Koch Peak (11,293 ft).

Magdalena Mountains w central New Mexico, in Socorro county, w of Socorro and the Rio Grande; largely within Cibola National Forest. Highest peak is South Baldy (10,787 ft).

Mahameru, Mount (Mount Mahameroe) Highest peak (12,060 ft) in Java, Indonesia, in the Semeru Mountains, 60 m. s of Surabaya; volcanic.

Mai Gudo Peak (*c.* 11,120 ft) in sw Ethiopia, 30 m. ese of Jimma, in the mountains between Omo, Gibbe and Gojab rivers.

Maipo Pass (11,230 ft) in the Andes, on the Argentina-Chile border, at the s foot of Maipo Volcano, on the road between San Rafael (Argentina) and El Volcán (Chile).

Maipo Volcano (17,355 ft) in the Andes, on the Argentina-Chile border, 65 m. se of Santiago (Chile).

Majestic Mountain (10,125 ft) in the Rocky Mountains, w Alberta, near the British Columbia border, in Jasper National Park.

Maladetta (Maladeta) Highest massif of the central range of the Pyrenees, in n Huesca and Lerida provinces, ne Spain, near the French border. Highest peaks are Pico de Aneto (11,168 ft), Pico del Medio (11,004 ft) and Pico de la Maladeta (10,866 ft).

Malaspina Glacier se Alaska, w of Yakutat Bay; belongs to glacier system of St Elias Mountains.

Malinche (Malintzi or Malinzi) Dormant volcano (14,636 ft) in central Mexico, on the Puebla-Tlaxcala border, 16 m. ne of Puebla; has several extinct craters.

Malte Brun Range W central South Island, New Zealand, in the Southern Alps; extends 7 m. N-S between Murchison and Tasman glaciers; highest peak is Mt Malte Brun (10,421 ft).

Maluti Mountains Branch of the Drakensberg, W Basutoland; extend NE-SW and rise to 11,000 ft in Machache Peak.

Mana Pass (*c.* 18,000 ft) in S Zaskar Range of the Kumaun Himalayas, SW Tibet, 23 m. N of Badrinath (India).

Manaslu (Kutang I) Eighth highest peak (26,658 ft) in the world, in the central Nepal Himalayas, N Nepal, 38 m. N of Gurkha.

Manzano Range Central New Mexico, E of Rio Grande; extends *c.* 40 m. N from Mountainair. Highest peak is Manzano Peak (10,103 ft).

Marcellina, Mount Peak (11,349 ft) in the Rocky Mountains, Gunnison county, W Colorado.

Marconi, Mount (10,190 ft) in the Rocky Mountains, SE British Columbia, near the Alberta border, 60 m. N of Fernie.

Marcus Baker, Mount (13,250 ft) in the Chugach Mountains, S Alaska, 55 m. WNW of Valdez.

Mareka Peak (11,360 ft) in the Drakensberg, in Basutoland, just W of Natal border.

Margherita, Mount Highest summit (16,795 ft) of the Ruwenzori, in E central Africa, on the Congo-Uganda border, 30 m. ESE of Beni. Third highest peak in Africa.

Markagunt Plateau High tableland in SW Utah, chiefly in Iron county, rising to 11,315 ft in Brian Head peak.

Markham, Mount A triple-peaked mountain (15,100 ft) in Antarctica, S of Shackleton Inlet, at W edge of Ross Shelf Ice.

Marmolada Highest peak (10,964 ft) in the Dolomites, N Italy, 25 m. ESE of Bolzano; has glaciers.

Marmolejo, Cerro Andean peak (20,000 ft) on the Argentina-Chile border, 27 m. SSW of Tupungato and 50 m. SE of Santiago.

Marmot Peak (11,841 ft) in the Rocky Mountains, between Chaffee and Park counties, central Colorado.

Maroon Peak (14,126 ft) in the Elk Mountains, W central Colorado, 12 m. SW of Aspen.

Marra Mountains Highest section of the Nile-Lake Chad watershed, in Darfur province, W Sudan, W of El Fasher. Extend *c.* 100 m. and rise to *c.* 10,000 ft.

Marvine, Mount Highest peak (11,600 ft) in Fish Lake Plateau, S central Utah, 25 m. ESE of Richfield.

Marysvale Peak (10,943 ft) in the Sevier Plateau, Piute county, SW central Utah, 7 m. ENE of Marysvale (city).

Masherbrum Peak (25,660 ft) in the Kailas-Karakoram Range of the Karakoram mountain system, Kashmir, 45 m. NE of Skardu.

Massive, Mount Central Colorado, in the Sawatch Mountains, 5 m. NNW of Mt Elbert, 10 m. WSW of Leadville.

It is the second highest peak of the Rocky Mountains of the U.S.A.

Mather, Mount (12,015 ft) in the Alaska Range, S central Alaska, in Mt McKinley National Park, 140 m. N of Anchorage.

Matterjoch (Théodule) Pass (10,892 ft) linking Italy with Switzerland, near the Matterhorn, in the Pennine Alps.

Maudit, Mont Peak (14,649 ft) of the Mont Blanc massif, on the French-Italian border, just NE of Mont Blanc.

Mau Escarpment Section of the W rim of the Great Rift Valley in W Kenya, W and S of Nakuru; rises to 10,000 ft.

Medicine Bow Mountains NW extension of the Front Range in N Colorado and SE Wyoming; extend *c.* 100 m. NNW from Cameron Pass to Medicine Bow town. Chief peaks are Elk Mountain (11,162 ft) and Medicine Bow Peak (12,005 ft), both in Wyoming.

Mejicana, Cumbre de la Andean mountain (20,500 ft) in Sierra de Famatina, N central La Rioja province, Argentina, 23 m. NW of Chilecito.

Mengene Dag Peak (11,844 ft) in E Turkey, near the Iran border, 40 m. ESE of Van.

Merbabu, Mount (Mount Merbaboe) Volcanic peak (10,308 ft) in central Java, Indonesia, 30 m. WNW of Surakarta.

Mercan Dagi Peak (11,315 ft) in the Mercan Mountains, which extend 40 m. S of the Euphrates. Peak is 13 m. SSE of Erzincan, E central Turkey.

Mercedario, Cerro Andean peak (21,885 ft) in SW San Juan province, Argentina, near the Chile border, 60 m. SW of Tamberías.

Mescit Dag Peak (10,680 ft) in the Coruh Mountains, NE Turkey, 13 m. SE of Ispir.

Mettelhorn Peak (11,184 ft) in the Pennine Alps, S Switzerland, 2 m. N of Zermatt.

M'Goun, Djebel (Ighil M'Goun) Peak (13,353 ft) of the High Atlas, S central Morocco, 50 m. NE of Ouarzazate.

Michelson, Mount Highest point (9,239 ft) of the Brooks Range, NE Alaska.

Mikeno, Mount Second highest peak (*c.* 14,600 ft) of the Virunga range, E Congo, near the Ruanda-Urundi border, 20 m. S of Rutshuru. Extinct volcano.

Miller, Mount (11,000 ft) in the Chugach Mountains, S Alaska, 30 m. NNE of Cape Yakataga.

Minarets, The Odd formation of jagged summits (*c.* 12,000 ft) in the Sierra Nevada, E California.

Minas, Sierra de las E central Guatemala. Range extends *c.* 60 m. E-W along the Alta Verapaz-Zacapa department border, between Polochic River (N) and Motagua River (S); rises to *c.* 10,000 ft.

Mineral Mountains Beaver county, SW Utah; extend 25 m. N from Minersville. Highest point 11,200 ft.

Miño Volcano Andean peak (18,440 ft) in N Chile, near the Bolivia border. Loa River rises at its NE foot.

Mischabelhörner   Group of peaks in the Pennine Alps, s Switzerland, near Zermatt. Highest peak is the Dom (14,923 ft); other peaks include Täschhorn (14,744 ft), Nadelhorn (14,206 ft) and Lenzspitze (14,098 ft). Mischabeljoch, a pass, is just s of the Täschhorn, at 12,644 ft.

Mishmi Hills   Range in NE Assam, India, N and E of Sadiya. Rise to *c.* 15,000 ft.

Mission Range   In the Rocky Mountains of NW Montana; rises between Flathead Lake and Swan River and extends *c.* 45 m. s towards Missoula. Highest point is McDonald Peak (10,300 ft).

Mist Mountain   (10,303 ft) in the Misty Range of the Rocky Mountains, SW Alberta, near the British Columbia border, 50 m. SW of Calgary.

Mittaghorn   Peak (12,796 ft) in the Bernese Alps, s central Switzerland, 13 m. s of Interlaken.

Mittelhorn   Peak (12,163 ft) in the Bernese Alps, s central Switzerland, 4 m. E of Grindelwald.

Mogollon Mountains   SW New Mexico, just E of San Francisco River, in Gila National Forest, near the Arizona border. Chief peaks are Mogollon Mountain (10,788 ft) and Whitewater Baldy (10,892 ft).

Mohinora, Cerro   Peak (13,097 ft) in Sierra Madre Occidental, Chihuahua, N Mexico, 80 m. NNE of Culiacán.

Mojones, Cerro   Andean volcano (19,650 ft) in N Catamarca province, Argentina, 30 m. N of Antofagasta.

Mokrye Gory (Milryye Gory)   Highest central range of the Lesser Caucasus; extends *c.* 35 m. s from upper Khram River at Tsalka; rises to *c.* 10,500 ft.

Molina Pass   (12,500 ft) in the Andes, on the Argentina-Chile border, 20 m. SW of Maipo Volcano, on the road between San Rafael (Argentina) and Rancagua (Chile).

Moloch, Mount   (10,195 ft) in the Selkirk Mountains, SE British Columbia, 26 m. NNW of Revelstoke.

Monarch Mountain   (11,714 ft) in the Coast Mountains, w British Columbia, 200 m. NW of Vancouver.

Monarch Pass   (11,312 ft) in the Sawatch Mountains, central Colorado, between Chaffee and Gunnison counties. Crossed by highway.

Monitor Range   Central Nevada, largely in Nye county, E of Toquema Range. Highest peak is Monitor (10,856 ft), *c.* 60 m. NE of Tonopah. Other high peaks are Antelope Peak (10,207 ft) and Summit Mountain (10,466 ft).

Monmouth, Mount   (10,470 ft) in the Coast Mountains, SW British Columbia, 120 m. NNW of Vancouver.

Mono Pass   (*c.* 10,600 ft) in the Sierra Nevada, E California, *c.* 10 m. SW of Mono Lake.

Monroe Peak   (11,226 ft) in Sevier Plateau, SW central Utah, 7 m. SSE of Monroe.

Mont Blanc de Seilon   Peak (12,700 ft) in the Pennine Alps, s Switzerland, 11 m. SE of Bagnes.

Mont Blanc du Tacul   Peak (13,940 ft) of the Mont Blanc massif, Haute-Savoie department, SE France, 5 m. s of Chamonix.

Montcalm, Pic de   Peak (10,105 ft) in the central Pyrenees, Ariege department, s France, near the Spanish border.

Mont Cenis   Alpine pass (6,831 ft) between the Cottian Alps and the Graian Alps, SE France.

Mor Dag   Peak (12,500 ft) in the Hakari Mountains, SE Turkey, near the Iran border, 13 m. NNE of Yuksekova.

Morgan, Mount   (13,739 ft) in the Sierra Nevada, Inyo county, E California, 19 m. w of Bishop.

Moroto, Mount   (10,000 ft) just E of Moroto (town), Northern Province, E Uganda, near the Kenya border.

Morrison, Mount   Highest peak (13,000–14,000 ft) of Formosa, in the central range, 33 m. E of Kiayi.

Morteratsch, Piz   Alpine peak (12,315 ft) in Upper Engadine, SE Switzerland, 8 m. SSE of St Moritz. Morteratsch Glacier, one of Switzerland's largest glaciers, descends N from the Italian border E of Piz Bernina and Piz Morteratsch to Bernina River.

Motilones, Serranía de los   Andean range on the Colombia-Venezuela border. It is a N part of the Cordillera Oriental. Extends *c.* 80 m. and rises to 12,300 ft.

Mourne Mountains   Range in s County Down, Northern Ireland, extending 15 m. NE-SW between Carlingford Lough and Dundrum Bay and rising to 2,796 ft in Slieve Donard, 2 m. SW of Newcastle.

Mucuchíes Pass (Timotes Pass)   Mérida state, w Venezuela, N of Pico Mucuñuque. Altitude *c.* 13,500 ft.

Mucuñuque, Pico   Peak (15,328 ft) in Andean spur, Mérida state, w Venezuela, 28 m. NE of Mérida.

Muerto, Cerro El   Andean mountain (21,450 ft) on the Argentina-Chile border, 30 m. WSW of Cerro Incahuasi.

Muir, Mount   (14,025 ft) in the Sierra Nevada, E central California, on Inyo-Tulare county border, just s of Mt Whitney.

Mulhacén (Muley-Hacén)   Highest peak (11,411 ft) of continental Spain, in the Sierra Nevada, Granada province, s Spain, 20 m. SE of Granada. Snowline at *c.* 10,000 ft.

Mummy Range   Spur of the Front Range in NE corner of the Rocky Mountain National Park, N Colorado. Chief peaks are Mt Dunraven (12,548 ft), Mt Chiquita (13,052 ft), Mt Chapin (13,059 ft), Mummy Mountain (13,413 ft), Mt Fairchild (13,502 ft), Ypsilon Mountain (13,507 ft) and Hague's Peak (13,562 ft).

Munday, Mount   (11,000 ft) in the Coast Mountains, w British Columbia, 170 m. NW of Vancouver.

Munku-Sardyk   Highest peak (11,453 ft) in the Eastern Sayan Mountains, on USSR-Mongolia border, w of Mondy. Has small glaciers.

Munzur Dag   Peak (10,460 ft) in E central Turkey, 13 m. E of Kemaliye, in the Munzur Mountains, a range which extends 55 m. s and E of the Euphrates. Sometimes spelled Monzur.

Murat Dag   Peak (11,545 ft) in E Turkey, 27 m. SE of Karakose.

Murchison, Mount   (10,659 ft), SW Alberta, near the

342

British Columbia border, in the Rocky Mountains, and included in Banff National Park.

Mururata Peak (18,965 ft) in the Cordillera de La Paz, w Bolivia, 19 m. ESE of La Paz.

Musinia Peak (10,986 ft) in the Wasatch Plateau, central Utah, 16 m. SSE of Manti.

Mustang Mountain (10,316 ft) in the White Mountains, sw Nevada, near the California border, 60 m. WNW of Goldfield.

Muttler Peak (10,820 ft) in the Rhaetian Alps, E Switzerland, 5 m. NW of the Swiss-Austrian-Italian border.

Muveran, Grand Peak (10,043 ft) in the Bernese Alps, sw Switzerland, 11 m. w of Sion.

Muzart Pass (11,480 ft) in the central Tien Shan, near Muzart village, NW Sinkiang province, China.

Muztagh Ata Range Sinkiang province, China. Extends 200 m. NNW-SSE parallel to the E edge of the Pamir. Rises to 25,146 ft in the Kungur Massif, 70 m. sw of Kashgar. The peak Muztagh Ata (24,388 ft) is 95 m. sw of Kashgar. Sometimes called Kashgar Range and Bolor Tagh.

Nacimiento, Cerro del Andean peak (21,300 ft) in w Catamarca province, Argentina, near the Chile border, 23 m. sw of Cerro Incahuasi.

Nanga Parbat, Mount (10,780 ft) in the Rocky Mountains, on the Alberta-British Columbia border, at the w edge of Banff National Park.

Nangpa La Pass (19,050 ft) in the E Nepal Himalayas, on Nepal-Tibet border, 34 m. s of Tingri (Tibet).

Napa, Cerro Andean peak (18,880 ft) on the Chile-Bolivia border.

Narym Range Branch of the sw Altai Mountains, East Kazakhstan oblast, Kazakh SSR. Extends 90 m. w along Narym River to Irtysh River; rises to 11,270 ft in the E.

Naryn-Tau Range in the Tien Shan mountain system, Kirghiz SSR. Extends c. 80 m. E-W, s of Naryn River and E of Naryn; rises to 13,000 ft.

Nassau Range w central New Guinea, adjacent to Orange Range and forming w part of Snow Mountains; extends c. 200 m. E from the isthmus SE of Vogelkop peninsula to Orange Range. Contains Mt Carstensz (c. 16,400 ft, highest peak in the island) and Mt Idenburg (c. 15,750 ft).

Natazhat, Mount (13,480 ft) in the St Elias Mountains, s Alaska, 150 m. NNW of Yakutat.

Natu La Pass (c. 14,000 ft) in the sw Assam Himalayas, on the Sikkim-Tibet border, 15 m. ENE of Gangtok. Connects with main India-Tibet trade route.

Navajo Mountain (10,416 ft) in s Utah, near the Arizona border, 11 m. s of junction of San Juan and Colorado rivers.

Negra, Cordillera w section of the Cordillera Occidental of the Andes, Ancash department, w central Peru. Extends 110 m. SSE from Santa River to the area of Chiquián. Rises to 14,764 ft.

Negro Muerto, Cerro Andean volcano (19,190 ft) in N Catamarca province, Argentina, at the s end of the Sierra de Calalaste, 60 m. sw of Antofagasta.

Neiges, Piton des Highest peak (10,069 ft) in Réunion island, 14 m. s of Saint-Denis, at the center of a three-lobed volcanic massif.

Nelson Peak (10,772 ft) in the Selkirk Mountains, SE British Columbia, 60 m. sw of Banff.

Nemrut Dag Peak (10,010 ft) in E Turkey, 20 m. NNE of Bitlis.

Nesthorn Peak (12,533 ft) in the Bernese Alps, s Switzerland, 7 m. NNW of Brig.

Neumayer Escarpment Antarctica, forming the E side of the polar plateau of New Schwabenland; highest altitude 12,000 ft.

Nevado, Cerro Pre-Andean peak (12,500 ft) in s central Mendoza province, Argentina, 70 m. s of San Rafael.

Nevado, Cerro el Andean peak (14,960 ft) in Meta intendancy, central Colombia, in the Cordillera Oriental, 33 m. wsw of Villavicencio.

Never Summer Mountains Range of the Rocky Mountains in N Colorado, extending for c. 20 m. N-s along the Continental Divide. Chief peaks are Mt Cumulus (12,724 ft), Mt Nimbus (12,730 ft), Mt Cirrus (12,804 ft), Howard Mountain (12,814 ft) and Mt Richthofen (12,953 ft).

Ngoc Ang Highest peak (10,500 ft) of the Annamese Cordillera.

Nieves Negras Pass (12,500–13,000 ft) in the Andes, on the Argentina-Chile border, at the s foot of San José Volcano.

Niti Pass (16,627 ft) in SE Zaskar Range of the Kumaun Himalayas, near the India border, in sw Tibet.

Nivelle, Mount (10,620 ft) in the Rocky Mountains, SE British Columbia, near the Alberta border, 50 m. SSE of Banff.

Nokilalaki, Mount (10,863 ft), central Celebes, Indonesia, 45 m. NNW of Poso.

Nopala, Cerro Peak (10,170 ft) in Hidalgo, central Mexico, 6 m. SSE of Huichapan.

North Maroon Peak (14,000 ft) in the Elk Mountains, Pitkin county, w central Colorado.

Nukatl Range (Nukatl' Range) N spur of the E Greater Caucasus, in s central Dagestan Autonomous SSR. Extends in an arc 30 m. N, forming right watershed of the Avar Koisu; rises to 12,860 ft.

Nu Mountains Outlier of the Tibetan highlands, NW Yunnan province, China. Extends c. 250 m. N-s between Mekong (E) and Salween (w) rivers, rising to 15,800 ft.

Nyamlagira (Nyamuragira) Active volcano (c. 10,000 ft) in the Virunga range, E Congo, N of Lake Kivu and 15 m. NE of Sake, in the s part of the Albert National Park.

Nyenchen Tanglha (Nyenchhen Thanglha) Moun-

343

tain range of the SE Trans-Himalayas, SE Tibet. Extends *c.* 550 m. E-w. Highest point is Nyenchen Tanglha peak (23,255 ft), 60 m. NW of Lhasa.

Nyiragongo Active volcano (*c.* 11,400 ft) in the Virunga range, E Congo, near the Ruanda-Urundi border, NE of Lake Kivu and 12 m. N of Goma, in the s part of the Albert National Park. Also called Tshaninagongo.

Oberaarhorn Peak (11,949 ft) in the Bernese Alps, s central Switzerland, 13 m. s of Meiringen.

Oberalpstock Mountain (10,925 ft) in the Glarus Alps, s central Switzerland, 5 m. NW of Disentis.

Obergabelhorn Peak (13,340 ft) in the Pennine Alps, s Switzerland, 4 m. WNW of Zermatt. The Untergabelhorn (11,138 ft) is SE.

Obstruction Mountain (10,394 ft) in the Rocky Mountains, sw Alberta, near the SE edge of Jasper National Park, 60 m. SE of Jasper.

Occidental, Cordillera Name applied to several mountain ranges in Spanish-speaking countries, especially in the Andes. In Bolivia, the term refers to the main range of the Andes, in Peru to the westernmost part of the main range. In Ecuador it forms the western of two ranges enclosing the central tableland, and in Colombia it is the westernmost of the three main cordilleras which fan out N to the Caribbean.

Ojos del Salado, Cerro Andean peak (*c.* 22,550 ft) on the Argentina-Chile border, 15 m. wsw of Cerro Incahuasi; it is the second highest peak in the western hemisphere.

Olan, Pic d' Peak (11,739 ft) of the Massif du Pelvoux, Dauphiné Alps, SE France, 10 m. NE of Saint-Firmin.

Olancha Peak (12,135 ft) in the Sierra Nevada, E California, on the Inyo-Tulare county border, 24 m. s of Lone Pine.

Olca, Cerro Andean peak (17,420 ft) on the Chile-Bolivia border.

Old Baldy Peak (14,125 ft) in Sierra Blanca of Sangre de Cristo Mountains, just NE of Blanca Peak.

Oldenhorn Peak (10,256 ft) in the Diablerets of the Bernese Alps, sw Switzerland, 9 m. NW of Sion. Also called Becca d'Audon.

Oldhorn Mountain (10,125 ft) in the Rocky Mountains, w Alberta, near the British Columbia border, in Jasper National Park, 11 m. sw of Jasper.

Olivares, Cerro de Andean peak (20,512 ft) on the Argentina-Chile border, 40 m. wsw of Rodeo, Argentina.

Ollagüe, Cerro Andean peak (29,260 ft) on the Chile-Bolivia border.

Olperer Highest peak (11,414 ft) of Tuxer Alps, Tyrol, w Austria, 8 m. ENE of Brenner Pass.

Olympus, Mount (10,132 ft) in the Rocky Mountains, sw Alberta, near the British Columbia border, in Jasper National Park, 50 m. SE of Jasper.

On-take Peak (10,108 ft), central Honshu, Japan, 36 m.

sw of Matsumoto. 14th-century Shinto shrine and several small lakes on the summit.

Oquirrh Mountains NW Utah, extending *c.* 30 m. s from Great Salt Lake. Rise to *c.* 11,000 ft.

Orange Range Central New Guinea, forming the E section of the Snow Mountains. Extends *c.* 200 m. E from Nassau Range to the border of the Australian territories. Rises to *c.* 15,585 ft in Mt Wilhelmina.

Oriental, Cordillera Name applied to several mountain ranges in Spanish-speaking countries, especially in the Andes. In Bolivia, the term refers to a branch range of the Andes, bounding the Altiplano on the E, its highest section being known as Cordillera de la Paz. In Peru, it is the easternmost range between Nudo de Vilcanota and Nudo de Pasco. In Ecuador, it forms the eastern of two ranges enclosing the central tableland. In Colombia, it is again the easternmost of the three main cordilleras which fan out N to the Caribbean.

Orny, Pointe d' Peak (10,751 ft) in the Pennine Alps, sw Switzerland, 7 m. s of Martigny-Ville.

Ortiga, Cordillera de la Andean range in NW San Juan province, Argentina, near the Chile border; extends *c.* 30 m. N-s and rises to *c.* 18,860 ft.

Oseras, Altos de las Andean massif (12,565 ft) in the Cordillera Oriental, w central Colombia, 60 m. ssw of Bogotá.

Oso, Mount Peak (13,706 ft) in the Rocky Mountains, La Plata county, sw Colorado.

Ötztal Alps E division of the Central Alps along the Austro-Italian border, chiefly in s Tyrol, Austria; extend E from the Rhaetian Alps at Passo di Resia to Zillertal Alps at Brenner Pass. Highest peak is Wildspitze (12,379 ft).

Ouray Peak (13,955 ft) in the s tip of the Sawatch Mountains, 18 m. sw of Salida.

Overo, Cerro Andean volcano (15,630 ft) in Mendoza province, Argentina, 45 m. SE of Rancagua (Chile).

Oxford, Mount Peak (14,000 ft) in the Rocky Mountains, Chaffee county, central Colorado.

Pacajes y Carangas, Cordillera de Section of the Western Cordillera of the Andes on the Chile-Bolivia border; extends *c.* 140 m. s from the Peru border to Isluga Volcano and rises to 21,390 ft in the Sajama.

Paghman Mountains s outlier of the Hindu Kush, in E Afghanistan, forming watershed between the Helmand and Kabul river basins. Rises to 15,417 ft 22 m. NW of Kabul.

Pagoda Peak (13,491 ft) in the Front Range, N Colorado. Rises on the sw slope of Longs Peak, 25 m. NW of Boulder.

Pagosa Peak (12,674 ft) in the San Juan Mountains, Mineral county, sw Colorado, 12 m. NNW of Pagosa Springs (town).

Palandoken Dag Peak (10,249 ft) in E central Turkey, 10 m. ssw of Erzurum.

Palomaní Andean peak (18,924 ft) in the Nudo de Apolobamba, on the Peru-Bolivia border, 45 m. sw of Huancané.

Palomo, Cerro del Andean peak (15,930 ft) in O'Higgins province, central Chile, 40 m. SE of Rancagua.

Palpana, Cerro Andean peak (19,815 ft) in N Chile, near the Bolivia border.

Pambrun, Mount (10,400 ft) in the Selkirk Mountains, SE British Columbia, 50 m. NE of Nelson.

Pamir-Alai One of the main mountain systems of Central Asia, in the USSR, China and Afghanistan. Extends from the Tien Shan (N) to the Hindu Kush and Kunlun mountains (s). Includes the Pamirs, Trans-Alai Range, Peter the First Range and Akademiya Nauk Range.

Panamint Range Desert range (c. 6,000–11,000 ft), mainly in Inyo county, E California, near the Nevada border and along the w side of Death Valley; rises to 11,045 ft at Telescope Peak.

Pan de Azucar Andean peak (15,320 ft) in the Cordillera Central, sw Colombia, 25 m. SE of Popayán.

Pando, Cerro Peak (10,375 ft) in the continental divide, on the Panama-Costa Rica border.

Pangong Range SE extension of the Kailas-Karakoram Range, E Kashmir and w Tibet; extends c. 170 m. WNW-ESE between Pangong Tso (lake) and Ladakh Range, rising to 22,060 ft in w.

Paramillos, Sierra de los (Sierra de Uspallata) Sub-Andean range in Mendoza province, Argentina, w and NW of Mendoza; extends c. 70 m. s from San Juan province border and rises to over 11,000 ft.

Páramo Cendé Peak (11,653 ft) on the Trujillo-Lara border, NW Venezuela, in N Andean spur.

Parang Pass (18,300 ft) in the SE Punjab Himalayas, Kangra district, NE Punjab, India.

Park Cone Peak (12,102 ft) in the Rocky Mountains, Gunnison county, w central Colorado.

Park Range Colorado and Wyoming, in the Rocky Mountains; extends c. 200 m. NNW from NW Park county, central Colorado, into Carbon county, s Wyoming. Highest peak is Mt Lincoln (14,284 ft).

Park View Peak (12,433 ft) in the Front Range, N Colorado, between Grand and Jackson counties.

Paropamisus Mountains w outlier of the Hindu Kush in NW Afghanistan, extending c. 300 m. along the right (N) watershed of the Hari Rud, between the Iran border and the Koh-i-Baba. Rises to over 11,000 ft 50 m. ENE of Herat.

Parpaillon, Chaine du Offshoot range of the Cottian Alps, SE France, along the Basses-Alpes-Hautes-Alpes border. Extends c. 30 m. from Savines (w) to the Italian border sw of Monte Viso. Rises to 11,057 ft at the Pointe de la Font-Sancte.

Pasco, Nudo de High mountain knot of the Andes in the Pasco department, central Peru, considered

to be the junction of the cordilleras Occidental, Central and Oriental converging from N and s. The massif consists of several peaks, the highest of which is 15,118 ft.

Pasochoa, Cerro (Cerro Pasuchoa) Extinct Andean volcano (13,776 ft), Pichincha province, N central Ecuador, 18 m. s of Quito.

Pass Mountain Peak (11,400 ft) in the Rocky Mountains, Park county, central Colorado.

Pastos Grandes, Sierra de Sub-Andean mountain range in w Salta province, Argentina, w of Poma. Extends c. 35 m. N-s and rises to 20,175 ft in the peak Nevado Pastos Grandes, 28 m. wsw of San Antonio de los Cobres.

Patamban, Cerro Peak (12,303 ft) in Michoacan, N central Mexico, 18 m. ssw of Zamora.

Patascoy de Santa Lucía, Cerro Andean peak (c. 13,000 ft) in Putumayo commissary, sw Colombia, 25 m. SE of Pasto.

Patkai Range Culminating section of the Naga Hills, on the Burma-India border; rises to 12,553 ft in the Saramati.

Patos, Cerro Andean volcano (18,900 ft) in N Catamarca province, Argentina, 15 m. NW of Antofalla volcano.

Patos, Cerro de los Andean peak (15,960 ft) on the Argentina-Chile border.

Patterson, Mount (10,490 ft) in the Rocky Mountains, sw Alberta, near the British Columbia border, in Banff National Park, 60 m. NW of Banff.

Pavant Mountains In Fishlake National Forest, Millard and Sevier counties, sw central Utah; extend c. 45 m. N from the Tushar Mountains along the w bank of the Sevier River and rise to 10,082 ft in Mt Catherine.

Pax, Cerro Andean peak (10,990 ft) on the Ecuador-Colombia border, 33 m. ssE of Ipiales.

Payachata, Nevados de Andean massif on the Chile-Bolivia border, 80 m. WNW of Arica. Includes two snow-capped peaks, Cerro de Pomarepe (20,472 ft) and Cerro de Parinacota (20,767 ft).

Payún Plateau Sub-Andean highland in s Mendoza province, Argentina, E of the Río Grande; generally over 5,000 ft, rising to 12,075 ft.

Peale, Mount Highest peak (13,089 ft) in La Sal Mountains, E Utah, 20 m. SE of Moab, near the Colorado border.

Pede Peak (17,699 ft) 2 m. N of Pede (town), s Tibet, on Lake Yamdrok Tso.

Peinado, Cerro Andean volcano (18,830 ft) in w Catamarca province, Argentina, 30 m. NNE of Cerro Incahuasi, at the sw tip of the Sierra de Calalaste.

Pelagatos, Nevado Peak (16,168 ft) in Ancash department, w central Peru, in the Cordillera Occidental of the Andes, 30 m. wsw of Buldibuyo.

Pelat, Mont Highest peak (10,017 ft) of the Provence Alps, Basses-Alpes department, SE France, 4 m. NE of Allos.

Pele La Pass (11,055 ft) in Black Mountain Range, central Bhutan, 19 m. w of Tongsa.

Peña Blanca, Cerros Andean massif (19,750 ft) in

Atacama province, N Chile, near the Argentina border.

Peña Negra Pass (14,100 ft) in the Andes, on the Argentina-Chile border, on the road between San Juan (Argentina) and Coquimbo (Chile).

Peña Nevada Peak (11,955 ft) in the Sierra Madre Oriental, N Mexico, 45 m. w of Ciudad Victoria.

Penibética, Cordillera Mountain system of Andalusia, in SE and s Spain, forming a wide arc c. 600 m. long from Cape Nao (Alicante province) to Point Marroquí (Cádiz province). Its principal range is the Sierra Nevada, the highest peak of which is the Mulhacén (11,411 ft).

Penitentes, Cordón de los Andean range in NW Mendoza and sw San Juan provinces, Argentina. Extends c. 20 m. N of Aconcagua massif; contains a number of peaks over 18,000 ft.

Pequop Mountains NE Nevada, in E Elko county, E of Ruby Mountains. Highest point is Spruce Mountain (11,041 ft), in the sw spur.

Perdido, Monte Peak (10,997 ft) in the central Pyrenees, NE Spain, near the French border, 14 m. SSE of Luz (France).

Perijá, Sierra de Andean range on the Colombia-Venezuela border, N spur of the Cordillera Oriental. Extends c. 190 m. NNE-SSW and rises to 12,300 ft.

Perote, Cofre de Peak (14,048 ft) in Veracruz, E Mexico, 15 m. w of Jalapa. Extinct volcano. Also called Nauhcampatépetl.

Peteroa Volcano Andean volcano (13,420 ft) on the Argentina-Chile border, 40 m. ESE of Curicó.

Peters Dome Mountain (10,500 ft) in the Alaska Range, s central Alaska, in Mt McKinley National Park, 140 m. NNW of Anchorage.

Petersgrat Ridge (10,532 ft) in the Bernese Alps, s central Switzerland, 8 m. sw of Mürren.

Peter the First Range Branch of the Pamir-Alai mountain system, Tadzhik SSR. Extends 90 m. from Stalin Peak to the area of Garm; rises to 20,840 ft at Kirov Peak and to 24,590 ft at Stalin Peak. Has many glaciers.

Petrov Glacier On s slope of the Terskei Ala-Tau, in Kirghiz SSR. Has a meteorological observation post at 12,045 ft.

Picacho del Carmen, Cerro Highest peak (10,925 ft) in Guanajuato, central Mexico, in the Sierra Madre, 14 m. ENE of Alvaro Obregón.

Pichu Pichu, Nevado de Volcanic massif, Arequipa department, s Peru, just SE of El Misti, E of Arequipa; comprises several peaks, rising to c. 18,400 ft.

Pico Blanco Peak (11,696 ft) in the Cordillera de Talamanca, SE Costa Rica, 22 m. E of Buenos Aires.

Pie de Palo, Sierra del Pampean range in E San Juan province, Argentina, E of San Juan. Extends c. 40 m. N-S and rises to c. 10,000 ft.

Piedra Pomez, Campo de Sub-Andean plateau (c. 13,000 ft) in Puna de Atacama, N Catamarca province, Argentina, at the SE foot of the Sierra de Calalaste.

Piedras Blancas Andean massif (15,623 ft) in Mérida state, w Venezuela, in the Sierra Nevada de Mérida, 22 m. NNE of Mérida.

Pinaleno Mountains Range in Graham county, SE Arizona, sw of Safford, in part of Crook National Forest. 40 m. long, 8 m. wide. Highest peaks are Mt Graham (10,713 ft) and Hawk Peak (10,600 ft).

Pine Valley Mountains Dixie National Forest, Washington county, sw Utah, N of St George; rise to 10,324 ft.

Pingüicas, Cerro Peak (10,469 ft) in Queretaro, central Mexico, 3 m. WNW of Amoles.

Pintada Peak (13,176 ft) in the San Juan Mountains, Rio Grande county, s Colorado.

Pioneer Mountains Spur of the Bitterroot Range of the Rocky Mountains in sw Montana, extending N to the Continental Divide. Highest point is Torrey Mountain (11,170 ft).

Pioneer Peak Mountain (22,600 ft) in the Karakoram; first climbed by Martin Conway, 1892.

Pircas Pass (16,000 ft) in the Andes, on the Argentina-Chile border, on the road between Tupungato (Argentina) and El Volcán (Chile).

Pir Panjal Range s lateral range of the Punjab Himalayas, sw Kashmir and NW India; extends c. 200 m. SE from Jhelum River to upper Beas River, forming w border of the Vale of Kashmir. Rises to over 19,000 ft in the s. Pir Panjal Pass (11,462 ft) is 35 m. ssw of Srinagar.

Pisgah, Mount Peak (10,085 ft) in the Front Range, between Clear Creek and Gilpin counties, central Colorado.

Pissis, Monte Andean peak (22,240 ft) on the Catamarca-La Rioja province border, Argentina, 73 m. w of Fiambalá.

Piuquenes Pass (13,220 ft) in the Andes, on the Argentina-Chile border, 20 m. ssw of Tupungato peak, on the road between Tunuyán (Argentina) and El Volcán (Chile).

Piuquenes Mountain (19,685 ft) 8 m. N of Piuquenes Pass.

Piz Buin Peak (10,880 ft) in the Silvretta Group of the Rhaetian Alps, on the Swiss-Austrian border, E of Klosters.

Piz d'Err Peak (11,094 ft) in the Rhaetian Alps, SE Switzerland, 8 m. WNW of St Moritz.

Piz Duan Peak (10,279 ft) in the Rhaetian Alps, SE Switzerland, 9 m. sw of Sils im Engadin.

Piz Julier Peak (11,103 ft) in the Rhaetian Alps, SE Switzerland, 4 m. w of St Moritz.

Piz Kesch Highest peak (11,223 ft) in the Albula Alps, SE Switzerland, 9 m. N of St Moritz.

Piz Languard Peak (10,715 ft) in the Rhaetian Alps, SE Switzerland, 2 m. E of Pontresina.

Piz Linard Peak (11,200 ft) in the Rhaetian Alps, E Switzerland, 11 m. E of Davos; highest in the Silvretta Group.

Piz Lischanna Peak (10,202 ft) in the Rhaetian Alps, E Switzerland, 3 m. SE of Schuls.

Piz Medel   Peak (10,542 ft) in the Lepontine Alps, E central Switzerland, 6 m. SSE of Disentis.

Piz Ot   Peak (10,662 ft) in the Albula Alps, SE Switzerland, 3 m. NNW of St Moritz.

Piz Quatervals   Peak (10,396 ft) in the Rhaetian Alps, E Switzerland, 9 m. W of Ofen Pass.

Piz Sesvenna   Peak (10,523 ft) in the Rhaetian Alps, E Switzerland, on the Italian border, 7 m. NE of Ofen Pass.

Pizzo Rotondo   Peak (10,483 ft) in the Lepontine Alps, s Switzerland, 7 m. W of Airolo.

Planchón   Andean peak (13,025 ft) on the Argentina-Chile border.

Plomo, Nevado del   Andean peak (19,850 ft) on the Argentina-Chile border, 30 m. s of Aconcagua peak.

Pobeda Peak   Highest point (24,406 ft) in the Tien Shan mountain system, and second highest peak in the U S S R. Situated on the China-U S S R border, 100 m. E of the lake Issyk-Kul, 10 m. s of the peak Khan Tengri.

Poboktan Mountain   (10,920 ft) in sw Alberta, near the British Columbia border, in the Rocky Mountains, and included in Jasper National Park.

Pocitos, Cerro   Peak (16,463 ft) to the N of the salt desert Salar Pocitos in the Puna de Atacama, W Salta province, Argentina.

Pole Creek Mountain   Peak (13,740 ft) in the San Juan Mountains, sw Colorado, 13 m. E of Silverton.

Portillo, Cordón del   Andean range in w Mendoza province, Argentina, w of San Carlos; extends *c.* 35 m. s from Tupungato peak, rising to over 17,000 ft.

Portillo, Paso del   Andean pass (*c.* 13,500 ft) on the Argentina-Chile border, on the road between San Juan (Argentina) and Ovalle (Chile).

Posets, Pico   Peak (11,046 ft) in the central Pyrenees, Huesca province, NE Spain, 12 m. W of Pico de Aneto.

Potato Peak   (*c.* 10,200 ft), Mono county, E California, 12 m. N of Mono Lake.

Potro, Cerro del   Andean peak (19,125 ft) on the Argentina-Chile border.

Pourri, Mont   Alpine peak (12,428 ft) in the Savoy Alps, Savoie department, SE France, 8 m. SE of Bourg-Saint-Maurice.

Powell, Mount   (13,398 ft) in Gore Range, N central Colorado, 35 m. N of Leadville.

Premier Group   Short range of high peaks in the Rocky Mountains, SE British Columbia, 70 m. W of Jasper, overlooking the Fraser River valley. Highest point is Mt Sir Wilfrid Laurier (11,750 ft).

Presanella, La   Glacier-topped N arm of the Adamello mountain group, N Italy, separated from it by the upper Sarca River. Highest peak is Cima Presanella (11,666 ft), 8 m. ESE of Ponte di Legno.

Princeton, Mount   (14,177 ft), central Colorado, in Collegiate Range of the Sawatch Mountains, sw of Buena Vista.

Pshish   Peak (12,430 ft) in the main range of the w Greater Caucasus, on the Russia-Georgia border, 30 m. NNE of Sukhumi.

Ptarmigan Peak   1. Peak (13,736 ft) in Park Range, N central Colorado.
2. Peak (12,400 ft) in the Williams River Mountains, N central Colorado, *c.* 50 m. W of Denver.

Pular, Cerro   Andean peak (20,375 ft) in N Chile, near the Argentina border.

Púlpito   Andean peak (12,834 ft) in Táchira state, w Venezuela, 32 m. NE of San Cristóbal.

Pulsatilla, Mount   (10,060 ft) in the Rocky Mountains, sw Alberta, near the British Columbia border, in Banff National Park, 23 m. NW of Banff.

Punilla, Sierra   Sub-Andean mountain range on the La Rioja-San Juan province border, Argentina, w of Guandacol; extends *c.* 65 m. N-s and rises to over 15,000 ft.

Puntas Negras, Cordón de   Andean massif on the Chile-Argentina border; rises to *c.* 22,000 ft.

Puntiagudo, Cerro (Cerro Lamas)   Andean mountain (19,350 ft) on the Argentina-Chile border, 32 m. wsw of the Cerro Incahuasi.

Puquintica, Cerro   Andean mountain (18,897 ft) on the Chile-Bolivia border.

Puracé Volcano   Active volcano (15,420 ft) in Cauca department, sw Colombia, in the Cordillera Central, 17 m. ESE of Popayán.

Purple Peak   (12,900 ft) in the Rocky Mountains, Gunnison county, w central Colorado. Also known as Slate Peak.

Pyramid Peak   1. Mountain (10,020 ft) in the Sierra Nevada, E California, just sw of Lake Tahoe.
2. Mountain (14,000 ft) in the Elk Mountains, w central Colorado, 10 m. ssw of Aspen.

Qara Dag   Mountain range in Azerbaijan, NW Iran, between the rivers Tabriz and Aras; rises to *c.* 10,000 ft.

Queen Alexandra Range   Antarctica, w of the Beardmore Glacier, at the head of Ross Shelf Ice. Rises to 14,603 ft in Mount Kirkpatrick.

Queen Bess, Mount   (10,700 ft) in the Coast Mountains, sw British Columbia, 150 m. N of Vancouver.

Queen Mary, Mount   (10,600 ft), SE British Columbia, near the Alberta border, in the Rocky Mountains, 40 m. s of Banff.

Quemado, Cerro   Inactive volcano (10,430 ft) in sw Guatemala, 3 m. s of Quezaltenango.

Quichagua, Sierra de   Sub-Andean mountain range in w Jujuy province, Argentina, 20 m. SE of Rinconada; extends *c.* 25 m. NE-sw and rises to *c.* 14,000 ft.

Quilindaña, Cerro   Andean peak (16,000 ft) in E central Ecuador, SE of Cotopaxi volcano and 40 m. ssE of Quito.

Quincy Adams, Mount   (13,560 ft) on the Alaska-British Columbia border, in the Fairweather Range, 5 m. E of Mount Fairweather.

347

Quindío, Nevado   Andean peak (16,900 ft) in the Cordillera Central, just w of Nevado del Tolima and 20 m. NW of Ibagué. At the s foot is Quindío Pass, and s again of this is another pass (10,760 ft) carrying part of the Pan American Highway.

Rabbit Ears Mountain   Peak (10,719 ft) in the Rocky Mountains, NW Colorado, 12 m. ESE of Steamboat Springs.

Rae, Mount   (10,576 ft) in the Misty Range of the Rocky Mountains, sw Alberta, near the British Columbia border, 50 m. SE of Banff.

Raft River Mountains   Range in Minidoka National Forest, NW Utah; extend E-W along the Idaho border, rising to 10,000 ft.

Ramada, Cordillera de la   Andean range in sw San Juan province, Argentina, near the Chile border; rises to c. 20,500 ft.

Rantemario, Mount   Highest peak (11,286 ft) in Celebes, Indonesia, at the base of the sw peninsula, 30 m. ssw of Palopo.

Ratz, Mount   (10,290 ft), NW British Columbia, near the Alaska border, in the Coast Mountains.

Razorback   Mountain (10,667 ft) in the Coast Mountains, sw British Columbia, 170 m. NNW of Vancouver.

Redcloud Peak   (14,050 ft) in the San Juan Mountains, sw Colorado, 16 m. NE of Silverton.

Red Mountain Pass   (11,018 ft) in the San Juan Mountains, sw Colorado, 6 m. ESE of Telluride.

Red Mountains   Spur of the Continental Divide in the s part of Yellowstone National Park, NW Wyoming. Highest point is Mount Sheridan (10,385 ft).

Redoubt, Mount   Active volcano (10,198 ft) in s Alaska, w of Cook Inlet, 110 m. wsw of Anchorage.

Red Slate Mountain   (13,152 ft) in the Sierra Nevada, E California, c. 25 m. s of Mono Lake.

Reeds Peak   (10,011 ft) in Black Range, sw New Mexico, 35 m. w of Hot Springs.

Regal Mountain   (13,408 ft) in the Wrangell Mountains, s Alaska, 130 m. NE of Cordova.

Remote Mountain   (11,000 ft) in the Coast Mountains, sw British Columbia, 190 m. NW of Vancouver.

Resthaven Mountain   (10,253 ft) in the Rocky Mountains, w Alberta, near the British Columbia border, at N edge of Jasper National Park, 70 m. NW of Jasper.

Rhaetian Alps   Division of the Central Alps along the Italo-Swiss and Austro-Swiss borders; extend from the Lepontine Alps to the Ötztal and Lechtal Alps. Highest peak is the Piz Bernina (13,304 ft) in the Bernina Alps.

Rhätikon   Mountain chain of the Rhaetian Alps, Grisons canton, Switzerland; highest peak (9,736 ft) is Scesaplana, on Austro-Swiss border.

Rheinquellhorn   Peak (10,499 ft) in the Adula group of the Lepontine Alps, SE Switzerland.

Rheinwaldhorn   Highest peak (11,173 ft) in the Adula group of the Lepontine Alps, SE Switzerland, 9 m. NNE of Biasca.

Rhonestock   Peak (11,811 ft) in the Alps, s central Switzerland, 13 m. SE of Meiringen.

Rhyolite Mountain   Peak (10,731 ft) in Front Range, Teller county, central Colorado.

Richardson, Mount   Peak (10,125 ft) in the Rocky Mountains, sw Alberta, near the British Columbia border, in Banff National Park, 32 m. NW of Banff.

Richthofen Mountains   N range of the Nan Shan, China, N of the lake Koko Nor; rise to 19,000 ft.

Rico, Páramo   Andean peak (13,779 ft) in the Cordillera Oriental, Santander department, N central Colombia, 18 m. NE of Bucaramanga.

Rila Mountains   Highest range in Bulgaria and the Balkan Peninsula, forming NW part of Rhodope Mountains; c. 50 m. E-W, c. 30 m. N-S.

Rimpfischhorn   Peak (13,787 ft) in the Pennine Alps, s Switzerland, 6 m. E of Zermatt.

Rincón, Cerro   Andean volcano (18,353 ft) on the Argentina-Chile border, 65 m. WNW of San Antonio de los Cobres.

Rincon Peak   (c. 11,600 ft) in the Sangre de Cristo Mountains, N New Mexico, 23 m. ENE of Santa Fe.

Rinderhorn   Peak (11,343 ft) in the Bernese Alps, s Switzerland, 7 m. N of Leuk.

Ringelspitz   Peak (10,666 ft) in the Glarus Alps, E Switzerland, 9 m. WNW of Chur.

Rinjani, Mount   Highest volcanic peak (12,224 ft) in Lombok, Indonesia, in the N part of the island.

Rio Negro, Cerro de   Andean peak (19,815 ft) in N Chile, E of the Salar de Atacama.

Rito Alto Peak   (13,573 ft) in the Sangre de Cristo Mountains, s central Colorado.

Ritter, Mount   (13,156 ft) in the Sierra Nevada, E California, 19 m. ssw of Mono Lake.

Ritzlihorn   Peak (10,782 ft) in the Bernese Alps, s central Switzerland, 7 m. SSE of Meiringen.

Rize Mountains   NE Turkey, s and E of Rize (town). Extend 80 m. sw-NE between the Black Sea and Coruh River; rise to 12,917 ft in Kackar Dag.

Roberts Mountains   Eureka county, central Nevada, SE of the Cortez Mountains. Rise to 10,125 ft in Roberts Creek Mountain, 30 m. NW of Eureka.

Rochebrune, Pic de   Peak (10,905 ft) of the Cottian Alps, SE France, 9 m. SE of Briançon.

Rogers, Mount   (10,525 ft) in the Selkirk Mountains, SE British Columbia, 40 m. NE of Revelstoke.

Rohtang Pass   (13,050 ft) in SE Pir Panjal Range of the Punjab Himalayas, NE Punjab, India, 55 m. ENE of Dharmsala.

Root, Mount   (12,860 ft) in the Fairweather Range, on the Alaska-British Columbia border, 7 m. N of Mount Fairweather.

Rosario, Peñón del Peak (11,214 ft) in central Mexico, on the Tlaxcala-Puebla border, 8 m. NW of Tlaxco.

Roseg, Piz Peak (12,933 ft) in the Bernina Alps.

Rosenhorn Peak (12,114 ft) in the Bernese Alps, s central Switzerland, 5 m. E of Grindelwald.

Royal Society Range Antarctica, on the w shore of Ross Sea, near the head of McMurdo Sound; highest point is Mount Lister (13,350 ft).

Ruby Mountains NE Nevada, largely in Elko county, extending c. 60 m. SSW from the East Humboldt Range through part of Humboldt National Forest. Rise to 11,400 ft.

Ruinette Peak (12,726 ft) in the Pennine Alps, s Switzerland, 11 m. SE of Bagnes.

Ruiz, Nevado del Andean volcanic peak (17,720 ft) in the Cordillera Central, w central Colombia, 20 m. SE of Manizales.

Rumiñahui, Cerro Extinct Andean volcano (15,482 ft), Pichincha province, N central Ecuador, 25 m. s of Quito. It is a twin peak.

Russell, Mount 1. (11,500 ft) in the Alaska Range, s central Alaska, 130 m. NW of Anchorage, in the SW corner of Mount McKinley National Park.
2. (14,190 ft), E California, in the Sierra Nevada, just N of Mount Whitney.

Sabinio, Mount Extinct volcano (c. 11,500 ft) in the Virunga range, E central Africa, NE of Lake Kivu.

Sacajaewea Peak (10,033 ft) in the Wallowa Mountains, NE Oregon, near Wallowa Lake.

Sacramento Mountains New Mexico and Texas, extending generally N-S. Sometimes defined as part of the s Rocky Mountains. Highest peak is Sierra Blanca (12,003 ft).

Safed Koh 1. w outlier of the Hindu Kush, one of the Firoz Koh ranges, in NW Afghanistan. Extends c. 100 m. along the left watershed of the Hari Rud; rises to c. 10,000 ft.
2. Range on Afghanistan-Pakistan border, extending 100 m. and forming s watershed of the Kabul River. Rises to 15,620 ft in the Sikaram.

Sahand Volcanic cone (12,140 ft) in Azerbaijan, NW Iran, 30 m. SSE of Tabriz. Snow-capped, with mineral springs.

Sailyugem Range Part of the Altai Mountains, on the USSR-Mongolia border. Extends NE from the Tabun Bogdo mountain knot; rises to 13,927 ft.

Saint Bride, Mount (10,875 ft) in the Rocky Mountains, SW Alberta, near the British Columbia border, in Banff National Park, 30 m. NW of Banff.

Saint Elias, Mount Peak (18,008 ft) in the St Elias Mountains, on the Yukon-Alaska border, 200 m. w of Whitehorse.

Saksak Dag Peak (10,335 ft) in E central Turkey, 25 m. s of Erzurum.

Salín, Cerro Andean volcano (19,880 ft) on the Argentina-Chile border.

Salmon River Mountains E Idaho, bounded on the s, E and N by Salmon River. Chief peaks are Bald Mountain (10,314 ft) and Twin Peaks (10,328 ft).

Salt River Range Rocky Mountains, w Wyoming, just E of the Idaho border. Extends c. 70 m. N-S between Salt and Greys rivers. Chief peaks are Virginia Peak (10,143 ft), Man Peak (10,327 ft) and Mount Wagner (10,745 ft).

Samdi Dag Peak (12,503 ft) in the Hakari Mountains, SE Turkey, 15 m. w of Semdinli.

San Antonio Peak Highest point (10,080 ft) in the San Gabriel Mountains, s California, 23 m. NW of San Bernadino. Popularly called Old Baldy.

San Bernardino Mountains s California, extending c. 55 m. SE from Cajon Pass at the E end of the San Gabriel Mountains to San Gorgonio Pass at the N end of the San Jacinto Mountains. Highest points are San Bernadino Mountain (10,630 ft) and Mount San Gorgonio (11,485 ft).

Sandia Mountains Central New Mexico, E of the Rio Grande. Highest point is Sandia Peak (10,695 ft).

Sanford, Mount Highest peak (16,208 ft) in the Wrangell Mountains, s Alaska, 100 m. NE of Valdez.

San Francisco, Cerro Andean volcano (19,750 ft) on the Argentina-Chile border. San Francisco Pass (15,505 ft) is at its NW foot.

San Gabriel Mountains Range in s California, extending c. 60 m. E-w from the E end of the Santa Susana Mountains to the NW end of the San Bernardino Mountains. Highest point is San Antonio Peak (10,080 ft).

Sangay Volcano Andean peak (17,454 ft) in E central Ecuador, 30 m. SE of Riobamba. Snow-capped, still active.

San Gorgonio, Mount Peak (11,485 ft) in the San Bernardino Mountains, s California, c. 80 m. E of Los Angeles.

San Jacinto Mountains Range in s California extending c. 30 m. SSE from the San Bernardino Mountains to the N end of the Santa Rosa Mountains. Highest peak is Mount San Jacinto (10,805 ft) at the N end of the range.

San José Volcano Andean peak (19,130 ft) on the Argentina-Chile border, 80 m. s of the Aconcagua.

San Juan Mountains Range of the Rocky Mountains in SW Colorado and N New Mexico. Highest peak is Uncompahgre Peak (14,306 ft).

San Lorenzo, Cerro Andean peak (12,140 ft) on the Argentina-Chile border.

San Luis Peak (14,149 ft) in the San Juan Mountains, SW Colorado, 9 m. N of Creede.

San Mateo Mountains 1. w central New Mexico, w of the Rio Grande. Chief peaks are San Mateo Peak and Vicks Peak, both over 11,000 ft.
2. NW New Mexico, just N of San Jose River. Highest point is Mount Taylor (11,389 ft).

San Miguel Mountains w spur of the San Juan Mountains, SW Colorado. Highest points are Dolores Peak (13,502 ft) and Mount Wilson (14,250 ft).

San Pedro Martír, Sierra Range in Lower California,

NW Mexico. Extends *c.* 90 m. and rises to 10,063 ft in Cerro La Encantada.

San Pedro Volcano   Andean peak (19,585 ft) in Antofagasta province, N Chile, near the Bolivia border.

Sans Toucher, Mont   Dormant volcano (4,855 ft) on Guadeloupe, just N of the Soufrière.

Santa Catalina, Sierra de   Range in NW Jujuy province, Argentina, near the Bolivia border. Extends *c.* 70 m. NNE-SSW and rises to *c.* 15,000 ft.

Santa Isabel, Nevado de   Andean volcanic peak (16,730 ft), w central Colombia, in the Cordillera Central, 21 m. SSE of Manizales.

Santa Marta, Sierra Nevada de   Andean massif in Magdalena department, N Colombia, on the Caribbean coast. Highest point is Pico Cristóbal Colón (18,950 ft).

Santa Victoria, Sierra   Sub-Andean mountain range on the Jujuy-Salta province border, w of Santa Victoria. Extends *c.* 40 m. N-S, forming the w watershed of the upper Bermejo River. Rises to *c.* 15,000 ft.

Santo Domingo, Sierra de   Range in w Venezuela, forming the NE section of the Andean spur, Sierra Nevada de Mérida; rises to 15,328 ft in Pico Mucuñuque.

San Valentín, Cerro   Peak (13,313 ft) in s Chile, 90 m. SSW of Puerto Aysén, in an area of snow-covered peaks and glaciers. It has the San Rafael Glacier on its w slope. Also called Cerro San Clemente.

Saraurcu, Cerro   Andean peak (15,341 ft) in N Ecuador, 40 m. E of Quito.

Sarikol Range   China-USSR border, forming the E edge of the Pamir. Extends parallel to the Muztagh Ata Range; rises to over 15,000 ft.

Sarrail, Mount   (10,400 ft) in the Rocky Mountains, SW Alberta, near the British Columbia border, 45 m. SSE of Banff.

Saskatchewan, Mount   (10,964 ft) in the Rocky Mountains, SW Alberta, in Banff National Park, 70 m. SE of Jasper.

Saugstad, Mount   (10,000 ft) in the Coast Mountains, w British Columbia, 50 m. E of Ocean Falls.

Saur Range   Northernmost outlier of the Tien Shan mountain system on the China-USSR border. Rises to 12,300 ft.

Savoy Alps   NW offshoots of the Graian Alps, SE France. Rise to 12,668 ft at the Grande-Casse.

Sawtooth Mountains   s central Idaho, NE of Boise, at the head of Salmon River. Highest peak is Castle Peak (11,820 ft).

Sawtooth Range   s part of the Sawtooth Mountains. Rises to 10,704 ft.

Scafell   Mountain group of the Cumbrians, s Cumberland, in the Lake District. It includes the highest peak in England, Scafell Pike (3,210 ft).

Schallihorn   Peak (13,050 ft) in the Pennine Alps, s Switzerland, NNW of Zermatt.

Scheerhorn (Grosses Scheerhorn)   Peak (10,820 ft)

in the Glarus Alps, E central Switzerland, 9 m. ESE of Altdorf. Kleines Scheerhorn (10,610 ft) is nearby.

Schienhorn   Peak (12,490 ft) in the Bernese Alps, s central Switzerland, 8 m. SSE of Mürren.

Scopi   Peak (10,506 ft) in the Alps, SE central Switzerland, 9 m. s of Disentis.

Seattle, Mount   (10,070 ft) in the St Elias Mountains, on the Yukon-Alaska border, 150 m. WSW of Whitehorse.

Sefton, Mount   Peak (10,354 ft) in the Southern Alps, w central South Island, New Zealand.

Sele La   Pass (12,000 ft) in the w Assam Himalayas, SW Bhutan, 16 m. SW of Paro.

Selkirk Mountains   Range of the Rocky Mountains, w of the main body of the Rocky Mountains, mainly in SE British Columbia. Extend 200 m. NW-SE, reaching to just within the U.S. in Idaho and Montana. Highest peak is Mount Sir Sanford (11,590 ft).

Semeru Mountains   Volcanic range in E Java, Indonesia. Extends *c.* 30 m. and rises to 12,060 ft in Mount Mahameru, the highest peak in Java.

Sentinel Mountains   Group in Ellsworth Highland, Antarctica; highest peak is Mount Ulmer (12,500 ft).

Sevier Plateau   Sevier, Piute and Garfield counties, s Utah. Extends N-S along the E bank of the Sevier River. Highest peak is Monroe Peak (11,226 ft).

Shackleton, Mount   (10,800 ft) in the Rocky Mountains, SE British Columbia, near the Alberta border, 50 m. s of Jasper.

Shakh-Dag   Range in the Lesser Caucasus, on the N shore of Lake Sevan. Rises to *c.* 10,900 ft.

Shandur Pass   Mountain pass (*c.* 12,250 ft) in the Hindu Kush, w Pakistan, 100 m. WNW of Gilgit.

Shavano Peak   (14,179 ft) in the s tip of the Sawatch Mountains, central Colorado, 14 m. WNW of Salida. The figure known as the Angel of Shavano is formed by melting snow in fissures on the peak.

Sheep Mountain   Peak (12,800 ft) in the Rocky Mountains, Park county, central Colorado.

Shell Creek Range   (12,000-13,000 ft), White Pine county, E Nevada.

Sherman, Mount   Peak (14,037 ft) in Park Range, central Colorado, 7 m. ESE of Leadville.

Shilla, Mount   Peak (23,050 ft) in the Zaskar Range of the SE Punjab Himalayas, NE Punjab, India, 110 m. ENE of Dharmsala.

Shipki Pass   (*c.* 15,400 ft) in the s Zaskar Range at the NW end of the Kumaun Himalayas, near the India-Tibet border.

Shirane, Mount   Peak (10,534 ft) in central Honshu, Japan, 20 m. w of Kofu. Its highest point is Kitadake.

Shkhara   Peak (17,037 ft) in the main range of the central Greater Caucasus, on the Russian-Georgian border, 40 m. sw of Nalchik.

Shoshone Mountains   Central Nevada, in Toiyabe National Forest. Highest points are North Shoshone

Peak (10,322 ft) and South Shoshone Peak (10,072 ft).

Siah Koh   sw outlier of the Hindu Kush in w Afghanistan. It is one of the Firoz Koh ranges; rises to *c.* 12,000 ft 80 m. ENE of Shindand.

Sicasica, Serranía de   w outlier of the Eastern Cordillera of the Andes, w Bolivia. Extends *c.* 90 m. NW from Colquiri to a point s of La Paz. Rises to 16,000 ft at the SE end.

Sidley, Mount   (12,000 ft) in the Executive Committee Range, Antarctica, in Marie Byrd Land.

Sierra Blanca   1. Range of the Sangre de Cristo Mountains in s Colorado. Highest points are Old Baldy (14,125 ft) and Blanca Peak (*c.* 14,363 ft).
2. Range of the Sacramento Mountains, s central New Mexico. Highest point is Sierra Blanca (12,003 ft), 33 m. NNE of Alamogordo.

Sierra Madre   Range in the Continental Divide, s Wyoming, forming an extension of the Park Range. Chief peaks are Vulcan Mountain (10,700 ft) and Bridger Peak (11,007 ft).

Sierra Nevada de Mérida   Mountain range in w Venezuela, forming a spur of the Andes. Extends *c.* 300 m. from the Colombian border NE to Barquisimeto at the foot of the Caribbean coastal range, and is 30–50 m. wide. Highest peak is La Columna (16,411 ft).

Signal Peak   (11,233 ft) in Sevier Plateau, sw central Utah.

Sikaram, Mount   Highest peak (15,620 ft) in the Safed Koh Range, on the Afghanistan-Pakistan border, 55 m. SE of Kabul.

Silberhorn   Peak (10,757 ft) in the Southern Alps, w central South Island, New Zealand.

Sillajhuay   Peak (19,695 ft) in the Andes, on the Chile-Bolivia border, NW of the Salar de Uyuni.

Silverheels, Mount   (13,825 ft) in the Rocky Mountains, Park county, central Colorado.

Silverthrone, Mount   (13,130 ft) in the Alaska Range, s central Alaska, 130 m. N of Anchorage, 10 m. ENE of Mount McKinley.

Silvrettahorn   Peak (10,656 ft) in the Silvretta Group of the Rhaetian Alps, on the Swiss-Austrian border, 10 m. E of Klosters.

Simen Mountains   Highest range in Ethiopia, Begemdir province, NE of Gondar. Rise to 15,157 ft in Ras Dashan.

Simon Peak   (10,899 ft) in the Rocky Mountains, w Alberta, near the British Columbia border, in Jasper National Park, 18 m. sw of Jasper.

Sincholagua, Cerro   Volcanic Andean peak (14,846 ft), Pichincha province, N central Ecuador, N of Cotopaxi volcano and 23 m. SSE of Quito.

Singalila Range   s spur of the E Nepal Himalayas, along the Nepal-India border. Extends *c.* 50 m. N-s. Highest point is Kanchenjunga (28,146 ft).

Siple, Mount   (15,000 ft) in Antarctica, at the E entrance of Marie Byrd Land.

Sir Alexander, Mount   (10,740 ft) in the Rocky Mountains, E British Columbia, 100 m. E of Prince George.

Sir Douglas, Mount   (11,174 ft) in the Rocky Mountains, sw Alberta, near the British Columbia border, 35 m. SSE of Banff.

Sir John Abbott, Mount   (11,250 ft) in the Premier Group of the Rocky Mountains, E British Columbia, 75 m. w of Jasper.

Sir John Thompson, Mount   (11,250 ft) in the Premier Group of the Rocky Mountains, E British Columbia, 70 m. w of Jasper.

Sir Mackenzie Bowell, Mount   (11,000 ft) in the Premier Group of the Rocky Mountains, E British Columbia, 70 m. w of Jasper.

Siroua, Djebel   Volcanic mountain in sw Morocco, forming a bridge between the High Atlas and the Anti-Atlas. Rises to 10,840 ft.

Sir Sandford, Mount   (11,590 ft) in the Selkirk Mountains, SE British Columbia, 55 m. NNW of Revelstoke.

Sir Wilfrid Laurier, Mount   (11,750 ft) in the Premier Group of the Rocky Mountains, E British Columbia, 70 m. w of Jasper.

Slamet, Mount   Volcanic peak (11,327 ft) in central Java, Indonesia, 55 m. SE of Cheribon.

Snake Range   White Pine county, E Nevada, near the Utah border, extending N-s. Highest points are Mount Moriah (12,049 ft) and Wheeler Peak (13,058 ft).

Sneffels, Mount   (14,143 ft) in the San Juan Mountains, sw Colorado, 5 m. N of Telluride.

Snowcrest Mountains   Range of the Rocky Mountains in sw Montana; extend *c.* 45 m. N from w of Ruby River, near the Idaho border. Highest peaks are Sunset Peak (10,573 ft) and Hogback Mountain (10,605 ft).

Snow Dome   Mountain (11,340 ft) in the Rocky Mountains, on the Alberta-British Columbia border, 60 m. SE of Jasper.

Snowmass Peak   (14,077 ft) in the Elk Mountains, w central Colorado, 13 m. wsw of Aspen.

Snow Mountains   Collective name for the mountain ranges of central New Guinea; the main sections are Nassau Range and Orange Range.

Socompa, Cerro   Andean peak (19,787 ft) on the Argentina-Chile border, 125 m. wsw of San Antonio de los Cobres (Argentina). At sw foot is Socompa Pass (12,657 ft).

Soldados, Cerro   Andean peak (13,576 ft) in s Ecuador, 13 m. w of Cuenca.

Solimanca, Nudo   Andean massif in the Cordillera Occidental, s Peru, 30 m. NNW of Chuquibamba. Its highest peak rises to 20,728 ft.

Solo, Cerro   Andean peak (20,300 ft) on the Argentina-Chile border, 26 m. wsw of the Cerro Incahuasi.

Sonora Peak   (11,429 ft) in the Sierra Nevada, E California, 35 m. NW of Mono Lake.

Sorcerer Mountain   (10,387 ft) in the Selkirk Mountains, SE British Columbia, 30 m. NNE of Revelstoke.

Sotará Volcano (15,026 ft) in Cauca department, sw Colombia, in the Cordillera Central of the Andes, 13 m. s of Popayán.

South Baldy Peak (10,787 ft) in the Magdalena Mountains, w central New Mexico, 17 m. wsw of Socorro.

Southern Alps Mountain range in w central South Island, New Zealand. Extends *c.* 200 m. NE-SW and rises to 12,349 ft in Mount Cook.

South River Peak (13,145 ft) in the San Juan Mountains, sw Colorado, 19 m. s of Creede.

Spanish Fork Peak (10,185 ft) in Wasatch Range, N central Utah, 7 m. E of Spanish Fork City.

Spanish Peaks 2 peaks of volcanic origin in the Sangre de Cristo Mountains, s Colorado. West Spanish Peak is 13,623 ft and East Spanish Peak, 4 m. ENE, is 12,683 ft.

Spring Mountains SE Nevada, near the California border, in Nevada National Forest. Rise to 11,910 ft in Charleston Peak, 32 m. w of Las Vegas.

Spurr, Mount (11,069 ft) in the Alaska Range, s Alaska, 80 m. w of Anchorage.

Squaw Mountain Peak (11,733 ft) in the Front Range, Clear Creek county, N central Colorado.

Srikanta Peak (21,449 ft) in the w Kumaun Himalayas, N Uttar Pradesh, India, 9 m. wsw of Gangotri.

Stanislaus Peak (11,202 ft) in the Sierra Nevada, Alpine county, E California, *c.* 40 m. SSE of Lake Tahoe.

Stanley Baldwin, Mount (10,900 ft) in the Premier Group of the Rocky Mountains, E British Columbia, 65 m. w of Jasper.

Stanley Peak (10,351 ft) in the Rocky Mountains, on the Alberta-British Columbia border, 20 m. w of Banff.

Stansbury Mountains In Wasatch National Forest, NW Utah, extending N from the Onaqui Mountains. Rise to 11,031 ft in Deseret Peak.

Steele, Mount (16,439 ft) in the St Elias Mountains, sw Yukon, near the Alaska border, 180 m. w of Whitehorse.

Stella, Pizzo di Glacier-topped peak (10,377 ft) in the Rhaetian Alps, N Italy, near the Swiss border.

Steller, Mount (10,000 ft) in the Chugach Mountains, s Alaska, N of the Bering Glacier, 90 m. E of Cordova.

Stephen, Mount (10,494 ft) in the Rocky Mountains, SE British Columbia, near the Alberta border, 40 m. WNW of Banff.

Stewart, Mount (10,871 ft) in the Rocky Mountains, sw Alberta, near the E edge of Banff National Park, 70 m. SE of Jasper.

Stewart Peak (14,032 ft) in the Rocky Mountains, Saguache county, s central Colorado.

Stockdale, Mount (10,100 ft) in the Selkirk Mountains, SE British Columbia, 65 m. sw of Banff.

Storm Mountain (10,372 ft) in the Rocky Mountains, on the Alberta-British Columbia border, 20 m. w of Banff.

Strahlhorn Peak (13,758 ft) in the Pennine Alps, s Switzerland, 7 m. E of Zermatt.

Stubai Alps NE group of the Ötztal Alps in the Tyrol, w Austria. Highest peak is Zuckerhütl (11,519 ft).

Suget Pass (17,600 ft) in the w Kunlun mountains, on the Kashmir-China border.

Sultan Mountain Peak (13,336 ft) in the San Juan Mountains, sw Colorado, near Silverton.

Sulzer, Mount (10,920 ft) in the St Elias Mountains, s Alaska, 160 m. ENE of Cordova.

Sumapaz, Páramo de Andean range in central Colombia, where the Cordillera Oriental splits into the high plateaus of Bogotá and Boyacá; rises to 13,715 ft.

Sumbing, Mount Volcanic peak (11,059 ft) in central Java, Indonesia, 35 m. NW of Jogjakarta.

Summit Peak (13,272 ft) in the San Juan Mountains, sw Colorado, 18 m. ENE of Pagosa Springs.

Sunbul Dag Peak (12,270 ft) in the Hakari Mountains, SE Turkey, 5 m. SE of Hakari.

Sundial Mountain (10,438 ft) in the Rocky Mountains, sw Alberta, near the British Columbia border, 50 m. SSE of Jasper.

Sunlight Peak (14,060 ft) in the San Juan Mountains, sw Colorado, *c.* 10 m. SSE of Silverton.

Sunshine Peak (14,018 ft) in the San Juan Mountains, sw Colorado, 15 m. NE of Silverton.

Sunwapta Peak (10,875 ft) in the Rocky Mountains, sw Alberta, near the British Columbia border, 50 m. SE of Jasper.

Suphan Dag Peak (14,547 ft; also given as 14,630 ft) in E Turkey, on the N shore of Lake Van, 22 m. SE of Malazgirt.

Sustenhorn Peak (11,507 ft) in the Alps of the Four Forest Cantons, s central Switzerland, 13 m. E of Meiringen.

Svanetian Range Spur of the central Greater Caucasus in Svanetia, NW Georgian SSR. Rises to *c.* 13,120 ft.

Sweetwater Mountains Range in California and Nevada, running N-S just E of the Sierra Nevada. Rises to 11,646 ft at Wheeler Peak, 28 m. NNW of Mono Lake.

Sylvia, Mount Second highest peak (12,897 ft) of Formosa, in the N central range, 33 m. SE of Sinchu.

Tabun Bogdo Mountain knot in the Altai Mountains, at the junction of the borders of China, Mongolia and the USSR. Rises to 15,266 ft in the Khuitun (or Hüyten), just inside the Mongolian People's Republic.

Tacaná Volcano (13,333 ft) in the Sierra Madre, on the Mexico-Guatemala border, 19 m. NE of Tapachula. It is the 2nd highest mountain in Central America.

Tacora, Cerro de Andean peak (19,520 ft) on the Peru-Chile border, 65 m. NE of Arica.

Tahsüeh Mountains Outlier of the Tibetan plateau in E Sikang province, China. Extend N-S between the rivers Yalung and Tatu and rise to 24,900 ft in the Minya Konka.

Tahtali Mountains Part of the Anti-Taurus range, s central Turkey, E of Kayseri. Rise to 10,020 ft in Bey Dag.

Tajumbina, Cerro Andean peak (13,533 ft) in sw Colombia, 37 m. ENE of Pasto.

Takatu Mountain N spur (c. 11,340 ft) of the Central Brahui Range, NE Baluchistan, w Pakistan, overlooking Quetta.

Takht-i-Sulaiman Twin peaks (11,290 ft and 11,085 ft) and highest points in the Sulaiman Range, w Pakistan, 55 m. wsw of Dera Ismail Khan.

Tala Peak (13,451 ft) in the Choke Mountains, NW Ethiopia.

Talamanca, Cordillera de Section of the continental divide in SE Costa Rica. Extends 100 m. NW-SE to the Panama border; rises to 12,533 ft in the Chirripó Grande.

Talas Ala-Tau Branch of the Tien Shan mountain system in NW Kirghiz, forming the s watershed of the upper Talas River. Rises to 13,200 ft.

Talgar Peak Highest peak (16,027 ft) of the Trans-Ili Ala-Tau, Kazakh SSR, 10 m. E of Alma-Ata.

Tamaná, Cerro Andean peak (13,780 ft) in w central Colombia, 45 m. w of Manizales.

Tancítaro Volcano (12,664 ft) at the s end of the Sierra de los Terascos, w Mexico, 22 m. wsw of Uruapan. Often snow-capped; surrounded by a crest of c. 250 smaller volcanoes. Paricutín volcano is just N.

Tang La Pass (15,219 ft) in the w Assam Himalayas, SE Tibet, 8 m. NNE of Phari.

Tang Pass Pass (16,760 ft) in the Tanglha Range, w China, on main trade route, 95 m. NNE of Nagchu.

Tarryall Mountains Part of the Front Range, central Colorado. Highest peak is Bison Peak (12,400 ft).

Taseko, Mount (10,057 ft) in the Coast Mountains, sw British Columbia, 140 m. N of Vancouver.

Tatlow, Mount (10,050 ft) in the Coast Mountains, sw British Columbia, 150 m. NNW of Vancouver.

Tatul, Sierra de Sub-Andean mountain range in Atacama province, N Chile. Extends 40 m. SE to the Argentina border. Rises to c. 18,000 ft.

Taylor, Mount Volcanic cone and highest point (11,389 ft) in the San Mateo Mountains, NW New Mexico, c. 55 m. wnw of Albuquerque.

Teide, Pico de Volcano (c. 12,200 ft) in Tenerife, Canary Isles. Has snow-capped cone; main crater is c. 200 ft in diameter and c. 100 ft deep. Occasionally smaller, active volcanoes appear near the summit.

Telescope Peak (11,045 ft) in the Panamint Range, E California, rising above Death Valley.

Temple, Mount (11,636 ft) in the Rocky Mountains, sw Alberta, near the British Columbia border, 30 m. wnw of Banff.

Tenduruk Dag Peak (10,870 ft) in E Turkey, 16 m. SE of Diyadin.

Ten Mile Peaks (12,800 ft) in the Rocky Mountains, central Colorado, 5 m. NW of Breckenridge.

Tennessee Pass (10,424 ft) in Park Range, central Colorado, 8 m. N of Leadville.

Teocalli Mountain Peak (13,220 ft) in the Rocky Mountains, Gunnison county, w central Colorado.

Teotepec, Cerro Highest mountain (12,149 ft) in Guerrero, sw Mexico, in the Sierra Madre del Sur.

Terascos, Sierra de los Mountain range in w Mexico, w and NW of Uruapan. Forms part of the w-E volcanic belt of central Mexico, c. 25 m. NE-SW.

Terrill, Mount (11,530 ft) in Fish Lake Plateau, s central Utah, 24 m. E of Richfield.

Terskei Ala-Tau Range of the Tien Shan mountain system in Kirghiz SSR. Extends 225 m. w from Khan Tengri peak to Chu River. Rises to 16,440 ft.

Tetnuld Peak (15,922 ft) in the main range of the central Greater Caucasus, on the Russia-Georgia border, 12 m. E of Mestia.

Thabantshonyana Highest peak (11,425 ft) in the Drakensberg, in Basutoland, just w of the Natal border.

Thaba Putsua Range Central Basutoland, extending 50 m. NE-SW and rising to 10,157 ft.

Thabor, Mont Peak (10,440 ft) of the Cottian Alps, SE France, near the Italian border, 8 m. sw of Modane.

Thachap Kangri Peak (20,970 ft) on the Chang Tang plateau, NW Tibet.

Thieralplistock Peak (11,109 ft) in the Bernese Alps, s central Switzerland, 11 m. SE of Meiringen.

Thompson Peak (10,546 ft) in the Sangre de Cristo Mountains, N central New Mexico, 8 m. E of Santa Fe.

Thorvald Nilson Mountains Massif (c. 13,000 ft) of Queen Maud Range, Antarctica.

Three Sisters 3 peaks of the Cascade Range, central Oregon, w of Bend. They are North Sister (10,094 ft), Middle Sister (10,053 ft) and South Sister (10,354 ft) All have large glaciers.

Tiedemann, Mount (12,000 ft) in the Coast Mountains, sw British Columbia, 170 m. NW of Vancouver.

Tiferdine, Djebel Peak (12,370 ft) of the High Atlas, central Morocco, 28 m. SE of Azilal.

Tilcara, Sierra de Sub-Andean mountain range in central Jujuy province, Argentina. Extends 45 m. and rises to c. 14,000 ft.

Timpanogos, Mount Highest peak (12,008 ft) in Wasatch Range, N central Utah, 10 m. N of Provo.

Tina, Monte Peak (10,301 ft) in s central Dominican Republic, in the Cordillera Central.

Tinajillas Pass In the Andes of s Ecuador, 21 m. s of Cuenca.

Tinguiririca Volcano Andean peak (14,100 ft) in central Chile, near the Argentina border, 40 m. SE of San Fernando.

Tirich Mir Highest mountain (25,263 ft) in the Hindu Kush, Chitral state, N North-West Frontier Province, Pakistan, 155 m. N of Peshawar.

Titan, Mount Cariboo Mountains, British Columbia;

353

believed to be highest peak (c. 11,750 ft) of the range.

Titlis Peak (10,639 ft) in the Alps of the Four Forest Cantons, central Switzerland, 3 m. SSE of Engelberg.

Tittmann, Mount (11,000 ft) in the St Elias Mountains, s Alaska, 120 m. NW of Yakutat.

Tlacotepec, Cerro Mountain (10,594 ft) in the Sierra Madre del Sur, Guerrero, sw Mexico, 38 m. NNW of Acapulco.

Tobacco Root Mountains Range of the Rocky Mountains in sw Montana. Highest peaks are Ward Peak (10,267 ft), Branham Peaks (10,420 ft) and Granite Peak (10,575 ft).

Toba-Kakar Range NE Baluchistan, w Pakistan. Extends 250 m. sw from Gumal River, parallel to the Afghanistan border. Highest peaks are Kand (10,955 ft). and Sakir (10,519 ft).

Toby, Mount (10,537 ft) in the Selkirk Mountains, SE British Columbia, 60 m. NE of Nelson.

Tocorpuri, Cerro de Andean peak (22,162 ft) on the Bolivia-Chile border.

Tödi Highest peak (11,886 ft) of the Glarus Alps, E central Switzerland, 8 m. ssw of Linthal.

Toiyabe Range Central Nevada. Extends N-s along the E bank of Reese River. Highest peaks are Mount Callahan (10,203 ft) in the N and Arc Dome (11,775 ft) in the s.

Tolima, Nevado del Andean volcano (18,438 ft) in the Cordillera Central, w central Colombia, 17 m. NNW of Ibagué.

Tolimán Inactive volcano (10,344 ft), sw central Guatemala, 3 m. sw of San Lucas.

Toluca, Nevado de Extinct volcano (15,020 ft) in Mexico state, Mexico, 13 m. ssw of Toluca.

Tontal, Sierra del Sub-Andean range in s San Juan province, Argentina, w of San Juan. Extends c. 50 m. N-s and rises to c. 13,500 ft.

Toquema Range Central Nevada, largely in Nye county. Extends N-s between Toiyabe and Monitor ranges. Highest point is Mount Jefferson (11,807 ft).

Tornado Mountain (10,169 ft) in the Rocky Mountains, on the Alberta-British Columbia border, 40 m. NE of Fernie.

Toros Dagi Mountain group in the Taurus, in the subrange known as the Bolkar Mountains, in Turkey. Rises to 11,762 ft in Medetsiz Dag.

Torreys Peak (14,264 ft) in the Front Range, central Colorado, c. 45 m. w of Denver.

Totora, Cordillera de Andean range in w San Juan province, Argentina. Curves c. 30 m. w-e forming an E spur of the Andes, rising to c. 17,500 ft.

Toubkal, Djebel Highest peak (13,665 ft) of the High Atlas, sw Morocco, 40 m. s of Marrakesh.

Tour Saillère Peak (10,571 ft) in the Pennine Alps, sw Switzerland, 7 m. WNW of Martigny-Ville.

Trans-Alai Range Branch of the Pamir-Alai mountain system extending c. 125 m. w from the USSR-China border along the Kirghiz-Tadzhik SSR border, forming the N border of the Pamir. Rises to 23,382 ft in Lenin Peak.

Trans-Ili Ala-Tau Range of the Tien Shan mountain system in Kazakh SSR. Extends w from Chilik River to the Chu-Ili Mountains. Rises to 16,027 ft in Talgar peak.

Treasure Mountain Peak (13,442 ft) in the Rocky Mountains, Gunnison county, w central Colorado.

Trebizond Mountains NE Turkey, extending 50 m. WNW-ESE between the Black Sea and Harsit River. Rise to 10,660 ft in Kemer Dag.

Tres Cruces, Cerro 1. Andean peak (10,640 ft) on the Ecuador-Peru border, in the Cordillera del Cóndor, 55 m. SSE of Loja.
2. Peak (10,308 ft) in Chiapas, s Mexico, in the main range of the Sierra Madre, 15 m. NW of Motozintla.

Tres Cruces, Cordillera de Part of the Eastern Cordillera of the Andes, w Bolivia. Extends 30 m. from La Paz River to Ichoca, rising to over 18,000 ft.

Tres Cruces, Nevados Andean volcanic mountains on the Argentina-Chile border, 30 m. wsw of Cerro Incahuasi. Peaks rise to 21,720 ft, 20,853 ft and 19,780 ft.

Tre Signori, Corno dei Peak (11,020 ft) at the s end of the Ortles group, 12 m. SE of Bormio, N Italy. Has several glaciers.

Tres Morros, Alto de Andean massif (c. 12,150 ft) in the N part of the Cordillera Central of N central Colombia, 75 m. NW of Medellín.

Trivor Peak (25,370 ft) in the Karakoram; first climbed by Wilfrid Noyce, 1960.

Tromen Volcano Sub-Andean peak (13,000-13,500 ft) in N Neuquén national territory, Argentina, 13 m. sw of Buta Ranquil.

Tronador, Monte Andean peak (c. 11,200 ft) on the Argentina-Chile border, 30 m. w of San Carlos de Bariloche. Its main peak is in Chile.

Troublesome Peak (11,500 ft) in the Rocky Mountains, Grand county, N Colorado.

Troya, Cerro Andean peak (11,485 ft) on the Colombia-Ecuador border, 5 m. s of Tulcán.

Truchas Name of 3 peaks in N New Mexico, in the Sangre de Cristo Mountains, c. 25 m. NE of Santa Fe, all over 13,000 ft.

Trugberg Peak (12,914 ft) in the Bernese Alps, s central Switzerland, 12 m. SSE of Interlaken.

Trujillo, Pico Peak (10,115 ft) in the Cordillera Central, central Dominican Republic, 35 m. sw of Santiago.

Tsar, Mount (11,232 ft) in the Rocky Mountains, SE British Columbia, near the Alberta border, 55 m. SSE of Jasper.

Tuitul, Cerro Andean peak (17,280 ft) in w Salta province, Argentina, 50 m. w of San Antonio de los Cobres.

Tunari Peak (17,060 ft) in the Cordillera de Cochabamba, central Bolivia, 15 m. WNW of Cochabamba.

Tupungatito Andean peak (18,500 ft) on the Argentina-Chile border, just sw of Tupungato peak. Sometimes called Bravard, the name also given to the peak (18,865 ft) just SE.

Turkestan Range Branch of the Tien Shan in w Tadzhik SSR. Extends *c.* 200 m. w from the Alai Range along the N watershed of the Zeravshan River. Rises to 13,800 ft.

Turrialba Volcano (10,974 ft) in the Cordillera Central, central Costa Rica, 8 m. NW of Turrialba.

Turugart Pass (12,155 ft) in the Kokshaal-Tau section of the Tien Shan, on the USSR-China border.

Tushar Mountains sw central Utah, extending s from the Pavant Mountains along the w bank of the Sevier River. Chief peaks are Circleville Mountain (11,276 ft), Mount Belknap (12,139 ft) and Delano Peak (12,173 ft).

Tutupaca Volcano Andean peak (19,048 ft) in s Peru, 55 m. ENE of Moquegua.

Tuxer Alps Group of the Eastern Alps in the Tyrol, w Austria, adjoining the Stubai Alps (w) and the Kitzbühel Alps (NE). Extend 20 m. NE from the Brenner Pass, rising to 11,414 ft in the Olperer.

Twins, The Mountain (12,085 ft) in the Rocky Mountains, sw Alberta, near the British Columbia border, 50 m. SE of Jasper.

Tyndall, Mount (14,025 ft) in the Sierra Nevada, E California, 6 m. NNW of Mount Whitney.

Ubinas Volcano Andean peak (17,390 ft) in s Peru, just NE of Nevado de Pichu Pichu.

Uinta Mountains Range of the Rocky Mountains in NE Utah and sw Wyoming. Extend E from the Wasatch Range through sections of Wasatch and Ashley national forests. Highest peak is Kings Peak (13,498 ft).

Ulmer, Mount Highest peak (12,500 ft) of the Sentinel Mountains, Ellsworth Highland, Antarctica.

Ulugh Muztagh Highest peak (25,340 ft) of the Kunlun, on undefined China-Tibet border.

Umango, Sierra de Sub-Andean range in La Rioja province, Argentina, w of Villa Castelli; extends *c.* 30 m. NE-sw and rises to *c.* 15,000 ft.

Unai Pass (10,525 ft) in the s outlier of the Hindu Kush in E central Afghanistan, 50 m. w of Kabul.

Uncompahgre Peak (14,306 ft) in the San Juan Mountains, sw central Colorado, 12 m. ENE of Ouray.

Uncompahgre Plateau Tableland in sw Colorado, extending *c.* 60 m. NW-SE between San Miguel and Gunnison rivers; rises to 10,338 ft in the SE tip.

United States Range N Ellesmere Island, Northwest Territories. Extends *c.* 250 m. WSW-ENE across the N part of the island from Nansen Sound to Lincoln Sea. Rises to over 11,000 ft.

Unwin, Mount (10,723 ft) in the Rocky Mountains, w Alberta, near the British Columbia border, 30 m. SE of Jasper.

Ute Peak Outlying peak (10,151 ft) of the Sangre de Cristo Mountains, N New Mexico, near the Colorado border, 8 m. wsw of Costilla.

Vallecito, Cerro Andean volcano (20,075 ft) in w Catamarca province, Argentina, near the Chile border, just SE of Cerro Colorados.

Valle Grande Mountains N New Mexico, NW of Santa Fe. Extend N-s from Jemez Creek to Rio Chama. The range surrounds an enormous crater called the Valle Grande. Highest point is Chicoma Peak (11,950 ft).

Valle Hermoso Pass (11,529 ft) in the Andes, on the Argentina-Chile border.

Vancouver, Mount (15,700 ft) in the St Elias Mountains, on the Yukon-Alaska border, 160 m. w of Whitehorse.

Van Mountains E Turkey, s and SE of Lake Van. Extend E to Iranian border and s to Buhtan River. Rise to 12,300 ft in Baset Dag.

Vanoise, Massif de la High mountain group of the Savoy Alps, SE France. Has glaciers. Rises to 12,668 ft at the Grande-Casse and 12,018 ft at the Grand-Motte.

Vasquez Mountains In the Front Range, N central Colorado, extending N-s between Williams and Fraser rivers. Chief peaks are Byers Peak (12,778 ft) and Vasquez Peak (12,800 ft), *c.* 45 m. w of Denver.

Vaux, Mount (10,891 ft) in the Rocky Mountains, SE British Columbia, 40 m. w of Banff.

Velasco, Sierra de Sub-Andean mountain range in central La Rioja province, Argentina. Extends *c.* 100 m. s from the Catamarca province border. Rises to *c.* 13,000 ft.

Velluda, Sierra Andean range in Bío-Bío province, s central Chile, 50 m. E of Los Angeles. Extends *c.* 15 m. SE to Argentina border. Rises to 11,745 ft.

Vercenik Dag Peak (12,175 ft) in the Rize Mountains, NE Turkey, 32 m. SE of Rize.

Verstanklahorn Peak (10,830 ft) in the Silvretta Group of the Rhaetian Alps, E Switzerland, E of Klosters.

Victor Emmanuel Range Central New Guinea; rises to 11,810 ft.

Vidal Gormaz, Cerro Andean peak (*c.* 18,000 ft) on the Argentina-Chile border, 70 m. sw of the Cerro Incahuasi.

Viejo, Cerro el Andean peak (13,451 ft) in the Cordillera Oriental of Colombia, 18 m. WNW of Pamplona.

Viento, Cordillera del Andean mountain range in N Neuquén national territory, Argentina. Extends *c.* 45 m. s from the Cerro Domuyo to Neuquén River and rises to *c.* 10,000 ft.

Vignemale Highest peak (10,821 ft) of the French Pyrenees, sw France, on the Spanish border, 23 m. s of Lourdes.

Vilcabamba, Cordillera Andean range in s Peru. Extends *c.* 160 m. NW, rising to 20,551 ft in Cerro Salcantay.

Vilcanota, Cerro de Andean range in s Peru, E of Cuzco city. Extends *c.* 130 m. sw to the Nudo de Vilcanota (17,988 ft).

Virginia Peak (10,530 ft) in Front Range, Jefferson county, central Colorado.

Vogelberg Peak (10,559 ft) in the Lepontine Alps, E Switzerland, 9 m. NNE of Biasca.

Volcán, Sierra del Sub-Andean range in N San Juan province, Argentina, extending *c*. 25 m. N from Rodeo; rises to *c*. 13,000 ft.

Vueltas, Cerro de las Peak (10,128 ft) in the Cordillera de Talamanca, s central Costa Rica, 3 m. SE of Copey.

Waddington, Mount (13,260 ft) in the Coast Mountains, sw British Columbia, 170 m. NW of Vancouver.

Wakhjir Pass (16,150 ft) in the E Hindu Kush, on the Afghanistan-China border.

Wallel Peak (10,830 ft) in the highlands of w central Ethiopia, 20 m. N of Saio.

Wallowa Mountains NE Oregon, in Wallowa county. Highest peak is Sacajaewea Peak (10,033 ft).

Walsh, Mount (14,780 ft) in the St Elias Mountains, sw Yukon, near the Alaska border, 170 m. w of Whitehorse.

Warner Mountains Range in the extreme NE of California and in s Oregon. Extends *c*. 85 m. N-S. Height is *c*. 5,000–10,000 ft.

Washburn Range U-shaped ridge in the Rocky Mountains, NW Wyoming, in the N part of Yellowstone National Park. Highest point is Mount Washburn (10,317 ft).

Wassuk Range E spur of the Sierra Nevada, w Nevada, just w of Walker Lake. Highest points are Cory Peak (10,516 ft) and Mount Grant (11,303 ft).

Weisskugel Peak (12,287 ft) in the Ötztal Alps, the Tyrol, on the Austro-Italian border. Has glaciers.

Weissmies Peak (13,209 ft) in the Pennine Alps, s Switzerland, 2 m. from the Italian border, 13 m. s of Brig.

Weissnollen Peak (11,815 ft) in Alps of the Four Forest Cantons, s central Switzerland, 11 m. ESE of Meiringen.

Wellhorn Peak (10,483 ft) in the Bernese Alps, s central Switzerland, 9 m. SSE of Brienz.

West Tavaputs Plateau High tableland in E Utah. Extends w from East Tavaputs Plateau to Wasatch Plateau. Rises to 10,047 ft in Mount Bartles and 10,285 ft in Bruin Peak.

Wet Mountains Range of the Rocky Mountains in s central Colorado, extending SSE from Arkansas River to Huerfano River. Rises to 12,334 ft in Greenhorn Mountain, in the s tip.

Wetterhorn Peak (14,020 ft) in the San Juan Mountains, sw Colorado, 9 m. ENE of Ouray.

Whale Peak (13,074 ft) in Front Range, between Park and Summit counties, central Colorado.

Wheeler Peak 1. Peak (13,058 ft) in the Snake Range, E Nevada, 36 m. SE of Ely. It is the highest point in the range and the 2nd highest in the state.
2. Peak (13,151 ft) in N New Mexico, in the Sangre de Cristo Mountains, 70 m. NNE of Santa Fe.

White Face Peak (11,494 ft) in the Rocky Mountains, Grand county, N central Colorado.

Whitehorn Mountain (11,101 ft) in the Rocky Mountains, E British Columbia, near the Alberta border, 55 m. WNW of Jasper.

White Pine Mountains E Nevada, in Nevada National Forest. Rise to 10,741 ft in Mount Hamilton and 11,493 ft in Duckwater peak.

White Rock Mountain Peak (13,532 ft) in the Rocky Mountains, Gunnison county, w central Colorado.

Whitewater Baldy Peak (10,892 ft) in the Mogollon Mountains, sw New Mexico, *c*. 45 m. NNW of Silver City.

Wildhorn Peak (10,664 ft) in the Bernese Alps, sw Switzerland, 8 m. N of Sion.

Wildspitze Highest peak (12,379 ft) in the Ötztal Alps, the Tyrol, w Austria, 25 m. SSE of Imst.

Wildstrubel Mountain in the Bernese Alps, s Switzerland. Highest peak is the Grosstrubel (10,649 ft), 8 m. of Sierre.

Wilhelmina, Mount Highest peak (*c*. 15,585 ft) of Orange Range, central New Guinea.

Williamson, Mount (14,384 ft) in the Sierra Nevada, E California, 6 m. N of Mount Whitney.

Williams River Mountains In the Front Range, N central Colorado, extending N-S between Blue and Williams rivers. Highest points are Williams Peak (11,619 ft), Ute Peak (12,298 ft) and Ptarmigan Peak (12,400 ft).

Willingdon, Mount (11,044 ft) in the Rocky Mountains, sw Alberta, near the British Columbia border, 50 m. NW of Banff.

Wilson, Mount Peak (14,250 ft) in the San Miguel Mountains, sw Colorado, 12 m. sw of Telluride. It is the highest point in the range.

Wilson Peak (14,026 ft) in the Rocky Mountains, Dolores county, sw Colorado.

Wind Mountain (10,190 ft) in the Rocky Mountains, sw Alberta, near the British Columbia border, 20 m. SE of Banff.

Windom Peak (14,091 ft) in the San Juan Mountains, sw Colorado, 13 m. SSE of Silverton.

Wind River Range Part of the Rocky Mountains of w central Wyoming. Extends *c*. 120 m. NNW from Sweetwater River, forming part of the Continental Divide. Highest point is Gannett Peak (13,787 ft).

Witherspoon, Mount (12,023 ft) in the Chugach Mountains, s Alaska, 40 m. WNW of Valdez.

Wood, Mount (15,880 ft) in sw Yukon, near the Alaska border, 200 m. WNW of Whitehorse.

Wyoming Range Part of the Rocky Mountains of w Wyoming, near the Idaho border. Extends *c*. 40 m. N-S and rises to 11,388 ft in Wyoming Peak.

Yale, Mount (14,172 ft) in the Collegiate Range of the Sawatch Mountains, 9 m. w of Buena Vista.

Yeguas Volcano Andean peak (11,500 ft) in Linares province, s central Chile, 45 m. ESE of Linares.

Yellowjacket Mountains E Idaho, just E of the Middle

Fork of Salmon River. They are a N extension of the Salmon River Mountains. Highest point is Mount McGuire (10,070 ft).

Yoli Pass (18,000 ft) in the E Hindu Kush, on the Afghanistan-China border.

Yucuyácua, Cerro Peak (11,076 ft) in Oaxaca, s Mexico, in the Sierra Madre del Sur, 60 m. w of Oaxaca.

Zangezur Range In the Lesser Caucasus, extending *c.* 100 m. s from a point E of Lake Sevan to the Aras River. Rises to 12,850 ft.

Zapaleri, Cerro Andean peak (18,514 ft) at the s end of the Cordillera de Lipez, at the junction of the Bolivia-Chile-Argentina borders.

Zaskar Range N lateral range of the Himalayas in Kashmir, Tibet and India. Extends *c.* 400 m. SE from Suru River to the upper Karnali River; highest peak is Kamet (25,447 ft) in the SE.

Zempoaltépetl Peak (11,142 ft) in s Mexico, 50 m. E of Oaxaca, at the E end of the Sierra Madre del Sur.

Zeravshan Range Branch of the Tien Shan mountain system in w Tadzhik SSR. Extends *c.* 200 m. w from the Alai Range along the s watershed of the Zeravshan River. Rises to 18,480 ft.

Zillertal Alps Range of the Eastern Alps on the Austro-Italian border, extending 35 m. NE into the Tyrol, Austria. Rise to 11,555 ft in the Hochfeiler.

Zinalrothorn Peak (13,860 ft) in the Alps, s Switzerland, *c.* 10 m. NNW of Zermatt.

Zinal, Pointe de Peak (12,448 ft) in the Alps, s Switzerland, *c.* 10 m. NNW of Zermatt.

Zirate, Cerro Peak (10,958 ft) in central Mexico, on the N shore of Lake Pátzcuaro, 25 m. w of Morelia.

Zirkel, Mount (12,220 ft) in Park Range, N Colorado, 20 m. WNW of Walden.

Zoji La Pass (11,578 ft) in the Punjab Himalayas, w central Kashmir, 40 m. ENE of Srinagar.

Zuckerhütl Highest peak (11,519 ft) of the Stubai Alps, on the Austro-Italian border, 20 m. SSW of Innsbruck.

Zunil Inactive volcano (11,591 ft) in sw Guatemala, 9 m. SE of Quezaltenango.

Acknowledgments

For permission to reproduce copyright material the Editor and the Publishers are grateful to: ABERDEEN JOURNALS LTD, for an extract from a report of the annual dinner of the Cairngorm Club in 1925; ALLEN & UNWIN LTD, for an extract from *From Adam's Peak to Elephanta* by Edward Carpenter, published by Swan, Sonnenschein & Co., London, 1903, and for an extract from Baedeker's *Switzerland*, 1867; THE ALPINE CLUB, for an extract from *Peaks, Passes and Glaciers* by Francis Fox Tuckett, published by Longmans, London, 1859; EDWARD ARNOLD LTD, for an extract from *The Exploration of the Caucasus* by Douglas Freshfield, and for an extract from *Among Karakoram Glaciers* by Jenny Visser-Hooft, both published by Edward Arnold Ltd; THE BODLEY HEAD and HARPER BROS, for an extract from *Men Against the Clouds* by Richard L. Burdsall and A. B. Emmons, published by The Bodley Head, 1935; JONATHAN CAPE LTD, for an extract from *Travels in Arabia Deserta* by C. M. Doughty, published by Jonathan Cape Ltd, 1936, and for an extract from *The Autobiography of a Mountain Climber* by Lord Conway of Allington, published by Jonathan Cape Ltd, 1920; JONATHAN CAPE LTD and THE BEACON PRESS, for extracts from *The Marches of El Dorado* by Michael Swan, published by Jonathan Cape Ltd, 1958; LONGMANS GREEN & CO. LTD, for an extract from *Climbs and Exploration in the Canadian Rockies* by H. E. M. Stutfield and J. N. Collie, published by Longmans, 1902, and for extracts from *Alpine Studies* by W. A. B. Coolidge, published by Longmans, 1912; THE MACMILLAN COMPANY, for an extract from *Our Southern Highlanders* by Horace Kephart, published by The Macmillan Company, New York, 1913; METHUEN & CO. LTD, for an extract from *Highest Andes* by Stuart Vines and Professor Bonney, published by Methuen & Co. Ltd; JOHN MURRAY LTD, for an extract from *This My Voyage* by Dr T. G. Longstaff, published by John Murray Ltd, 1950; PENGUIN BOOKS LTD, for an extract from *A Peak in the Cévennes* by André Chamson, reprinted in *Penguin New Writing 12* from *A Mountain Boyhood*; A. D. PETERS, for an extract from *Africa View* by Sir Julian Huxley, published by Chatto & Windus, 1931, and for an extract from *The Good Companions* by J. B. Priestley, published by Heinemann Ltd; A. D. PETERS and J. B. LIPPINCOTT CO., for extracts from *The Age of Mountaineering* by James Ramsey Ullman, published by J. B. Lippincott Co; THE ROYAL GEOGRAPHICAL SOCIETY, for extracts from *Exploration on and around Aconcagua* by E. A. Fitz Gerald, published by the Royal Geographical Society in the Geographical Journal, Vol 12, No. 5, 1898, and for an extract from *Kanghenjunga Climbed* by Charles Evans and George Band, printed in the Geographical Journal of March, 1956; PATRICK M. SYNGE, for extracts from his book *Mountains of the Moon*, published by Lindsay Drummond, London, 1937.

The color plates were supplied by: Barnaby's Picture Library (Plate 11); J. Allan Cash (Plate 2); the Central Office of Information (Plate 10, Crown Copyright photograph); Simon Clark (Plate 14); Anthony Huxley (Plate 3); the Mount Everest Foundation (Plates 8 and 9); the Pictorial Press (Plate 1); W. A. Poucher, F.R.P.S. (Plates 4, 12, 13, 15 and 16); Dr H. Tazieff, volcanologist (Plate 5); Tom Weir (Plate 7, photograph taken November 1952).

The painting of Fujiyama by Hokusai was reproduced by courtesy of the Victoria and Albert Museum, London.

The monochrome photographs in the text were supplied by: Aerofilms Ltd (pages 71 and 179); the British Overseas Airways Corporation (page 292); J. Allan Cash (pages 81 and 135); Ronald W. Clark (pages 18, 21, 33, 90, 125, 204, 210, 211, 223, 228, and 311); the Colorado State

Department of Public Relations (page 249); Hans Ertl (page 273); the Exclusive News Agency Ltd (pages 121, 152, 190, 215, 243 and 252); the Fédération Française de la Montagne (page 77); the French Government Tourist Office (pages 59 and 60); Gyger & Klopfenstein (pages 63, 140, 159, 176, 218 and 283); E. O. Hoppé (pages 83, 170 and 272); Hunting Aerosurveys Ltd (page 128); the Icelandic Embassy (page 166); the Istituto di Fotografia Alpina "Vittorio Sella" (page 184); the Keystone Press Agency Ltd (page 315); the Mount Everest Foundation (pages 26, 149, 169 and 182); the Mustograph Agency Ltd, (page 288); the United States National Park Service (pages 123, 131, 157, 187 and 197); the New Hampshire State Planning and Development Commission (page 313); the New York State Department of Commerce (page 56); the High Commissioner for New Zealand (pages 139, 267 and 294); the Oregon State Highway Department (page 105); Polar Photos (page 261); W. A. Poucher, F.R.P.S. (pages 99, 117 and 196); the Rumanian Legation (page 103); the Society for Cultural Relations with the USSR (pages 108, 299 and 303); the South African Tourist Corporation (pages 137 and 217); Hans Steiner (pages 12, 64, 67 and 93); the Tennessee Conservation Department (page 163); the Washington State Department of Commerce News Bureau (pages 237 and 256); Tom Weir (pages 84, 201 and 319); the Yugoslav National Tourist Office (pages 133 and 175).

The jacket picture, which shows a peak in the Andes, was supplied by Dr A. B. Cunningham.

The world map used as endpapers for this book is based on the Oblique Aitoff Projection. It is an "equal area" projection, which means that the relative sizes of all areas of land and sea are correct. Shapes tend to be distorted, especially around the edges of the map. In this projection, however, the earth has been tilted so that the North Pole and the major land areas are relatively undistorted.

Great care has been taken to trace all the owners of copyright material used in this book. If any have been inadvertently overlooked or omitted, acknowledgment will gladly be made in any future edition.

The line illustrations for the Glossary were drawn by Bruce Robertson. The index was compiled by Mary Still.

Index

The figures in **bold type** *indicate the pages on which illustrations will be found*

Boulaz, Loulou 160
Boulder Peak 236
Bou Naceur, Djebel 85, 327
Boundary Peak (Adirondacks) 57
  (Sangre de Cristo) 327
  (White Mountains) 313, 327
Bourcet, General 127
Bourdillon, T.D. 23, 113, 150, 201
Bourrit, Marc-Théodore 218, 219
Boussingault, Jean-Baptiste 122
Bouvier, Jean 209
Bowen Mountains 86
Braeriach 99
Brahui Range, Central 327
Branham Peaks (Tobacco Root
  Mountains) 354
Bran Pass 301
Brassington 248
Brasstown Bald 96
Bravard 327
Brazeau, Mount 327
Brazilian Highlands 209
Brea, Cordón de la 327
Breadalbane 89
Brec de Chambeyron 122
Brèche de la Meije 212
  de Roland 114
Brecon Beacons (Brecknock Beacons)
  327
Breithorn (Bernese Alps) 327
  (Lötschentaler) 327
  (Pennine Alps) 327
Bremble, Master John de 14, 161-2
Brenner Pass 68-9, 97
Brenta Alps 69
Brevoort, Marguerite ("Meta") 18-
  19, 23, 211, 212
Brewer, Mount 327
  William 19
Brian Head 327
Bridger Peak 327
Bristenstock 327
Broad Peak 327
Broad Stand 197
Brocherei, Joseph 188
Brocken 165, 327
Broghil Pass see Baroghil Pass
Brokeoff Mountain 198
Brooks, Mount 327
Brooks Range 98, *plate 2*
Bross, Mount 327
Broughton 106
Brown, Joe 23, 182, 183, 225
Browne, Belmore 206, 207
Bruce, 23, 148, 169, 181, 227

Bruce, Mount 312
Brüderlin, A. 158
Bruin Peak 328
Bryce, Mount 328
Bucegi Mountains 300
"Buddha's Glory" 238
Buey, Páramo del 328
Buffalo Peaks 328
Buhl, Hermann 23, 229-30
Bulgarian Alps 87
Bulgarka 87
Bullychoop Mountains 193
Bum La 328
Bunnabeola see Benna Beola
Burdsall, Richard. 178, 213,
  214
Bureya Range 190
Burji La 328
Burnaby, Mrs see LeBlond, Mrs
  Aubrey
Burton, Sir Richard 100
Burzil Pass 328
Büttlassen 328
Buz Dag 328
Byas Rikhi Himal 231
Byelukha see Belukha
Byrd, Admiral 254
Byukhasan see Hasan Dag

Cabral, John 93, 94, 112
Cacella, Stephen 93, 94, 112
Cachi, Sierra Nevado de 328
Cadibona Pass 209
Caesar, Julius 202
Cairngorm 99
Cairngorm Mountains **99**, 99-100
Cairntoul 99
Cajón, Sierra del (Sierra de Quil-
  mes) 328
Cakirgol Dag 328
Calalaste, Cerro 328
  Sierra de 328
Calchaquíes, Cumbres 328
California Geological Survey 19
Callahan, Mount (Toiyabe Range)
  354
Callaqui Volcano (Callaquén Vol-
  cano) 328
Camel's Hump (Ghats) 155
  (Green Mountains) 163
Cameron, Mount 328
  Una 189
Cameron Cone 248, 328
  Pass 328
Cameroon Mountain 100

Camino de los Andes see Uspallata
  Pass
Campanario, Cerro de 328
Campo Tencia 328
Canadian Geological Survey 82, 203
Canby Mountain 328
Canin, Mount 175
Cannon Mountain see Profile Moun-
  tain
Cantabrian Mountains (Cordillera
  Cantábrica) 100-101
Capac-Urcu see Altar, Cerro
Capillitas, Sierra see Atajo, Sierra
Capitan Mountains 328
Capitol Peak (Elk Mountains) 332
Carabaya, Cordillera de 125, 126,
  328
Carbon, Mount (Castle Peak) 328
Carbon Glacier 256
Carbonnières, Ramond de 16, 23
Cardamom Hills 155
Care Alto, Monte (Adamello) 323
Cariboo Mountains 101
Carihuairazo, Cerro 328
Carmel, Mount 102
"Carmen Land" 255
Carnes Mountain 328
Carnic Alps 69, 175
Carpathian Mountains 102-4, **103**
Carpe, Allen 101, 203, 208
Carpenter, Edward 57
Carrantuohill (Carrantuohil, Car-
  rantual) 104
Carrel, Felicité 211
  Jean-Antoine 211, 219
Carrie, Mount 236
Carson Range 280
Carter Dome 314
Carter-Moriah Range 313-4
Carstenz, Mount 232, 233, 234, 328
Cascade Range 56, 57, 104-6, **105**,
  115
Cassin, Riccardo 153, 161, 208
Castalian spring 245
Castelnau, Baron Emmanuel Boi-
  leau de 129, 212
Castle Naze 248
Castle Peak (Elk Mountains) see
  Carbon, Mount
  (Sawtooth Mountains) 328
  (Wrangell Mountains) 328
Catacombs Mountains 328
Cathédrale 129
Cathedral Peak (Alaska Range) 62
  (Sierra Nevada) 328

363